ECOLOGICAL BULLETINS No 20

Structure and Function of Tundra Ecosystems

T ROSSWALL and O W HEAL (Editors)

Papers presented at the IBP Tundra Biome V. International Meeting on Biological Productivity of Tundra, Abisko, Sweden, April 1974.

30150   007177014

Suggested citation:

Authors name. 1975. Name of paper. – In: Rosswall, T.
& Heal, O.W. (eds.) Structure and Function of Tundra
Ecosystems. Ecol. Bull. 20:000–000. Stockholm:
Swedish Natural Science Research Council.

Cover:

Swedish Tundra Biome site at Stordalen in mid-September.

ISBN 91-546-0188-6
Production and distribution: NFR Editorial Service
Original produced by Sundt & Co Offset, Stockholm
LF/ALLF 209 75 009
Printer: LiberTryck Stockholm 1975

PREFACE

At the Vth International Meeting on Biological Productivity of Tundra: IBP Tundra Biome, Abisko, Sweden, 16–24 April 1974, a series of papers was presented summarising the functional characteristics of the individual sites within the Tundra Biome. These papers have been brought together in the present volume. Another series of papers presented at the meeting developed between-site comparisons of the site characteristics and their productivity, examining trends within the Biome. This synthesis will appear in Tundra: Comparative Analysis of Ecosystems, ed. J.J. Moore, Cambridge University Press.

The use of units in this volume follows IBP recommendations for the use of the SI system (Quantities, units and symbols. Recommendations for use in IBP synthesis. Report of a SCIBP Working Group. London: ICSU/SCIBP. 1974, 53 pp.). Although calories were used as the unit of energy during IBP, all these values have been converted to joules (J) by multiplication by 4.184. An exception is the simulation modelling paper by Bunnell & Scoullar, in which calories were retained, as the model was implemented using this unit. All weights are given as dry weights (dw), unless otherwise stated.

The Abisko meeting was supported by grants from the Swedish Government, and the US and Canadian IBP Tundra projects; the generous support is gratefully acknowledged. On behalf of the participants we would also like to thank M. Sonesson, B. Svensson, B. Paulsen and J. Lindström as well as the staff of Abisko Tourist Hotel and Research Station for the planning and support before and during the meeting.

We would also like to acknowledge the assistance of G. Pettersson, who has had the job of retyping numerous drafts; G. Sunnerstrand and B. Myrvik, who have drawn many of the figures; P. Wigren, who has assisted in the preparation of many illustrations; R. Kumar, who has corrected the English language of papers from authors not having English as their mother tongue.

We are particularly grateful to the authors and their colleagues for their helpful cooperation in producing this volume.

Uppsala, Sweden and Grange-over-Sands, UK

August, 1975

T. Rosswall & O.W. Heal

3

3

CONTENTS

THE IBP TUNDRA BIOME – AN INTRODUCTION

T. ROSSWALL and O.W. HEAL

A major part of the effort in the PT section (Productivity of Terrestrial Communities) of the International Biological Programme has been the study of various ecosystems. Four major ecosystem types were recongised; Arid land, Grassland, Forest and Tundra, and within each of these Biomes, productivity studies have been carried out on a range of sites. The IBP Tundra Biome studies were initiated through two preparatory meetings (Moor House, UK, 1967 and Ustaoset, Norway, 1968). At those meetings a minimum programme (4) was adopted for the tundra studies to give the participating projects a common broad base for comparison. The cooperation was facilitated by further general meetings (Edmonton, Canada, 1969; Kevo, Finland, 1970; Leningrad, USSR, 1971; Abisko, Sweden, 1974), the present volume being the last of the series of proceedings (7, 14, 19). This last volume (14) comprises a series of papers which summarise the current understanding of the structure and function of the ecosystems which were involved in the IBP Tundra Biome. In addition, a number of international work groups concerned with specific components of the ecosystem were set up, and the results from these efforts have in part been published as proceedings from work group meetings (1, 8).

The main product from the Biome studies will be the intra-Biome syntheses, published by Cambridge University Press (12). In these, the variations in environment, composition and productivity of components of the ecosystem, and the rates of processes, will be examined across the whole series of sites. However, many important aspects of the structure and function of ecosystems will be obscured by such between-site comparisons because of the emphasis on components of the ecosystem. The papers in the present volume emphasise the interaction between components within a system, and the integrity of the system. Although such descriptions will appear as part of the national studies, the production of a set of comparable ecosystem descriptions is an international exercise, aimed to facilitate between-site and between-Biome syntheses.

At each site, intensive research has provided information on the components of the system – the species composition, population density, production and activity of the flora, fauna and microflora. These represent pieces of the jigsaw which, when combined, provide a picture of the ecosystem. It is recognised that, in the sense of Odum (13), an ecosystem is a relatively discrete unit within which energy and nutrients are fixed

7

and circulate, with only minor transfers across the ecosystem boundaries. Despite the acceptance by many people that an ecosystem is a distinct level of organisation, the study of ecosystems is in its infancy and few general principles on structure and function have been formulated. There is a feeling that there are many gaps in our measurements; we have too few data to produce a complete picture. Despite the complexity of the systems and the absence of data on some aspects, the IBP is at an end, and this provides a convenient opportunity to summarise the understanding of ecosystem dynamics, to look for general principles which will guide future research and, hopefully, management.

The approach to ecosystem synthesis adopted in this volume was for each national project to produce a "word model" for their site or sites. These are verbal descriptions which emphasise the functional characteristics of the ecosystem and its components, concentrating on major causal relationships which represent a series of hypotheses based on data and experience. The idea of a word model is that it is a first stage in the development of a more rigorous mathematical simulation of the ecosystem which can be used to explore the dynamics of the system (2). In a few cases mathematical models have been developed, and the final paper in the volume describes a model of the primary production, herbivory and decomposition processes in the wet coastal tundra at Point Barrow, Alaska. This is a mathematical formulation of the word model for Barrow, but it was also developed with the aim of using it for inter-site international comparisons, thus representing one way in which inter-site comparison and synthesis can be made while still considering the individual sites as functional units.

The word models for the various sites differ considerably in their approach. This reflects differences in 1) the ecology of the areas, e.g. the importance of large herbivores; 2) the economic and human interest, e.g. agriculture, hunting and industrial usage; 3) the degree of understanding of parts of the system, e.g. the absence of fauna and microflora research in some sites and 4) the attitudes of authors, e.g. some authors are more constrained by data than others. There are obvious differences in the definition of the ecosystem boundaries, some sites identifying boundaries on the basis of recognisable limits of plant communities, others, e.g. Devon Island in Canada and Hardangervidda in Norway, represent major landscape areas defined by topography.

There are many definitions of the term tundra, but we are here not concerned with this question, important though it is. The IBP Tundra Biome adopted a "liberal" classification (4), and the sites which have cooperated in the Tundra Biome studies are given in Fig. 1. Their selection was partly accidental, partly designed, but they comprise a wide range of conditions from high polar and alpine, through sub-polar and sub-alpine to relatively warm temperate bogs. Tundra is sometimes defined as areas with a mean annual air temperature below 0°C; if the temperature regimes of the IBP tundra sites (Fig. 2) are examined, the great variety of patterns reflect their geographical location, and the annual temperature course is more important to the biology of individual ecosystems than is the mean annual value.

The tundra sites have been grouped on combinations of the climatic and soil characteristics (6) and on their vegetation (17, 18). These groupings or classifications, summarised in Figs. 3–5, provide an ecological framework to which particular sites can be referred, and indicate the degree of ecological similarity between geographically dispersed sites.

8

Tundra areas, and the arctic region in particular, have recently proved to be of major importance to industrial society. The interest in the Arctic is mainly focussed on energy fuels, and the findings of appreciable amounts of oil and natural gases is at present the most important cause for industrial development in tundra (15). The introduction of industrial enterprises of the magnitude of oil extraction and transportation in fragile tundra environments has resulted in an increased interest in ecological aspects of the Arctic. It is important to understand the mechanisms controlling the structure and function of tundra ecosystems, in order to provide a scientific basis for management prescriptions which will minimise the effects of industrial exploitations.

Man has lived in tundra areas for a long time, and although native populations are but a small fraction of the total populations in circumpolar countries, they are an integral part of many tundra ecosystems through reindeer husbandry, hunting and fishing. Modern society is causing radical changes in ancient land use patterns through its effect on the wildlife resource and on the social structure and relationships of native peoples. The reciprocal relationship between man and tundra is discussed in some of the following papers, reflecting the increased interest in arctic people and their land use.

The tundra areas are also of considerable interest for tourism. This may in many cases be a threat, and alpine tundra areas close to winter/summer resorts have witnessed extensive destruction of the vegetation cover, and disturbance of wildlife. Some of the natural environments will be changed, e.g. by road and ski-lift constructions, but the changes should be only those which are necessary and within the carrying capacity of the area (5) so that the attractions which are the basis of the tourism industry are not destroyed (11). The Antarctic islands are also threatened by tourism (cf. 3, 9, 10), but this has to some extent been restricted by the Antarctic Treaty (op. cit.).

It is hoped that the IBP Tundra studies will form a useful basis for further specific investigations aimed at answering questions of importance to a balanced utilisation of the vast but fragile tundra ecosystems.

REFERENCES

1. Bliss, L.C. & Wielgolaski, F.E. (eds.) 1973. Primary Production and Production Processes, Tundra Biome. Edmonton: IBP Tundra Biome Steering Committee. 256 pp.
2. Brown, J., Pitelka, F.A. & Coulombe, H.N. 1970. A word model of the Barrow ecosystem. – In: Fuller, W.A. & Kevan, P.G. (eds.) Productivity and Conservation in Northern Circumpolar Lands, pp. 41–43. Morges, Switzerland: IUCN.
3. Collins, N.J., Baker, J.H. & Tilbrook, P.J. 1975. Signy Island, maritime Antarctic. – In: Rosswall, T. & Heal, O.W. (eds.) Structure and Function of Tundra Ecosystems. Ecol. Bull. 20: 345–374. Stockholm: Swedish Natural Science Research Council.
4. Dahl, E. & Gore, A.J.P. 1968. Proceedings Working Meeting on Analysis of Ecosystems: Tundra Zone. Ustaoset, Norway. Oslo: Norwegian IBP Committee (Mimeographed). 87 pp.
5. Franz, H. & Holling, C.S. 1974. Alpine Areas Workshop. IIASA Conference Proceedings CP–74–2. Laxenburg, Austria: IIASA. 80 pp.
6. French, D.D. 1974. Classification of IBP Tundra Biome sites based on climate and soil properties. – In: Holding, A.J., Heal, O.W., MacLean, S.F. & Flanagan, P.W. (eds.) Soil Organisms and Decomposition in Tundra, pp. 3–25. Stockholm: IBP Tundra Biome Steering Committee.

7. Heal, O.W. (ed.) 1971. IBP Tundra Biome Working Meeting on Analysis of Ecosystems, Kevo, Finland. Stockholm: IBP Tundra Biome Steering Committee. 298 pp.

8. Holding, A.J., Heal, O.W., MacLean, S.F. & Flanagan, P.W. (eds.) 1974. Soil Organisms and Decomposition in Tundra. Stockholm: IBP Tundra Biome Steering Committee. 398 pp.

9. Jenkin, J.F. 1975. Macquarie Island, Subantarctic. – In: Rosswall, T. & Heal, O.W. (eds.) Structure and Function of Tundra Ecosystems. Ecol. Bull. 20: 375–397. Stockholm: Swedish Natural Science Research Council.

10. Lewis-Smith, R.I. & Walton, D.W.H. 1975. South Georgia, Subantarctic. – In: Rosswall, T. & Heal, O.W. (eds.) Structure and Function of Tundra Ecosystems. Ecol. Bull. 20: 399–423. Stockholm: Swedish Natural Science Research Council.

11. McConnell, M.P. 1970. The potential for, and impact of tourism in the Northwest Territories. – In: Fuller, W.A. & Kevan, P.G. (eds.) Productivity and Conservation in Northern Circumpolar Lands, pp. 291–296. Morges, Switzerland: IUCN.

12. Moore, J.J. (ed.) In press. Tundra: Comparative Analysis of Ecosystems. Cambridge University Press.

13. Odum, E.P. 1971. Fundamentals of Ecology. 3rd ed. Philadelphia–London–Toronto: W.B. Saunders Co. 574 pp.

14. Rosswall, T. & Heal, O.W. (eds.) 1975. Structure and Function of Tundra Ecosystems. Ecol. Bull. 20: 1–450. Stockholm: Swedish Natural Science Research Council.

15. Sater, J.E., Ronhovde, A.G. & Van Allen, L.C. 1971. Arctic Environment and Resources. Washington, D.C.: The Arctic Institute of North America. 310 pp.

16. Schamurin, V.F., Polozova, T.G. & Khodachek, E.A. 1972. Plant biomass of main plant communities at the Tareya station (Taimyr). – In: Wielgolaski, F.E. & Rosswall, T. (eds.) Proc. IV. International Meeting on Biological Productivity of Tundra, Leningrad, USSR, pp. 163–170. Stockholm: IBP Tundra Biome Steering Committee.

17. Webber, P.J., Wielgolaski, F.E. & French, D.D. In press. A comparison of sites by multivariate methods. – In: Moore, J.J. (ed.) Tundra: Comparative Analysis of Ecosystems. Cambridge University Press.

18. Wielgolaski, F.E. 1973. Vegetation types and biomass in tundra. – Arctic and Alpine Res. 4: 291–305.

19. Wielgolaski, F.E. & Rosswall, T. (eds.) 1972. Proc. IV. International Meeting on Biological Productivity of Tundra, Leningrad, USSR. Stockholm: IBP Tundra Biome Steering Committee. 320 pp.

Note:

The volumes published by the IBP Tundra Biome Steering Committee are available from
Dr. T. Rosswall, Department of Microbiology, Agricultural College, S–750 07 Uppsala 7, Sweden:

Bliss and Wielgolaski (1) $ 4;
Heal (7) $ 3;
Holding *et al.* (8) $ 5;
Wielgolaski and Rosswall (19) $ 4;

Site abbreviations used in Figs. 3–5 arranged in alphabetical order of initial letters of abbreviation.

A   Abisko (Stordalen), Sweden (pp. 265–294)
  AH   Elevated area
  AP   Minerotrophic depression

AG   Agapa, USSR (pp. 141–158)
  AGB   Boggy community
  AGH   Spotted hummocky tundra
  AGP   Spotted polygonal tundra
  AGS   Spotted nanopolygonal tundra
  AGW   Wet tundra

B   Barrow, Alaska, USA (pp. 73–124)
  B2   Site 2, meadow
  B4T   Site 4, polygon trough
  B4B   Site 4, polygon dry basin
  B4R   Site 4, polygon ridge
  B4H   Site 4, high center polygon

D   Devon Island, Canada (pp 17–60)
  DC   Beach ridge crest
  DB   Beach ridge slope
  DM   Mesic meadow

DK   Disko Island, Greenland
  DKA   *Alchemilla*
  DKS   *Salix herbacea* heath
  DKSB   Snow bed
  DKF   Fell-field

G   Glenamoy, Ireland (pp. 321–343)
  GB   Bog
  GG   Grassland on bog
  GF   Forest on bog

H   Hardangervidda, Norway (pp. 225–264)
  HLH   Lichen heath
  HDM   Dry meadow
  HWM   Wet meadow
  HBF   Birch forest
  HSB   Snow bed
  HWT   Willow thicket

K   Kevo, Finland (pp. 193–223)
  KB   Birch forest
  KP   Pine forest
  KM   Low alpine heath
  KPa   Palsa bog

M   Macquarie Island, Subantarctic (pp. 375–397)
  M1   Grassland, site 1
  M2   Grassland, site 2
  M3   Herbfield, site 3
  M4   Herbfield, site 4

MH   Moor House, UK (pp. 295–320)
  MHC   *Calluna* bog (Sike Hill, dry)
  MHE   *Eriophorum* bog (Cottage Hill)
  MHS   *Sphagnum* bog

  MHJ   *Juncus* moor
  MHG   *Festuca-Agrostis* grassland

N   Niwot Ridge, USA
  NK   *Kobresia* dry meadow
  ND   *Deschampsia* wet meadow

P   Mt. Patscherkofel, Austria (pp. 125–139)
  PL   Loiseleurietum
  PLH   *Loiseleuria* heath
  PV   *Vaccinium* heath

S   Signy Island, maritime Antarctic (pp. 345–374)
  SMT   Moss turf
  SMC   Moss carpet
  SOM   Old moraine
  SMK   Marble knoll
  SG   Grassland

SG   South Georgia, Subantarctic (pp. 399–423)
  SGA   *Acaena*
  SGG   *Festuca*
  SGP   *Poa*
  SGR   *Rostkovia*
  SGF   Fell-field
  SGFS   Flush slope, *Juncus*

T   Tareya, USSR (pp. 159–181)
  TSC   Spot crust
  TSF   Spot fissure
  TRB   River bank
  TAT   *Astragalus-Dryas* tundra
  TP   Polygon, low centres
  TB   Polygon, borders
  TSD   Spotted *Dryas*-sedge mossy tundra
  THD   Hummocky *Dryas*-sedge mossy tundra
  TPB   Polygonal bog

Ary-Mas and Maria Pronchitsheva Bay have not been included in these analyses.

11

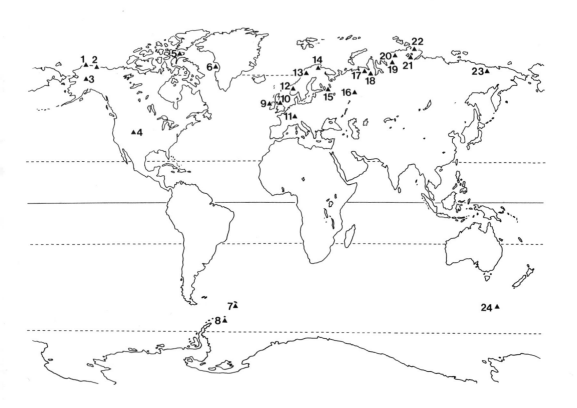

Figure 1. The IBP Tundra Biome sites
1. Barrow, 2. Prudhoe Bay, 3. Eagle Summit, 4. Niwot Ridge, 5. Devon Island, 6. Disko Island,
7. South Georgia, 8. Signy Island, 9. Glenamoy, 10. Moor House, 11. Mt. Patscherkofel and Hoher
Nebelkogel, 12. Hardangervidda, 13. Stordalen (Abisko), 14. Kevo, 15. Lammin-sou☆, 16. Petchora☆,
17. Sivaya Maska☆, 18. Harp, 19. Agapa, 20. Tareya, 21. Ary-Mas, 22. Maria Pronchitsheva Bay,
23. Kolyma, 24. Macquarie Island.

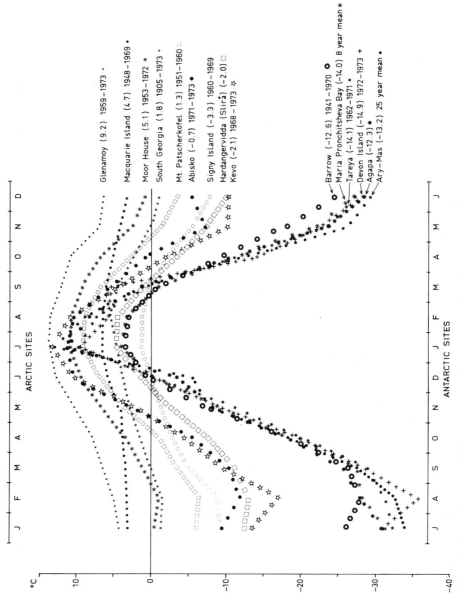

Figure 2. Annual patterns of air temperature at some tundra sites. Site names are given with mean annual temperatures in brackets and periods of observations. Data from (14).

13

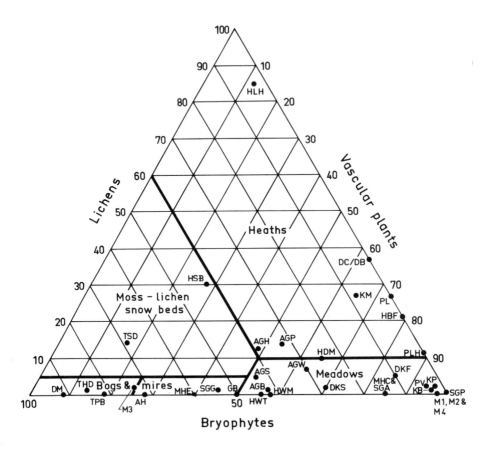

Figure 3. IBP Tundra Biome sites grouped according to percentage of vascular plants, bryophytes and lichens in relation to total aboveground living biomass. Diagram from (18), site data plotted from (16, 18) and the present volume.

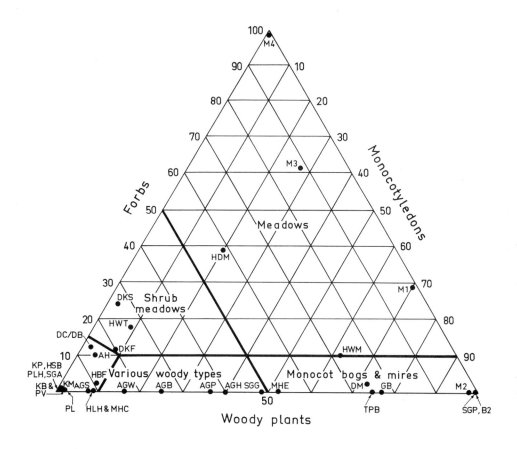

Figure 4. IBP Tundra Biome sites grouped according to vascular plant types present; percentage of woody plants, forbs and monocotyledons in relation to total aboveground living vascular plant biomass. Diagram from (18), site data plotted from (16, 18) and the present volume.

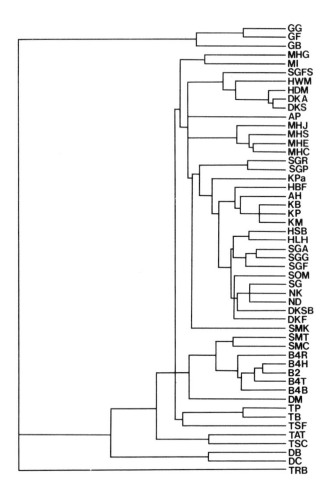

Figure 5. Classification of IBP Tundra Biome sites based on climate and soil data. Dendrogram showing clustering of sites by group mean cluster analysis. Site codes are given on p. 11. (Expanded version from (6).)

Rosswall, T. & Heal, O.W. (eds.) 1975.
Structure and Function of Tundra Ecosystems.
Ecol. Bull. (Stockholm) 20: 17–60.

DEVON ISLAND, CANADA

L.C. BLISS

INTRODUCTION

Site description

The Truelove Lowland (75°33′N, 84°40′W), one of five lowlands along the northeast coast of Devon Island, is 43 km^2 and consists of 41 % sedge-moss dominated meadows, 20 % cushion plant-lichen and -moss communities, mostly on gravelly raised beaches, 12 % dwarf shrub heath and grass communities in rocky sites, 22 % ponds and lakes, and 5 % lichen barrens on rocks and small coastal salt marshes (Fig. 1). To the east and south a plateau, covered with sedimentary rocks of probable Cambrian age, rises 300 m above the Lowland. The Devon ice cap to the south (12 to 15 km) rises from the nearly barren polar desert at ca 450 m to a maximum thickness of 2 080 m a.s.l.. Much of the island was deglaciated 8 700 years B.P. (2).

These coastal lowlands result from postglacial rebound following deglaciation. Radiocarbon dating has shown that the upper marine limit is at 76 m, dating to ca 9 450 B.P. With uplift, lagoons were cut off by raised beaches, resulting in the formation of shallow lakes (7 to 8.5 m deep, mean depths 2.9 to 3.2 m for the three deeper lakes — Fish, Immerk, and Loon). Shallower lakes have filled in with lacustrine sediments to form meadows.

The Truelove River which originates at the ice cap to the south, ca 30 km inland, provides a minor influence on the Truelove Valley (3.6 km^2) and the Lowland. The Gully River, which flows from the barren plateau to the east, provides a relatively rapid flow of water through Loon Lake and influences the sedge-moss meadows in the northeastern part of the Lowland from surface flow in spring (Fig. 1).

In the Lowland seven major topographic-plant community units are recognized with several subdivisions (Table 1). Many of the biological data are presented in relation to the land area of these units. Of these, hummocky sedge-moss meadows, raised beaches including the transition zone to meadows, and the rock outcrops were studied most intensively.

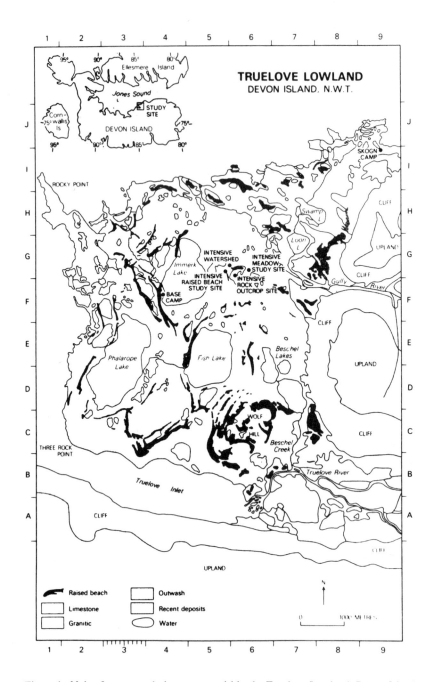

Figure 1. Major features and place names within the Truelove Lowland, Devon Island.

Table 1. Major topographic-plant community units within the Truelove Lowland

	Area (ha)	Lowland (%)
Salt water marsh	22	0.5
Lichen barren on limestone pavement	180	4.2
Cushion plant-lichen on raised beaches	215	5.0
on limestone pavement	26	0.6
on rock outcrops	52	1.2
Cushion plant-moss on raised beaches	274	6.4
separate from raised beaches	298	6.9
Dwarf shrub heath on rock outcrops	533	12.4
Hummocky sedge-moss meadow	883	20.6
Frost-boil sedge-moss meadow	796	18.4
Wet sedge-moss meadow	88	2.1
Lakes and ponds	933	21.7
Total	4 300	100.0

General research plan

The major objective was to determine energy flow through the system and its major components (functional groups of organisms, e.g. vascular plants, herbivorous invertebrates, mammalian carnivores; and landscape units, e.g. meadows vs. raised beaches). The Lowland was studied for four summers and one winter.

Following the systematic inspection of a series of meadows and raised beaches, a representative of each was selected and designated as the Intensive Study Site. These sites (Fig. 1) were within ca 700 m of each other. An adjacent rock outcrop was selected for more limited research (meteorology, plant production) and an adjacent small meadow watershed for part of the hydrology study. The intensive research program of meteorology, soils, energy and water flux, plant production, photosynthesis, invertebrates, decomposition and soil microbiology, and surface manipulation were all established within the intensive meadow and raised beach sites.

A number of meadows and raised beaches were studied so that the data would be representative of the biological diversity within the different meadows and raised beaches. Thus an extensive study program was established by each researcher in three to eight additional meadows and raised beaches for the study of permafrost, soils, meteorology, plant production and invertebrates. Research on the more mobile vertebrates (birds, muskox, lemming, hare, fox, weasel) was conducted whenever the animals could be found in the Lowland and Truelove Valley. The data collected, especially for muskox grazing and defecation and bird nesting, were related to the topographic-plant community units.

Site representativeness

Within The Queen Elizabeth Islands (ca 418 000 km^2) only ca 2 % of the land consists of sedge-grass tundra with raised beaches (5). The rest of the land is a polar semi-desert (43 %) with typically 5 to 2 % cover of flowering plants plus 30 to 50 % cover of lichens and mosses, polar desert (35 %) with 0 to 3 % plant cover including lichens and mosses, or ice caps (20 %).

If compared with other IBP tundra sites the lowland sedge meadows are most closely related in terms of ecosystem structure and function to the Low Arctic sedge-grass meadows at Barrow, Alaska and the hummocky sedge-moss meadows of the several sites on the Taimyr Peninsula. The areas of dwarf heath shrub, limited to the warmer and more wind protected sites (rock outcrops and sides of narrow valleys) are related to dwarf heath shrub communities of the Low Arctic. The cushion plant-lichen and cushion plant-moss communities of the raised beaches occur in similar coastal sites in the northern islands and are the dominant communities on Banks, Victoria, Prince of Wales, and King William Islands. In these latter islands, sedge-moss meadows are the second most important community (8). The plateau is typical of the Polar Desert in which plants are generally a minor feature. The area described in this paper is more lush biologically than most of the landscape because of its proximity to the edge of the plateau (0.5 km).

ENVIRONMENTAL CONDITIONS

Macroclimate

The long polar day in summer reduces the temperature gradient from low to high latitudes while the temperature gradient steepens in winter with the polar night. This semi-annual fluctuation strengthens and weakens the zonal air flow over the Arctic, resulting in shifts of the jet streams and the Arctic Front (9). With the weaker zonal flow in summer, cyclonic storms increase, yet are minor in these latitudes. This infrequency of cyclonic storms, the shallow pressure gradients in summer, and low annual precipitation result in a cold desert climate.

Truelove Lowland has mean monthly temperatures from June through August similar to those of Resolute Bay, Cornwallis Island (315 km to the west), but significantly cooler than Eureka, Ellesmere Island 510 km north of Devon. Precipitation in May through September is less in the Truelove Lowland than at Resolute Bay, but significantly greater than at Eureka. Approximately 50 % of the annual precipitation occurs as snow.

Using accumulated degree days above 0°C, the Intensive Meadow Site averaged 304 degree days (1.5 m) per year from 1971–73. Comparable data for the same years were 243 at Resolute Bay, 229 at Rea Pt., Melville Island, 162 at Isachsen, Ellef Ringnes Island, 333 at Eureka, Ellesmere Island, and 321 degree days at Barrow, Alaska. The Truelove Lowland was warmer than all but one station north of 74° and was comparable to Barrow, Alaska for the three summers.

20

Mesoclimate and microclimate

Mean weekly net radiation became negative the week ending 24 September, 1972 and became positive the week ending 30 May, 1973. Global radiation averaged 2.10 to 2.50 kJ cm^{-2} d^{-1} in late June, 1.36 to 1.78 in late July and 0.84 to 1.26 kJ cm^{-2} d^{-1} in late August each year (13). Most summers about 50 % of the global radiation occurs before 80 to 90 % of the Lowland is snow-free.

Mean weekly air temperatures at 1.5 m were 0°C or above 12 weeks in 1970 and 1971, 9 weeks in 1973 and only 7 weeks in the unusually cold and dry 1972 season. For much of July and August daily temperature averaged 3 to 5°C. On only 1 to 4 days per summer do maxima reach 10 to 15°C and these periods were often associated with föhn winds.

For three summers a network of weather stations gathered radiation, temperature, wind, and relative humidity data throughout the Lowland, on the plateau, and in the Truelove Valley. The Valley and the base of the west-facing cliffs are the first to warm in spring and become snow-free. These areas support early spring grazing of muskox and the Valley is a calving ground in May. Mean weekly temperatures show that Wolf Hill and rock outcrops warm up first in the Lowland and these sites plus the raised beaches are "hot spots" in summer (5° to 7°C) while meadows are somewhat cooler (4° to 5°C). The coastal fringe of rock and meadow is the last to warm and is always cool (2° to 3°C). By late August the Lowland is nearly iso-thermal (1° to 2°C) and by early September all areas are below 0°C (13).

One of the best indicators of macro- and mesoclimate is the ice-free season of the large lakes. Ice thickness generally averages 1.5 to 1.7 m on the three large lakes but only about 1 m on Loon and Beschel Lakes. Immerk Lake was ice-free 6 weeks in 1971, 3 weeks in 1973 and 1974, 2 days in 1970, and only a 50 % thaw in 1972. These events along with time of snow melt and general summer temperature regime have an influence on the biota, yet the year to year biological response (plant growth, nesting of birds, muskox grazing) was less dramatic than might be assumed.

Length of the growing season (daily mean temperature above 0°C at 10 cm) averaged 78 days in the meadow and 97 days on the raised beach in 1970 and 1971, but only 45 days in the meadow and 51 days on the raised beach the same two years using the criterion snowmelt to 50 % leaf coloration. The latter method is a more accurate measure of a plant growing season and is used elsewhere in this paper.

Precipitation was lowest in 1972 when there was little open sea and highest in 1970 and 1973, summers of more open sea (Table 2). Periods of heavy rain are infrequent; most occur as light drizzle for short time periods. By late August snow predominates over rain. Winter snow averaged 10 to 20 cm on the wind exposed crests of raised beaches, 20 to 40 cm on the sedge meadows, slopes of the raised beaches, and lake surfaces, and 50 to 150 cm in the raised beach to meadow transition zone and in rock outcrops.

Relative humidity was consistantly high, reflecting the abundant moisture supply from the lakes, ponds and saturated to near saturated meadow soils (Table 2).

Wind speed (10 m) generally averaged 2 to 3 m s^{-1} in June through August and only 1 to 2 m s^{-1} in winter. During periods of cyclonic storms and föhn winds, speeds of 25 to 35 m s^{-1} occurred, usually for less than 24 h (13). One to three föhn winds occurred

Table 2. Mean monthly climatic data, Base Camp, Truelove Lowland, summers 1970 through 1973

Variables	1970				1971			
	June	July	Aug.	Sept.	June	July	Aug.	Sept.
Radiation (kJ cm^{-2})	38.9	54.0	43.9	n.d.	87.0	72.0	32.2	16.0
Screen temperature ($^\circ$C)								
min	-0.6	1.1	0.4	-4.2	0.0	1.8	0.7	-4.7
mean	1.7	4.2	3.3	-1.7	3.5	4.5	2.7	-2.7
max	3.9	7.1	6.1	0.9	7.0	7.3	4.7	-0.6
Relative humidity air (%)	86	87	91	n.d.	88	83	79	85
Wind speed (10 m) (m s^{-2})	n.d.	2.7	3.6	3.0	1.1	2.7	3.7	2.2
Precipitation (mm)	25.8	9.2	17.3	17.1	0.0	15.3	34.8	13.2

Variables	1972				1973			
	May	June	July	Aug.	May	June	July	Aug.
Radiation (kJ cm^{-2})	64.0	81.6	66.1	39.7	89.1	81.2	58.2	31.4
Screen temperature ($^\circ$C)								
min	-15.2	-5.4	0.8	-0.1	-15.0	-1.4	1.4	2.5
mean	-10.5	-2.5	3.0	2.2	-10.1	1.6	3.9	5.6
max	-5.8	-0.5	5.3	4.4	-5.1	4.4	6.4	8.7
Relative humidity air (%)	83	82	86	87	80	85	87	85
Wind speed (10 m) (m s^{-1})	2.6	3.7	3.0	3.3	2.2	3.3	3.7	2.3
Precipitation (mm)	1.1	7.6	4.4	9.5	0.0	12.2	39.9	22.1

n.d. = not determined

each summer, and depending upon when they occurred, they had a profound biological influence. A föhn wind in late June 1970 melted most of the lowland snow in a 48 h period, leaving lemming without cover since summer burrows were still frozen. Late winds in 1971 melted much of the early snow, again exposing these animals to severe temperature conditions. Lemming numbers were much lower in 1970 and 1972 than in 1971 and especially in 1973 (14).

Microenvironmentally the raised beaches and sedge-moss meadows are very different, especially belowground. Profile data show that maximum temperatures occurred in mid-July, within 2 to 3 weeks of the solar high (Fig. 2). Temperatures were highest within the plant boundary layer, 1 to 2 cm on the raised beach and 2 to 15 cm on the meadow. In the warm 1971 summer, mean weekly surface and near surface temperatures reached 10°C to 15°C for three weeks at both intensive sites. The cool 1972 summer had mean weekly temperatures of 5° to 7°C for three weeks on the meadow and only 4°C for two weeks on the raised beach (13) (Table 3). Accumulated degree days above 0°C at 10 cm averaged 424 on the raised beach and 309 on the meadow (1971–73). In the meadow degree days totaled 443 in the warm 1971 summer but only 137 in the cool 1972 summer at 10 cm. At −5 cm, degree day accumulation was 2.2 to 4.9 times greater in the beach ridge than in the meadow soils.

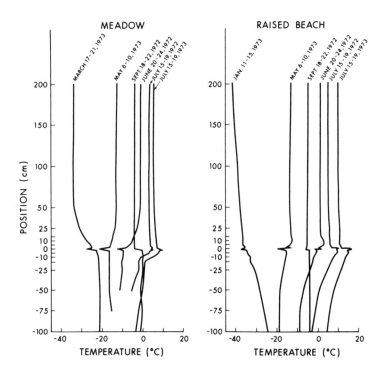

Figure 2. Temperature profiles (5 day means) for select periods that depict seasonal temperature for the Intensive Raised Beach Ridge and the Intensive Meadow Study Site in 1972 and 1973.

Table 3. Climatological summary for the Base Camp (raised beach), Devon Island in 1972–73.

Variables	J	F	M	A	M	J	J	A	S	O	N	D	Year
Radiation (kJ cm^{-2})	0	0	12.9	50.5	89.7	77.8	59.8	35.3	19.9	35.7	0	0	381.6
Screen temperature (°C)													
min	−46.1	−47.2	−48.3	−41.7	−26.7	−6.7	−2.5	−1.1	−20.6	−31.1	−40.6	−45.6	−29.9
mean	−30.8	−35.8	−28.7	−19.7	−9.3	0.4	9.6	5.6	−5.3	−14.2	−22.7	−28.2	−17.5
max	−20.5	−29.5	−17.0	−10.6	7.2	13.3	12.2	16.1	1.7	−4.4	−12.2	−20.5	5.4
Relative humidity air (%)	n.d.	n.d.	n.d.	78	80	85	87	85	79	81	n.d.	n.d.	82
Wind speed (10 m) (m s^{-1})	1.8	1.3	1.1	1.5	2.2	3.3	3.7	2.3	2.2	2.1	1.4	1.9	2.1
Precipitation (mm)	15.0	6.6	12.4	15.2	0	12.2	56.4	21.1	5.5	102.9	25.9	10.4	283.6
Snow depth (cm)	15	10	18	18	15	0	0	0	0	10	18	13	–

n.d. = not determined

Wind speeds at 25 cm at the intensive sites and 40 cm at the extensive study sites generally averaged 1 to 2 m s^{-1} (Table 3) except at the Cliff Base and Plateau Stations where weekly averages were often 2 to 6 m s^{-1} or greater.

Soils in the hummocky sedge-moss meadow were always at or near saturation below 3 to 5 cm. In this surface layer soil water potential was generally above −2 bars. The sandy-gravelly beach ridge soils are better drained, thaw to a greater depth (80 to 100 cm) and have considerably lower soil water potentials (−10 to −30 bars, average −20 bars) (1). Dissipation of global radiation differs greatly in relation to site and sunny vs. cloudy conditions (Table 4). Net radiation (R_n) accounts for only 57 to 67 % of global radiation on a cloudy day but 80 to 90 % on a sunny day. Because of the general plant and soil resistances to water loss on the raised beach, latent heat flux (LE) accounts for a much smaller component of net radiation than does sensible heat (H). The magnitude of these components is reversed in the meadow where there is much more water available (1).

On the beach ridge, surfaces covered by crustose lichens conserve soil moisture compared with fruticose lichen and bare soil surfaces. In these sites LE for vascular plants is a relatively small component. This helps to explain why vascular plants appear to be more numerous and to grow better in association with crustose lichens than in sites with few lichens in polar semi-deserts in the western and southern arctic islands.

Table 4. **Radiant energy flow (J cm^{-2} min^{-1}) on the raised beach and hummocky sedge-moss meadow for clear sky and overcast conditions**

Site	$L_d^{☆}$	R_t	R	L_μ	R_n	H	LE	G
Sunny period								
Raised beach	2.24	1.74	0.27	2.33	1.39	1.06	0.21	0.12
Meadow	2.24	1.74	0.19	2.23	1.56	0.62	0.80	0.14
Cloudy period								
Raised beach	1.85	0.70	0.15	2.00	0.40	0.26	0.11	0.04
Meadow	1.85	0.70	0.05	2.03	0.47	0.16	0.26	0.05

☆ L_d = longwave incoming, R_t = shortwave incoming, R = reflected shortwave,

L_μ = longwave up, R_n = net radiation, H = sensible heat, LE = latent heat flux, G = soil heat flux.

Permafrost

Permafrost underlies the area to an estimated depth of 250 m on Rocky Point along the coast and 500 to 650+ m on the Lowland and plateau. Eleven holes drilled to a depth of 1 to 9 m revealed that mean annual temperature was generally $-15°C$ in the upper 1 to 5 m (12). The geothermal gradient was greatest in granite-gneiss and lowest in the plateau dolomite. Beach ridges and meadows were somewhat intermediate. Thermal conductivity and snow depth are important factors in thickness of the active layer and in permafrost temperatures. Active layer thickness on the plateau averaged 30 to 40 cm in 1971 and 1972, but was 60 to 70 cm in the wetter and warmer summer of 1973. Average thaw depth was 30 to 50 cm in the sedge-moss meadows and ice-wedge polygons. Depth of thaw was greater on the raised beaches and coastal limestone (60 to 120 cm) and deepest on the inland rock outcrops (110 to 220 cm).

Soils

Soils of the area belong to the Cryosolic Order, soils of permafrost regions. The hummocky sedge-moss and wet sedge-moss meadows are underlain by mineral soils (Gleysolic Static Cryosols) and organic soils (Fibric-Organo Cryosols). The mineral soils generally lack gley colors or mottles, are low in organic matter and are near neutrality (46). The organic soils have a lower pH and are very low in mineral content (Table 5). Peats are at least 30 to 50 cm in depth, in places extending to 70 to 80 cm. The frost-boil sedge-moss meadows with more active soil churning have soils similar to the hummocky sedge-moss meadows (Gleysolic Turbic Cryosols).

Soils of the raised beaches correlate well with topographic position and plant communities. Regosolic Static Cryosols occur on the well-drained crests, Brunisolic Static Cryosols occur on the slopes with cushion plant-lichen communities and in the transition zone to meadows with cushion plant-moss communities. These soils are neutral to alkaline, low in available nutrients and the Brunisolic soils (arctic brown) have a weakly oxidized B-horizon with an accumulation of mobile humus (1 to 2 % carbon) (46).

Within the granite-gneiss rock outcrops, where a *Cassiope* heath predominates, Regosolic Static Cryosols occur. These soils are slightly acid and have a partially humified organic layer that overlays a humus-rich mineral horizon.

Soils of the plateau show little variation and development. These Gleysolic Turbic Cryosols are developed from highly calcareous glacial till. There are only slight color changes and no evidence of soil development with depth. These soils are very subject to freeze-thaw cycles and to mass flow in the direction of subsurface water flow (46).

Hydrology

Within the High Arctic, water budgets are dominated by snow (65 to 85 %) rather than rain and most small watersheds discharge 80 to 90 % of their annual runoff over a 2 to 3 week period. Where drainage patterns are well developed and with little rain the landscapes (upper 5 to 10 cm) become relatively dry by early August.

In the Truelove Lowland this pattern is modified by the addition of water from the plateau via Gully River and several small streams at the base of the east cliff (Fig. 1).

Table 5. Physical and chemical analyses of soils from the two intensive study sites within the Truelove Lowland and the polar desert of the plateau

Measurement	Raised beach (Brunisolic static cryosol)				Hummocky sedge meadow (Fibric organo cryosol)		Plateau (Gleysolic turbic cryosol)	
1. Horizon	Ahk	Bmk	Ck	Ck	Of$_1$	Of$_2$	Ckgy$_1$	Ckgy$_2$
2. Depth (cm)	0–10	10–26	26–46	46–62	31–23	23–0	0–21	21–36
3. pH (H$_2$O)	7.8	8.0	8.1	8.1	6.5	6.2 (6.1–6.8)	7.8	7.7
4. Moisture (% dw, range) ☆☆	20(10–31)	7(4–14)			617 (277–1476)	329 (106–1075)		
5. Bulk density (g cm^{-3})	1.3	1.6	1.6	1.6	0.2+ (0–30)	0.2+ (10–13 cm)		
6. Maximum thaw (cm)	58(45–73)☆				27(21–30)		36–70	
7. Gravel (%) (>2 mm)	17	57	50	64			Est.<20	Est.<20
8. Sand (%) (2–.05 mm)	92	97	91	90			22	20
9. Silt (%) (.05–.002 mm)	6	2	9	8			53	48
10. Clay (%) (<.002 mm)	2	1	0	1			25	32
11. Total organic C (%)	3.7	trace	0.0	0.0	38.1	42.2	0.2	0.0
12. Total nitrogen (%)	0.12	0.03	0.01	0.01	3.06	2.68	0.03	0.03
13. C/N	31				12.5	15.7		
Exchangeable cations (meq 100 g^{-1}) Only on soils with pH <7.5								
14. Calcium					110.7	93.5		
15. Magnesium					32.5	23.4		
16. Sodium					0.2	0.2		
17. Potassium					0.4	0.2		
18. Hydrogen					13.0	22.3		
19. C.E.C. (meq 100 g^{-1})					132.5	127.9		
Sol. (available) nutrients (ppm)								
20. Nitrate – N	1	0	0	0	4	6		
21. Phosphorus – P	1	1	1	1	0	0		
22. Potassium	12	5	3	5	129	47		
23. Sodium	1	1	1	2	21	25		
Soil temperature (°C) ☆☆	1970 (5 cm)	1971	1970 (10 cm)	1971	1970 (5 cm)	1971	1970 (10 cm)	1971
24. July mean min.	5.3	5.6	4.4	6.3	2.9	2.2	1.8	–0.1
25. July mean max.	13.0	17.3	10.3	12.6	5.7	3.7	3.4	0.4
26. July mean	8.8	11.1	7.7	9.3	4.1	2.9	2.3	0.1

Sources: Data from Walker and Peters unless otherwise stated; ☆ Svoboda (44); + Muc (25); ☆☆ Courtin & Labine (13).
Methods: 3 – water saturated paste; 5 – core techniques; 7 – sieve techniques; 8, 9, 10 – pipette for raised beach samples (organic matter removed), hydrometer for plateau (organic matter only removed); 11 – total carbon (dry combustion) minus $CaCO_3$–C (manometric determination); 12 – macro-Kjeldahl; 14, 15, 16, 17 – atomic absorption on ammonium acetate extract; 18 – NaOH titration on barium acetate extract; 20 – $CuSO_4$–Ag_2SO_4 extraction; 21 – NH_4–H_2SO_4 extraction; 22 – NH_4Ac extraction; 23 NH_4Ac extraction; 24, 25, 26 – Grant recorder.

These streams and river provide water all summer to the sedge meadows in the Gully River and Beschel Lakes drainages. These waters increase the flushing rate within Loon and Beschel Lakes compared with the other three large lakes. This helps to explain the lower production of Loon Lake as discussed later. The Truelove River water has a minor influence on the Truelove Valley and Lowland.

Early snowmelt runoff is rapid over a surface with only a 1 to 2 cm thaw. The meltwater soon establishes a shallow and unstable surface flow. In the Intensive Watershed, maximum flow from meltwater was 100 l s^{-1} km^{-2} in 1972, 63 l in 1973 and with a 56 % increase in mean snow depth, flow peaked at 116 l s^{-1} km^{-2} in 1974 (38).

After the peak in surface flow, there is a steady decline in flow rate with most surfaces relatively dry by late July. Flow increases or is reinitiated by the few rains of a frontal or undefined origin. Most rains are of low intensity and yield little water ($<$ 0.5 mm). This lateral flow of water is more important in the hummocky than in the frost-boil meadows and helps to explain their location and plant production dynamics. Most hummocky sedge-moss meadows are located near the base of the east cliff, along Gully River and west and north of the larger lakes where there are streams that cut through or around the younger and often more pronounced raised beaches. Surface flow of water moves 4 to 11 % of the litter within a meadow (25), but only a small amount (0.1 %) is removed via stream flow because plants act as a barrier to lateral movement.

Water budget studies in the Intensive Watershed Site (0.1 km^2), a hummocky sedge-moss meadow, in 1972 and 1973 show that in these contrasting cool-dry and warm-wet summers the proportions of snow and rain and the ways in which water was dissipated changed considerably (Table 6). Evapotranspiration and runoff both increased in magnitude in the warmer season. The Gully River Watershed is much larger (22.4 km^2), is at a higher elevation, and receives more precipitation. Its hydrologic regime is similar to other high arctic rivers in showing a spring snow melt flood and a high response to rain. Throughout the summer, flow rates decreased. The Truelove River Watershed drains the ice-cap, the barren plateau and the U-shaped river valley. After snowmelt most of the water comes from the ice-cap. Throughout the summer, maximum diurnal flow lags the solar high by ca 12 h (16).

Table 6. **Water budget (mm) for the Intensive Watershed study site on the Truelove Lowland**

Year	Precipitation			Run-off	Snow-evaporation	Evapo-transpiration	Change in storage
	Snow	Rain	Total				
1972	132	36	168	66	32	69	+ 1
1973	111	73	184	83	41	121	−61

PALEOECOLOGY

Due to the shallow nature of peats in the Lowland, it is difficult to obtain Post-Wisconsin paleobotanical information. Cores taken to a depth of 170 cm in the raised center of an ice-wedge polygon contained thin peat horizons. The basal peat in this locality was radiocarbon dated by Barr (7) to be 2 450 ± 9 years. The pollen spectrum is poor quantitatively and qualitatively. Pollen of *Salix arctica* Pall., Cyperaceae, and Poaceae is most numerous and shows no major shift in importance with depth. The spectrum corresponds qualitatively to present vegetation (18).

Macrofossil plant remains were well preserved throughout the profile. Mosses, rich in species diversity predominate but with considerable amounts of *Salix* and *Dryas* leaves and twigs below 125 cm. No seeds or fruits were found, probably the result of low production and their harvest by birds and lemming. The limited data do not permit an evaluation of oscillating climate as has been possible in Greenland and northern Ungava (18).

PRIMARY PRODUCTION

Plant communities

Of the 18 units (14 plant communities) mapped in the Lowland (26), seven were studied in greater detail. These included three types of sedge meadow, two cushion plant types on raised beaches, a dwarf heath shrub type within rock outcrops, and coastal salt marshes. Communities were based upon general plant growth form and percent cover of the species. Those sampled communities with a similar floristic and structural composition were grouped together to comprise a community type.

Meadows

Within the Lowland, sedge dominated meadows on the poorly drained lands around lakes and between raised beaches occupy the greatest area (41 %). Hummocky sedge-moss meadows (50 % of meadow complex) occur on moist to wet soils where there is little churning of surface soils (Fig. 3). The dominant species in decreasing order are *Carex stans* Drej., *Eriophorum angustifolium* Honck., *Salix arctica*, *Carex membranacea* Hook., *Polygonum viviparum* L., and *Arctagrostis latifolia* (R. Br.) Griseb (25). A total of 29 flowering plants were sampled in 12 sites (stands) and 30 species of bryophytes in 4 sites. *Cinclidium arcticum* (B.S.G.) Schimp and *Drepanocladus revolvens* (Sev.) Warnst accounted for 27 % of the bryophyte cover (88 %) (18). Peats are generally shallow (10 to 15 cm). Mosses form the hummocks and sedges then occupy these sites. These meadows are more common near the base of the cliff and the north and west part of the Lowland where there is more surface water after snowmelt.

Frost-boil sedge-moss meadows (45 % of meadow complex) occur on 1 to 5° slopes, down from hummocky sedge meadows or downslope from raised beaches and rock outcrops. They are most important in the central and southern part of the Lowland, adjacent to the large lakes. These meadows are saturated after snowmelt but are drier in late summer. Frost-boils account for 42 % of the surface. While some have active soils,

Figure 3. Hummocky sedge-moss meadow at the Intensive Study Site. *Carex stans* dominates with lesser amounts of *C. membranacea* and *Arctagrostis latifolia.*

Figure 4. Crest of the Raised Beach Intensive Study Site. The frames in the foreground are insect emergence traps, stakes mark plots for vegetation sampling, and the large white box houses the meteorological recording instruments.

most "boils" are covered with blue-green algae, a few mosses, and where most stable, *Carex membranacea* occurs (25). Of the 25 species of vascular plants sampled at 5 sites, *Eriophorum triste* (Th. Fr.) Hadac & Löve, *Carex membranacea, C. stans, C. misandra* R. Br., *Salix arctica*, and *Arctagrostis latifolia* are the most important (25). The drier site meadow mosses predominate (*Orthothecium chryseum* (Schwaegr. *ex* Schultes) B.S.G., *Ditrichum flexicaule* (Schwaeger.) Hampe, and *Campulium arcticum* (Williams) Mitt.; 19 species were sampled at one site (28). Moss cover averaged 78 %.

The wet sedge-moss meadows, located along streams, account for only 5 % of the meadow complex. The peats (30 to 50+ cm) are saturated with slow moving water. Of 21 vascular plant species sampled at three sites only *Carex stans* has a high cover (25). Sixteen species of bryophytes were sampled at one site; *Drepanocladus revolvens, Messia triquetra* (L. *ex* Richt.) Aongstr., *Calliergon giganteum* (Schimp.) Kindb., and *Cinclidium arcticum* were most important (28). Moss cover averaged 93 %.

The meadow complex is most closely related to the sedge meadow tundra of the Low Arctic (8).

Raised beaches

Another important habitat type in the Lowland is the raised beach complex (11.4 %). Physiographically and ecologically it is divided into a crest and slope complex (cushion plant-lichen community) and a transition (cushion plant-moss community) downslope that typically grades into a hummocky sedge-moss meadow. An additional 1.8 % of the Lowland is covered by the former and 6.9 % by the latter community types (Table 1). An additional 4.2 % is a lichen barren with limited amounts of cushion plant cover on limestone pavement. A total of 24.3 % of the Lowland is covered by this general type of vegetation which is most closely related to the Polar Semi-desert complex of the High Arctic.

Vascular plants account for only 20 % cover on the crest zone of the raised beaches. *Dryas integrifolia* M. Vahl., *Carex nardina* Fries, *Saxifraga oppositifolia* L., and *Salix arctica* provide nearly all of the cover (44) (Fig. 4). Fifteen lichen species provide 38 % cover, 10 moss species 5 % and 37 % is bare gravel and sand. Of the lichens, *Alectoria pubescens* (L.) R.H. Horne, *Thamnolia vermicularis* (Sev.) Ach., *Umbilicaria arctica* (Ach.) Nyl. and *Leconora epibryon* (Ach.) Ach. are most important (32). Winter snow cover averages 10 to 20 cm.

The slopes have deeper snow cover (30 to 40 cm), low soil moisture and a higher vascular plant (35 %) and lichen (40 %) cover. Cover for *Dryas* is increased nearly threefold while *Salix* is greatly reduced. *Carex rupestris* All. not present on the crest, is the third most important species (44). *Lecanora epibryon, Thamnolia*, and *Hypogymnia subobscura* (Vain.) Poelt. are the most important lichens (32).

The lower slopes (transition zone), where snow is deeper (50 to 150 cm) and melts later (2 to 4 weeks) than on the crest, form a physiographic and ecologic unit. Here vascular plants account for 58 %, mosses 29 %, and lichens 13 % cover. *Dryas* and *Carex rupestris* increase in cover and *Cassiope tetragona* (L.) D. Don. is prominent. Of the 25 species of moss, *Tortella arctica, Tomenthypnum*, and *Aulocomnium turgidum* (Wahlenb.) Schwaegr. are most important (28).

Rock outcrops

This habitat is the most diverse floristically and ecologically of the three major units. Six plant community types are recognized (10), although the dwarf shrub heath type predominates (48 %). Where winter snow melts in late June or early July *Cassiope tetragona* with lesser amonts of *Salix, Dryas, Saxifraga oppositifolia, Carex rupestris* and *C. misandra* occur. There are typically 28 to 31 vascular plant species and 32 bryophyte species present. Important mosses include *Ditrichum flexicaule, Hylocomium splendens* (Hedw.) B.S.G., *Distichium capillaceum* (Hedw.) B.S.G., and *Polytrichum juniperinum* Willd. *ex* Hedw. (10, 28). The most common lichens are *Cetraria nivalis* (L.) Ach., *Thamnolia vermicularis*, and *Dactylina arctica* (Hook.) Nyl.

Rhacomitrium lanuginosum forms large mats among the rocks and *Alectoria ochroleuca* (Hoffm.) Mass., *A. nigricans* (Ach.) Nyl., *Umbilicaria lyngei* (Ach.) Tuck. and *U. arctica* (Ach.) Nyl. lichen communities are common on rocks and the former two species grow loosely on moss.

Small late snow-bed communities (23 %) occur where snow melts in mid-July. *Alopecurus alpinus* J.N. Smith., *Saxifraga cernua* L., *S. nivalis* L., *S. tenuis* Sm., *Oxyria digyna* (L.) Hill and *Luzula nivalis* (Laest.) Beurl. are common along with the mosses *Polytrichastrum alpinum* (Hedw.) Smith, *Hylocomium splendens*, and *Tomenthypnum nitens* (Hedw.) Loeske (10).

In small dry sites near the top of rock masses, small (15 %) grass-rush communities are found. *Hierochloe odorata* (L.) Beauv., *Poa glauca* Vahl., *Festuca brachyphylla* Schultes, Lindb., *Luzula confusa* and *Potentilla hyparctica* Malte dominate (10). Cushion plant-lichen communities also occur.

Salt marshes

Where lagoons occur along the coast, narrow bands (10 to 30 m) of salt marsh occur (19). *Puccinellia phryganodes* (Trin.) Scribn. and Merr. is the only abundant species although scattered plants of *Carex ursina* Dew., *Stellaria humifusa* Rottb. and *Cochlearia officinalis* L. ssp. *groenlandica* Hult. occur.

Standing crop and net plant production

As used here, standing crop (phytomass) may include all or part of the following: live, attached dead litter, aboveground or belowground material. Net production refers to plant growth of that year and productivity refers to rate of production. Belowground, unless otherwise stated, refers to rhizome and root material. Stem bases of sedges contained within the moss mat are considered part of aboveground phytomass. Data presented are mean values for four hummocky sedge-moss meadows but for only one study site in each of the other plant community – habitat types.

Sedge meadows

Within the meadow complex, vascular plant and total standing crop were greatest in the hummocky sedge-moss meadow (Tables 7 and 8). Net production and bryophyte standing crop were greater in the wet sedge-moss meadows. Root and rhizome production were greatest here, probably the result of more uniform plant density, slightly higher soil nutrient content, and better aeration from flowing water.

Bryophytes contributed 40 to 42 % of the total standing crop in the wet sedge-moss and frost-boil sedge-moss meadows and 28 % in hummocky sedge-moss meadows, yet their net production accounted for 59 % in the wet sedge meadow and only 8 to 18 % in the other two types. Bryophyte production was exceptionally high along stream banks (28), with growth of individual shoots nearly 10 times greater than in the hummocky sedge-moss meadows.

Assuming only one crop of algae was produced per year (single celled algae), soil algal production was estimated to be 4 g m^{-2} in the hummocky sedge-moss meadows (Table 8) (42). Bluegreen algae comprise 75 to 90 % of the total algal standing crop. No estimates were made for algae growing on the mosses. Production in this microhabitat may have been several times that within the soil. Mats of *Nostoc commune* Vaucher form a prominent feature of meadows, averaging 17 mg m^{-2} in hummocky sedge-moss meadows and 9 mg m^{-2} in wet sedge-moss meadows (42).

As in other tundra sedge-moss communities, belowground production constituted the major part of plant growth (70 to 80 %). *Carex stans*, the major contributor to production, reached a peak plant height 30 days after snowmelt. At that time about 32 % of the aboveground tissue was alive. Although about 50 % of *Carex* living shoot tissue occurs in the moss layer (3 to 5 cm), only about 10 % annual aboveground production occurs here because these shoot bases live several years (25).

These plants carry about 10 % of their green tissue over winter and this tissue continues to function the next year. Some of this green tissue is consumed by muskox in winter. Only 2 to 8 % of the *Carex stans* flower each year. About 55 % of the sedge root system is alive and roots and rhizomes live 3 to 4 years; shoots live 5 to 6 years before flowering and dying (25). Aboveground plant production averaged 42 to 47 g m^{-2} in 1970–1972, being greatest the warmest year (1971) in the hummocky sedge-moss meadow (25). Using the potential growing season (snowmelt to 50 % leaf coloration) of 50, 55, and 45 days in the hummocky sedge-moss meadow, daily productivity averaged 2.79, 2.80, and 3.37 g m^{-2} in 1970–72 respectively. Although the length of the growing season varied by 20 %, plant production varied by only 9 % indicating that these high arctic plants are adapted to "near normal" plant growth even in colder and drier summers.

Belowground production accounted for 69 to 70 % of total production in the hummocky sedge meadow and 74 % in the frost-boil sedge-moss community (25).

Raised beaches

Standing crop and net annual production are significantly less on the beaches than in the meadows, the product of a very different plant growth form and microenvironment. Plant cover and net production were significantly greater in the cushion plant-moss (transition) than in the cushion plant-lichen community (crest and slope) (58 % vs. 20 % vascular plant cover and 53 vs. 23 g m^{-2} net production). The high standing crop of the crest and slope compared with the transition (462 vs. 453 g m^{-2} respectively) results from many dead plants on the slope (44). In contrast with meadows where woody plants provide 19 to 28 % of aboveground production, on the beaches they constitute 60 to 75 % of aboveground production. Roots contribute only 14 % to total production (43).

Dryas integrifolia was the major producer in the two plant communities and along

Table 7. Plant phytomass (g m^{-2}) for the major plant communities (habitat types) at the peak of aboveground standing crop, Truelove Lowland. The mean values are based upon 1 to 3 years of data

	Plant Community						
Component	Hummocky sedge-moss meadow	Wet sedge-moss meadow	Frost-boil sedge meadow (total area) ☆	Rock outcrop Dwarf shrub heath (total area) ☆☆	Raised beach Crest & slope Cushion plant-lichen	Raised beach Transition Cushion plant-mosses	Plateau
Lowland areas (ha)	883	88	796	533	292	572	n.d.
Vascular plants							
Aboveground							
Green	35	40	27	16	18	48	5
Non-green live	51	38	29	30	71	78	10
Dead	187	120	101	65	298	192	19
Belowground							
Rooting depth (cm)	25	25	25	12	20	20	10
Live	1 085	691	353	215	57	50	4
Dead	938	604	313	72	n.d.	n.d.	n.d.
Mosses							
Green live	194	385	150	} 130	15	600	232
Brown live	714	712	400	{			
Lichens	0	0	0	8	49	23	0
Algae	4	2	1	n.d.	n.d.	n.d.	n.d.
Total	3 208	2 592	1 374	536	498	991	270
Vascular Plant Ratios							
Ratio live above:dead above	1:2.2	1:1.5	1:1.8	1:1.4	1:3.3	1:1.5	1:1.2
Ratio live below:dead below	1:0.9	1:0.9	1:0.9	3:1.0	n.d.	n.d.	n.d.
Ratio live above:below	1:12.6	1:8.9	1:6.3	1:4.7	1:0.6	1:0.4	1:0.3

☆ Vegetation occupies 51 % of total area   ☆☆ Vegetation occupies 32 % of total area   n.d. = not determined

Table 8. Net plant production (g m^{-2}) for the major plant communities (habitat types) in the Truelove Lowland. The mean values are based upon 1 to 3 years of data

	Hummocky sedge-moss meadow	Wet sedge-moss meadow	Frost-boil sedge meadow		Rock outcrop Dwarf shrub heath		Raised beach Crest & slope	Raised beach Transition	Plateau
			Data expressed:		Data expressed:		Cushion plant-lichen	Cushion plant-moss	
			vegetated area (51 %)	total area	vegetated area (32 %)	total area			
Lowland areas (ha)	883	88	796		533		292	572	n.d.
Vascular plants									
Aboveground									
Monocotyledons	32.5	44.1	38.2	19.1	0.8	0.3	1.0	2.3	0
Forbs	4.5	1.5	3.2	1.6	1.5	0.5	4.9	5.0	2.0
Woody plants	7.7	0	16.4	8.2	15.6	5.0	9.3	20.0	0
Belowground	103.6	129.7	118.6	59.3	89.6	28.5	2.6	4.6	0.4
Total vascular plants	148.3	175.3	176.4	88.1	107.5	34.3	17.8	31.9	2.4
Mosses	33.0	102.6 ☆	15.0	7.5	20.0	8.4 ☆☆	2.0	20.0	5.0
Lichen	0	0	0	0	3.5	1.1	2.5	1.5	0
Algae	4.0	2.0	2.0	1.0	n.d.	n.d.	>0.1	n.d.	0
Total	185.3	279.9	193.4	96.6	131.0	43.8	22.4	53.4	7.4

n.d. = not determined

☆ Based upon 15 % streamside habitat with 293 g m^{-2} net production and 85 % wet meadow habitat with 69 g m^{-2} net production.

☆☆ Includes 2 g m^{-2} estimated moss production of *Rhacomitrium lanuginosum* upon rocks.

with *Saxifraga oppositifolia* has leaves that function for two years; *Cassiope tetragona* leaves function for five years. *Dryas*, a conservative species, produces 2 to 3 leaves per shoot each year and only 8 % of the aboveground standing crop is green tissue. Along with low photosynthetic rates (21) this helps to explain low rates of annual production. Shoot growth is greater on the southeast side of clumps and leaves are inclined on this exposure which reduces the angle of incidence and therefore leaf temperature. Most species complete their shoot growth 2 to 3 weeks after snowmelt. In contrast with meadows, most roots are alive.

Mosses and lichens each contributed about 10 % to total production on the crest and slope, but lichen production dropped to 3 % in the transition zone while moss production increased to 37 % (Table 8). Lichen cover and standing crop showed little variation in relation to age of raised beaches. On a younger ridge (3 300 B.P.), lichen cover averaged 33 % (22 to 54 %) and standing crop 31 g m^{-2} (13 to 97 g m^{-2}) while on the Intenstive Study Site (7 500 B.P.) cover averaged 35 % (25 to 59 %) and standing crop 39 g m^{-2} (26 to 58 g m^{-2}) (45). Vascular plant cover and standing crop of vascular plants also varied little with increased age of the beaches (beaches < 6 200 B.P. averaged 27.1 g m^{-2} and > 7 000 years B.P. 28.4 g m^{-2} net production) (45). Although accurate estimates of production are not possible, net production probably averages 2 to 10 % of the standing crop of fruticose and foliose lichen species (1 to 3 g m^{-2}).

Using a potential growing season of 60, 55, and 45 days in 1970–72 respectively, daily productivity of vascular plants averaged 0.37, 0.39, and 0.56 g m^{-2} in the three years for a net production of 22 to 25 g m^{-2} (44). On these drier sites, production was highest in the cool and drier year (25 g m^{-2}) than in the warmer summers.

Rock outcrops

Within the granite-gneiss rocky sites, standing crop of vascular plants was similar to the raised beaches, yet plant production, species composition, and the component contribution of belowground production was very different (Tables 7, 8) (10). In *Cassiope tetragona*, the dominant species of the dwarf shrub heath community, leaves turn green 3 to 8 days after snowmelt and flower 21 to 25 days after melt. Shoot growth occurs slowly much of the summer with individual shoots producing flowers about every 2 to 4 years. About 50 % of the shoots produced flowers in 1972 following the warm 1971 summer (10). Many shoots live 30 to 60 years. Green tissue is a small component of the aboveground biomass (14 to 21 %) with *Cassiope* contributing 80 to 94 % of the total and 65 % of net annual aboveground production.

In mesic sites with deeper soils, a more lush vascular plant cover occurred. Standing crop and net production averaged 2 655 and 153 g m^{-2} respectively. In more typical sites with lower soil moisture levels (70 % of these heath communities), the values were 1 673 and 108 g m^{-2} respectively (10). Since only 32 % of the rock outcrops contain vascular plant communities these values are greatly reduced when expressed on the basis of the total area (Tables 7, 8). Mosses and lichens are important contributors to these communities. In addition the standing crop of large mats of *Rhacomitrium lanuginosum* averaged 4 928 g m^{-2} on dry rocky sites and *Hylocomium splendens* 2 218 g m^{-2} in mesic sites between rocks (45).

Plateau

Less detailed data were gathered from this Polar Desert, but the data show that mosses predominate (86 % of standing crop). Most vascular plants form small rosetts and have leaves that remain green more than one year. Estimates of annual production were 10 to 15 g m^{-2} in this unusually "lush" polar desert site within 0.5 km of the edge of the plateau (44). As on the raised beaches, root standing crop is small with most roots produced each year. Further inland toward the ice cap, including 20 m from the ice in early August, total plant cover was less than 2 % over vast areas (Fig. 5). Here annual plant production is less than 0.5 g m^{-2}.

Figure 5. Polar desert at 400 m, Devon Island. The complex pattern of sorted polygons (1 to 2 m) and strips have < 2 % vascular plant and moss cover. Note Devon Icecap in background.

Production processes

Photosynthesis and respiration

Field and laboratory measurements of net assimilation were made on *Dryas*, but only field measurements for *Carex stans* (21, 22). *Dryas* leaves turn red then green over a ten day period after snowmelt. Leaf temperatures were 2° to 8°C higher in red leaves, possibly an adaptation to initiating a more rapid start in photosynthesis, since the leaves are not photosynthetically active for several days after snowmelt. When the red leaves begin to fix CO_2 the rates are higher than when the leaves turn green. This was especially true in the cooler 1972 summer (21).

Average rates of net assimilation over time were 0.5 to 1.5 mg CO_2 g^{-1} h^{-1} with maximum whole plant rates (ca 7 mg CO_2 g^{-1} h^{-1}) occurring at "night" when leaf temperatures were lower. Fixation rates of single leaves in the laboratory were higher, (14.5 mg CO_2 g^{-1} h^{-1}) at 15°C and were still 4 mg CO_2 g^{-1} h^{-1} at < –1°C. Maximum fixation rates in summer were reduced only 35 % (at 15°C) after cold treatment, indicating that they maintain a considerable degree of cold hardiness in summer. Above 10 to 12°C, rates of respiration increase more rapidly than photosynthesis (0.19 mg CO_2 g^{-1} °C^{-1} between 0° and 12° and 0.43 above 12°C).

Dryas leaf temperatures rise to 30° to 40°C (max 47°) on clear days when adjacent ambient temperature is 5° to 10°C, indicating high resistance to water vapor and CO_2 exchange. Spectral radiation data show no diurnal shift in red: far red ratio throughout the summer. Thus it is doubtful that a "physiological night" occurs (22).

Carex stans, the dominant meadow sedge, responds quite differently. Maximum mean hourly values of 15 to 16 mg CO_2 g^{-1} h^{-1} were very common. Light compensation occurs at 0.04 J min^{-1} vs. ca 0.17 J min^{-1} in *Dryas*. In contrast with *Dryas*, *Carex* has a mid-day photosynthetic lag and rates are lower at "night" with a low sun angle. These results are comparable to others working with tundra sedges, grasses, and cushion plants.

A regression model (49), derived from field data and expressing net assimilation as a function of radiation and temperature, indicated an above- and belowground production of 56 g m^{-2} of *Dryas* cushion (100 % cover) by 20 August. This is in reasonable agreement with Svoboda's (44) measured 78 g m^{-2} (using 100 % plant cover).

The agreement is equally good for the *Carex* model, as Muc (25) reported 138 g m^{-2} of monocotyledon production and the model predicted 126 g m^{-2} by 30 August (49). *Carex* root growth continues 2 to 3 weeks after cessation of shoot growth.

Plant water relations

Water loss from *Dryas* plants was less than for lichen or bare soil microsites on the raised beach (1). These plants maintained low leaf water potentials (ψ), −20 to −40 bars, mean −32 bars. Soil water potentials in the rooting zone (−5 to −10 cm) averaged −20 bars (1). The apparent high leaf resistances to water loss help explain the low rates of net assimilation, slow growth rates, and long life (30+ years) of the cushion plants.

Although *Carex stans* is rooted in a saturated soil, leaf ψ is lower than might be expected, averaging −14 bars (−4 to −40 bars). Low leaf ψ indicates water deficit that results from the inability of the plant to absorb water from cold and poorly aerated soil.

Even under controlled environmental conditions, these plants maintained low leaf ψ (−8 to −16 bars) with normal soil watering. Dormant leaves maintained potentials of −33 to −60 bars. Such values probably help maintain cold hardiness by increasing solute concentration (1).

Leaf resistances were greater in *Dryas* (20 s^{-1} cm^{-1}) than in *Carex* (16 s^{-1} cm^{-1}) on a sunny day, but remained higher in the latter species on a cloudy day (16 vs. 5 s^{-1} cm^{-1}) than in *Dryas* (1). The combined high leaf resistance of *Carex* and canopy resistance of moss result in about equal amounts of water loss from the two microsites.

Carbohydrate reserves

In *Carex stans* and *C. membranacea* there was an early season depletion and a late season carbohydrate accumulation, reserves being used for early season growth. Oligosaccharides were 10 to 50 times greater than monosaccharides while starches accounted for only 20 to 30 % of total carbohydrate content (24).

Oligosaccharides also predominate in the total carbohydrate content of cushion plants. While seasonal shifts occurred in *Dryas* and *Saxifraga oppositifolia*, they were less pronounced than in the sedges and reserves were a smaller percentage of dry weight than in the sedges. The high proportion of oligosaccharides is probably related to high frost resistance (43).

HERBIVORES

As in most ecosystems, diversity of herbivore species, biomass, and production are relatively small. The soil invertebrate component is the most diverse. The fauna includes only one large herbivore, the muskox (*Ovibos moschatus* Zimmermann), one microtine, the collared lemming (*Dicrostonyx groenlandicus* Traill), and one important avian grazer, the greater snow goose (*Chen caerulescens* L.). Arctic hare (*Lepus arcticus monstrabilis* Nelson) occurs in the Lowland but in only small numbers and Peary's caribou *(Rangifer tarandus pearyi* J.A. Allen) was present in the recent past (10—20 years). Of the invertebrates, some species of Tardigrada, Nematoda, Diptera, Hymenoptera and all Lepidoptera are herbivores.

Invertebrates

Populations

At least 200 species of insects occur on the Lowland with the 45+ species of chironomid and 23 species of muscoid flies being energetically the most important, and numerically almost equal to the Collembola. Other orders include 31 species of Collembola, 6 Anoplura, 13 Lepidoptera, 1 Trichoptera, 3 Coleoptera and 36 Hymenoptera. There are 9 species of Araneida (20) and 19 known species of Acarina. The insect orders Hemiptera, Orthoptera, and Neuroptera, which are important in lower latitudes, are absent from the Lowland. Other important groups not found here but which occur in low arctic and alpine tundras are: Mollusca, Myriapoda, Isopoda, Pseudoscorpionida, and Opilonida (35). This reduction in diversity attests to environmental severity; yet for this latitude, the invertebrate fauna is comparatively diverse.

Invertebrates are slow to mature at this latitude. Sharp (39) reported it takes 1—2 years for the collembolan *Hypogastrura tullbergi* Schaeffer to reach sexual maturity, and it can then survive an additional 3—4 years. An intensive life history study of *Gynaephora groenlandica* Homeyer and *G. rossii* Curtis (moths) indicates these species may take 10 or more years to complete their life cycle (37).

The best estimates of population size for 11 groups are given in Table 9. With the exception of Collembola and Nematoda all groups have greater densities in the hummocky sedge meadow than on the beach ridge (36). Using pitfall traps, Collembola were most active in June whilst mites were most active in July and August, 1973 (39). Much of the invertebrate activity occurs in the 0—5 cm layer in the meadows and 0—10 cm layer in the drier raised beaches. The cushion plant-moss community of the raised beach transition zone has much higher populations of nematodes (30) and somewhat higher populations of Collembola (39) than the crest, with its lower organic content and drier soil.

Production

Protozoa, including naked amoebae, ciliates, and testates, are estimated to produce a minimum of 1.5 g m^{-2} yr^{-1} total tissue in the hummocky sedge-moss meadow. This calculation uses 2—6 generations yr^{-1} (36). Protozoa are the most important invertebrate group in the meadow, and are suspected to be more important than shown here.

Table 9. Estimated mean populations (seasonal averages) of various invertebrate groups in Truelove Lowland. All data are numbers $\times 10^3$ m^{-2}. Data are from Ryan (36) Sharp (39) and Procter (30)

	Raised beach	Hummocky sedge meadow
Nematoda	3 840	1 273
Rotifera	0.2	6.0
Enchytraeidae	9.7	33.3
Tardigrada	2.5	4.2
Copepoda	0	30.0
Ostracoda	0	0.6
Cladocera	0	0.03
Acarina	7.4	9.6
Collembola	18.2	7.0
Diptera Nematocera	0.3	11.2

Soil invertebrates, especially Nematoda and Enchytraeidae, are the next most significant energy releasers (30, 36). These and other soil invertebrates feed on bacteria, fungi, and decaying organic material. Herbivory is a minor component of invertebrate consumption. Mean production estimates for adult Chironomidae and Sciaridae are 10 mg m^{-2} yr^{-1} on raised beaches and 90 mg m^{-2} yr^{-1} in the sedge meadows (36). The meadow values are greater than those reported for lakes (66 mg m^{-2} (23)). Preliminary annual production estimates for the Nematoda on the raised beaches and sedge meadows are 931 mg m^{-2} and 163 mg m^{-2} respectively (30). All the invertebrates (including Protozoa) at the hummocky sedge meadow produce 56.5 kJ of tissue and respire on an average 100.4 kJ m^{-2} yr^{-1}. On the raised beach ridge site the total is 31.0 kJ tissue produced and 25.1 kJ respired. Total invertebrate production is estimated to be 2.6 g m^{-2} yr^{-1} on the hummocky sedge-moss meadows and 1.4 g m^{-2} yr^{-1} on raised beaches (36).

Consumption and bioenergetics

Larvae of the two *Gynaephora* species feed on *Dryas integrifolia, Saxifraga oppositifolia* and *Salix arctica*. Field studies and calculations based on ground surface temperatures show that larvae grow to about 2.2 times their initial weight per average year (37). Efficiency of conversion of digested food into production is low (24 %) when compared to other Lepidoptera. This results from feeding on mature leaves, and because the larvae frequently stop feeding yet continue to metabolize energy. In an average generation 68 % of the digested energy is lost by respiration while 32 % remains as produced animal tissue, including 4 % viable egg tissue. These larvae consume 0.1 % of the net aboveground vascular plant production of raised beaches (37).

Procter (31) has measured respiration rates of 14 species of invertebrates at 2°, 7°, and 12°C. In all cases, respiration rates were highest at 12°. Oxygen consumption per unit weight ranged from 5.0 μl mg^{-1} dw h^{-1} at 12°C for *Daphnia pulex* Leydig, to 0.3 for the mite *Hermannia subglabra* Berlese at 12°C. For most species, oxygen consumption ranged from 0.7 to 1.3 μl mg^{-1} dw h^{-1}. For most species, Q_{10} was between 2 and 4, although Q_{10} of 6.5 for *Gynaephora rossii*, 8.0 in a *Lebertia* sp. (Acarina), and 8.8 in *Folsomia agrelli* Gisin (Collembola) suggest a breakdown in metabolic regulation (31).

Vertebrates

Populations

Arctic hare is a minor species on the Lowland, with an estimated 5–10 animals, probably because *Salix arctica* is not an abundant forage species and because of recent hunting pressure.

Collared lemming occurred in relatively small numbers most years. Estimates were 744, 1 404, 278, and 7 200 lemmings in 1970 through 1973 respectively (14). In 5 of the 7 years for which data were available, numbers of lemming declined from July to August and built up during the following winter. There is no evidence for a three–four year cycle in these animals.

Low population levels in 1972 may have resulted from high mortality due to insufficient snow cover, or inaccessibility of food due to heavy snow crust in early winter 1971, the result of the fall föhn winds. The sudden snowmelt in late June 1970 (föhn winds) prior to the thaw of summer burrows influenced the population size that year.

The data indicate that males reach puberty at a smaller size in years of a low population. Females bear only one or two litters in summer in contrast with more southern populations. Litter size averaged 5.7 with a slight increase (not statistically significant) in years of high numbers. The overall sex ratio was 50 % male, but males formed a much smaller component in the non-breeding population (31–48 %) (15).

In general summer burrows are on the raised beaches or rock outcrops, while winter nests are in the beach ridge transition to frost-boil sedge meadows or back slopes of raised beaches that terminate abruptly in meadows, sites of deep winter snow. Burrow density was geatest in the ice-wedge polygons (533 ha^{-1}), intermediate in the beach ridges (115 ha^{-1}) and lowest in the meadows (27 ha^{-1}). On the beach ridges and meadows most burrows are under rocks, microsites that thaw to a greater depth because rocks act as a heat sink (14).

Muskox population dynamics were studied all four years. Based upon one or more aerial surveys each year the total population along the northeast of Devon was 154 animals in 1970, 149 in 1971, 257 in 1972, and 271 in 1973 (17). There have been good calf crops each year and if cows breed only every other year then 75 % of cows eligible for breeding in the fall of 1971 produced a calf in 1972 (17) and about 43 % of all cows had calves in 1973 (calculated from (17)). Some cows may breed in successive years. The large increase in animal numbers from 1971 to 1972 is due to incomplete coverage in the 1970 and 1971 surveys which took place after the animals dispersed into valleys and uplands for summer feeding (17).

Snow geese are the only important avian herbivore in the Lowland with 22–26 birds in three of the four years. A few pairs nest in the area. Several hundred birds return to the nearby Sparbo-Hardy Lowland each summer mostly as a non-breeding population.

Consumption and bioenergetics

It is known that arctic hare generally feed on *Salix arctica*. The field bioenergetic studies used only this species and it was observed that only growing tips were consumed (40). Energy consumed by an adult male and a juvenile female (40) were significantly higher than laboratory data for the same animals under cold stress studies (47). This indicates that the species can reduce its energy requirements in periods of temperature stress and that the combination of reduced basal metabolism and thermal conductance are distinct physiological adaptations for this species which lives in a cold environment with a low primary production (47).

Lemming craters were examined (701) in September 1971 and 96 % terminated in one of four species of Dicotyledons. *Dryas* accounted for 43 %, *Saxifraga oppositifolia* 37 % and *Salix arctica* 12 %. *Carex* shoots are used in winter nests, but there was no evidence that sedges were used for food. Summer observations of plants near winter nests show that many shoots of *Saxifraga oppositifolia* and *Dryas integrifolia* had been utilized (15).

The diet of muskox consists mostly of monocotyledons although they utilize *Salix arctica* where it occurs in mats on Rocky Point. Based upon the number of muskox days on the Lowland, their "average" daily intake requirements, and the known standing crop of forage, it was estimated that < 1 % of potential herbage is removed. In 1972, six meadows were sampled in which ca 19 % of the total area was grazed and 15 % of the potential aboveground biomass was harvested. Almost regardless of area, 80 % of the estimated biomass had been harvested in each crater (8). Similar sampling in 1973 showed that on the average 24 % of the area of individual meadows had been grazed and that 85 % of the assumed biomass had been removed in each crater (17).

Feeding experiments on captive muskox at Fairbanks provided a digestibility of 64 % based upon three methods that gave results with no significant differences (17).

The 12 month study of muskox in 1972—73 showed that of the total population, 17 % utilized the Lowland throughout the year (17) and that the Lowland and Valley comprise 16 % of the total lowland area available to the population. This Lowland plays a more significant role than this at key seasons for there is a greater percentage of sedge meadows in this Lowland than in the others. In 1972—73, 30—40 % of the total herd was in the Lowland from January through March and 26 % in April (17). From June through November only 6—10 % of the total herd was present. This dramatically demonstrates the importance of these limited oases for winter grazing. The peak count of 115 animals in February contrasts with the 20—25 animals in July and August for each of the four years of the study.

Further evidence of seasonal utilization and habitat selection by muskox comes from the data on dung production and distribution. In hummocky sedge-moss meadows, standing crop of winter dung averaged 3.0 and 3.9 g m^{-2} and summer dung 0.5 and 0.6 g m^{-2} in 1972 and 1973. These values are much higher than for raised beaches (0.8 and 1.3 in winter, 0.3 and 0.5 g m^{-2} in summer) during the same two years (11). Muskox rarely defecate while grazing and they graze very little on the beaches. They do, however, seek these drier sites for resting and ruminating (Fig. 6), and defecate at the end of the resting period. In general the amount of time spent grazing, ruminating, and resting does not change very much from summer to winter, again indicating the efficiency of these animals.

Based upon decomposition-accumulation comparisons and carbon loss studies, the time required for dung decomposition is 10 to 12 years on raised beaches but only 5 to 6 years in meadows. In the meadows dung is often found half-buried by mosses (11).

Figure 6. Cushion plant moss community with muskox, near Beschel Creek.

CARNIVORES AND INSECTIVORES

With the low vertebrate herbivore base it is obvious that the carnivore standing crop and production would also be low. The major carnivore species are the arctic fox (*Alopex lagopus* L.), short-tailed weasel (*Mustela erminea* L.), long-tailed jaegers (*Stercocarius longicauda* Vieillot) and parasitic jaegers (*S. parasiticus* L.). Of the insectivores the two principal species are lapland longspurs (*Calcarius lapponicus* L.) and snow bunting (*Plectrophenax nivalis* L.). Several species of duck nest and feed on the Lowland as do the red-throated loon (*Gavia stellata* Pontoppidan).

Vertebrates

Populations

Arctic fox spend much of the winter on the sea ice scavenging polar bear kills and return to the land in May for denning. Foxes were observed on the Lowland each year but were studied only from 1970 to 1972. In 1971 there were four foxes from May through July and six foxes from August through October. No young were produced on the Lowland from 1970–72 (33) but the one active den produced several whelps in 1973. No estimate was made of weasel production.

There was an average of 46 long-tailed jaegers and 13 parasitic jaegers on the Lowland in the four years. Only two pairs of long-tailed jaeger and 2 to 5 pairs of parasitic jaegers nested on the Lowland in 1970 and 1972. Snow bunting averaged 338 (144 to 603) over the four years. This principal passerine species spends about five months on the Lowland. Data from 1970–72 indicate that the post fledgling count declined from 421 to 321 birds but increased to 603 in 1973. In 1972 there was a 76 % recruitment of young birds; mean clutch size was 3.6 (29). The 82 breeding lapland longspurs had only a 51 % recruitment of young in 1972; mean clutch size was 4.3. Post-breeding bird density of passerines was 35.4 km^{-2} on the Lowland (29) for four years, densities lower than the Alaskan and European IBP tundra sites.

Consumption and production

Field observations and gut analyses showed that foxes prey or scavenge on at least 12 species of birds and mammals. In summer they cache eggs and consume them in fall before returning to the sea (33).

Feeding experiments were conducted on Devon during the summer and four animals were taken south for winter feeding tests. The bioenergetic data indicate that the five foxes estimated to have occupied the Lowland from 1 May through 30 September would have consumed 157.5 kg of biomass. This is more energy than in the small vertebrates that the Lowland supports. Thus the fox must range over other lowlands in order to obtain this magnitude of food (33). Data of Pattie (29) show that arctic fox accounted for 42 % of nest predation in 1972, a year in which 63 % of all observed nests were predated.

Bioenergetic studies on a weasel indicate that the daily consumption of an adult averaged 15.4 g d^{-1}. This again illustrates the high percentage utzilization of small vertebrates that must take place to keep these carnivores alive. Weasels predated an average 12 % of lemming nests each winter (33).

Snow buntings feed on seeds upon arrival, shift to spiders, and by late June to insects. In early August the young birds and molting adults shift to ripening fruits and seeds.

Feeding experiments showed that adult bunting ingest 9.7 g d^{-1}, a consumption of 222 kJ bird^{-1} d^{-1} (29). Digestive efficiency was 40 % for seeds and 73 % for invertebrates. Metabolic requirements were 104 kJ bird^{-1} d^{-1}, nestlings used 103 kJ bird^{-1} d^{-1} and hatching a clutch of five eggs required 149 kJ (29).

DECOMPOSERS

In this high arctic ecosystem, as with the other ecosystems studied within the Tundra Biome, the main pathways of energy and nutrients are from plants to soil organisms. The complexity of soil organism interreactions are far greater than aboveground and only a few were investigated in this study. It is evident that the meadow system is more complex because of a greater plant production and a microenvironment conducive to greater microbial activity than on the raised beaches.

Decomposition

Carex litter and standing dead decomposed at about the same rate the first two to three years (Table 10). Each year a greater loss occurred over winter than during the 50 day growing season. This may result from leaching during spring melt.

Filter paper decomposed much faster in the warmer but drier beach ridge soils than in the colder and wetter meadow soils (Table 10). Maximum decomposition occurred at a greater depth in the meadow peats (50). Total organic carbon was 3.7 % in the upper 10 cm of the raised beach soils (only a trace below this depth) and 38 to 42 % in the meadow peat (46).

As discussed earlier, Protozoa, Nematoda, and Enchytraeidae are the most significant energy releasers. They feed on bacteria, fungi, and other invertebrates.

Physiology

Fungi

Fourteen species of fungi were grown under standard temperature regimes (5°, 10°, 15°, 20°C) and maximum growth was generally at 20°C although all species showed significant growth at 5°C. This suggests the species are cold-tolerant rather than cold adapted (50). Four fungal species were grown on four carbohydrate substrates and humic acid. Although growth was less on humic acid, all species utilized this substrate in contrast with bacteria tested (50).

Bacteria

Three bacterial isolates from the intensive meadow site showed temperature ranges for growth characteristic of facultative psychrophiles; optimal temperatures were 30 to 35°C. *Pseudomonas* sp. and *Arthrobacter* sp. grew below 0°C but *Bacillus* sp. would

Table 10. Decomposition of organic materials (weight loss) at the two intensive study sites and laboratory analyses of litter respiration (means ± 95 % confidence limits)

1. Whatman filter paper (n=5) (%)

Soil depth (cm)	Time (months) since burial							
	10	11	12	13	14	22	23	24
Hummocky sedge-moss meadow								
0	0	0	0	0	0	0	0	0
5	0	0	0	0	0.1(0–6)	0	0	17(0–35)
15	0	0	0	0	0.6(0–2)	13(0–30)	0.3(0–1.2)	32(18–45)
Raised beach ridge-crest								
0	0	0	0	0	0	0	0	0
5	n.d.			19(1–37)	37(0–82)	22(0–52)	53(47–59)	71(57–83)
15				0	15(0–46)	20(17–22)	59(52–67)	44(29–57)

2. Litter (n=3) (%)

	Time (months) since placing in field					
	12	14	24	25	26	37
Carex litter	18(9–27)	20(n.d.)	25(14–37)	n.d.	30(31–39)	37
Carex standing dead	15(0–30)	18(10–27)	n.d.	30	n.d.	n.d.

3. Respiration (μl O_2 g^{-1} h^{-1}) (n=5 - *Carex*; 3 - *Dryas*)

	Moisture (% ww)	Temperature regime					
		0°	5°	10°	15°	20°	25°
Carex stans green leaves	79 %	76(40–112)	185(104–265)	530(305–755)	625(419–830)	793(690–896)	2 175(1 550–2 799)
Standing yellow leaves	45 %	14(4– 25)	14(1– 28)	35(8– 62)	97(46–149)	109(68–150)	486(226– 746)
Standing grey leaves	73 %	47(45– 49)	59(55– 64)	144(105–182)	340(195–486)	471(329–612)	683(495– 873)
Dryas green leaves	50 %	48(27– 68)	99(97–101)	168(132–205)	207(158–257)	122(60–183)	175(92– 259)
Brown leaves	2.3 %	0	0	25(17– 33)	34(18– 50)	17(8– 27)	94(67– 120)
Brown-grey leaves	2.4 %	0	0	13(7– 18)	n.d.	7(3– 11)	54(11– 92)
Grey leaves	1.4 %	0	0	13(6– 19)	16(5– 38)	5(3– 12)	32(18– 46)
Grey fragmenting leaves	3.3 %	0	0	20(9– 50)	28(2– 54)	31(19– 96)	113(17– 242)

n.d. = not determined

not grow at 0°C or below (27). Freeze-thaw studies showed that survival of the above species was greater in drier soils and slow thawing (4 days) was more detrimental than fast thaw (4 h) for all but *Arthrobacter* sp.

All three species were capable of efficient growth at low concentrations of glucose. When subjected to starvation, *Pseudomonas* sp. remained 100 % viable for more than 30 days, *Arthrobacter* sp. for 10 days, and *Bacillus* sp. for < 2 days. Respiration dropped to 2–28 % of the rate during active growth and there was a rapid breakdown of cellular protein, carbohydrate, and RNA after onset of starvation (27).

These data indicate that these bacteria are well adapted to living under the reduced temperature and nutrient regimes of these high arctic soils.

Biomass and production

Fungi

Although the number of species of fungi identified was about the same in the two sites investigated (Table 11), mycelial length and biomass were much greater in the meadow soils. Mycelial length decreased about 8 and 5 fold from the upper to the lowest level in the meadow and beach ridge soils respectively. In general mycelial content increased during spring. At both sites sterile forms were the major component. Other important species were *Cylindrocarpon* sp. nov., *Chrysosporium panorum* (Link) Hughes and *Phoma herbarum* Westend (50).

The minimum fungal production between August 1970 and July 1971 was 16 g m^{-2} in the meadow but only 2 g m^{-2} in the raised beach soils (upper 5 cm). As there was no account of fungal death rates and grazing by microfauna, fungal production was no doubt much higher.

Table 11. **Standing crop and production data for bacteria and fungi at the two intensive study sites, Truelove Lowland.**

Component	Hummocky sedge-moss meadow depth (cm)		Raised beach crest depth (cm)	
	0–5	10–15	0–5	10–15
Bacteria				
Number of genera	9	n.d.	9	n.d.
Plate count (no. g^{-1} × 10^6)	481	4	12	2
Biomass (g m^{-2})	0.529	0.003	0.062	0.011
Fungi				
Number of genera	19	n.d.	22	n.d.
Mycelium length (m g^{-1})	1 472	143	83	3
Biomass (g m^{-2})	4.5–20.3	n.d.	1.3–8.7	n.d.
Protozoa (no. g^{-1})	5.3 × 10^8	n.d.	n.d.	n.d.
Blue-green algae (cells g^{-1})	1.8 × 10^5	n.d.	72	n.d.

n.d. = not determined

Bacteria

There were 9 taxonomic groups of bacteria identified in the soils from the two sites with *Streptomyces* and members of the *Flavobacterium/Cytophaga* group being the most important in the raised beach soils and *Arthrobacter* the most important genus in the meadow soils.

Bacteria were far more abundant in the meadow soils (Table 11) which probably reflects soil moisture and organic substrate. Numbers decrease with depth, but more rapidly in the meadow soils. In the meadow soils there was an early spring peak in numbers followed by a decline, while numbers increased all summer in the raised beach soils (50).

Nutrient Budget

The Truelove Lowland ecosystem is low in nutrients (soil, water, vegetation). Long term stimulation of plant growth around old whale bones (3 to 5 000 years) attests to this as do the fertilizer studies. An increase (50 to 200 %) in plant flowering occurred in several species three years after treatment with an N-P-K fertilizer (56 and 336 kg ha^{-1} of each element). The response of species was variable, *Cerastium alpinum* showed a 15 fold increase in growth, *Saxifraga oppositifolia* increased 3 fold, but *Dryas integrifolia* only an 0.5-fold increase (4).

The rate of nitrogen fixation is low with bacteria and single celled blue-green algae being most important. Fixation was estimated to be 380 and 120 mg N m^{-2} yr^{-1} in the hummocky sedge-moss meadows (1971 and 1972), but only 30 and 7 mg N m^{-2} yr^{-1} on the raised beach. The lower rates occurred in the cooler and drier summer (42). *Peltigera aphthosa* (L.) Willd. and *Nostoc commune* are nitrogen fixers but because of their small standing crop and meadows with a relatively dry surface in summer, their contribution is small. Legumes are not present at this latitude and *Dryas* is not a fixer either. Nitrogen fixation appears greatest near the aerobic/anaerobic interface and *Bacillus* sp. is assumed to be an important fixer. Nitrate nitrogen was absent from the soil and when added (1 ppm), decreased N-fixation by 56 % (41).

In a model of nitrogen flow in the hummocky sedge-moss meadow, it was estimated that in the time peat has accumulated (> 2000 years), as much as 1 940 g N m^{-2} have accumulated in the peat while only 37 g N m^{-2} were tied up in the live and dead sedges, mosses, and algae combined (6). Nitrogen flow is highly limited within this system with only small quantities entering via precipitation and leaving via stream flow. The same is true for phosphorus and this element may actually be more limiting to plant growth than nitrogen (6). Thus the total system with its diverse land (dry and wet sites) and lake-pond subsystems appears to produce and maintain low nutrient levels with little leakage to the sea or removal via birds and mammals.

ECOSYSTEM ENERGY FLOW

This system is largely a detritus system in which solar radiation → plants → decomposers and organic matter storage is the main pathway. Herbivores and carnivores, while

Table 12. Live standing crop and net annual production of various communities on Truelove Lowland and plateau, expressed as energy constants (kJ m^{-2})

	Vascular plants		Mosses	Lichen	Algae	Total
	Aboveground	Belowground				
Standing Crop						
Cushion plant-lichen	1 824	1 167	272	841	0	4 104
Cushion plant-moss	2 581	1 025	10 920	393	n.d.	14 919
Frost-boil sedge-moss	1 088	6 720	10 012	0	17	17 837
Dwarf shrub heath	3 397	18 912	7 389	410	n.d.	30 108
Hummocky sedge-moss	1 674	20 656	16 527	0	67	38 924
Wet sedge-moss	1 519	13 154	19 966	0	33	34 672
Polar desert (plateau)	301	75	4 222	0	0	4 598
Semi-desert (raised beach)	2 130	1 113	4 531	661	0	8 435
Wet sedge-tundra (all meadows)	1 402	14 008	13 351	0	42	28 803
Total Lowland	1 602	8 422	9 506	205	21	19 756
Net production						
Cushion plant-lichen	326	63	38	50	0	477
Cushion plant-moss	552	105	364	33	n.d.	1 054
Frost-boil sedge-moss	565	1 121	146	0	17	1 849
Dwarf shrub heath	423	1 904	364	59	n.d.	2 750
Hummocky sedge-moss	858	1 979	602	0	67	3 506
Wet sedge-moss	895	2 477	1 874	0	33	5 279
Polar desert (plateau)	42	8	92	0	0	142
Semi-desert (raised beaches)	418	79	167	46	0	710
Wet sedge tundra (all meadows)	724	1 619	460	0	42	2 845
Total Lowland	544	1 004	331	17	21	1 917

of great interest and use to people, form a small biomass and energy flow component. Since lemming and muskox utilize at most 3—4 % of aboveground standing crop, most primary production goes to the soil decomposer and storage component. Mosses, while comprising 33 % of the plant energy standing crop, are not utilized by vertebrates and are little used by invertebrates. Muskox density (ca 1 km^{-2}) is not very different from that of native herbivores in more temperate regions. The low lemming density (73 km^{-2}) and very low arctic hare density further reduce the overall role of vertebrate herbivores. In other tundra systems and in grasslands the rodent herbivores perform a more central role.

Although we have dealt with this lowland and valley as one total system, biological-ly it is three systems — aquatic, raised beaches, and sedge-moss meadows. The meadow system with its grazing muskox and snow geese has a primary production efficiency much larger than the raised beaches with their thin cover of cushion plants, lichens, and mosses and limited grazing by lemming (Tables 12, 13). Plant production efficiency is similar to that of temperate region ecosystems although total production and length of the growing season are considerably less.

Table 13. Net annual production and efficiency of annual production for the various plant communities and system components based upon the length of the growing season (50 to 60 days)

Component	Net production (kJ m^{-2})	Total radiation (kJ m^{-2})	Efficiency (%) Total radiation	PAR [*]
Polar desert (plateau)	138	11.72 x 10^5	0.01	0.03
Polar semi-desert (raised beach)	711	11.13 x 10^5	0.06	0.16
Sedge-moss meadows (all meadows)	2 845	9.04 x 10^5	0.31	0.79
Hummocky sedge-moss meadow	3 506	9.04 x 10^5	0.39	1.03
Total Lowland	1 916	9.62 x 10^5	0.20	0.50

[*] PAR (photosynthetically active radiation) = 40 % of total radiation; efficiency was calculated on the basis of radiation received during the growing season for each component part and the con-tribution (%) which that component provides to the total lowland (raised beach types, meadow types, dwarf shrub heath, etc. — see Table 12).

Based upon growing season measurements, net radiation (52 %) is a somewhat larger component of total radiation than in some temperate regions. Photosynthetically ac-tive radiation (PAR) appears to be lower than in temperate regions which effectively in-creases percent efficiency of primary production (Table 13). Data from other high arctic sites are necessary before this can be substantiated.

Within the hummocky sedge-moss meadow system 2 % of plant production is utiliz-ed by vertebrate and invertebrate herbivores, the remaining 98 % goes directly to the decomposer complex (Fig. 7) (48). Fungi are the largest users of energy within the decomposer subsystem, bacteria of less importance. Within the soil invertebrates, protozoa are the most important in terms of energy flow, followed in order by the Enchytraeidae, Nematoda, Diptera, and Crustacea (Harpacticoids) (36). The "ivores" in Fig. 7 refer to the fungal, bacteria, and protozoa feeders, mostly Nematoda and Collembola. Carnivore standing crop and production energy are not presented because of the difficulty in determining the amount of time a given number of fox and jaegers spend on this Lowland each summer. Their energy demands are such that they must roam over adjacent lowlands as well.

Using only the crest and slope portions of the beach ridge system (most of the invertebrate and all of the microflora were from this part), 92.5 % of plant production is utilized directly by the decomposer complex (Fig. 8) (48). Within the decomposer complex, fungi are again the most significant energy using group and bacteria a very minor component. Nematoda are the most significant energy users of the invertebrate groups followed by Enchytraeidae, Collembola, and Diptera (36). The role of Protozoa is not known, but would appear to be minor in relation to the meadows. The "ivores", Nematoda and Collembola, utilize 14 % of the available energy, a much higher proportion than in the meadow (1.4 %). Estimated numbers of these groups are also much greater in this habitat (Table 9) although the standing crop and production of the "ivores" is comparable in the two systems. Estimates of vascular plant production are ten times greater in the meadow vs. beach ridge while soil organic matter is five times greater. Decomposition rates are much faster (filter paper – Table 10) in the warmer but drier beach ridge soils.

Vascular plants consumed by herbivores are reasonably high in caloric content (19.2 to 22.2 kJ g^{-1}) and are high in protein content (6 to 9 % in winter, 17 to 21 % in summer). This is probably essential to herbivores that are under considerable thermal and nutrient stress for many months per year.

Based upon the four years of study the system appears to be in reasonable balance. Plant and animal production changed little from year to year, except lemming, although summer climatic conditions were highly variable (degree days above $0°C$, mean monthly temperature, precipitation, ice-free season of the larger lakes, and length of growing season).

The system is dependent upon the greater number of hours of sunshine and probably the strong and weak föhn winds that characterize the eastern arctic islands. The presence of impounded water across the Lowland and the ability of it to retain its limited pool of nitrogen and phosphorus are essential features. All of these characteristics combine to make this and similar sites, with their three subsystems, far more productive than most of the land at this latitude. It is only the few sites north of $73°N$ with this combination of warmth, water and a more continuous mantle of vegetation that can support this level of biotic diversity and production. They are like miniatures of the systems which cover large areas of the southern high arctic islands.

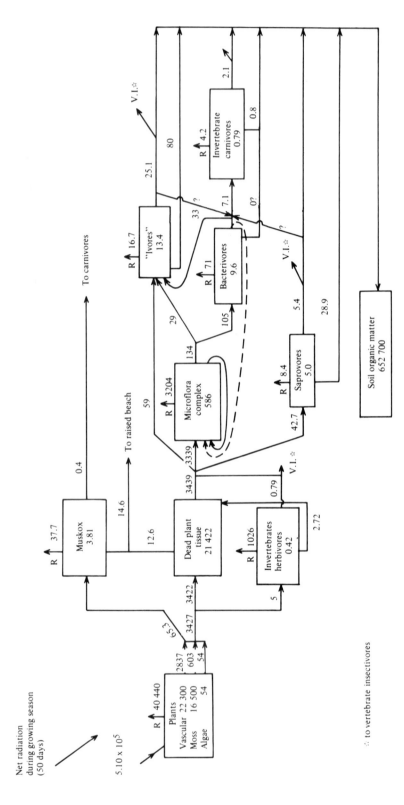

Figure 7. Energy flow diagram for the sedge-moss meadow system. Standing crop (boxes) and energy flow (arrows) are expressed in kJ m^{-2}. Respiration (R) is given for all components along with energy estimates for regecta. Ivores are fungal, bacteria, and protozoa feeders, insectivores are seed and insect feeding birds.

☆ to vertebrate insectivores

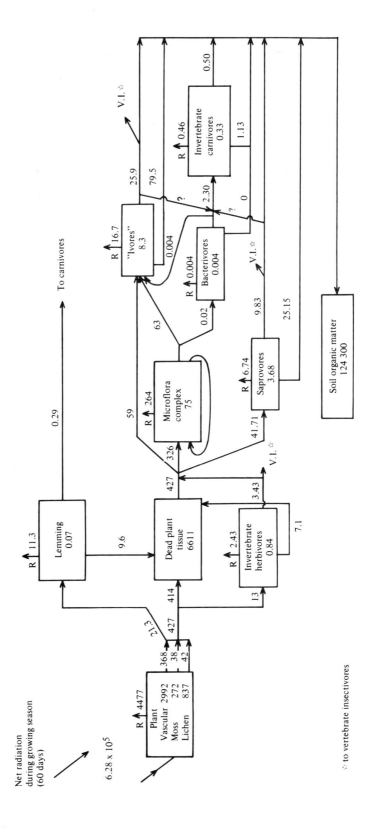

Figure 8. Energy flow diagram for the beach ridge (crest and slope) system. See Fig. 7 caption for details on the components.

53

AQUATIC SYSTEM

Groups of lakes are uncommon at these latitudes and their presence adds to the biological diversity of the Lowland, although they are low in species richness. The impoundment of water by raised beaches and its slow release to the sea has permitted the high level of plant production in the meadows.

Of the lakes and ponds in the Lowland, only three are deep enough to contain arctic char (*Salvelinus alpinus* L.); Loon, Fish and Immerk lakes (Fig. 1). These lakes were studied in 1973 to permit comparisons with the intensive study at Char Lake, Cornwallis Island and to provide additional information on this land-water system.

Immerk and Fish Lakes are roughly 100 ha while Loon Lake is much smaller (16 ha). All three are shallow (mean depth 2.9 to 3.2 m) with maximum depths of 7 to 8.5 m. Loon Lake is fed by Gully River from the plateau while Immerk and Fish Lakes have drainage basins of sedge-moss meadows, raised beaches and rock outcrops. Ice thickness was only 1 m on Loon and Beschel Lakes near the base of the cliff while Immerk and Phalerope Lakes had ice thickness of 1.75 m. Snow depth averaged 32 to 37 cm in late May (23). The lakes did not become ice-free until late July or early August.

Temperature profiles showed that prior to ice melt in May—June, temperatures were $0°C$ under the ice and $1°C$ at the bottom. The three deeper lakes reached temperature maxima of at least $4.5°$ to $5°$ in August while ponds warmed to $8°C$. As the ice pan melted, mixing became complete and isothermal conditions continued for some time, indicating continuous water mixing.

In general, conductivity increased during the summer for both inflow and outflow waters of a lake and lake water conductivity slowly dropped (23). Similar patterns of conductivity changes as well as levels (100 to 200 μ mho cm^{-1}) have been recorded in other arctic lakes with a similar geology.

When an arctic lake freezes it becomes a system isolated from the atmosphere and thus over winter, losses from the oxygen pool can be attributed to lake metabolism. Daily rates of oxygen metabolism were converted to yearly rates m^{-2} of lake bottom. The value of 69.2 g O_2 m^{-2} yr^{-1} is very close to the data of Appolonis (3) gathered in 1961—62 (69.4 g O_2 m^{-2} yr^{-1}). Calculated values for Fish and Loon Lakes were 54.2 and 33.7 respectively (23). This latter figure is more comparable to Char Lake. In these lakes, as with Char Lake, primary production results mostly from benthic algae, although in Char Lake, ca 20 % of production is from aquatic mosses.

Chlorophyll a concentration was used as a measure of phytoplankton. The results showed that chlorophyll a was highest in May and decreased throughout the summer in all but Immerk Lake. Here peak values of 1 mg m^{-3} were reached in early July. In Fish Lake peak chlorophyll a reached 2.6 mg m^{-3} in late May, declining to 0.4 mg m^{-3} by early August. Loon Lake with a greater flushing of water from the Gully River and with water of lower conductivity, also had a much lower concentration of chlorophyll a (0.2 to 0.7 mg m^{-3}), again more comparable with Char Lake. Carbon production data show that production was high just below the ice in all of the lakes.

Species diversity of zooplankton is very limited, based upon late July — early August sampling. Two species of crustacea and four of rotifers were sampled in Fish Lake while the other two lakes contained only three species in total. Numbers of crustacean zooplankton were also much higher in Fish Lake (4 784 m^{-3}) than in Loon Lake (141 m^{-3}). The lakes produce considerable numbers of chironomids (midges) with emergence peaks occurring in the 2 to 4 m zone. Total emergence from 19 June to 9 August amounted to 1.56 kJ m^{-2} (66 mg m^{-2}). As with other northern lakes there were two peaks in emergence (23).

Arctic char is the only fish species, a landlocked population for the streams do not permit a sea run. The fish grow slowly the first 10 to 14 years (20 cm) when growth rate increases. Char of 54 cm were about 26 years old, much larger and older than in Char Lake on Cornwallis Island (27 cm at 20 years). These char reach a larger size and an older age than do fish from other landlocked lakes that have been studied (23).

Char feed predominantly on the crustacean *Mysis relicta*, chironomid larvae and some zooplankton in winter. In summer their diet consists almost exclusively of chironomid pupae and adults.

These data indicate that high arctic lakes with a polar desert watershed (Char Lake and Loon Lake) have a lower production than lakes with a watershed of relatively lush vegetation (Immerk and Fish Lakes). Lake metabolism, mean summer chlorophyll, and early growth rates of Arctic char are greater in Immerk and Fish Lakes than in Loon and Char Lakes (23). Biological structure and species diversity are similar in all of the lakes. The major controls seem to be temperature and low nutrient input.

MAN'S INFLUENCE ON HIGH ARCTIC ECOSYSTEMS

Wildlife utilization by the Eskimo

Although the Eskimo (Inuit) have occupied these northern islands for at least 3 000 years including Dorset and Thule cultures in this and adjacent lowlands, they migrated out of the area at least 200 to 300 years ago. The federal government reintroduced people from Pond Inlet and Port Harrison to Craig Harbour in 1953, and in 1956 they moved to Grise Fiord. Their population has grown from 36 to 96 people in only 20 years. Until recently most food and income were derived from wildlife (13 to 18 hunters) but now considerable income comes from wages. Throughout the years the value of imported food (mostly carbohydrates) has risen from $500 per annum to $23 000 in 1971–72 (Riewe in 9).

There are several important aspects of this population of native people. Firstly, as with other Eskimo and northern Indians, their diet was mostly protein rather than carbohydrate. Secondly, as with most Eskimo, this community received most of its food from the sea rather than the land, and thirdly the people harvested a great number of wildlife species for food and furs (ca 19 species) (34). Ringed seal (*Phoca hispida* Schreber) formed the basis of the diet of these people. Polar bear (*Ursus maritimus* Phipps) accounted for 55 % of the furs sold, arctic fox provided an additional 15 % and muskox 16 %. Of the total energy (7.99 x 10^8 kJ) harvested by the Grise Fiord people in 1971–72, 10 % was consumed by people, 18 % by 50 dogs, 67 % by decomposers and scavengers, and 5 % shipped south as crafts and furs (34). This means that a considerable amount of food energy is derived from imported food.

Significant shifts in hunting methods, species utilized and the economy of these people have occurred in 20 short years. Initially hunters and trappers used dog teams (average annual cost per year $12) but since the late 1960s the Eskimo have switched to snowmobiles at a yearly cost of $1 075 in depreciation and operating costs (Riewe in 9). This has raised the average annual hunting costs from $572 in 1965–67 using dogs to $1 846 in 1969–72 using snowmobiles. This shift has made the hunters more mobile in seeking game, has resulted in overhunting caribou and in providing large quantities of meat no longer consumed by dogs (150 down to 50). In 1971–72 a greater proportion of the economy resulted from wages, carvings, and handicrafts ($78 000) than money earned or in kind derived from meat harvested ($29 200) and furs sold ($19 000) (Riewe in 9). This contrasts with the Sachs Harbour, Banks Island, people who derive nearly all of their income from fox trapping and most of their meat from caribou rather than from seals. This southern high arctic area with its greater proportion of sedge meadows and cushion plant-lichen vegetation supports a much larger wildlife population of lemming, fox, snow geese, muskox and Peary's caribou (34) and therefore a more viable population of native people living off the land than is possible in the northern islands.

In the past, most energy harvested was utilized in one form or another by Grise Fiord people and their dogs; lesser amounts by scavengers and decomposers. Today this pattern is reversed. The use of machines and modern hunting equipment has enabled these people to harvest a greater number of mammals, birds, and fish. This plus a rapidly expanding population is placing a greater strain on these terrestrial and aquatic northern high arctic ecosystems to produce an adequate amount of wildlife in the future.

Perturbations

Muskox grazing and vehicle usage are two potential perturbations subject to man's control. The potential effects of these are indicated in two separate sets of experiments.

Simulated grazing

Clipping experiments revealed that at the beginning of the second year, belowground carbohydrate reserves were ca 50 % lower, yet production the second year of clipping showed little reduction. There was no indication that clipping stimulated growth (4). These data together with general observations of plant growth in muskox feeding crater sites of the previous winter, and the exclosures, indicate that muskox grazing has little direct impact on the vegetation. The 1972–1973 yearly average of ca 40 animals in the 37 km^{-2} land area is not resulting in overgrazing.

Simulated surface blading

Removal of plant cover in a sedge meadow resulted in a 15 % increase in the active layer. Radiant energy measurements showed that albedo decreased 55 %. Convection plus evapotranspiration decreased from 98 to 93 % of net radiation. Soil heat flux increased from 2 to 7 %, but this small component resulted in little additional soil thaw (4). Measurements of active layer depths elsewhere in these northern islands show that removal of vegetation has little effect on soil thaw, probably less than associated soil compaction. In the western Queen Elizabeth Islands, surface erosion and gullying are more serious problems than in the eastern islands. Soil erosion is more intense because of less plant cover, small root systems less capable of holding soil, slow plant growth, and a lack of soil particle cohesion due to low levels of iron oxides (5).

Should lowlands such as this one be subjected to heavy summer vehicle use, long term reduction of potential grazing could be serious, witness the slow rate of plant recovery in 10 year old tracks in this Lowland (4).

ACKNOWLEDGEMENTS

Many groups of people have contributed to the success of this project. Major funding was provided by the following federal and provincial agencies: NRCC–IBP , Department of Environment and the Canadian Wildlife Service within the DOE, Arctic Land Use Research programme and the Environmental-Social Program Northern Pipelines Committee, both of the Department of Indian and Northern Affairs, Division of Building Research of NRCC, Polar Continental Shelf Project of the Department of Energy, Mines, and Resources, Alberta Environment, and University of Manitoba Northern Studies Committee. The Arctic Institute of North America managed the Base Camp facilities. The University of Alberta, University of Calgary, Laurentian University, and University of Manitoba provided teaching assistantships for some of the graduate students.

The Executive of the Arctic Petroleum Operators Association and 24 member companies and consortia provided financial support. Special thanks are due King Resources Co. (1970), Sun Oil Co. (1971) and Imperial Oil Ltd. (1972, 1973) for transportation support between Edmonton and Resolute.

The Polar Continental Shelf Project provided most of the logistic support from Resolute to Devon Island and Panarctic Oils, Elf Oil, and Sun Oil provided most of the inter-island logistic support for the surface disturbance studies. Environmental instruments were loaned by the Atmospheric Environmental Service of the Department of the Environment.

The Department of Botany, University of Alberta absorbed many of the associated administrative costs of this project which is gratefully acknowledged.

This study could not have been done without the research of the various graduate students, faculty members, and their field assistants. The success of this project results from their effective research although the writer assumed responsibility for interpreting their studies.

REFERENCES

1. Addison, P.A. 1975. Studies on evapotranspiration and energy budgets on the Truelove Lowland. – In: Bliss, L.C. (ed.) Truelove Lowland, Devon Island, Canada: A High Arctic Ecosystem. Edmonton: University of Alberta Press.
2. Andrews, J.T. 1970. A geographical study of postglacial uplift, with particular reference to Arctic Canada. – Inst. Brit. Geogr., Spec. Publ. 2. 156 pp.
3. Appolonio, S. 1962. Unpublished report of freshwater research undertaken on the Truelove Lowland, 1961–1962.
4. Babb, T.A. & Bliss, L.C. 1974. Effects of physical disturbance on arctic vegetation in the Queen Elizabeth Islands. – J. Appl. Ecol. 11: 549–562.
5. Babb, T.A. & Bliss, L.C. 1974. Susceptibility to environmental impact in the Queen Elizabeth Islands. – Arctic 27: 234–237.
6. Babb, T.A. & Whitfield, D.W.A. 1975. Nitrogen and phosphorous cycles on the Truelove Lowland. – In: Bliss, L.C. (ed.) Truelove Lowland, Devon Island, Canada: A High Arctic Ecosystem. Edmonton: University of Alberta Press.
7. Barr, W. 1971. Postglacial isostatic movement in northeastern Devon Island: a reappraisal. – Arctic 24: 249–268.

8. Bliss, L.C. 1975. Tundra grasslands, herblands, and shrublands and the role of herbivores. – In: Kesel, R.H. (ed.) Grassland Ecology, A Symposium. Geoscience and Man 10: 51–79.

9. Bliss, L.C., Courtin, G.M., Pattie, D.L., Riewe, R.R., Whitfield, D.W.A. & Widden, P. 1973. Arctic tundra ecosystems. – Ann. Rev. Ecol. Syst. 4: 359–399.

10. Bliss, L.C. & Kerik, J. 1973. Primary production of plant communities of the Truelove Lowland, Devon Island, Canada – rock outcrops. – In: Bliss, L.C. & Wielgolaski, F.E. (eds.) Primary Production and Production Processes, Tundra Biome, pp. 27–36. Edmonton: IBP Tundra Biome Steering Committee.

11. Booth, T. 1975. Muskox dung decomposition: turnover rates and its possible role on the Truelove Lowland. – In: Bliss, L.C. (ed.) Truelove Lowland, Devon Island, Canada: A High Arctic Ecosystem. Edmonton: University of Alberta Press.

12. Brown, R.J.E. 1974. Permafrost investigations in the Truelove Lowland, Devon Island, N.W.T. – In: Bliss, L.C. (ed.) Truelove Lowland, Devon Island, Canada: A High Arctic Ecosystem. Edmonton: University of Alberta Press.

13. Courtin, G.M. & Labine, C.L. Micrometeorological studies of the Truelove Lowland. – In: Bliss, L.C. (ed.) Truelove Lowland, Devon Island, Canada: A High Arctic Ecosystem. Edmonton: University of Alberta Press.

14. Fuller, W.A., Martell, A.M., Smith, R.F.C. & Speller, S.W. 1975. High arctic lemmings (*Dicrostonyx groenlandicus*): II. Demography. – Can. J. Zool. (in press).

15. Fuller, W.A., Martell, A.M., Smith, R.F.C. & Speller, S.W. 1975. Hich arctic lemmings (*Dicrostonyx groenlandicus*): I. Natural history observations. – Can. Field Nat. (in press).

16. Holecek, G. & Vosahlo, M. 1974. Hydrology. Progress Report, Devon Island Project. 36 pp.

17. Hubert, B.A. 1975. Productivity of Muskox. – In: Bliss, L.C. (ed.) Truelove Lowland, Devon Island, Canada: A High Arctic Ecosystem. Edmonton: University of Alberta Press.

18. Jankovska, V. & Bliss, L.C. 1975. Pollen and macroscopic analysis from the Truelove Lowland. – In: Bliss, L.C. (ed.) Truelove Lowland, Devon Island, Canada: A High Arctic Ecosystem. Edmonton: University of Alberta Press.

19. Jefferies, R.L. 1975. Plant communities of muddy shores of arctic North America. – Can. J. Bot. (in press).

20. Leech, R.E. & Ryan, J.K. 1972. Notes on Canadian arctic spiders (Araneida), mainly from Devon Island, N.W.T. – Can. Ent. 104: 1787–1791.

21. Mayo, J.M., Despain, D.G. & van Zinderen Bakker, E.M. 1973. CO_2 assimilation by *Dryas integrifolia* on Devon Island, Northwest Territories. – Can. J. Bot. 51: 581–588.

22. Mayo, J.M., Hartgerink, A.P., Despair, D.G., Thompson, R.G., van Zinderen Bakker, E.M. & Thompson, S.D. 1975. Gas exchange studies of *Carex* and *Dryas*. – In: Bliss, L.C. (ed.) Truelove Lowland, Devon Island, Canada: A High Arctic Ecosystem. Edmonton: University of Alberta Press.

23. Minns, C.K. 1975. Limnology of three lakes on the Truelove Lowland. – In: Bliss, L.C. (ed.) Truelove Lowland, Devon Island, Canada: A High Arctic Ecosystem. Edmonton: University of Alberta Press.

24. Muc, M. 1973. Primary production of plant communities of the Truelove Lowland, Devon Island, Canada-sedge meadows. – In: Bliss, L.C. & Wielgolaski, F.E. (eds.) Primary Production and Production Processes, Tundra Biome, pp. 3–14. Edmonton: IBP Tundra Biome Steering Committee.

25. Muc, M. 1975. Ecology and primary production of the lowland sedge-moss meadow communities. – In: Bliss, L.C. (ed.) Truelove Lowland, Devon Island, Canada: A High Arctic Ecosystem. Edmonton: University of Alberta Press.

26. Muc, M. 1975. Plant communities of the Truelove Lowland. – In: Bliss, L.C. (ed.) Truelove Lowland, Devon Island, Canada: A High Arctic Ecosystem. Edmonton: University of Alberta Press.

27. Nelson, L. 1975. Growth and survival characteristics of three arctic soil bacteria. – In: Bliss, L.C. (ed.) Truelove Lowland, Devon Island, Canada: A High Arctic Ecosystem. Edmonton: University of Alberta Press.

28. Pakarinen, P. & Vitt, D.H. 1973. Primary production of plant communities of the Truelove Lowland, Devon Island, Canada – moss communities. – In: Bliss, L.C. & Wielgolaski, F.E. (eds.) Primary Production and Production Processes, Tundra Biome, pp. 37–46. Edmonton: IBP Tundra Biome Steering Committee.

29. Pattie, D.L. 1975. Population levels and bioenergetics of arctic birds on the Truelove Lowland. –

In: Bliss, L.C. (ed.) Truelove Lowland, Devon Island, Canada: A High Arctic Ecosystem. Edmonton: University of Alberta Press.

30. Procter, D.L.C. 1975. Nematode densities and production on the Truelove Lowland. – In: Bliss, L.C. (ed.) Truelove Lowland, Devon Island, Canada: A High Arctic Ecosystem. Edmonton: University of Alberta Press.

31. Procter, D.L.C. 1975. Invertebrate respirometry. – In: Bliss, L.C. (ed.) Truelove Lowland, Devon Island, Canada: A High Arctic Ecosystem. Edmonton: University of Alberta Press.

32. Richardson, D.H.S. & Finegan, E. Primary production of plant communities of the Truelove Lowland, Devon Island, Canada – lichen communities. – In: Bliss, L.C. & Wielgolaski, F.E. (eds.) Primary Production and Production Processes, Tundra Biome, pp. 47–55. Edmonton: IBP Tundra Biome Steering Committee.

33. Riewe, R.R. 1975. Mammalian carnivores utilizing the Truelove Lowland. – In: Bliss, L.C. (ed.) Truelove Lowland, Devon Island, Canada: A High Arctic Ecosystem. Edmonton: University of Alberta Press.

34. Riewe, R.R. 1975. The utilization of wildlife in the Jones Sound region by the Grise Fiord Inuit. – In: Bliss, L.C. (ed.) Truelove Lowland, Devon Island, Canada: A High Arctic Ecosystem. Edmonton: University of Alberta Press.

35. Ryan, J.K. In press. Comparison of invertebrate species lists from IBP tundra sites. – In: Moore, J.J. (ed.) Tundra: Comparative Analysis of Ecosystems. Cambridge University Press.

36. Ryan, J.K. 1975. Synthesis of energy flows and population dynamics of the Truelove Lowland invertebrates. – In: Bliss, L.C. (ed.) Truelove Lowland, Devon Island, Canada: A High Arctic Ecosystem. Edmonton: University of Alberta Press.

37. Ryan, K.J. & Hergert, C.R. 1975. Energy budget for *Gynaephora groenlandica* (Homeyer) and *G. rossii* (Curtis) on the Truelove Lowland. – In: Bliss, L.C. (ed.) Truelove Lowland, Devon Island, Canada: A High Arctic Ecosystem. Edmonton: University of Alberta Press.

38. Rydén, B.E. 1975. Hydrology of the Truelove Lowland. – In: Bliss, L.C. (ed.) Truelove Lowland, Devon Island, Canada: A High Arctic Ecosystem. Edmonton: University of Alberta Press.

39. Sharp, J. 1975. Population dynamics and biology of collembola on the Truelove Lowland. – In: Bliss, L.C. (ed.) Truelove Lowland, Devon Island, Canada: A High Arctic Ecosystem. Edmonton: University of Alberta Press.

40. Smith, R.F.C. & Wang, L.C.H. 1975. Arctic hares on the Truelove Lowland. – In: Bliss, L.C. (ed.) Truelove Lowland, Devon Island, Canada: A High Arctic Ecosystem. Edmonton: University of Alberta Press.

41. Stutz, R.C. & Bliss, L.C. 1975. Nitrogen fixation in soils of Truelove Lowland, Devon Island, N.W.T. – Can. J. Bot. (in press).

42. Stutz, R.C. 1975. Biological nitrogen fixation in High Arctic soils. – In: Bliss, L.C. (ed.) Truelove Lowland, Devon Island, Canada: A High Arctic Ecosystem. Edmonton: University of Alberta Press.

43. Svoboda, J. 1973. Primary production of plant communities of the Truelove Lowland, Devon Island, Canada – beach ridges. – In: Bliss, L.C. & Wielgolaski, F.E. (eds.) Primary Production and Production Processes, Tundra Biome, pp. 15–26. Edmonton: IBP Tundra Biome Steering Committee.

44. Svoboda, J. 1975. Ecology and production of raised beach communities. – In: Bliss, L.C. (ed.) Truelove Lowland, Devon Island, Canada: A High Arctic Ecosystem. Edmonton: University of Alberta Press.

45. Vitt, D.H. & Pakarinen, P. 1975. The bryophyte vegetation, production and organic component in Truelove Lowland. – In: Bliss, L.C. (ed.) Truelove Lowland, Devon Island, Canada: A High Arctic Ecosystem. Edmonton: University of Alberta Press.

46. Walker, B.D. & Peters, T. 1975. Soils of the Truelove Lowland and plateau. – In: Bliss, L.C. (ed.) Truelove Lowland, Devon Island, Canada: A High Arctic Ecosystem. Edmonton: University of Alberta Press.

47. Wang, L.C.H., Jones, D.L., MacArthur, R.A. & Fuller, W.A. 1973. Adaptation to cold: energy metabolism in a typical lagomorph, the arctic hare (*Lepus arcticus*). – Can. J. Zool. 51: 841–846.

48. Whitfield, D.W.A. 1975. Energy budgets and ecological efficiencies in a high arctic system. – In: Bliss, L.C. (ed.) Truelove Lowland, Devon Island, Canada: A High Arctic Ecosystem. Edmonton: University of Alberta Press.

49. Whitfield, D.W.A. & Goodwin. 1975. Comparison of the estimates of annual vascular plant production made by harvesting and by gas exchange. – In: Bliss, L.C. (ed.) Truelove Lowland, Devon Island, Canada: A High Arctic Ecosystem. Edmonton: University of Alberta Press.
50. Widden, P. 1975. Microbiology and decomposition studies on the Truelove Lowland. – In: Bliss, L.C. (ed.) Truelove Lowland, Devon Island, Canada: A High Arctic Ecosystem. Edmonton: University of Alberta Press.

Rosswall, T. & Heal, O.W. (eds.) 1975.
Structure and Function of Tundra Ecosystems.
Ecol. Bull. (Stockholm) 20: 61–72.

MARIA PRONCHITSHEVA BAY, USSR

N.V. MATVEYEVA, O.M. PARINKINA, Yu.I. CHERNOV

INTRODUCTION

The intensive IBP study site is situated on the eastern coast of the Taimyr Peninsula on the northern shore of Maria Pronchitsheva Bay at a latitude of 75°30′ N (Fig. 1). The site is situated at 30–40 m a.s.l. There is a plain dissected by a network of streams with steep banks and one depression containing a lake. As a result of frost action the interfluve and slope surfaces are broken into polygons of various sizes with diameters ranging from 0.5 to 10 m. One of the characteristic features of the landscape is the presence of massifs consisting of numerous hills, so-called *baidjarakhi*, separated by troughs, 3–6 m wide. The basal diameter of the hills is 8–10 m, their height varying between 0.5 and 3 m. The frost cracks cut the surface of all interfluves into polygons of 0.5–0.8 m diameter with vegetation cover only in small troughs and bare ground on polygons. The disturbance of soil cover by frost action causes the thawing of fossil soil ice, which leads to landslide formations. The size of the landslide areas occupies several thousand square metres; there is one active and several stabilized landslides in the region.

No biological research has previously been carried out in the region. The present study was undertaken in the vicinity of the meteorological station. The site, lying in the arctic tundra subzone, was selected with a view of obtaining some data for comparison with those from typical tundra in the region of the IBP Tareya station (Western Taimyr). The present study was conducted over two summers (1972 and 1973).

ENVIRONMENTAL CONDITIONS

Climate

Negative air temperatures predominate in the annual cycle (Table 1). The mean annual temperature is about −15°C, and the mean January and July temperatures are −31°C and 4° respectively. The relative humidity is 80 %, nearly constant throughout the year; the mean wind speed fluctuates from 2 to 5 m s^{-1}. The yearly precipitation is 220 mm, and the duration of snow cover 280 days. The snow cover at interfluves does not exceed

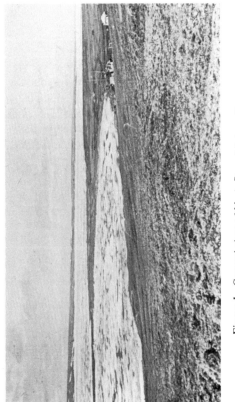

Figure 1. General view of Maria Pronchitsheva Bay.

Table 1. Climatic means for 8 years for Maria Pronchitsheva Bay

Variables	J	F	M	A	M	J	J	A	S	O	N	D	Year
Temperature (°C)													
Air	−31.2	−28.2	−27.3	−19.9	−9.0	−0.5	4.0	3.4	−0.8	−10.4	−22.1	−27.1	−14.0
Soil surface	−33	−32	−30	−20	−11	−1	5	4	−1	−5	−23	−31	−15
Relative humidity (%)	85	84	86	85	86	90	85	91	90	86	85	85	86
Wind velocity (m s^{-1})	4.5	4.4	5.4	5.3	5.2	5.4	4.6	4.5	5.3	5.5	5.2	5.0	5.0
Precipitation (mm)	9.5	8.3	11.1	13.8	11.6	17.6	38.6	20.5	39.0	22.7	17.4	9.3	219.4
Snow depth (cm)	12	14	15	18	30	16	0	0	2	5	8	6	86

20—25 cm and is thickest in May. There are no places where the snow cover lasts over many years. The snowfree period begins in late June and ends in mid-September.

M. Pronchitsheva Bay and the Laptev Sea are under ice during the greater part of year; the water freezes at the end of September, and the ice begins to break at the middle or end of July. The Laptev sea is never completely free from ice. Snow often falls during the summer but usually melts within two days. Permafrost underlies the entire area, the depth of the active layer being no more than 60 cm at the various habitats, including the southern slopes.

Microclimatic conditions vary little between different habitats (Table 2). On sunny days there is a temperature difference of only 1—2°C between the soil surface and 2 and 5 cm depths of communities at interfluves and southern slopes in meadow communities. This slight difference disappears on cloudy days. The vegetation cover has a slight influence on the temperature regime in soils; in bright weather the bare ground becomes warmer than that under a moss layer, the difference being about 6°C, which in cloudy weather reduces to 2°C. The temperature difference between the soil surface and 2 and 5 cm depths on bare ground is 1—2°C on sunny days and 0—1°C on cloudy days. The corresponding values for mossy troughs are 4—6°C and 2—3°C respectively.

Table 2. Soil moisture and soil temperature data of the sites at M. Pronchitsheva Bay

Site	Moisture (% of fw)			Temperature (°C)		
	I	II	III	I	II	III
Mossy *Salix polaris* mesic frost-boil tundra; spot, 0–2 cm	20.4	17.1	25.8	7.7	8.6	6.4
Mossy *Salix polaris* dry frost-boil tundra; spot, 0–2 cm	19.6	18.4	21.8	7.3	8.6	5.3
Herb grass meadow on southern slope, 1–5 cm	30.9	28.8	34.2	8.2	9.7	5.8

I   – mean for the summer month (14–7 to 12–8 1973)
II   – mean for the period of (14–7 to 31–7 1973)
III – mean for the period of (1–8 to 12–8 1973)

Soils

The soil cover is about 50–60 cm deep, and reaches down to the permafrost level. The soil texture is medium loamy. The soil chemical analysis data for the four sites studied are given in Table 3.

Table 3. Soil characteristics of sites at Maria Pronchitsheva Bay

Community type	Elements of nanorelief and sample depth (cm)	pH		Exchangeable bases (meq 100 g^{-1}) Ca^{++} and Mg^{++}	Humus after Tjurin (%)	Mobile form (mg 100 g^{-1})	
		H$_2$O	KCl			K$_2$O	P$_2$O$_5$
Mossy *Salix polaris* mesic frost-boil tundra	frost-boil						
	0–2	6.6	5.7	14.2	2.7	14.5	6.2
	2–10	6.6	5.6	14.4	2.5	15.9	5.0
	12–26	6.9	5.7	14.9	2.4	20.8	8.7
	26–41	7.1	6.1	14.7	2.4	22.2	6.2
	trough						
	10–18	7.1	5.7	15.2	5.4	16.9	1.2
Mossy *Salix polaris* dry frost-boil tundra	frost-boil						
	0–2	6.7	5.8	14.5	2.6	14.1	15.0
	2–10	7.2	5.7	14.6	2.8	12.1	7.5
	10–27	6.8	5.8	15.0	2.9	13.1	8.7
	27–43	7.1	6.2	14.5	2.8	13.6	10.0
	lichen crusts						
	0–2	5.8	5.2	14.7	6.3	21.7	14.0
	trough						
	5–15	5.5	4.7	15.0	20.4 ☆	12.4	14.0
Lichen-*Dryas* fell-field on skeleton soil	bare ground						
	0–2	6.3	5.3	13.6	2.1	22.6	15.0
	lichen crusts						
	0–2	5.6	5.3	14.3	11.3 ☆	12.1	12.1
	Dryas octopetala						
	0–2	5.7	5.1	17.1	36.8 ☆	8.4	2.5
	2–10	5.9	5.2	16.8	25.1 ☆	14.5	12.5
	Novosieversia glacialis						
Herb-grass meadow on southern slope	0–5	6.6	6.5	17.0	16.0 ☆	22.6	9.3
	5–10	6.0	4.9	13.8	3.8	10.7	10.0
	10–30	6.8	6.1	14.9	3.3	15.9	12.5
	31–50	7.2	6.5	15.7	4.6	12.7	15.0
	51–57	7.4	6.4	15.6	4.1	12.4	15.0

☆ Loss on ignition (%)

PRIMARY PRODUCTION

The main vegetational features are as follows: i) extremely slight vertical differentiation, the plant cover is not more than 10 cm high, only generative shoots of certain species reach up to 15 cm, rarely 20 cm; ii) a great proportion (50–60 %) of bare ground (frost-boils) at interfluves and in the stream valleys with plant cover only in troughs. Areas with continuous vegetation cover are rare, and usually only in depressions with enough deep snow in winter; iii) absence of polygonal wet meadows or bogs; iv) absence of shrubs as an element of vegetation, with only a prostrate shrub, *Salix arctica* Pall, being found rarely. The species diversity of dwarf shrubs is also poor; *Salix polaris* Wahlenb. is widespread in zonal communities and *Dryas octopetala* L. occurs only on skeleton soils; v) absence of sedges in interfluve communities, where *Luzula confusa* Lindeb., *L. nivalis* (Laest.) Beurl., *Alopecurus alpinus* Sm., *Poa alpigena* (Fr.) Lindm. and *Arctagrostis latifolia* (R.Br.) Griseb. are found instead. Sedges grow in the stream valleys and waterways. The genera with highest species diversity are *Saxifraga* and *Draba*.

Vegetation communities and dynamics

Intensive investigations have been carried out at four different habitats.

Site 1. Mossy *Salix polaris* mesic frost-boil tundra

The community contains 60 species, including 26 phanerogams, 12 mosses and 22 lichens. The surface is broken up into regular polygons with a diameter of 0.5 m, the distance between polygon centres being 0.6 m. The troughs form a network with about 144 frost boils per 100 m^2, occupying 55 % of the community area. The active soil layer is 0.50 m at polygons and 0.45 m in troughs. The vegetation on polygons is very poor; vascular plants and crustaceous lichens are occasionally found. The lichens form compact crusts, one centimetre thick, at polygon margins – the first stage in succession on bare ground. The main lichens are *Pannaria pezizoides* (Web.) Trev., *Ochrolechia gyalectina* (Nyl.) Zahlbr., *Psoroma hypnorum* (Vahl.) Grey, *Rinodina turfacea* (Ach.) Koerb. Troughs are completely moss-covered with *Hylocomium splendens* (Hedw.) B.S.G. var., *alaskanum* (Lesq. et James) Limpr., *Tomenthypnum nitens* (Hedw.) Loeske predominating and *Aulacomnium turgidum* (Wahlenb.) Schwaegr. and *Ptilidium ciliare* (L.) Hampe occur in small numbers. The species diversity of mosses is poor. The thickness of the moss layer in troughs is 7 cm. Few phanerogams are found in the moss layer, only their generative shoots rising slightly above it. The most abundant is *Salix polaris*; other important species are *Alopecurus alpinus* and *Poa alpigena*. The floristic composition of the community as a whole is enriched by specific species found on the bare ground; more than half of the occurring phanerogams and lichens are only found at frost boils. The annual aboveground production of vascular plants is 20 g m^{-2} at frost boils and 35 g m^{-2} in troughs.

Site 2. Mossy *Salix polaris* dry frost-boil tundra

The community contains 71 species including 32 phanerogams, 13 mosses and 26 lichens. The surface is broken up into regular polygons with a diameter of 0.6 m, the distance between polygon centres being 0.7 m. The area of bare ground (on polygons) is

50 % of the total, and there are 113 frost-boils per 100 m^2. There is much gravel on the polygons, and the depth of the active layer is 60 cm. The troughs form a network, and are completely covered by vegetation, with the mosses *Hylocomium splendens* var. *alaskanum* and *Aulacomnium turgidum* dominating with *Rhacomitrium lanuginosum* (Hedw.) Brid., *Tomenthypnum nitens* and *Ptilidium ciliare* being less abundant. The thickness of the moss layer in troughs is 6 cm. The floristic composition and abundance of vascular plants is poor in troughs; *Salix polaris* is the most abundant. Other species, e.g. *Alopecurus alpinus*, *Poa alpigena*, *Luzula nivalis*, *Stellaria ciliatosepala* Trautv., occur with high frequency but low abundance. The polygons, concave in surface with mossy troughs, have no continuous vegetation cover. Lichens are more abundant and form crusts, 1–2 cm thick, along small cracks in the soil; *Parmelia omphalodes* (L.) Ach., *Ochrolechia gyalectina* and *Pannaria pezizoides*. Lichens settle on dead mosses or vascular plants, and humus and fine earth accumulate under the crusts. The polygons contain in decreasing order of occurrence: *Salix polaris*, *Saxifraga platysepala* (Trautv.) Tolm., *Luzula nivalis*, *Alopecurus alpinus*, *Poa alpigena* and *Saxifraga nivalis* L. Although the vegetation on polygons is sparse, it is richer in phanerogam and lichen species than in troughs. Plants are generally less than 5 cm in height. The annual aboveground production of vascular plants is 21 g m^{-2} on polygons and 33 g m^{-2} in troughs.

Site 3. Lichen-*Dryas* fell-field on skeleton soil

This stand contains 68 species: 30 phanerogams, 6 mosses and 32 lichens. There is a skeleton soil with a 40 cm active layer, frost cracks cutting the whole surface. *Dryas octopetala* forms prostrate mats 2–3 cm in depth covering 20–25 % of the community area. There are sporadic specimens of other species in the *Dryas* mats, e.g. *Novosieversia glacialis* Bolle ap. Fedde, *Poa alpigena* and *Salix polaris*. The microclimatic and soil conditions are most favourable here with a thick humus-turf horizon (10–15 cm in depth), while the remaining area is primitive skeleton soil with a high percentage of gravel in the active layer. The gravel area between *Dryas* mats is covered to 50 % by crustaceous lichen, with accumulations of humus and fine earth. The most abundant species are *Ochrolechia* spp., *Parmelia omphalodes*, *Hypogymnia subobscura* (Vain.) Poelt., *Solorina crocea* (L.) Ach., *Lecidea* spp. and *Sphaerophorus globosus* (Huds.) Vain. The gravels are covered by epilithic lichens. The liverwort, *Gymnomitrium corallioides* Nees, is one of the first species to settle on bare ground together with crustaceous lichens. There is practically no vertical differentiation in vegetation: the thickness of plant cover is 5 cm, with single generative shoots of *Novosieversia glacialis* reaching to 10 cm.

Site 4. Herb-grass meadow on southern slopes

The community contains 52 species including 30 phanerogams, 9 mosses and 13 lichens. The active layer is 60 cm with roots reaching the permafrost. The dominating phanerogams are *Poa alpigena*, *Alopecurus alpinus*, *Luzula confusa*, *Saxifraga cernua* L., *S. caespitosa* L., *S. hieracifolia* Waldst. et Kit., *S. hirculus* L., *Stellaria ciliatosepala* Trautv., and *Cerastium bialynickii* A. Tolm., with a total cover of 40–50 %. There are very few mosses and lichens at this subsite. The thickness of the plant cover is 18–15 cm. Annual aboveground production of vascular plants is 72 g m^{-2}.

Mossy *Salix polaris* communities (sites 1 and 2) are zonal types of vegetation and occur at the interfluves in mesic soil. Lichen-*Dryas* fell-field (site 3) is the extreme type of vegetation on skeleton soil occurring in very severe microclimatic conditions being the first stage of succession. Herb-grass meadow (site 4) is the optimal type of vegetation occupying the most favourable environments with regard to soil and microclimate.

All successions in vegetation are very slow owing to low plant productivity. The main dynamic processes in zonal types take place at frost boils where crustaceous lichens are of major importance, forming compact crusts and yielding the largest biomass. Phanerogams are less important in the processes of colonization of bare ground, but when they die they make good substrate for crustaceous lichens. Certain vascular plants that form compact cushions or tussocks can significantly modify the environment. A thick humus-turf horizon, 10 cm deep, is being formed under the large old cushions of *Novosieversia glacialis, Dryas octopetala, Saxifraga caespitosa* and *S. hirculus* and offers good conditions for microorganisms and soil invertebrates.

Standing crop and production

Annual aboveground production of vascular plants was measured at three stands (sites 1, 2 and 3). The data for graminoids, mixed herbs and dwarf shrubs (*Salix polaris*) are given in Table 4. *Salix polaris* (only leaf weight was measured) is the most productive in tundra, and production is equal in the zonal types (sites 1 and 2). In herb-grass meadows, grasses and herbs have the main green mass, which is only twice as large as that in tundra communities. The weight of standing dead is twice the annual mean mass of green material, indicating that the standing dead remains attached for a number of years. Although the total phytomass was not determined, it may be assumed that in tundra communities mosses yield the highest proportion of total phytomass followed by phanerogams and lichens.

FAUNA

There is a sharp fall in species diversity of animal populations compared with the adjoining southern subzone. Some of the invertebrate groups or species of the typical tundra (Tareya) are absent here, e.g. Rhopacolera, Cicadoidea, Hemiptera, Psillidae, Curculionidae, Lycosidae, *Nematus crassipes* (Thomson) and Lithobiidae. Some groups are represented by a few species: Araneida — one *Erigone* sp.; Staphylinidae — one *Tachinus* sp.; Carabidae — 2–3 *Pterostichus* spp.; Chrysomelidae — one *Chrysolina* sp.; Tipulidae — 3 species. Only 34 species of birds were found. Among them were typical high arctic species such as *Calidris testacea* Pall., *C. alba* Pall., *C. canutus* (L.), *Arenaria* and *Eudromias morinellus* L., which are very abundant. *Calidris* species commonly found in typical tundra (Tareya), such as *Calidris temminckii* Leisl., *C. minuta* Leisl. and *C. alpina* (L.) are absent here.

The fall in diversity of animal species is accompanied by a rise in individual populations, leading to decreased polydominance. The populations of individual species, e.g. *Tipula carinifrons* Holm. are significantly larger than in southern tundras.

Tachinus sp. and *Erigone* sp. are the most abundant species at the study site. The numbers of *Eisenia nordenskiöldi* Eis. in arctic frost-boil tundras is higher than in zonal

Table 4. Annual aboveground production of vascular plants (mean data from 30 replicates, size of plot 10 x 10 cm; air dry weight; July 1973)

Plant groups / Community type	Graminoids	Mixed herbs	Dwarf shrubs *Salix polaris* $g\ m^{-2}$	Green mass	Standing dead
Mossy *Salix polaris* mesic frost-boil tundra (site 1)					
frost boil	11.3	12.0	8.5	20.2	44.0
troughs	3.5	0	31.6	34.8	4.3
Mossy *Salix polaris* dry frost-boil tundra (site 2)					
frost-boil	10.5	11.7	1.6	21.0	79.7
troughs	5.8	2.9	26.6	32.9	7.2
Herb-grass meadow on southern slope (site 4)	36.8	30.0	1.6	71.5	138.0

tundras which occur on the interfluves in typical tundra. Collembola numbers remain about the same as in typical tundra. Although animal species are fewer than in typical tundra, total zoomass is much higher because the species able to survive in such severe conditions have large populations. In comparison with typical tundra, each species has a high proportion of the total biomass which is large. The biomass is fairly stable because although standing crop is high, the rates of trophic dynamics are low. The zoomass in the main nanorelief elements varies between 25 and 65 g m^{-2} (fw), which is significantly higher than in zonal stands of typical tundra. The numbers of *Eisenia nordenskiöldi* on bare ground reach 80 ind m^{-2} (23 g m^{-2}), but under the moss layer is decreases to 6 m^{-2}. On bare ground the numbers of Enchytraeidae are about 500 m^{-2} (1.4 g m^{-2}) and under the moss layer up to 1 500 m^{-2} (4.3 g m^{-2}). Numbers of *Tipula carinifrons* change from 10 m^{-2} on bare ground to 60 m^{-2} (33 g m^{-2}) under the thick moss layer in troughs. As compared with bare ground, the density of animal populations increases under moss turfs and the thin moss layer at polygon margins, but decreases significantly in troughs with a thick moss layer where conditions are less favourable. One of the most characteristic features of animal populations in the arctic tundra is the small difference between zonal communities and optimal meadow communities; total zoomass is approximately the same in tundras on interfluves and in meadow stands on southern slopes. Total zoomass in herb-grass meadows is 30 g m^{-2} with the same species composition as in tundras. Owing to the extremely severe climate and resultant low energy flow, conditions do not appear more favourable on southern slopes as compared to the interfluves as is the case in more southerly regions. For this reason the distribution of zoomass is very uniform throughout the whole region. One of the causes of higher overall zoomass is the absence of a continuous moss layer in plant communities leading to higher soil temperatures. Besides, the heterogeneity of the vegetation cover provides diverse and favourable conditions for the development of certain groups of invertebrates. The uniform conditions can be demonstrated by the change in size of *Eisenia nordenskiöldi:* in typical tundra (Tareya) its size on southern slopes is three times as large as in interfluve zonal tundra communities (about 500 and 1 500 mg respectively); in arctic tundra (M. Pronchitsheva Bay) the maximal biomass of *Eisenia nordenskiöldi* is approximately equal in all environments, about 350 mg.

MICROORGANISMS

One of the most peculiar features of microbial distribution in arctic tundra soils is a remarkable relative decrease in numbers in the optimal meadow communities. This phenomenon has not been explained satisfactorily. The quantity of viable microflora decreases gradually with depth. But in both the mesic and dry sites of the mossy *Salix polaris* frost-boil tundra, an increase in numbers was observed at depths of 12—36 cm and 10—27 cm respectively. This is possibly explained by the higher content of Ca, P and humus (Table 3).

As pointed out earlier for the Tareya station soils a characteristic of the soils of the eastern Taimyr is that bacteria predominate over fungi and actinomycetes. While fungi and actinomycetes are observed mainly in the upper horizons, bacteria are detected

Table 5. Viable microbial counts in profile of soils investigated (numbers $\times 10^3$ g^{-1})

Site	Depth (cm)	Soil extract agar	Utilizers of mineral N	Utilizers of organic N	Ammoni-fyers	Oligo-nitro-philic	Anaerobic nitrogen fixing	Nitri-fying	Denitri-fying	Clostridium butyricum anaerobic	Cellulolytic anaerobic	Cellulolytic aerobic	Fungi	Actino-mycetes
Mossy *Salix polaris* mesic frost-boil tundra	0–2	2 550	3 540	1 960	950	2 270	–	0.25	0.95	2.5	–	0.95	1.6	–
	2–12	1 790	1 800	1 310	1 500	1 500	–	–	–	4.5	–	–	0.23	–
Spot	12–36	3 000	3 600	1 800	4 500	2 600	0.003	–	–	0.95	–	–	0.5	–
	36–41	970	1 000	1 130	250	970	0.15	–	–	0.15	–	–	0.1	–
Mossy *Salix polaris* dry frost-boil tundra	0–2	2 900	5 300	740	2 500	5 500	4.5	0.025	0.95	25	–	–	3.3	33.0
	2–10	730	730	500	15	660	–	–	0.06	15	–	–	0.006	–
Spot	10–27	900	960	760	45	1 200	0.04	–	–	45	–	–	0.01	–
	27–43	350	520	330	40	344	0.3	–	–	25	–	–	–	–
Herb-grass meadow on southern slope	0–10	259	202	350	450	570	0.09	–	0.95	1.5	–	–	2.3	16.3
	10–30	330	290	229	950	234	0.25	–	0.09	0.45	–	–	2.6	–
	30–50	340	290	243	450	163	0.25	–	–	0.95	–	–	–	–
	52–57	22	21	97	200	130	0.15	–	0.09	0.09	–	–	–	–

– not detected

throughout the soil profile down to the very permafrost level. The utilizers of mineral nitrogen, oligonitrophilic bacteria and bacteria growing on soil extract agar predominate (Table 5). Ammonifyers are widely distributed. Nitrogen-fixing aerobic bacteria (*Azotobacter*) were not detected and numbers of anaerobic nitrogen fixing bacteria are very low. Nitrifying bacteria were not detected in most soils and extremely weak nitrification was observed in only two cases. Denitrifying bacteria were observed in the upper horizons of most soils. Cellulolytic bacteria, both anaerobic and aerobic, are practically absent in the soils studied.

Some preliminary data on the microbial development in the root region (Table 6), show that soil close to *Dryas octopetala* roots contained about twice as many bacteria as soil from bare ground. Samples from the root region of *Novosieversia glacialis* contained 3–30 times greater microbial populations as compared with bare ground. On the other hand, inhibition of microbial development was detected under the lichen crust, where soil samples contained 2 to 30 times fewer microbial cells than bare ground.

Table 6. The effect of plant roots on microbial populations (numbers x 10^3 g^{-1})

Microorganisms	Bare ground	*Dryas octopetala* root region	*Novosieversia glacialis* root region	Soil under lichen crust
	0–2 cm	1–5 cm	1–5 cm	1–3 cm
Bacteria on soil extract agar	1 000	2 100	3 600	63
Utilizers of mineral nitrogen	1 090	1 980	3 520	64
Utilizers of organic nitrogen	590	143	770	20
Ammonifyers	150	450	4 500	25
Oligonitrophilic	750	450	2 660	39
Fungi	14	20	42	8
Actinomycetes	11	9	86	–

– not detected

The severe environmental conditions cause a sharp decrease in bacterial production compared with that in the subzone of typical tundra (Tareya). Tha maximum value for bacterial production in soils of Maria Pronchitsheva Bay is close to the minimum values found for typical tundra (0.1–0.2 %, Table 7).

Table 7. Bacterial production and generation rates in arctic tundra

Site	Depth (cm)	Bacterial production within one summer month (% of soil dw)	Average generation rate (h)
Mossy *Salix polaris* mesic frost-boil tundra; spot	0–2	0.15 0.15	28 28
Mossy *Salix polaris* dry frost-boil tundra; spot	0–2	0.23	35
Herb grass meadow on southern slope	1–5	0.11	31

Spatial variation in the severe environmental conditions do not strongly influence bacterial production. Maximum production is about twice the minimum value in this arctic zone, compared with 18 times in typical tundra.

Rosswall, T. & Heal, O.W. (eds.) 1975.
Structure and Function of Tundra Ecosystems.
Ecol. Bull. (Stockholm) 20: 73–124.

BARROW, ALASKA, USA

F.L. BUNNELL, S.F. MACLEAN, Jr. and J. BROWN

INTRODUCTION

Geographical location

Barrow is situated at the northern extremity of the Alaskan Coastal Plain province, on a triangular-shaped land mass bounded by the Chukchi Sea on the west, and the Beaufort Sea and Elson Lagoon on the east (71°18′N, 156°40′W) (Fig. 1). The land mass is characterized by low relief, and dominated by ice-wedge polygons, shallow, oriented lakes and drained lake basins. Small ponds and lakes cover 20 % of the landscape. Coastal bluffs, stream banks, and shores of drained lakes represent the maximum relief, with much of the remaining tundra surface showing relief features of less than 2 m. Relief forms are accentuated where drainage gradients are steepened along edges of streams or shorelines due to thermal erosion of the ice wedges. Several of these characteristics are shown in the aerial view of the US Tundra Biome terrestrial sites (Fig. 2).

Vegetation and soil characteristics vary along a moisture-dominated gradient ranging from drier, elevated beach ridges and upland meadow communities through wet meadow and marsh types to emergent aquatics and open water in small ponds and lakes. On raised center polygons a similar moisture-dominated gradient extends from the drier, raised centers through rims to the relatively moist troughs. The depth of seasonal soil thaw averages 40 cm in wet mineral soils but varies from 20 to 80 cm depending on organic matter and moisture contents. The seasonally thawed soil is underlain by perennially frozen ground to several hundred meters which has a mean annual temperature of approximately −10°C.

The wet, marsh-dominated tundra of the Barrow area is characteristic of a narrow belt of coastal tundra which gives way to a more varied, tussock- and shrub-dominated tundra tens of kilometers inland. The vertebrate fauna is also simpler than other coastal as well as inland areas. In particular, caribou (*Rangifer tarandus* (L.) Hamil.-Smith) and ground squirrels (*Spermophilus*) are largely absent and collared lemmings (*Dicrostonyx*) are not abundant at Barrow. Polygonized ground and the shallow, oriented lakes are ubiquitous on the Arctic Coastal Plain.

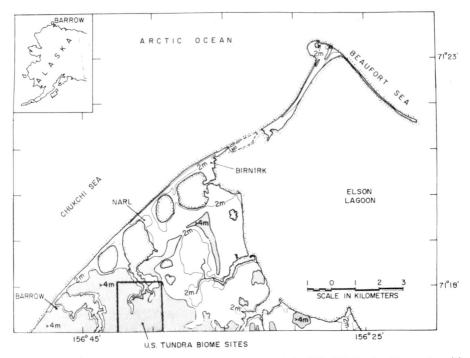

Figure 1. Index map of Alaska showing the Barrow area and the U.S. IBP Tundra Biome site with 2- and 4-m contour intervals.

Figure 2. Aerial photograph looking north across the U.S. Tundra Biome site. The ice-covered Arctic Ocean is in the background.

History

The Arctic Coastal Plain is composed of Pleistocene-aged, near-shore marine deposits composed of admixtures of silts, fine sands and gravels. Fluvial, lacustrine and eolian processes along with frost action have modified the upper 3 to 5 m of sediments. The northern extension of the coastal plain comprising the Barrow area is recently emergent bearing a sequence of uplifted beach ridges that become less defined inland and south-westward. Radiocarbon age determination from the reworked deposits of the first in-land beach ridge yielded a date of 25 000 years B.P. Based on a number of radiocarbon dates, the majority of the soils and surficial features of the present Barrow land surface are not older than 8 000–10 000 years and perhaps considerably younger.

The village of Barrow, which is the largest Eskimo town in the State of Alaska (population 2 100), is located within the general study area. Earliest known human habitation of the area occurred at the Birnirk Site which was drowned by an encroaching sea and abandoned some 1 200–1 500 years ago.

Several government-operated facilities, including the Naval Arctic Research Laboratory, NARL, are situated 6 km north of Barrow Village. NARL has supported research on tundra ecology since 1947; the National Weather Service has operated a first-order weather station at Barrow since 1920.

ENVIRONMENTAL CONDITIONS

Climate

Macroclimate

The regional climate consists of long, dry, cold winters and short, moist, cool summers. The sun is above the horizon continuously from 10 May to 2 August, and below between 18 November and 24 January. Table 1 contains monthly means of several key climatic parameters for Barrow.

As measured by 5-year running means for individual months, the mid-1950s and the late 1960s were cooler than the long-term means. Indirect evidence of climate trends based on geothermal analyses indicates a 4°C warming in ground temperatures over the past century. Table 2 demonstrates that July temperatures during the IBP study years were generally warmer than normal.

Air temperatures remain below freezing through most of the year with only 87 days showing a mean daily temperature greater than 0°C. Air temperatures below freezing are observed in every month of the year. A gradual warming trend begins in April with a definite transition toward summer during May. Snowmelt, however, is not initiated until mid-June. The end of the short summer is reached by mid-September and by mid-November one half of the daily mean temperatures are −18°C or lower. Coastal temperatures are affected noticeably by the wind and ice conditions although, even before the shore ice goes out, the ocean is an important moderator of climate. The Arctic Ocean generally becomes ice-free during late July or early August. During periods of open water, air temperatures are considerably cooler when winds are off the oceans as compared to periods of southerly winds. The occurrence of cloudiness, precipitation and heavy fog is associated with the presence of ice-free ocean.

Table 1. Monthly normals (1941–1970) for air temperature (°C), precipitation (mm), windspeed (m s^{-1}) and solar radiation (kJ cm^{-2}), Barrow, Alaska (from National Weather Service)

	J	F	M	A	M	J	J	A	S	O	N	D	Year
Solar radiation (kJ cm^{-2}) ☆	0	4.4	22.8	48.2	68.0	68.9	57.3	33.5	15.0	5.4	0.5	0	324
Temperature (°C)	−25.9	−28.1	−26.2	−18.3	−7.2	0.6	3.7	3.1	−0.9	−9.3	−18.1	−24.6	−12.6
Precipitation (mm)	5.8	5.1	4.8	5.3	4.3	8.9	22.4	26.4	14.7	14.0	7.6	4.8	124.2
Windspeed (m s^{-1})	5.0	4.9	5.0	5.2	5.2	5.1	5.2	5.5	5.9	6.0	5.6	5.0	5.3

☆ 14-year mean

Table 2. Summer climate for IBP years as compared with the 30-year normals

	Temperature (°C)			Precipitation (mm)		
	June	July	Aug.	June	July	Aug.
1970	0.5	3.2	1.7	0.5	3.8	8.9
1971	1.7	4.7	0.8	3.1	24.4	8.9
1972	0.3	6.1	4.8	1.3	2.8	28.5
1973	0.7	4.3	4.3	19.8	26.9	55.9
1941–70 Normal	0.6	3.7	3.1	8.9	22.4	26.4

A large part of the annual precipitation (40 %) occurs as rainfall during the short summer season. Although evaporation apparently equals precipitation, the lack of drainage due to the impervious nature of permafrost results in soils close to saturation most or all of the growing season. Summer monthly precipitation during the IBP study period extended to both extremes. The summer of 1973 was extremely wet while early summer of 1970 was unusually dry.

Variation of windspeed during the year is small, with fall months being the windiest. Relatively high sustained windspeeds suggest strong, drying effects in the vegetation. However, the potential drying effects in summer by strong winds are modified by the concomittant high relative humidities. Fogginess and cloudiness persist through the summer with average humidities for the months of June through September consistently above 80 % and usually above 90 % throughout the day.

Microclimate

During any particular growing season at Barrow, dramatic changes in microclimate occur over time and, to a more limited extent, space. The most dramatic differences occur during the brief spring and autumn with the transition from a snow-covered to a snow-free surface and vice versa. Other, less dramatic differences in microclimate are associated with specific terrain parameters such as microrelief and vegetative structure.

Based on energy balance the seasonal climatic cycle of arctic tundra can best be divided into six distinct periods:
1. Pre-melt — late May and early June.
2. Snowmelt — early June to mid-June.
3. Post-melt — mid- to late June.
4. Summer — July and August.
5. Freeze-up — mid-September to October.
6. Winter — November to mid-May.

Annual variations in the starting date and duration of these periods occur, but each period has both its own characteristic energy balance components (Fig. 3) and physical appearance of the tundra surface. Typical temperature profiles of several conditions are presented in Fig. 4. The Arctic Coastal Plain snowpack consists of four zones in the approximate order from top to bottom: 1) fresh new snow, with variable crystal forms and a density of 0.15 to 0.20 g cm^{-3}; 2) wind slab, hard, fine-grained with density 0.35 to 0.45; 3) medium-grained snow 0.23 to 0.35; and 4) depth hoar consisting of loosely

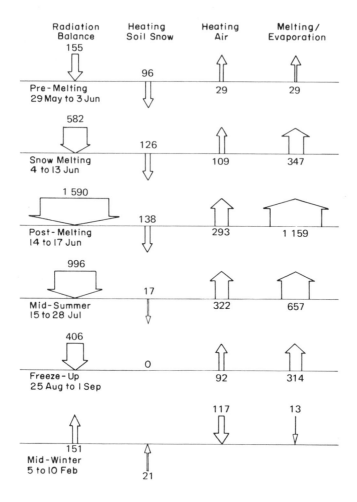

Figure 3. Heat balance of the arctic tundra for six different characteristic periods. The width and direction of the arrows and numbers at the base of each arrow indicate energy flux directions and rates (J cm^{-2} d^{-1}) (modified from Weller & Holmgren, 1974).

bonded crystals possessing a density of 0.20 to 0.30. This forms the principial subnivean environment for the lemmings.

Changes through the period of snowmelt are large. The average snow cover of 35 to 45 cm is removed within 2 to 3 weeks, soil surface temperatures increase by 15°C and the dry snow environment with high reflectivity is replaced by a saturated, water-logged tundra surface with low reflectivity. The first snow-free patches of tundra occur on knolls and tufts of tall vegetation. These absorb solar radiation and quickly heat up to 10°C above the temperature of surrounding snow-covered terrain. During the period of snowmelt plants are thus exposed to both rapidly increasing surface temperatures and rapidly increasing light. Early in spring, lemmings concentrate their activities in low-lying areas where the snow remains longest, thus minimizing exposure to predators. As the snow pack becomes isothermal and loses structure, the subnivean space collapses and low-lying areas are subject to flooding. Lemmings are then forced to more elevated habitats where they are subject to environmental extremes and exposed to avian predation. Meltoff is a period of heavy mortality for lemmings.

The dramatic change that occurs during snowmelt is associated with changing albedo at the surface. Dry snow which is present for about 9 months of the year at Barrow has an albedo of approximately 85 %. During melting this drops steadily. Dry tundra has a mean albedo of about 20 % which is reduced to 10 % whenever rain or snowmelt produce extensive areas of water. As the growing season progresses, the roughness of the tundra surface increases. The increase in terrain roughness and reduction in wind speed near the surface contribute to the temperature increase observed within the vegetative canopy (Fig. 4).

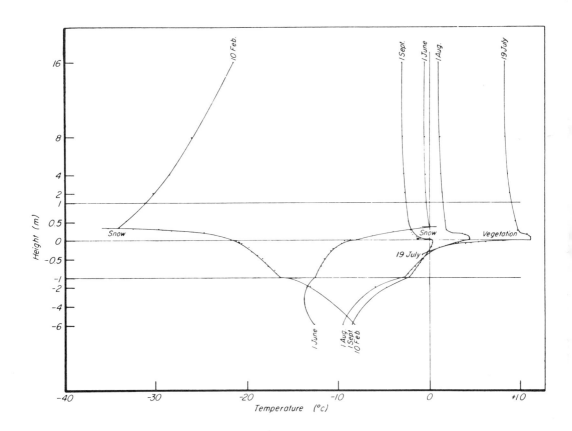

Figure 4. Typical temperature gradients in air, snow, vegetation and soil. Note the effect of snow (10 February and 1 June) and vegetation (1 August and 19 July) on the soil surface temperature. The vertical height scale from +1 to −1 m is expanded. (Weller & Holmgren, 1974.)

The sharp gradient in air temperature within the vegetative canopy means that organisms in the upper canopy levels of 20 to 30 cm height are as much as 2°C cooler than organisms at the soil surface. Windspeed may double between the surface and 10 to 20 cm in height. For substrates with little capacity to retain or replenish water, the difference in windspeed may be significant. Thus, standing dead vegetation in the upper canopy may be too dry over much of the summer for decomposition to occur, while moderate rates of decomposition might occur at lower canopy levels.

By the time the tundra surface refreezes in early September, radiation has dropped appreciably and evaporation has been reduced. Soon thereafter snow covers the tundra again and the radiation balance becomes negative. Organisms living in the soil near the surface are again subject to a major change in temperature, although the rate of change is buffered by the zero curtain (a period after soil freezing has begun in which a zone of soil remains isothermal as the latent heat of fusion is being extracted). During this period soil organisms remain active. The air temperature falls much more rapidly than soil temperature; as a result, surface-dwelling organisms such as lemmings may experience low temperatures and exposure to wind without the protection of snow accumulation.

Microrelief at the Barrow site, particularly in well polygonized areas, influences both the amount of standing water and related albedo and the density of vegetation and associated thermal and windspeed gradients. Thus, somewhat different microclimates are associated with polygon rims as compared to polygon troughs. The seasonal course of soil temperatures under three polygon microrelief types (troughs, rims, centers) is shown in Fig. 5.

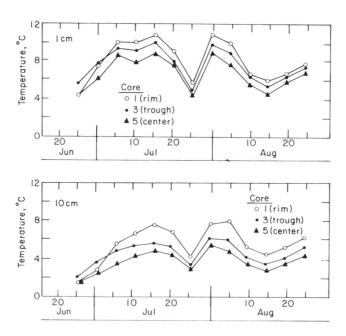

Figure 5. Seasonal course (5-day means) of 1972 summer soil temperature on a polygon trough, rim and center at 1-cm and 10-cm depth.

Hydrology

The hydrologic year can be divided into three seasons that are directly related to the six energy-balance periods that characterize the arctic tundra. Table 3 gives estimates of the water balance for the tundra near Barrow for these seasons and periods.

Table 3. Water balance estimates for Alaskan arctic coastal tundra

Hydrologic Season	Period	Measured precipitation (mm)	Estimated runoff (mm)	Estimated evapotranspiration (mm)
Snow accumulation	Freeze-up	36.2	0	5.0
	Winter	71.1	0	0
	Pre-melt	5.2	0	2.0
Runoff	Snow-melt	3.3	100.0	2.0
Evapotranspiration	Post-melt	5.0	0.3	11.4
	Summer	54.2	2.7	51.5
Annual		175.0	103.0	71.9

Hydrologic activity during the freeze-up and winter period is minimal except for the gradual increase in the snowpack. During the pre-melt period, the radiation balance becomes positive, and the available energy is used to ripen the snowpack and heat the surface soil. The annual snowmelt runoff is the most significant hydrologic event of the year; typically 100 mm of water runs off in a 7- to 10-day period. Most fluvial processes of erosion and deposition occur at this time. Following spring runoff, the tundra is left saturated and covered with numerous ponds of all sizes and shapes. Evapotranspiration then becomes the dominant process during the post-melt period, with 4 to 5 mm d^{-1} evaporating from open water areas. In the two-month summer period, open-water evaporation rates decrease to 3 mm d^{-1}. Transpiration rates are typically 1/10 of open-water evaporation rates; evapotranspiration accounts for about 95 % of the precipitation in an average summer. During rainless periods, runoff may cease and many tundra ponds dry up. However, during occasional periods of sustained summer precipitation, such as are likely to occur in August, as much as 70 % of precipitation runs off. Spring and summer runoff occur almost exclusively at the surface, with negligible contributions from soil moisture.

Soils

Soil morphology and classification

The majority of the Barrow soils have formed on flat to very gently sloping topography under cold temperatures and high moisture conditions which favor the accumulation of organic matter. A high proportion of the soils have a tripartite morphology consisting of a histic or organic-rich surface horizon; a horizon of silty clay to silt loam textured mineral material, commonly gleyed and with variable amounts of included and/ or enmixed organic materials. This horizon is commonly coextensive with an underlying organic-rich horizon. The sequence of horizons has been interpreted as reflecting that burial of organic materials by lacustrine sediments as a result of the thaw lake cycle, or in some cases by frost churning. The surface horizon and mottling within the mineral horizons are the product of the current soil forming processes of organic matter accumulation and gleyzation. Leached soils, represented by the Arctic Brown soil, are present only on coarser textured deposits on primary land surfaces and are not represented within the Biome sites.

Few of the Barrow soils have a sufficient thickness and/or percentage of organic material to be classified as organic soils, Histisols, in the US National Soil Taxonomy. Most belong to the mineral soil order of Inceptisols. Because all of the soils are cold and have a cryic temperature regime, the prefix Cry is added to each subgroup name. The term Pergelic preceeding the subgroup name indicates the presence of perennially frozen ground.

The soils occur along a topographic gradient ranging from the relatively freely drained and weakly leached Pergelic Cryochrepts (Arctic Brown) to those developed under conditions of extreme wetness, the Pergelic Cryaquepts and Histic Pergelic Cryaquepts (Half Bog soils). Intermediate and somewhat better drained elements of the topographic-moisture gradient have Histic Pergelic Cryaquepts and Pergelic Cryaquepts developed in association with weakly expressed, low center polygons and low, raised center polygons (Meadow Tundra). Somewhat higher on the gradient where the low center polygonal pattern is strongly developed, an association of soils occurs composed of Pergelic Cryohemists in the depressed polygon centers, Histic Pergelic Cryaquepts or Pergelic Cryosaprists on the polygon rims and Pergelic Cryaquepts or Pergelic Cryohemists in the troughs. These soils repeat in cyclic fashion from polygon to polygon. Their generally better drainage is reflected in an increase in mottling in the subsurface horizons and evidence of cryoturbation, especially in the soils of the rims.

Pergelic Cryosaprists occur in the centers of prominent raised center polygons. On coarser-textured and better drained mineral soil slopes Aeric Pergelic Cryaquepts may be found.

Local, recent disturbance to the tundra surface has resulted in thermokarst depression of the troughs associated with low, raised center and low center polygons. Continued degradation of the perennially frozen ground together with thermal erosion may result in the conversion of the present Histic Pergelic Cryaquepts to Pergelic Cryaquepts and Pergelic Cryohemists to Pergelic Cryosaprists through the oxidation and/or erosion of the organic surface horizon as a result of better drainage in the polygon centers.

Soil physical properties

The wet meadow soils have physical properties typical of peat soils. During the summer a high temperature gradient exists between the heated surface and the underlying permafrost boundary. The surface may reach temperatures of 25°C while soil horizons at 20 to 30 cm never rise much above 2°C. Soil surface temperatures are modified by canopy absorption of radiation, while thermal conductivity of the soil varies directly and markedly with the moisture and mineral contents. Strong prolonged warming of the surface tends to dry out the surface horizons causing a decrease in thermal and hydraulic conductivities and, hence, in heat and moisture fluxes. Intermittent wetting of the surface by precipitation or dew formation can increase the surface thermal and hydraulic conductivity. By their drying action, prolonged warm spells actually can reduce thermal flux, thaw depth, and soil evaporation, but not transpiration of vascular plants. Maximum heat flux and thaw depth are obtained with frequent wetting of the soil surface combined with intermittent periods of moderate to high temperature.

Soil moisture contents at depths greater than about 4 cm are high, normally at least 85 % of water-holding capacity. At these depths soil moisture tensions almost never exceed 100 millibars; consequently vascular plants rarely experience moisture stress.

Bulk densities range from 0.05 g cm^{-3} in the surface moss layer, to as high as 1.5 g cm^{-3} in the silt-loam layers, decreasing again to about 0.6 in the buried peat layer. The upper organic layer of low bulk density is highly porous (pore volumes of 90–93 %); the mineral layers are less so (45–65 %); while the buried peat layers contain 80–88 % pore volume. The stratification of organic matter content and pore volume affects the movement of air and water in the soil. With the high moisture contents and reduction of pore volume in the mineral layers the soil environment becomes rapidly anaerobic. Root activity of some plants is inhibited and the decomposer community shifts from fungal to bacterial dominance.

Chemical properties

The wet meadow soils are highly organic, strongly to very strongly acid, generally have a low percentage base saturation, and are therefore classified as oligotrophic. Since decomposition products of organic matter are generally acid, the cation exchange capacity and exchangeable acidity usually vary directly, while pH and percent base saturation vary inversely with the organic content. Both the cation exchange capacity and percent base saturation correlate directly with clay content.

Given these general relations, the Cryohemist soils are less fertile than the Cryaquept soils which contain a mineral horizon. Furthermore, the latter soils contain buried organic horizons of increased fertility and pH. In these buried horizons compaction and deaeration of the organic matter mixed with mineral material apparently increase the humification and the base saturation. Subsoil components thus store a considerable percentage of the base nutrients and frequently contain sufficient nutrients to meet the annual requirements of the biotic portion of the ecosystem.

The organically bound nutrients, principally N and P, are stored in large quantities in the soil organic matter but are released only slowly as available N and P. Soluble N, P and S levels are very low, indicating relatively low rates of mineralization and high rates of uptake or assimilation. Available N is present largely as the cation NH_4^+. It is stored on the soil exchange complex and appears to be mineralized and localized principally in the subsoil organic layers during the latter part of the summer. During the first week of July to the beginning of September, available N appears to move by diffusion upwards from the subsoil towards the root zone. Some downward movement of available N must occur at some point in the season. Such cyclical, seasonal movement may also occur to some degree with the various bases, and nutrient limitation of primary production by this mechanism may occur.

Soluble iron is generally high, the level increasing directly with pH and being rather independent of redox potential which suggests strong chelation. A pronounced peak in soluble Fe and P occurs in the late summer which may be connected with the activity of Fe-fixing bacteria. Soluble Al (possibly chelated) levels are also high and may be attributable to the high levels of exchangeable Al which are thought to be a principal source of acidity in Histisols. The colloidal organic content of the soil solution is high and stores a limited amount of N and P which may be readily hydrolyzed to available N and P.

PRIMARY PRODUCTION

Community classification

The vascular vegetation of the Alaskan Coastal Plain is meadow-like, with sedges, grasses, forbs and a few dwarf shrub species. The well known decline in species numbers that occurs with increased latitude is observed among vascular plants as well as insects and other organisms. Near Umiat, just beyond the southern boundary of the coastal plain vegetative province, there are about 250 vascular plant species, but only 150 of these reach the proximity of the sea coast. In the immediate coastal area near Barrow, there are only about 100 vascular plant species with 96 bryophyte and 57 lichen species known. The northward reduction in the number of species is accompanied by a steady decline in the abundance of shrubs, particularly Ericaceae. This reduction in species diversity northward is related both to reduction in topographic and habitat diversity and to severity in climates northward.

The general summer aspect of coastal tundra vegetation is that of uniform yellow-brown grassland relieved only by the appearance of greener vegetation in the wetter areas including the network of troughs between polygons. The drab color of the vegetation results from the accumulation of dead vascular plant parts. On the wetter, lower areas such as basins or polygon troughs, this dead vegetation is depressed by the weight of drifting snow and accumulated melt water. Thus, although primary production is greater on the wetter soils, less dead vegetation remains standing and the aspect is greener.

In the Barrow tundra with its low relief, differences in the composition of vegetation of uplands and lowlands are not pronounced. All species of the extensive marshes also occur on the uplands and most of those of the driest upland sites also can be found wherever hummocks appear in the wetter areas. The vegetative composition assumes a fine-grained mosaic of recurring assemblages distributed over and differentiated by the geomorphic structures of polygons. Marked differences are restricted to localized habitats such as marine beaches or eroding bluffs.

The vegetation continuum in areas of low relief with little surface drainage has been divided into eight commonly occurring plant assemblages or noda. Each nodum is named on the basis of its moisture regime, dominant and/or characteristic species, and general habitat. Table 4 lists some species, the principal soil types, and the characteristic microrelief of these noda. Gradient analysis methods have permitted an assessment of the substrate conditions controlling plant and vegetation distribution. The most important substrate complexes are soil moisture, soil oxidation-reduction potential as indicat-

Table 4. Characteristics of the eight vegetation noda of the meadows and polygonized tundra at Point Barrow

Nodum	Principal species	Principal soils ☆	Major microrelief type(s)	Area (%)
I. Dry *Luzula confusa* heath	*Luzula confusa, Potentilla hyparctica, Alectoria nigricans, Pogonatum alpinum,* and *Psilopilum cavifolium*	Upland Tundra Pergelic Cryaquept/Pergelic Cryosaprist	High center polygons	3
II. Mesic *Salix rotundifolia* heath	*Salix rotundifolia, Arctagrostis latifolia, Saxifraga punctata, Sphaerophorus globosus,* and *Brachythecium salebrosum*	Upland Tundra and Frost Medallion Ruptic Histic Pergelic Cryaquept/ Pergelic Cryaquept/Aeric Pergelic Cryaquept	Low center polygons and sloping creek banks	7
III. Mesic *Carex aquatilis-Poa arctica* meadow	*Carex aquatilis, Poa arctica, Luzula arctica, Cetraria richardsonii, Pogonatum alpinum*	Upland Tundra Pergelic Cryaquept/Pergelic Cryosaprist/ Pergelic Cryohemist	Hummocky polygon rims and centers and dry, flat polygonized sites	41
IV. Moist *Carex aquatilis-Oncophorus wahlenbergii* meadow	*Carex aquatilis, Oncophorus wahlenbergii, Dupontia fischeri, Peltigera aphthosa* and *Aulacomnium turgidum*	Upland Tundra Pergelic Cryaquept/Pergelic Cryohemist	Moist, flat sites and drained polygon troughs	21
V. Wet *Dupontia fischeri-Eriophorum angustifolium* meadow	*Dupontia fischeri, Eriophorum angustifolium, Cerastium jenisiense, Peltigera canina* and *Campylium stellatum*	Meadow Tundra/Half bog Pergelic Cryaquept	Wet, flat sites and polygon troughs	7
VI. Wet *Carex aquatilis-Eriophorum russeolum* meadow	*Carex aquatilis, Eriophorum russeolum, Saxifraga foliolosa, Calliergon sarmentosum* and *Drepanocladus brevifolius*	Meadow Tundra/Half bog Histic Pergelic Cryaquept/Pergelic Cryohemist	Low polygon center and pond margins	15
VII. *Arctophila fulva* pond margin	*Arctophila fulva, Ranunculus pallasii, Ranunculus gmelini, Eriophorum russeolum* and *Calliergon giganteum*	Meadow Tundra/Half Bog/Bog Pergelic Cryaquept	Pond and stream margins	2
VIII. *Cochlearia officinalis* meadow and creek bed	*Phippsia algida, Ranunculus pygmaeus, Stellaria humifusa, Saxifraga rivularis* and *Arctagrostis latifolia*	Alluvium Pergelic Cryaquept/Aeric Pergelic Cryaquept	Snowbeds, creek banks and creek sides	4

☆ Two soil nomenclatures are used: see Tedrow & Cantlon, 1958 (top line of each nodum) and Soil Survey Staff, 1974.

ed by the relative presence or absence of hydrogen sulphide, and soluble phosphate levels. Fig. 6 shows the position of the major vegetation noda within the continuum formed by these complex gradients. This framework also permits the description of plant productivity and standing crop estimates in terms of the important substrate gradients.

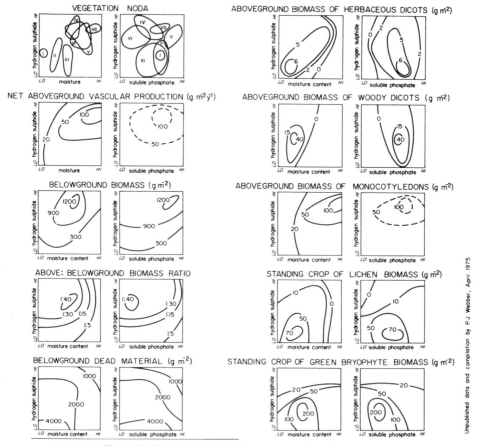

Figure 6. Gradient analysis of meadows and polygons.

Species diversity and productivity patterns

Throughout the tundra zone there is a positive correlation between floristic diversity and primary productivity, and Barrow conforms to the trends. However, within the Barrow site this relationship is controlled by site moisture regime. Almost monospecific stands of monocotyledons in the wettest meadows have the highest production. Productivity decreases from these sites down a complex moisture gradient concomittant with an increase in floristic diversity. At the driest end of the gradient the decrease in both diversity and productivity is rapid to very low values.

Vascular plants

Plants taken from beneath the snow in early June show photosynthetic competence;

86

however, there is no evidence that growth or production is actually initiated until the plants are released from snow cover, about 5 June to 14 June. From this time until the onset of fall freezeup, about 5 September, CO_2 assimilation is possible. Within the predominant grass-sedge or wet meadow community the period of most rapid vascular plant growth is still more restricted, occurring between 14 June and 1 August. Not surprisingly, vascular plants comprising the wet meadow community show most of the physiological responses associated with rapid growth over a short period. These include efficient use of a low energy environment, increased respiration rates, large carbohydrate reserves associated with starch degradation at low temperatures, and vegetative reproduction. Meltoff occurs very near the summer solstice when radiation is maximal. Because there is very little persistent chlorophyllous tissue in the dominant grasses and sedges, canopy development must occur very rapidly if the plants are to make efficient use of the declining radiation.

At the onset of the growing period the low availability of photosynthetic tissue, and therefore the efficiency of solar energy interception, places more limitation on community production than do the limitations of low temperature and low light intensity which are prevalent throughout the growing season. Since the period of maximum standing crop is narrowly defined, phenomena which affect the availability or exposure of photosynthetic tissue at the beginning of the growing season alter the period of growth and total community production. Early snowmelt probably increases the annual production while very high numbers of overwintering lemmings can reduce it dramatically.

Within the plants themselves, the overwintering ability possessed by partially formed reproductive structures and partially developed leaves represents an adaptation for early resumption of spring growth and quick utilization of the greater amounts of radiation present at the beginning of the growing season. Similarly, the apparent mobilization of carbohydrate reserves from belowground biomass and effective translocation of carbohydrates at temperatures near $0°C$ are equally likely to be adaptations to the restricted growing season.

Immediately after snowmelt, relative growth rates for the vascular plant community are rapid, 0.20 to 0.25 g g^{-1} d^{-1}, declining to about 0.03 g g^{-1} d^{-1} within 10 days. Early season growth includes translocation from belowground storage as well as CO_2 assimilation. Maximum aboveground standing crops vary with the meteorological conditions of the season and with the size of the lemming population. Representative peak aboveground biomasses for the wet meadow communities at Barrow range from 60 to 100 g m^{-2}. Since the dead remains of several years' previous growth may remain standing, the combined live and dead vascular plant material varies between 150 and 300 g m^{-2} at maximum aboveground standing crop. In specific moist and nutrient-rich habitats where monospecific graminoid stands become established, live vascular plant standing crops of up to 200 g m^{-2} may occur. The most productive stands are generally located in standing water and have very erect leaves.

While the date of initiation of new growth (defined as green biomass > 5 g m^{-2}) may differ by 19 days (for *Dupontia*) to 38 days (for *Eriophorum*) between years depending upon meteorological and lemming factors, the time of maximum standing crop is more narrowly defined and occurs within about 5 days of 1 August. The factors stimulating cessation of aboveground growth are not clear. A shortening of the photoperiod is not initiated until 2 August; however, incoming radiation is already declining in late

June, and air temperature in July.

Allocation to aboveground biomass thus ceases about one month before photosynthesis and other growth processes are curtailed by fall freezing. Substantial CO_2 uptake occurs during August and photosynthate is incorporated into belowground reserves which may permit rapid initiation of growth in the following spring. Spring growth, however, is not extensively dependent on stored reserves. Despite the severe environment and short growing season a significant developmental senescence occurs. In the 10- to 20-day period following maximum standing crop, *Eriophorum angustifolium* Honck. experiences a decrease in biomass at rates of up to 0.07 g g^{-1} d^{-1}, while *Dupontia fischeri* R. Br. loses biomass at rates of 0.02 to 0.03 g g^{-1} d^{-1}. While much of this loss represents conversion of green to standing dead, there appears to be transfer of both mobile organic compounds and minerals to subsurface components. The rates of withdrawal of nitrogen, potassium and phosphorus are more rapid than the rate of biomass loss during senescence, and significant withdrawal of these three elements may occur before biomass growth is terminated.

The seasonal course of belowground biomass is masked by the large amount accumulated and by large variability between microsites and within sample dates. Apparent increases in live, belowground biomass have been measured. Over the sample period, the proportion of the live biomass made up of rhizomes initially decreases, only to increase later, suggesting translocation downward in late season. Much of the vascular plant standing crop occurs belowground, and at maximum aboveground standing crops the ratio of live biomass belowground to that aboveground is frequently 10:1. Standing crops of dead material belowground are usually much larger than the live crops and are more evenly distributed with depth; whereas 60 to 80 % of the live material is contained within the upper 10 cm of soil as little as 50 % of the dead material is resident there. The difference is likely associated with the higher microbial activity and decomposition rates in the upper 10 cm. Roots appear to live 2 to 10 years and to exhibit an annual production of 65 g m^{-2} (disregarding potential losses to decomposition which would increase production estimates). Rhizomes usually live longer than roots and have a lower rate of annual production.

Most of the apparently living standing crop belowground occurs within the upper zone of the active layer. The major portion of the belowground standing crop is thus within soil that is thawed by late June and which does not freeze again until early September.

With the short growing season and unfavorable climatic conditions, vegetative reproduction is more reliable than sexual reproduction and both flowering and successful seed set are reduced. Among the rhizomatous monocotyledons, vegetative reproduction is common although many species may develop flowers. Less than 2.5 % flowering shoots occur in two *Eriophorum* species, about 10 % in *Dupontia* and about 7 % in *Carex*. Asexual reproduction, including apomixis and vivipary, also occurs probably representing an adaptive response to the short growing season.

Bryophytes

The bryophyte association at Barrow consists of heterogeneous assemblages of taxa scattered through the communities, rather than as mosaics of pure clumps. Thus, with a few exceptions such as the clumped shoots of *Lophozia ventricosa* (Dicks.) Dum. or areas where the vascular plant biomass is low, the abundant bryophytes are relatively inconspicuous and hidden by the vascular overstory. The inconspicuous nature of the bryophyte contribution is misleading since bryophytes are represented by about the same number of species as are the vascular plants and may contribute significantly to aboveground primary production.

Within the wet meadow where aboveground productivity of vascular plants reaches 60–100 g m^{-2}, annual bryophyte production ranges up to 160 g m^{-2}. On these meadow areas the largest contribution to bryophyte biomass is made by pleurocarpous mosses, followed by acrocarpous mosses and leafy liverworts; on drier sites dense tufts of acrocarpous mosses may have even higher biomass. Thalloid liverworts are not abundant and *Sphagnum* species are restricted to local depressions and the edges of some polygon rims. Vascular plants in wet meadows are represented by 20 or more species while bryophytes are represented by about 27 species.

As it does with other organisms, microrelief influences the abundance and distribution of bryophytes. At the beginning of the growing season, bryophyte biomass on the edge of polygon rims may be two to three times as great while values in the low center polygons may be only half as much as those in meadows. The larger biomass values represent temporary nutrient sinks particularly for the trace elements such as boron, copper and molybdenum. Although concentrations of macronutrients during the growing season are generally lower than those found in vascular plants, concentrations of the trace elements and calcium are generally higher in the bryophytes. The capacity of the bryophytes to accumulate essential microelements may be important to general nutrient budgets since these elements might otherwise be lost during spring runoff. Similarly, the switch in lemming diet towards bryophyte foodstuffs during the winter may result, not simply because of the reduced vascular biomass present, but also because of the high concentration of certain nutrients, especially calcium, within the bryophytes.

Since decomposition rates of bryophytes are generally somewhat lower than vascular plants, their importance in nutrient cycling can be assessed in terms of absolute amounts temporarily immobilized as well as in terms of concentrations presented to foraging herbivores. Thus, while aboveground portions of live vascular plants may contain 1.5 to 2.0 g N m^{-2} or 0.1 to 0.2 g Ca m^{-2}, bryophytes may contain 2.0 to 3.2 g N m^{-2} and 1.5 to 2.0 g Ca m^{-2}.

Lichens

Both biomass and diversity of lichen species are strongly influenced by and inversely correlated with substrate moisture. On the poorly drained areas where runoff water accumulates for 2 to 3 weeks at the beginning of the summer, lichens are entirely absent with the exception of some water-transported fragments. Sites where soil moisture levels are consistently above 100 % (dw) typically contain only *Peltigera apthosa* (L.) Willd. and *P. canina* (L.) Willd. Although biomass of *Peltigera* in these areas is only about 10 g m^{-2}, the areas may contribute significantly to input of nitrogen to the Barrow ecosystem through nitrogen fixation. *Peltigera apthosa* and *P. canina* are the major nitrogen-fixing lichens of the Barrow area. Nitrogen concentrations of these species exceed typical values for Barrow lichens (0.5–0.7 %) and are as high as or higher than those of vascular plants, ranging from 2.4 to 4.2 %. Although no clear causal relationship is apparent, soils of the wetter areas where *Peltigera* and blue-green algae are abundant, show unusually high levels of nitrogen.

It is noteworthy that unlike many tundra regions, lichens of the Barrow region play a very limited role in vertebrate trophic relations. Caribou are infrequent migrants to the Barrow area and lemming stomachs seldom contain more than 2 % lichens. Cycling of lichen constituents such as nitrogen must proceed through the saprovore and decomposer food chains. On better drained meadow sites or areas of polygonized ground, where soil moisture levels vary between 30 and 100 %, soil lichens may attain biomass levels exceeding 50 g m^{-2}, but lichens are usually outcompeted by bryophytes and vascular plants. Diversity also increases on drier sites and the genera *Cetraria, Cornicularia, Thamnolia, Alectoria, Cladonia* and *Dactylina* are represented as well as *Peltigera*. Lichens attain their best expression on the driest sites such as tops of high center polygons and frost boils where surface soil moisture levels are less than 30 %. In these areas more than 20 lichen species may be represented in a 10 cm^2 area and biomasses of more than 60 g m^{-2} are attained.

Algae

Algae are ubiquitous, occurring in the moss layer and upper few centimeters of soil over all microtopographical areas of the Barrow site. Because of the generally moist nature of much of the site, the species composition of the algae approximates that of aquatic environments and includes planktonic forms. Green algae are most prevalent and include coccoid and filamentous, single-celled and multi-cellular types. Diatoms, euglenoids and filamentous blue-greens are also present. Over small areas there is no consistent trend in species diversity or abundance. A single species may dominate a local microsite with numbers as high as 10^7 g^{-1} soil; other microsites may have 10 or more species each represented by fewer cells. *Nostoc commune* Vauch. and its various phenotypes are common and significant in the general nitrogen balance of the system since they contribute importantly to nitrogen fixation.

At the time of meltoff, algal biomass is about 0.15 g m^{-2} in the upper 2 cm of soil and slightly less in the moss layer. During the growing season biomass decreases to between one-half and one-tenth the biomass initially present, perhaps in response to protozoan and invertebrate grazing. The generally moist nature of the Barrow site supports significant numbers of aquatic fungi, many of which are parasitic on algae (R. Seymour, pers. comm.). The significance of these parasites in reducing algal biomass cannot be judged but nearly 85 % of algae examined contained at least one fungal parasite. There is some indication that algal biomass may begin to increase in September, although it is equally likely that much of the return to early season levels occurs under the snow immediately prior to meltoff.

Standing crops, productivity and diversity of the algae appear largely moisture-limited. The moss layer, which is more exposed to drying than the soil beneath it, generally has a lower productivity than the soil layers. Thus, as the season progresses and the moss layer dries, the amounts of *Nostoc* available to fix nitrogen gradually decline. In general, moister sites such as troughs and wet meadows, show higher standing crops and productivity than more mesic sites except during periods of precipitation when algal production on even the drier polygon ridges is high. Although standing crops and apparent productivity of the soil algae appear to decrease during the snow-free season there is an increase in species diversity. The increase may be a response to ameliorated temperature conditions concomitant with readily available moisture. The influence of moisture is most apparent after periods of precipitation, when both species diversity and algal cell abundance increase. It appears that the longer the period of available moisture, the greater the expression of algal diversity.

Production processes

Gas exchange patterns

Uptake of CO_2 by lichens and algae is relatively insignificant in the terrestrial plant community. Thus vascular plants and bryophytes make the largest contributions to community incorporation of organic matter. Early in the season uptake of CO_2 is limited by the ability to intercept light. This condition persists until the leaf area index approaches 1.0, near the end of July. Early season uptake of CO_2 is further limited by the incomplete competence of the photosynthetic structures. At this time high mesophyll resistances associated with low carboxylation activity limit the photosynthetic rate. Before the vascular canopy develops, bryophytes intercept radiation more effectively than vascular plants and likely are more important to CO_2 uptake early in the season.

Photosynthetic rates of vascular plants are characterized by responses similar to other plants possessing the C3 pathway. Light-saturated rates of young, expanded leaves are typically between 8 and 20 mg CO_2 dm^{-2} h^{-1}, although rates as high as 30.8 mg CO_2 dm^{-2} h^{-1} have been measured. These maximum photosynthetic capacities are highly correlated with ribulose-1,5-diphosphate carboxylase activity. Under optimal conditions, mesophyll resistances to CO_2 uptake are 3 to 5 times greater than resistances imposed by the leaf epidermis and stomata, which show minimal values of 1 and 3 cm s^{-1}.

Light saturation in Barrow monocotyledons is attained around 1.7 to 2.1 J cm^{-2} min^{-1} (wave bands from 400 to 700 nm). Since these light intensities are attained only on relatively clear days around solar noon, the leaves of most plants are seldom light-saturated, and CO_2 uptake within the community should be closely coupled to radiation. Temperature optima for Barrow monocotyledons also are higher than the usual ambient temperatures. For intact leaves, temperature optima are about $15°C$. Despite the fact that neither light nor temperature consistently approach the optimum levels, the broad response curves against both light and temperature permit the photosynthetic apparatus to function near optimally over the natural daily range of temperature, and to maintain at least low rates of photosynthesis over the entire 24 h period at least to late July.

General growth strategies of the whole monocotyledon plant also facilitate efficient CO_2 uptake. Barrow monocotyledons show a pattern of successive leaf replacement with full photosynthetic competency attained as each leaf approaches maximum expansion. Thus a complement of at least one competent leaf is retained throughout the season even as leaf turnover results in senescence of older leaves. The result is that the whole plant achieves maximum rates of CO_2 uptake early in the season. With progression of the season the high daily rates decrease both as a result of increasing senescence and a deteriorating radiation regime.

Because of the low light required for compensation, community photosynthesis is positive for 24 h on most days until the sun sets on 2 August. Similarly, because the leaves are seldom light-saturated and meltoff occurs only shortly before the time of maximum light intensity, community CO_2 uptake is strongly coupled with radiation. Leaf resistances remain low during the season indicating that transpiration is potentially high. Low irradiances and high air humidities, however, result in a low water vapor density gradient. Therefore, transpiration rates are low. Slight midday depressions in CO_2 uptake do occur and are associated with small increases in resistances.

Daily rates of CO_2 uptake as high as 300 mg CO_2 dm^{-2} d^{-1} result in a high seasonal total. Community uptake is maximal just prior to maximum standing crop and is significantly influenced by temperature, radiation, and species composition. About one-third of the seasonal uptake occurs after maximum standing crop and is either utilized or stored below ground. Independent estimates indicate that seasonal uptake ranges between 6 000 and 7 000 mg CO_2 dm^{-2}. The bulk of this carbon is derived from community respiratory sources rather than from direct atmospheric drawdown.

Water relations patterns

Plants in the wet meadow are rarely stressed to the level of complete stomatal closure. In moist years water potentials may range between -1 bar at midnight to about -10 bars at midday, while unusually warm and dry years produce potentials of -18 to -25 bars. Water potentials associated with a leaf resistance of about 20 s cm^{-1} vary with species and range from -9 to -10 bars for *Arctophila fulva* (Trin.) Anderss. and *Dupontia fischeri* to -14 for *Eriophorum angustifolium* and -18 bars for *Salix pulchra* Cham. Water potentials at these values are rarely attained in the field and most Barrow plants experience little water stress.

The relationship between water potential and the saturation deficit is linear with a slope of about -0.8 to -1.8 bars/% saturation deficit for most species studied. *Eriophorum angustifolium* shows a somewhat reduced response to saturation deficit and has a slope of -0.2 bars/% saturation deficit.

Minimum leaf resistances are about 1 and 3 s cm^{-1} for all species, while root resistances to water uptake vary widely with the rate of transpiration.

Effect of plant geometry

The plant community of the wet meadow tundra is well adapted to intercepting the relatively low levels of solar radiation. Graminoid species with leaves inclined about $65°$ predominate. By the time of maximum standing crop the leaf area indices range between 0.6 and 1.0 for living material and from 0.0 to 1.5 for standing dead material. At the latitude of the Barrow site, the average solar altitude on 21 June is $25°$ declining to about $19°$ by 21 August. At these low solar altitudes the erect leaves provide almost complete interception of solar radiation, and measured interception efficiencies range between 0.72 on 15 June to 1.0 at the end of August.

Under the conditions prevailing at Barrow, leaf area indices of 0.5 and 1.0 intercept 62 % and 94 % of the incoming radiation on 21 June, increasing to 68 % and 98 % on 21 August. A leaf area index of 1.0 has an intercepting path length of about 2.6 on 21 June which increases to 3.0 in July and August. By contrast, at $40°N$ a leaf area index of 7.0 would be required to produce the same intercepting path length.

Plant constituents

Concentrations of nitrogen, phosphorus and potassium in aboveground monocotyledon biomass peak during the second week of the growing season, then decline steadily at a rate more rapid than can be explained by senescence. The rapid decline of concentrations is primarily due to dilution by structural material during the growing season. A steady increase in calcium concentrations during the growing season reveals the continued increase in cell wall contents.

Concentrations at the time of early season peak values range from 2.5 to 3.5 % for nitrogen, 2.0 to 2.5 % for potassium, and about 0.4 to 0.7 % for phosphorus. By the onset of senescence these values have declined to 1.5 to 2.0 % for nitrogen, 0.8 to 1.5 % for potassium, and 0.1 to 0.25 % for phosphorus. Calcium concentrations begin at levels of 0.05 to 0.15 % and increase to about 0.15 to 0.30 % during the growing season. Amounts of nutrients resident in aboveground, live, monocotyledon biomass at time of maximum standing crop are thus about $1.7 \, \text{g N m}^{-2}$, $0.8 \, \text{g K m}^{-2}$ and $0.15 \, \text{g m}^{-2}$ of both phosphorus and calcium. Representative transients are illustrated in Fig. 7.

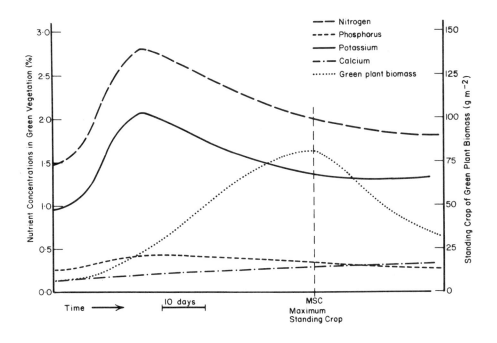

Figure 7. Representative patterns of nitrogen, phosphorus, potassium and calcium concentrations in green vascular biomass during the growing season (maximum standing crop usually about 1 August).

93

Barrow monocotyledons store all the nutrients required for the spring flush of growth in the rhizome and stem base. Significant absorption of nutrients from the soil does not begin until early July. Absorption from the soil becomes progressively more important in August as depth of thaw proceeds and continues well into September when aboveground biomass is no longer increasing. The nutrient stores of the rhizome and stem base, which may be depleted in the spring, apparently are not replenished by nutrient uptake and translocation from senescing aboveground parts until later in the season.

The mineral composition of dicotyledons differs from that of the monocotyledons primarily in the cations. In the dicotyledons calcium and potassium are present at concentrations about twice those found in monocotyledons. The different cation status is probably assocaited with the different microsite preferences shown by the two groups. Whereas the monocotyledons are dominant in the wetter, more acid microsites, dicotyledons prefer the better drained, drier and less acid areas. In these latter areas, cations are more generally available to plants and this increased availability may be expressed as higher cation concentrations in the vascular plants. Furthermore, mycorrhiza are consistently associated with dicotyledons and absent in monocotyledons. The mycorrhizal association probably contributes to higher phosphorus levels in dicotyledons.

Carbohydrates appear to be translocated at high rates (i.e., comparable to temperate zone plants) even at the existing low temperatures. The allocation of this assimilate varies among species but is available for root growth and production as soon as photosynthesis commences even though temperatures in the lower part of the root zone may be at $0°C$. In *Dupontia*, tillers show a high degree of independence although leaves from one tiller will partially support rhizomes and roots of adjacent tillers.

Early in the season total nonstructural carbohydrate (TNC) levels in rhizomes and stem bases drop slightly as new shoot material is produced. At no time, however, do levels of TNC drop below 15 % of the dry weight of the organ. Sugar pools are maintained at stable levels in leaves and stems although polysaccharides vary to a greater extent and decrease through the season as do lipids. Upon the addition of fertilizer, especially phosphorus or nitrogen and phosphorus, the plants respond by rapidly increasing leaf areas concommitant with a general decrease in TNC. There is no increase in carboxylation activity but carbohydrates are withdrawn from the rhizome. The response confirms the hypothesis that the most significant control of inorganic nutrients is on the allocation of carbohydrates to leaf material and not on the photosynthetic process directly. The control of organic nutrients on carbohydrate allocation accounts for a portion of the spatial variation in observed primary production.

The common growth forms at Barrow possess little structural tissue aboveground. Thus, in comparison with plants of other areas, most plant components are chlorophyllous. The seasonal progression of chlorophyll is quite synchronous among all species, with maximum standing crops (450 mg m^{-2}) and concentrations (85 mg g^{-1}) preceding peak plant biomass by 10 and 20 days respectively. The patterns of chlorophyll suggests that senescence is initiated before peak biomass, a pattern that is also characteristic of alpine graminoids and coincides with the withdrawal of inorganic nutrients from aboveground biomass. The retention of chlorophyll until 1 September further suggests that CO_2 uptake is significant between peak season and freezeup.

Few plant species at Barrow invest in compounds that are costly to synthesize. Neither the graminoid nor dicotyledon growth forms store large quantities of lipids or other high

94

energy compounds. Although there is some variation between species, energy contents of aboveground components are typically slightly less than 18.4 kJ g^{-1} (uncorrected for ash which ranges between 3 and 14 %). Roots and other subsurface components have slightly lower energy contents.

HERBIVORES

Overview and generalizations

Plant consumption at Barrow is dominated by a single species, the brown lemming [(*Lemmus sibericus* (Kerr) (=*trimicronatus* (Richardson)]. Because the density of this species varies in a cyclic fashion over a period of 3 to 5 years, grazing pressure also varies in a cyclic fashion. Lemmings do not hibernate but are active throughout the year, and maximum densities are attained through reproduction during the winter. The heaviest grazing pressures are therefore concentrated on low standing crops of green vegetation (stem bases) when the vegetation is dormant. During periods of high lemming density (up to 200 ha^{-1}) grazing activities can cause widespread destruction of the habitat. As well as reducing the standing crop of herbs and mosses, lemming activities may uproot rhizomes, alter the thermal regime of soil and the depth of thaw, and modify the rates of decomposition. Long-term effects include alteration of vegetation composition and the microtopography. Lemmings may also influence the spatial distribution of nutrient concentrations by their patterns of grazing and fecal deposition.

Other vertebrate herbivores are present at Barrow (Table 5) but never achieve the high densities of the brown lemming nor do they undergo such dramatic changes in density. Geese (*Anser, Branta*), collared lemmings (*Dicrostonyx*), and caribou (*Rangifer*) which are common elsewhere on the tundra, attain only low densities in the Barrow area and some mammalian herbivores characteristic of tundra, such as ground squirrels (*Spermophilus*) and hares (*Lepus*), are entirely absent. Avian consumers are primarily insectivorous although some, such as the Lapland longspur (*Calcarius lapponicus* Ridgway) and snow bunting (*Plectrophenax nivalis* L.), consume seeds prior to and subsequent to the midsummer period of abundant insects. The redpoll (*Acanthis flammea* (L.)), a seed specialist, can be common in summers when seeds of the previous year's crop are abundant. Tundra arthropods are primarily saprovores and do not feed extensively on live plant tissue.

Invertebrates

The invertebrate fauna of Barrow is particularly low in aboveground or canopy-dwelling herbivores. Sawfly (Hymenoptera: Tenthredinidae) and lepidopteran larvae occur on willows and other dicotyledonous plants. These plants, however, are not generally abundant. One leafhopper (Homoptera: Cicadellidae) and one leaf beetle (Coleoptera: Chrysomelidae) occur, but again, are not abundant. Root-piercing nematodes are present but the total effect of invertebrate herbivory is very small.

Table 5. Major terrestrial vertebrates of the Barrow, Alaska, tundra

H = herbivore, H_g = granivore, C_v = carnivore on vertebrates, C_i = carnivore on invertebrates.

Taxon	Trophic function	Density	Biomass (g ww)	Duration of residence
Mammalia				
Insectivora				
Sorex cinereus	Scavenger; C_i	Uncommon	4 g	Resident
Sorex arcticus	Scavenger; C_i	Uncommon	7 g	Resident
Carnivora				
Alopex lagopus	Scavenger; C_v	0–1 km^{-2}	2.8–4 kg	Resident but varies seasonally
Mustela erminea	C_v	0–2 km^{-2}	100–140 kg	Resident
M. nivalis	C_v	0–25 km^{-2}	40–70 g	Resident } when lemming density permits
Artiodactyla				
Rangifer tarandus	H	Uncommon visitant	90–100 kg	Seasonal visitant
Rodentia				
Lemmus trimucronatus (= *sibericus*)	H	<1–200 ha^{-1}	ca 60–80 g exceptionally 125 g	Resident
Dicrostonyx groenlandicus	H	<1–25 ha^{-1}	ca 60 g exceptionally 125 g	Resident
Aves				
Anseriformes				
Polysticta stelleri	C_i	Up to 1 km^{-2}	750–1 000 g	
Clangula hyemalis	C_i	ca 0.5 km^{-2}	650– 850 g	
Anas acuta	C_i,H	Variable; up to 2 km^{-2}	750–1 000 g	♂ 20 days; ♀ 70 days
Strigiformes				
Asio flammeus	C_v	0–2 km^{-2}	♂–250 g, ♀–400 g	90 days
Nyctea scandiaca	C_v	0–2 km^{-2}	♂–1750 g, ♀–2100 g	100 days (occasionally resident)
Charadriiformes				
Xema sabini	C_i	Colonial; breeds inland and on offshore islands		
Sterna paradisea	C_v	0–15 km^{-2}	♂–650 g, ♀–740 g	
Stercorarius pomarinus	C_i	ca 4 km^{-2}	180–200 g	
Pluvialis dominica	C_i	Patchy; ca 2 km^{-2}	95–115 g	
Arenaria interpres	C_i	ca 10 km^{-2}	55–60 g	80 days
Calidris alpina	C_i	nil – 20 km^{-2}	65–100 g	♂40 days; ♀ 60 days
C. melanotos	C_i	ca 4 km^{-2}	30–35 g	♂60 days; ♀ 50 days
C. bairdii	C_i	ca 4 km^{-2}	22–26 g	50–60 days
C. pusilla	C_i	Variable; 2–25 km^{-2}	50–60 g	♀ 30 days; ♂70 days
Phalaropus fulicarius	C_i			
Passeriformes				
Calcarius lapponicus	C_i; H_g	ca 40 km^{-2}	23–28 g	80 days
Plectrophenax nivalis	C_i; H_g	Mostly anthropogenic	26–36 g	100 days

Vertebrates

A pattern of alternating high and low densities of brown lemmings is clear, but the precise population levels and timing of demographic events differ from cycle to cycle (Fig. 8). In addition, the population characteristics in relatively high, dry habitats differ from those in low, wet habitats. During a "typical" cycle, however, densities, averaged over several habitats span several orders of magnitude, from less than 1 to 200 animals (excluding sucklings) per hectare.

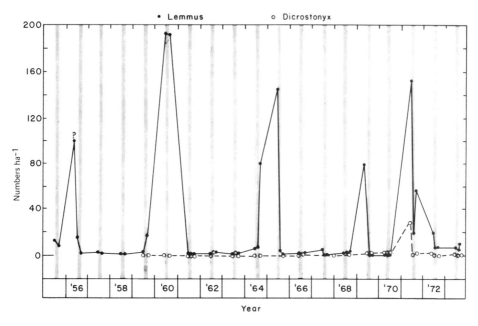

Figure 8. Fluctuations in mammalian herbivore densities at Barrow (based on trapline data from Pitelka 1973).

Year-to-year variation in winter reproduction is a major feature of lemming population cycles. The causes are not altogether clear. Winter temperature, interacting with snow depth and structure, clearly has an effect. The Barrow snow cover is shallow and provides relatively little insulation; ground surface temperatures of $-25°C$ and below are regularly recorded. Such conditions must create an energetic stress for lemmings, and it appears that winter reproduction is inhibited by low temperature and unusually shallow snow.

Snow structure may be equally important. During winter, lemmings forage in a subnivean space consisting of depth-hoar, very coarse, crystalline snow. In some years, fall rains produce a very hard layer in the snow, sometimes extending to the ground surface. This layer prevents depth-hoar formation, and lemmings may be excluded from a portion of the habitat. The phenomenon is seen following sping melt-off as very intense but patchy grazing pattern. If sufficiently extensive, such conditions may delay or even abort a population rise to a cyclic high.

Densities build up to peak levels under the winter snow pack, and highest levels occur just before snowmelt when breeding ceases. Populations usually decline during the summer and winter following a peak and reach their lowest levels by the second summer. The decreasing trend reverses during the second or third winter following a peak and the cycle is completed the next year. A seasonal pattern is superimposed upon the cyclic pattern. Breeding is restricted to the summer (June—August) and winter after the snow pack has formed (November—April). During other times, particularly snowmelt and freezeup, the population must decline no matter what the cyclic trend is. This pattern of population dynamics imposes a similar pattern on production, consumption and energetics.

The average daily metabolic rates of arctic microtines tend to be higher than those for other rodents, an apparent adaptation that allows maintenance of body temperature under winter snow where temperatures may reach $-25°C$. One might expect total population energy budgets of lemmings to be higher than those for temperate microtines, but apparently this is not so because temperate populations may reach high densities for longer periods of time. The total population respiration of lemmings calculated over a "standard" cycle varied between $0.63-210$ kJ m^{-2} yr^{-1}.

Total annual production for lemming populations at Barrow has been calculated by summing the energy channeled into reproduction and growth. The range of values during the course of the population cycle was $0.04-10.5$ kJ m^{-2} yr^{-1}. In temperate rodent populations, net secondary production represents a small part of the energy flow, averaging 2.8 % of respiration. Calculations for brown lemmings at Barrow indicate a larger value (4.9 %), probably because lemmings have longer breeding seasons and larger litter sizes than most temperate rodent populations.

The diet of brown lemmings varies with season and with habitat, both of which influence availability of forage. In general, lemmings at Barrow consume monocotyledons (*Carex*, *Dupontia*, and *Eriophorum*) and mosses (*Polytrichum*, *Dicranum* and *Calliergon*). Mosses form 5—20 % of summer diets and 30—40 % of winter diets. Availability of monocotyledons is dramatically reduced during winter; only the bases of leaves and stems provide suitable forage. Because digestibility of forage is low (about 35 % of energy for monocotyledons and about 25 % of energy for mosses), consumption rates are higher than might be expected. Total consumption of forage during the standard cycle varies from $1.7-700$ kJ m^{-2} yr^{-1}.

The nutrient content of monocotyledon forage is sufficient for body maintenance but may allow severe nutrient depletion in lactating females. Consumption of mosses provides a more concentrated nutrient source and also, because of the low digestibility of mosses for energy, requires a higher gross intake of forage to satisfy energy requirements. Thus, mosses may be a critical nutrient supplement. A diet of mosses, alone, will not sustain a lemming. The low digestibility of monocotyledons for energy may be an adaptation to increase gross intake of nutrients in the diet. If this is so, nutrient intake, rather than energy, may be the most critical factor influencing the evolution of lemming nutritional behavior and physiology.

Year-to-year variation in plant nutrient content is surprisingly high, particularly in habitats of low nutrient status. Since lemming reproduction appears to be sensitive to nutrient content of the forage at the levels found in natural Barrow vegetation, such year-to-year variation may influence reproductive intensity and act as an important modifier of cyclic pattern.

Functional effects

Because of the cyclic nature of lemming populations, the effect of their grazing varies enormously. At low population levels lemming consumption is less than 0.1 % of aboveground net primary production. Consumption over the year of the population peak (ca 700 kJ m^{-2} yr^{-1}) amounts to about 25 % of the annual aboveground net primary production, and 10 % of the total net primary production. This consumption, however, is distributed over the plant productivity of two different seasons; a period of plant growth occurs at the same time as the major population decline in most seasons. Thus an increasing lemming population may consume up to 40 % of the aboveground production of the prior season, while a declining population usually consumes less than 15–25 % of the production of the ensuing season. If the effect of lemming activity is to reduce plant production in the summer of the population high (as in 1964–1965), the percentage of production that is consumed will increase.

Plant-herbivore interactions are further complicated by the asynchrony between plant growth and lemming consumption. During the period of summer activity, plant growth occurs far more rapidly than lemming consumption. Even peak lemming populations are not able to consume a significant fraction of plant growth. Aboveground plant growth ceases in August, and by September live aboveground vascular plant biomass is reduced to overwintering values of 5–10 g m^{-2}. This biomass must support the lemming population for the entire winter and the major pre-high population increases usually are made on these low plant biomasses. Since each grass or sedge shoot provides only a small quantity of food, a lemming must fell many shoots to meet its daily energy and nutrient requirement during winter. During the pre-high winter grazing is complete; essentially the entire aboveground vascular plant biomass is consumed. Even in years of low to moderate lemming abundance patches of complete winter grazing of vascular vegetation are evident. In some years at places of heavy grazing, lemmings disturb the moss layer to forage extensively on stem bases and rhizomes. The former contain the growth meristems, while the latter are major storage reservoirs of energy and nutrients, some of which are used for early season plant growth in the following season. Thus, grazing during the winter of increase prior to the high has a far larger effect upon plant growth than does the summer grazing of the population high. The most important direct effect of grazing is probably removal of growth points through consumption of meristematic tissue.

Nutrient turnover

Of the food consumed by lemmings, the majority (about 70 %) is immediately returned to the tundra as feces. Assimilated energy is largely used in respiration, while assimilated nutrients are used in body maintenance with associated urinary loss. The feces and urine accumulate over a winter of grazing, and release a significant quantity of readily leachable and soluble nutrients with the spring melt. Thus there is a meltoff flush of nutrient availability associated with lemming grazing. The movement of meltwater may result in nutrient enrichment of impoundments where meltwater accumulates, and of tundra ponds.

Lemming feces consist of small particles of vegetation and are deposited on the ground surface where temperature and moisture conditions are favorable for decomposition. Measures of microbial respiration from decomposing lemming feces are of the same magnitude as from decomposing standing dead vegetation, but certain elements such as phosphorus are leached extremely rapidly. Thus, while the feces retain their structural integrity and are present in high densities within the Barrow soil, the material within them is primarily resistant polysaccharides.

In the course of winter grazing lemmings fell vegetation, converting standing dead to litter on the surface of the tundra. The latter decomposes more rapidly due to more favorable temperature, moisture and nutrient conditions. This, again, contributes to rapid nutrient turnover. Fig. 9 illustrates the effect of lemming density on decomposition of vascular plant vegetation. Note the accumulation of dead vegetation over the period prior to high lemming density and rapid disappearance during the high year.

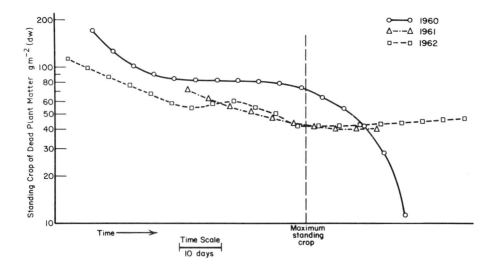

Figure 9. Patterns of total vascular plant standing dead and litter during the summer years of high (1960) and low (1961, 1962) lemming density. Maximum standing crop usually about 1 August (Bunnell 1973).

Lemmings may likewise influence nutrient distribution. Winter activity is localized in polygon troughs and other low areas of maximum snow accumulation. Activity of reproductive females is localized around a winter nest constructed of dead graminoids and placed on the tundra surface. Lemmings make foraging trips to other habitats, but spend the majority of their time in these favored habitats. Thus, while foraging may occur extensively, fecal deposition tends to be localized and the result is a net movement of nutrients into favored habitats. While the net movement in any single year may be small, lemming-mediated nutrient transport accumulated over a sequence of population cycles may be largely responsible for contemporary patterns of nutrient distribution, which impact heavily upon ecosystem function.

Physical effects

Consumption of over-wintering plant biomass by lemmings may be total, but this accounts for only a fraction of the annual net primary production. More important, in terms of plant processes, is consumption of stem bases and rhizomes. Such removal significantly influences the plants' capacity for rapid growth in the following summer. Rapid leaf development is important if plants are to make efficient use of the available radiation; thus even a small delay in spring growth may have a large effect upon production.

Winter grazing also removes standing dead leaf tissue from the vegetative canopy, thus increasing efficiency of light interception by green tissue in the ensuing spring, and enhancing production. It follows that moderate winter grazing favors plant productivity, while severe and/or sustained grazing has a depressing effect.

Even within their favored habitats lemming movement is largely confined to runway systems. Where runways are constructed and used over a sequence of cycles in polygonal ground, they may become channels for runoff, and thus are subject to erosion. As a result, runway construction interacts with landscape forming processes on a very fine scale.

Effects on community structure

The non-random selection of forage and severe grazing intensities provide at least the potential for interaction between lemmings and community structure. The growth form of the dominant Barrow monocotyledons — large, belowground storage of energy and nutrients; relatively protected meristem; sequence of tillers leading up to the production of a flowering tiller; capacity for vegetative reproduction — would seem to make them relatively resistant to grazing, and thus favored under a regime of periodic heavy grazing. As a result, grazing may help sustain the monocotyledon dominance of the Barrow system. *Saxifraga cernua* L., an important dicotyledon of the low, wet habitats favored by lemmings, has small bulbils along the stem that are capable of sprouting. Lemming activity may contribute to the spread of this species.

The effects of lemmings may be assessed in exclosures. In old exclosures around the Barrow area, there is generally a buildup of standing dead vegetation, increased thickness of the moss layer, shallow depth of seasonal thaw, decreased vascular plant productivity, and a change in species composition. The grass *Calamagrostis holmii* Lange seems particularly prevalent where lemmings are excluded.

CARNIVORES

Overview and generalizations

Carnivory at Barrow is supported by both herbivore- and saprovore-based food chains. The dominant herbivore is a vertebrate (the brown lemming) and carnivores in the herbivore-based food chain are also vertebrates, predatory birds and mammals. The marked population cycles of lemmings produce similar cycles of predator abundance. In a year of abundant lemmings, pomarine jaegers (*Stercorarius pomarinus* (Temminck)), snowy owls (*Nyctea scandiaca* (L.)), short-eared owls (*Asio flammeus* (Pontoppidan)), least weasels (*Mustela nivalis* L.), ermine (*M. erminea* L.) and arctic fox (*Alopex lagopus* (L.) Kaup) all may be abundant. During low lemming densities these predators are scarce or absent (Table 5.)

Invertebrate saprovores and microbivores support both invertebrate and avian predators. The combined saprovore and microbivore fauna provides an abundant and consistently more reliable food source than do the lemmings. Thus, carnivores in the saprovore-based food chain do not show wide annual fluctuations. Dominant inverteberate predators include carabid beetles and larvae of the cranefly *Pedicia hannai antenatta* Alex. Tundra graminoids set seed infrequently and insectivory is the most common trophic mode among tundra birds. The shorebirds, especially sandpipers of the genus *Calidris* (*C. alpina* L., *C. melanotos* (Vieillot), *C. bairdii* (Coues), *C. pusilla* L.) are particularly conspicuous insectivores. The two important passerine species, Lapland longspur (*Calcarius lapponicus*) and snow bunting (*Plectrophenax nivalis*) are partially graminivorous in early and late season, but support essentially all their breeding activities by feeding on tundra arthropods.

Invertebrates

Predatory invertebrates, like other trophic groups, are greatly limited in diversity. Only one spider family (Linyphiidae) achieves any degree of diversity and abundance; Lycosidae is represented by a single, uncommon species and no other spider families have been observed at Barrow. Several species of carabid beetle (*Pterostichus* spp.) exist at combined densities of 30 to 60 m^{-2}. Because the adult life of these species is prolonged, larvae and adults coexist in the soil. Staphylinid beetles are smaller, but exist at similar or greater densities. Mesostigmatic mites are moderately abundant (600–7 000 m^{-2}) and most of these are predatory. The most important predatory invertebrate, however, is the cranefly (*Pedicia hannai*) which attains larval densities of 200 m^{-2} and a biomass approaching 1 g m^{-2}.

Population energetics have been investigated only in the cranefly larva (*Pedicia hannai*). The productivity to respiration ratio declines with development; overall, it is 0.59 over the four-year development period. A larval population of 200 m^{-2} gives a productivity of 7.6 kJ m^{-2} yr^{-1} and population respiration of 11.3 kJ m^{-2} yr^{-1}, with an adult emergence of approximately 10 m^{-2} yr^{-1}.

Enchytraeidae dominate the invertebrate biomass and these form the most likely food source for invertebrate predators. Collembola are also abundant and may be important as prey.

Vertebrates

Populations

Densities of lemming predators vary markedly with season and stage of the lemming population cycle. Avian predators are migratory and only snowy owls are present in the winter (and these only rarely in a pre-high year). Most owls arrive between late April and late May, jaegers arrive in late May to early June. At peak lemming densities, snowy owls may nest at 0.5–1 pair km^{-2}, and pomarine jaegers at 7 pairs km^{-2}. In years of low lemming numbers neither owls nor jaegers nest in the Barrow area. Nesting owls produce clutches of up to 11 eggs, with clutch size at least partially adjusted to lemming density; jaegers lay clutches of two. The estimated food requirements of snowy owls during fall and winter (4–7 lemmings d^{-1}) prohibits their presence in most years.

The numeric response of least weasels to lemming density involves both immigration from adjacent areas and reproduction. It appears largely over the winter that precedes the lemming high. Peak weasel density at meltoff of the lemming high year may be quite high (up to 25 km^{-2}). Since weasels are not migratory they remain into the post-high winter until the lemming population has declined to the point that it will no longer support predators. As a result, least weasels exert heavy predation pressure on a declining lemming population. After the decline weasels may become locally extinct in the immediate Barrow area until the next increase in lemming abundance.

Unlike other predators, arctic foxes are more common in winter than in summer. Major denning areas are inland from Barrow, possibly due to a greater abundance of nesting waterfowl providing a more dependable food source. In September and October young of the year as well as some older animals disperse from the denning sites, moving toward and along the coast seeking areas of high food availability. Carcasses of sea mammals, birds and other carrion form the major portion of their winter diet but as the lemming population increases, foxes prey actively on lemmings. The numeric response of arctic foxes is thus primarily one of immigration.

Nine of the common bird species of the Barrow area rely upon tundra arthropods during the breeding season (7 species of shorebirds and 2 buntings). Collectively, these species nest at densities of 80–100 pairs km^{-2}. Although abundance of species within this group may change from year to year their overall abundance and impact is more consistent than is the case for predators relying upon lemmings.

Tundra bird populations arrive in the first days of spring melt, and commence breeding activities immediately. This is necessary to ensure that the young are produced at the time of the mid-season peak in adult insect activity. Early season bird activities are supported, in large part, by Diptera larvae, especially crane flies (Tipulidae), and by fat reserves. When adult insects appear in early July the birds shift their foraging attention to these. Late-season activities are again supported by Diptera larvae, especially Chironomidae. The shorebird species differ in social system organization and in duration of residence on the tundra. For example, in the dunlin (*Calidris alpina*) the mating system is monogamous, and both adults remain on the tundra through August; in pectoral sandpipers (*C. melanotos*) mating is polygamous or promiscuous and males leave the Barrow tundra by early July. Such social system differences may contribute to the coexistence of ecologically similar species using a resource base that is low in diversity.

Production

Production of predators may be great during a lemming high, particularly if high lemming density persists well into the summer. Fledging success of pomarine jaegers varies between zero and 55 % of eggs laid. Comparable fledging success leads to greater productivity of owls, because of their larger clutch size.

Least weasel females collected near Barrow appear to have a larger litter size than do temperate weasels. The larger litter sizes and the absence of delayed implantation give them a high reproductive potential and may explain the rapid and extreme numeric response to increasing lemming density. While arctic foxes, pomarine jaegers and snowy owls respond to the dramatic changes in lemming densities through migratory or other dispersal patterns, the least weasel relies heavily on its reproductive potential.

Both snowy owls and arctic foxes have been shown to have exceptional insulation, thus reducing metabolic rates to feasible levels during the winter. Foxes rely heavily upon carrion and upon fat reserves to survive the winter. The major fox production occurs at inland denning sites with a more diverse prey base.

The bioenergetics of Barrow carnivores are poorly known. Metabolic rates of the four *Calidris* sandpipers increase with decreasing temperature over the entire range of ambient temperatures normally encountered at Barrow. Thus, these birds, and likely the other vertebrate insectivores as well, are always using extra energy to compensate for heat loss. As a result only 2 to 3 % of the total energy consumed by insectivorous birds ($17-21 \times 10^5$ kJ km^{-2} season^{-1}) contributes directly to secondary productivity. Annual secondary productivity also can be assessed in the form of surviving young birds leaving the system. Expressed in energetic terms secondary productivity of the insectivorous avifauna amounts to about 4×10^4 kJ km^{-2} season^{-1}.

Functional effects

Feeding by insectivorous birds serves to bring energy and material from belowground components of the system into circulation aboveground. A portion of the large nutrient reserve present in the subsurface portions of the Barrow ecosystem are thus transferred into avian production and secondarily into prey for the vertebrate carnivores predating upon these birds. These latter predators, such as the snowy owl, least weasel and jaegers, preferentially take lemmings, but insectivorous birds can supplement a dwindling availability of lemmings. By acting as a supplementary food source, insectivorous birds sustain the impact of vertebrate carnivores on a declining lemming population. The effect of lemming predators appears to be a reinforcement in both amplitude and period of cyclic trends in lemming numbers.

Lemming predators tend to nest and roost on mounds, polygons, or other elevated sites. Such sites receive nutrient enrichment from predator feces and remains of prey. This enrichment may be the only mechanism of nutrient movement against the topographic gradient. Areas enriched by predators show a conspicuous vegetative response in species composition and amount of growth.

Soil arthropods exist in such large numbers and biomass levels that it seems unlikely that insectivorous birds could have significant effects on larval insect populations. It has been estimated that during the season the four *Calidris* sandpiper species consume a maximum of 14 000 cranefly (Diptera: Tipulidae) larvae ha^{-1}, or about 1 % of the total population. Because of the low productivity to biomass ratio of tundra invertebrates 1 % represents a larger harvest of prey productivity than comparable predation in other ecosystems. However, even with predation concentrated on the large, fourth-instar Diptera larvae, avian predators take less than 10 % of the productivity of their major prey.

During the brief mid-summer period of insect emergence the common avian insectivores, plus additional ones which do not breed at Barrow (e.g. *Stercorarius longicaudus* Vieillot), join in the harvest of adult insects. By the time emergence has ended they have cropped about 30 % of the adult insects from the tundra surface. These heavy predation rates probably elicit a "predator swamping" mechanism and thus reinforce the brevity and synchrony of insect emergence.

DECOMPOSITION AND SOIL PROCESSES

Overview and generalizations

Activities of the Barrow microbiota are restricted by frequent freeze-thaw cycles, acidic pH, low oxygen levels, extremely low levels of available nitrogen and phosphorous, and the extent of enzymatic adaptation for cold-tolerant metabolism. Community structure shows low diversity and microbial counts are lower at Barrow than in tundra soils at lower latitudes. Decay rates within the growing season are broadly comparable with rates from more temperate regions, but the brevity of the growing season produces low annual decay rates. Although microbial respiration continues at temperatures as low as $-7°C$, little decomposition occurs at these temperatures. Both moisture and temperature exert strong influences on microbial respiration rates and account for much of the seasonal variation in weight loss from litter and standing dead. In part the accumulation of large amounts of litter and standing dead aboveground results from the slow movement of aboveground dead into the litter and soil layers. When lemmings are abundant or where vehicular traffic has depressed dead vegetation, decomposition rates are increased (Fig. 9). Maximal rates of decomposition in the soil occur where the soil is warmer, better drained and inhabited by abundant invertebrates.

Rates of decomposition

Within three years following death most of the natural organic substrates lose 60 % of their original weight. Although loss rates within a specific year vary with weather conditions, about half of the three year loss occurs in the first year. First year losses from *Carex aquatilis* Wahlenb. and *Eriophorum angustifolium* average 26.6 % and 27.7 % of initial weight, respectively. A portion of the first year loss not attributable to microbial respiration is through translocation to stem bases and subsurface components, but most is through leaching.

Particular chemical constituents are lost at different rates and to a large extent rates and patterns of weight loss can be predicted from chemical composition. Some inorganic nutrients, particularly phosphorus and potassium, are lost rapidly, 70–80 % may be removed within the first year. On the other hand, much of the calcium remaining after plant death is immobilized in the cell walls and is lost very slowly. The different loss rates for specific organic constituents produce a departure from a simple exponential decay. Rapidly metabolized compounds represented by ethanol soluble (Fig. 10a) have an average annual loss rate of 49 % yr^{-1} while the more recalcitrant compounds are lost at a rate of 11 % yr^{-1}. Combination of these two exponential loss rates generates the pattern of total weight loss observed.

Although substrate chemistry is an important determinant of the total weight loss the rate at which a particular chemical constituent is lost is a function of temperature, oxygen, moisture and the physical geometry of the substrate. Fig. 10b illustrates the loss rates of a single chemical constituent, cellulose, in three different microclimates. In the soil and standing dead canopy, cellulose loses weight at a rate of 1.4 % yr^{-1}; in the litter layer, weight loss averages 3.5 % yr^{-1}. Much of this difference in weight loss is attributable to differences in microclimate. The half saturation moisture levels for effective microbial respiration are 60–75 % in standing dead substrates and about

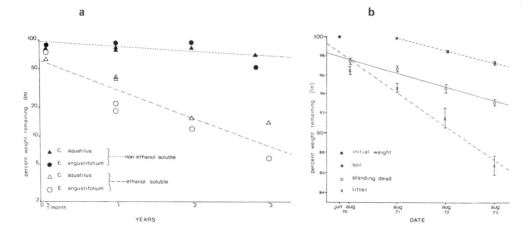

Figure 10. Decay rates of naturally occurring organics (a) and cellulose filter paper (b) in the Barrow environment. Ethanol soluble and non-ethanol soluble compounds represent a simple partitioning of the total organic constitutents in *Eriophorum angustifolium* and *Carex aquatilis* (modified from Bunnell, Tait & Flanagan, ms).

120 % in the litter layer. Although soils are moist, the Barrow site is windy and moisture levels in the standing dead canopy may fall to 40–60 % while in the litter layer moisture levels seldom fall below 500 %. Thus, conditions are less often satisfactory for decomposition within the standing dead canopy than within the litter layer. As a result rates of weight loss from natural substrates within the standing dead canopy usually decline to 4–5 % yr^{-1} after the first year, but increase to 7–16 % yr^{-1} once the material enters the litter layer. The low rates of weight loss from cellulose in the soil (Fig. 10b) are puzzling because the soils are also moist (although cooler than the litter layer) and about 40 % of the soil fungi are cellulolytic.

Rates of weight loss from a specific chemical constitutent within any canopy level or soil horizon are the result of respiration of microbes using the substrate as an energy source, leaching and comminution. Physical breakdown of substrates occurs during freezing and thawing but its relative contribution to weight loss is not quantified. Similarly, total biomass of soil invertebrates shows a clear inverse relationship with accumulated organic matter, but an unequivocal causal relationship linking invertebrate communities with decomposition cannot be established. Leaching contributes significantly to weight loss, particularly in newly dead material that has passed through its first winter. Leachate from aboveground substrates during meltoff probably accounts for the relatively high rates of soil respiration during that period.

Despite significant contribution of comminution and leaching much of the variation in annual patterns of weight loss is related to the influences of temperature, moisture and oxygen on microbial respiration. The response of microbial respiration to these meteorological variables has been expressed as

$$R(T,M) = \frac{M}{a_1 + M} \times \frac{a_2}{a_2 + M} \times a_3 \times a_4^{(T-10)/10} \tag{1}$$

where $R(T,M) = \mu l\,CO_2$ respired g^{-1} substrate h^{-1} at temperature T and moisture M.

T = temperature in $^\circ C$,

M = moisture as % dry weight,

a_1 = % water content at which substrate is 'half-saturated' with water or respiratory activity is at half its optimal value,

a_2 = % water content at which gas exchange is limited to half its optimal value,

a_3 = substrate specific respiration rate at $10^\circ C$ when neither moisture nor oxygen are limiting, and

a_4 = Q_{10} coefficient.

Equation 1 is useful in predicting the response of microbial respiration from a variety of substrates under most temperature and moisture combinations (Fig. 11a). Respiration rates at $10^\circ C$ with moisture unlimiting decline with age of substrate. For example, in *Eriophorum angustifolium* the rate declines from 777 $\mu l\ O_2\ g^{-1}\ h^{-1}$ for newly dead material to 184 $\mu l\ O_2\ g^{-1}\ h^{-1}$ for two-year-old material. The decline in microbial respiration with age is related to substrate chemistry in a predictable fashion.

Much of the microflora is cold-tolerant and significant portions are psychrophilic (have an optimum for growth at or below $10^\circ C$). In the phyllosphere, litter and soil, psychrophilic fungi comprise 5.5, 7.5 and 15.6 % of the mycofloras respectively. The remaining fungi are cold-tolerant mesophiles able to grow and/or respire at $-5^\circ C$, but with growth and respiration optima usually between 20 and $30^\circ C$. About 80 % of the cellulose-decomposing bacteria tested can grow at $0^\circ C$ when using glucose as the sole carbon source. Most yeast isolates from Barrow soils also are cold-tolerant, demonstrating growth at $0^\circ C$ with optimal temperatures of $20-25^\circ C$. Some, however, are strict psychrophiles demonstrating growth at $0^\circ C$, temperature optima around $10^\circ C$ and maximal temperatures at $20^\circ C$. The Q_{10} $(0-10^\circ C)$ for most standing dead substrates varies from about 2 to 3 while total litter shows a Q_{10} of 3.7.

As aboveground material ages and becomes more pitted and porous, the moisture range over which microbial respiration is unconstrained broadens. This trend is reversed belowground because compaction reduces pore size of the aging material. Within the soil Q_{10} values are typically 1.7 to 1.9 and increase with depth. These observations suggest that microbial populations have a narrower temperature range with depth. In particular, microorganisms in the litter layer continue respiration at lower temperatures than do microorganisms deeper in the profile. Surface layers are subject to wider ranges in both temperature and moisture than are the deeper layers. Thus it is not surprising to find the deeper communities apparently adapted to narrower temperature and moisture conditions than surface communities.

Patterns of soil respiration differ over the microsites of polygonized ground. Polygon rims and troughs evolve approximately twice as much carbon as polygon basins; carbon evolution from meadow soils is still higher possibly reflecting the higher bacterial biomasses. Over the 85-day period from 26 June to 10 September, 159 g C m^{-2} were evolved from meadow soils. This sum is approximately equivalent to net primary production during the same period. Soil respiration closely tracks temperature at 2 cm depth during midseason, but departs early and late in the season due to changes in substrate and soil moisture (Fig. 11b).

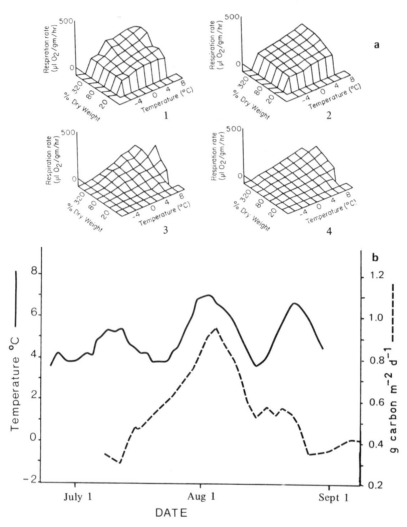

Figure 11. a. Patterns of microbial respiration. Respiration rates as they are influenced by temperature and moisture in one- and two-year old *Carex aquatilis* are illustrated as 1) and 3). The comparable rates predicted by equation 1 are illustrated as 2) and 4). b. Carbon evolution from a polygon basin soil in relation to soil temperature. Both carbon evolved and soil temperature are 10-day running means.

Anaerobic bacteria are important in the decomposition process at Barrow, but little CH_4 is evolved from the soil surface because of the action of methane-oxidizing bacteria, unless the soils are perturbed. By the end of the first year of operation of the soil plot heated to simulate pipeline conditions, the permafrost was thawed to 1 m and the plot ponded. Under these conditions 46–65 % of the gas evolved was methane; usually less than 1 ppm of the gas evolved from wet meadow soils is methane. Over a one-year period soils of the largely anaerobic, heated plot showed a reduction of 21 % in energy content of the soil over unheated controls.

Microbial biomass

Fungi including yeasts

In better drained habitats the plateable microflora of the upper few cm is dominated by fungi (Table 6). Although species diversity within the fungi is low (60–100 species of Basidiomycetes and Ascomycetes including Discomycetes), individual species are often found in great numbers. Parasitic species are generally rare, but saprophytes are common as are mycorrhiza formers. The aquatic fungi are an exception; the greatest proportion of this group are algal parasites (R. Seymour, pers. comm.). Mycorrhizal formers attain their highest biomass levels in the restricted, somewhat drier plant communities where vascular plants other than graminoids are more abundant. As well as facilitating nutrient flux in their role as mycorrhizal formers, three species of filamentous fungi are associated with algae (basidiolichens) and are to this extent contributing to nitrogen fixation. The fungal saprovores represent the primary microbial element decomposing lignin, cellulose, and other macromolecular substances.

Table 6. Mean seasonal abundance of Barrow microflora

Microfloral type	Depth	Polygon trough	Polygon rim	Polygon basin	Wet meadow
Algae					
Biomass (g dw m^{-2})	moss layer	0.13	0.15	0.24	0.11
	0–1 cm	0.17	0.20	0.40	0.13
Bacteria					
Aerobic plate count (nos. g^{-1} dw)	0–2 cm	1.05×10^7	1.13×10^6	5.74×10^5	7.73×10^6
Biomass (g dw m^{-2})	0–2 cm	8.21×10^{-4}	3.72×10^{-4}	1.37×10^{-4}	2.12×10^{-3}
Direct counts (nos. g^{-1} dw)	0–2 cm				3.51×10^9
	2–7 cm				10.40×10^9
	7–12 cm				7.53×10^9
Yeasts					
Plate count (nos. g^{-1} dw)	0–2 cm	2.4×10^4	3.5×10^5	4.8×10^3	1.7×10^5
Biomass (g dw m^{-2})	0–2 cm	0.0004	0.0156	0.0002	0.0042
Fungi					
Mycelial length (m g^{-1} dw)	standing dead	2 047	2 754	657	2 072
	litter	1 038	2 426	2 650	2 442
	1–2 cm	733	1 436	867	1 398
	6–7 cm	366	456	262	339
Biomass (g dw m^{-2})	standing dead	0.81	1.09	0.26	0.82
	litter	0.11	0.25	0.27	0.22
	1–2 cm	0.43	1.87	0.75	0.64
	6–7 cm	0.53	1.52	0.29	0.29

Density of the filamentous fungi increases under the snow, either in the late fall or early spring, to a seasonal high around meltoff. At this time, dry polygon tops, polygon troughs, and basins attain levels near the surface (1–2 cm depth) of 500–700 m g^{-1} of mycelium. At the same depth the more productive polygon rims and wet meadows attain levels of 1 300–2 700 m g^{-1} of mycelium. A general decline in biomass is observed in early summer followed by a slow recovery on the less productive areas and a rather rapid recovery in the polygon rims and wet meadows. This biomass increase culminates in late July to early August when the majority of Basidiomycetes fruit. The pattern of an early season increase, gradual decline, and late season recovery occurs throughout the soil profile to a depth of at least 7 cm. Fungi in the standing dead and litter layers follow a similar temporal pattern, but at much higher levels of density (2 000–2 500 m g^{-1}) (Table 6). Following fruiting of the Basidiomycetes a slow decline in biomass occurs prior to the late fall or early spring increase.

Fungal biomass changes are correlated with temperature over the preceding 10 days but are more strongly influenced by soil moisture. Below 4 cm in depth, response to surface abiotic factors is damped. The filamentous fungi are more severely restricted to the organic peat layer than are the bacteria, and density declines rapidly with depth over the upper 7 cm. Within the soil the major portion of fungal biomass is present in the top 4 cm, declining from 700–1 400 m of mycelium g^{-1} at 1 to 2 cm depth to 260–460 m g^{-1} at 6 to 7 cm depth (Table 6). Because of the increase in bulk density with depth, fungal biomass declines less rapidly than fungal hyphal lengths, particularly in well aerated profiles. Virtually no filamentous fungi are found in the silty mineral horizon below the peat layer.

The sharp cessation in filamentous fungal biomass at the peat/silt interface is probably a function of available organic substrate, moisture and oxygen levels. Optimal conditions for the fungi appear to range over soil moisture levels of 300 to 500 % (less frequently up to 700 %) associated with bulk densities of 0.3 to 0.4 g cm^{-3}. Soil moisture levels are usually well above 300 % and the major limitation appears to be due to impeded gas exchange in horizons with high bulk density.

Yeast populations vary dramatically between years but are consistently higher prior to meltoff and in the fall than they are at mid-season. During these pre-melt and late summer periods they probably make an important contribution to decomposition. Some antagonism apparently exists between yeasts and bacteria since maximum yeast biomass occurs in late summer (August) when bacterial biomass is at a minimum.

Yeasts at the Barrow site appear to be unimportant in anaerobic decomposition and are largely restricted to the upper, organic soil layers. Few yeasts are found below the upper 5 cm of soil and they attain their highest numbers in areas of maximum moss growth (Table 6). The yeasts isolated have been identified as *Cryptococcus laurentii* (Kuff.) Skinner var. *magnus* Lodder et Kreger-van Rij which is frequently an epiphyte (S. Shadomy, pers.comm.). Yeasts are epiphytic on mosses and probably are important decomposers of moss components, releasing trace elements accumulated in the moss layer. In general, yeast biomasses vary in magnitude from a high of 0.0156 g g^{-1} on the polygon rims to a low of 0.0002 g g^{-1} in the polygon basins.

Bacteria

Plateable bacterial biomass is small (Table 6), but direct counts in moister habitats such as the wet meadow indicate that they can constitute 75 % of the total microfloral biomass. Fewer strictly aerobic bacteria are found at Barrow than commonly are observed in temperate soils, but there are more facultative and strictly anaerobic bacteria present. One of the reasons for a marked discrepancy between soil plate count determinations

(10^6 g^{-1}) and direct microscopic counts (10^{10} g^{-1}) in the wet meadow is the fact that many strictly anaerobic bacteria exist even in the upper 2 cm of the soil. Methane producers are present on these wet sites. Methane oxidizing bacteria have been isolated from the wet meadow, and may intercept methane before it is detected.

Bacteria isolated from Barrow soils have the physiological potential to influence flux of nitrogen, sulphur, iron and phosphorus as well as carbon. A large number of aerobes and anaerobes have the potential for ammonification and the high rates of ammonification in some of the anaerobic horizons indicates that this potential is achieved. Nitrification is rare although the potential is also present at the Barrow site. Both *Nitrosomonas* and *Nitrobacter* are found, but their numbers and activity are low except under favorable conditions. In most years the poorly drained sites typical of Barrow encourage few nitrifiers and are more favorable to the denitrifiers such as *Pseudomonas* spp. *Pseudomonas* species are present in the wet meadow and the moist troughs of polygonized areas. Bacteria contribute little to nitrogen fixation at Barrow. *Clostridium* spp. which fix nitrogen are rare in the wet meadow, although they do occur in increased numbers in disturbed, anaerobic areas such as old vehicle tracks. *Azotobacter* spp. are present in low numbers in both the wet meadow and polygonized areas.

Strictly autotrophic thiobacilli are rare at Barrow, but there is some evidence that weak sulphur oxidation occurs at 0 to 2 cm depth. While this reaction may be weak it is probably important in supplying a small quantity of sulphate for plant growth. The bacteria reducing sulphate to sulphide have not been identified but their activity has been observed. A variety of iron-oxiding bacteria have been observed. They do not function as important decomposers but may help generate insoluble iron phosphate compounds. Iron reducing bacteria have also been observed but their role in the Barrow ecosystem is unclear.

Maximum bacterial biomass occurs at the moment of thaw, then drops sharply with thaw followed by a small mid-season peak in July. In colder, wetter years the mid-season peak occurs later in July than in warm years. Minimum bacterial biomass occurs in late August when yeast biomass is at its peak. There is a gradual return to early season biomass levels during the "zero-curtain" period of September, which is accompanied by *Eriophorum* root death at depth and the provision of further substrate.

Bacteria, along with cellulolytic filamentous fungi, appear to be the primary colonizers of dead plant material in soils. In the surface organic layers bacterial counts are directly related to the quantity of primary production while counts in the lower mineral layers are directly related to the quantity of roots and depth of the root zone. Greatest numbers of soil bacteria thus occur in wet meadow sites and polygon troughs, while lowest bacterial numbers occur in the low center polygon basins (Table 6). Bacterial counts on graminoid surfaces are 100 times greater than in the soil away from the roots indicating that bacteria compete for root exudates and available substrates.

Soil protozoans

At the beginning of the growing season, shortly after meltoff, low numbers of ciliates are present in the wet organic soils. Protozoan biomass in the polygonized areas is very low at this time and does not build up until later as the yeasts decline and bacterial biomasses increase. As the season progresses and the soils become progressively better drained the ciliates give way to amoebas and flagellates, particularly *Bodo minimus* Klebs., *Masti-*

goamoeba longifilum Stokes and *Amoeba proteus* (Pallas) Leidy. These species are grazing not only bacterial populations but blue-green and green algae as well, and may be contributing to the fluctuating biomass patterns observed in the soil algae. Biomass of the soil protozoans attains levels of 0.05 to 0.15 g m^{-2} in the upper 1 cm.

Invertebrate biomass and production

The major invertebrates involved in decomposition and soil processes are Nematoda, Enchytraeidae (Annelida), Acarina, Collembola and Diptera (Table 7).

Soil nematodes include plant-parasitic, predatory, and "free-living" (largely microbivore) forms. They appear to be less significant than in other ecosystems, but their high weight-specific metabolic rate contributes to their importance in the dynamics of the soil system.

While Lumbricidae are entirely lacking from Barrow, Enchytraeidae are particularly abundant and strongly dominate soil invertebrate communities. The most abundant species, a large *Mesenchytraeis* sp., alone attains a biomass of up to 2.5 g m^{-2} in polygon troughs. Enchytraeidae, collectively, comprise 50–75 % of the invertebrate biomass across all habitats. Contrary to most faunal and floral groups enchytraeid diversity (14 species) is high compared with many other ecosystems. Between-habitat variation in community organization correlates significantly with variation in the vegetation.

Collembola occur at densities comparable to or greater than most terrestrial ecosystems, while mite density at Barrow is lower. The Collembola to mite ratio increases along a gradient of increasing soil moisture. The small prostigmatid mites are more abundant than the larger Cryptostigmata (Oribatei). Thus, mean individual and total community biomass of mites is small. Collembola communities show strong and consistent dominance by one species, *Folsomia quadrioculata* Tullberg, in all habitats. Among the mites, in contrast, abundance and biomass are much more equitably distributed amongst species, and strong shifts in species importance occur between habitats.

Among the higher insects Diptera are by far predominant. Three species of craneflies (Diptera: Tipulidae) are particularly abundant and conspicuous. Density of larvae of *Pedicia hannai antenatta*, a predatory species, may exceed 200 m^{-2} in wet habitats; larvae of the larger, saprovorous species, *Tipula carinifrons* Holm, may exceed 100 m^{-2} in mesic habitats. At peak densities biomass of these larvae approaches 1 g m^{-2} for each species.

Tundra invertebrates occur mainly in the upper horizons of the soil, where temperature and aeration are maximal. In mites, approximately 95 % of the individuals occur in the top 2.5 cm. This stratification, and their generally greater abundance in drier habitats and low abundance in low polygon basins (Table 7), suggest that mites are relatively intolerant of anaerobic conditions. Between-habitat differences in mite community organization correlate with differences in soil moisture. Enchytraeidae, which live in interstitial water and are thus aquatic organisms, occur at greater depth (66 % in the top 2.5 cm), and at greatest abundance in wetter habitats. They are the only invertebrates to achieve significant biomass in the low-centered polygon basins. Collembola demonstrate a less clear density response to soil moisture than other invertebrates. Their density is severely reduced in polygon basins.

The relatively high densities and invertebrate biomass values are, in part, a result of prolonged life cycles. Both *P. hannai* and *T. carinifrons* require at least four years to

Table 7. Densities and biomasses of major groups of invertebrates involved in decomposition processes

Habitat	Nematoda		Enchytraeidae		Acarina		Collembola		Total Biomass[2]	Organic matter (0–20 cm, kg m^{-2})
	Density[1]	Biomass[2]	Density[1]	Biomass[2]	Density[3]	Biomass[2]	Density[3]	Biomass[2]		
Meadow	650 000	65	56 700	2 300	26 200	110	96 800	484	2 960	28.8
Polygon trough	700 000	70	93 600	4 132	23 700	90	162 800	814	5 110	23.5
Polygon basin	120 000	12	25 200	1 847	9 560	26	24 400	112	2 010	42.7
Polygon rim	1 120 000	112	12 900	651	72 700	153	83 700	419	1 340	45.0
Mean of all habitats	800 000	80	46 100	2 119	40 500	124	90 700	454	2 780	31.5
Number of species recorded	n.d.		14		37		37			

1. Number m^{-2} to a depth of 15 cm
2. mg dw m^{-2} to a depth of 10 or 15 cm
3. Number m^{-2} to a depth of 10 cm

n.d. = not determined

complete larval development. In poor years growth is retarded and the life cycle is consequently lengthened. Prolonged life cycles are also seen in the dominant enchytraeid worm (*Mesenchytraeis* sp.) and collembole (*F. quadrioculata*). Prolongation of the life cycle is necessitated by the low annual growth rate. It results in overlapping generations and high abundance and biomass, especially relative to productivity.

Microorganism-invertebrate interactions and trophic relationships

Nearly all invertebrate feeding activity occurs in the soil. Most invertebrates feed upon dead organic matter directly and/or upon decomposer microorganisms. In organic-rich tundra soils, soil organic matter provides an almost limitless, but poor quality, food source. Microorganisms are present in moderate density and provide higher quality food. It appears likely that foraging upon microbes is the most prevalent trophic function of animals in the tundra. Consumption of microbial tissue by microbivores may equal the average annual biomass of microbes.

The biomass of soil micro-invertebrates (Nematoda, Enchytraeidae, Acarina, Collembola) is positively correlated with net annual primary production and negatively correlated with accumulated organic matter. Thus, greatest invertebrate biomass occurs in habitats of highest annual turnover of both energy and nutrients. Although the relationship is strongly driven by Enchytraeidae, because of their high biomass, it is stronger for the microfauna as a whole than it is for Enchytraeidae alone.

ENERGY AND NUTRIENT CYCLING

Energy — an overview and hypothesis

Essentially the entire aboveground portion of tundra monocotyledons grows and dies each season. Belowground portions are more persistent, with major sections of the root system lasting from two to ten years, depending upon species. Still there is a large annual production and death of rootlets and root hairs. The result is little accumulation of, and rapid turnover of energy in, the living portion of the ecosystem.

A very large amount of energy resident in Barrow tundra is contained in the pool of dead organic matter, which amounts to 22–45 kg m^{-2}, depending upon habitat, in the top 20 cm of the soil (Table 7). Because the greatest accumulation is associated with least primary productivity, dead organic matter represents between 50 and 400 times the annual net primary production. Thus, the rate of decomposition and nutrient release imposes major constraints upon patterns of energy flow in general.

Relative to primary production, consumption by animals is probably higher in the Barrow tundra than in most other ecosystems. Consumption by herbivores ranges from nil to ca 700 kJ m^{-2} yr^{-1} over a 3- to 5-year lemming cycle. Despite the absence of herbivore diversity, the long-term average consumption by herbivores is high. Based on periodic years of high consumption and productivity, the longterm average activity of vertebrate carnivores is likewise high.

Density and biomass of soil invertebrates are comparable to other ecosystems, despite the low primary production. Activity of soil invertebrates is limited by length and tem-

114

perature of the growing season, to which they show only partial physiological adaptation. Thus, the ratio of productivity to biomass tends to be low. Nevertheless, a large proportion of the energy of the Barrow tundra system passes through soil saprovore, and especially, microbivore populations. Annual consumption and production in the saprovore-based system is much greater than in the herbivore-based system, even given the periodic years of high consumption by lemmings.

Given the spatial and year-to-year variation in data, it is difficult to assemble a total energetic budget that can be used to determine whether a given area of the Barrow tundra is currently accumulating organic matter. Certainly, the large amount of organic matter indicates that accumulation has occurred at a significant rate in the past. Whether this organic matter is the result of rapid accumulation leading to contemporary steady-state conditions, or of continuing, gradual accumulation, is unclear.

The various estimates of production and decomposition for the terrestrial system suggest that any deviation from steady state is in the direction of a surplus of production over decomposition, i.e. accumulation. Measurements in Barrow ponds suggest a deficit in production relative to decomposition. Thus the general pattern seems to be one of accumulation of organic matter in terrestrial tundra and degradation in ponds. Superimposed upon this pattern is an inverse correlation between primary production and accumulation in terrestrial tundra habitats. The most productive terrestrial habitats have the least accumulated organic matter and must be accumulating very slowly, if at all. In habitats of relatively large accumulation of organic matter, primary production is low. If contemporary production rates have prevailed during the period of accumulation, then a very large proportion of annual production must be allocated to accumulation to account for the present organic matter pool. If, however, we postulate a decline in the rate of primary production with accumulation, possibly due to nutrient limitation, the current accumulation of organic matter can be explained without invoking a massive disbalance between rates of production and decomposition (Fig. 12b).

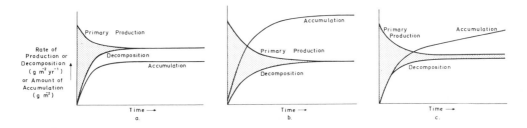

Figure 12. Hypothesized relationships between primary production, decomposition, and organic matter accumulation in the Barrow tundra. a) Model tending toward steady state, for a habitat of high decomposition potential. b) Model tending toward steady state, for a habitat of low decomposition potential. c) Non-steady state model, tending towards a condition of continuing accumulation.

The simple model of Fig. 12a and b tends toward a steady-state equilibrium between production and decomposition in all habitats. As depicted in Fig. 12, factors favoring the accumulation of organic matter (low decomposition rate) also may reduce primary production through lower soil temperature and nutrient limitation. The apparent tendency toward accumulation of organic matter in the Barrow terrestrial tundra suggests that 1) recurrent disturbances prevent the attainment of the steady state, so that at least some habitats are always in a state of development, or 2) the model is wrong. Habitat composition of Barrow tundra appears to be very dynamic; as polygonization occurs in flat, meadow tundra due to the action of ground ice, polygons coalesce to form ponds and lakes, and aquatic habitats are drained to produce meadows. This has been termed the thaw-lake cycle. Within this hypothesis, habitats exposed by draining of lakes would be low in organic matter and thus would be sites for accumulation. The recurrent nature of the thaw-lake cycle might assure that a steady-state equilibrium is never reached.

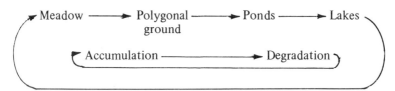

The alternative hypothesis is that, at least in some habitats, an equilibrium between production and decomposition never exists; accumulation continues until conditions change (Fig. 12c). This appears to be the case, for example, in peat-depositing bogs. This situation could be accommodated in the model of decomposition and accumulation simply by providing for decline in decomposition rate (g CO_2 released g^{-1} substrate) with depth. Where decomposition rate is slow and/or drops off rapidly with depth accumulated material may reach the depth of negligible activity and then contribute nothing to total decomposition. The result would be continuing accumulation as some increment of the annual production is added to the deep deposits, below the level of active decompositon, each year.

Since the amount accumulated at Barrow is nowhere great, this hypothesis requires that eith r 1) the Barrow tundra system, as we now know it, is young and has not had time for a large accumulation of peat to develop, or 2) recurrent changes or disturbances reverse the pattern of accumulation in any habitat.

Nutrient budgets and limitations

Nutrients, like energy, are concentrated in the soil organic matter. Static budgets of the top 10 cm of the Barrow ecosystem reveal that most of the nutrient capital is in a soil pool which is not directly available to plants (Fig. 13). Thus, like energy, the percentage of nutrient capital resident in the living components of the ecosystem is small (less than 1 % for both nitrogen and phosphorus). Distribution of both energy and nutrients within the tundra ecosystem is therefore markedly different from other ecosystems, such as rainforest, where the biota constitutes a significant reservoir.

Because the pools of soluble soil nitrogen and phosphorus are small relative to exchangeable pools, which are in turn small relative to non-exchangeable pools, there must be continual turnover in these pools within a growing season to satisfy plant requirements. To replenish the quantity absorbed by plants, soluble plus exchangeable nitrogen

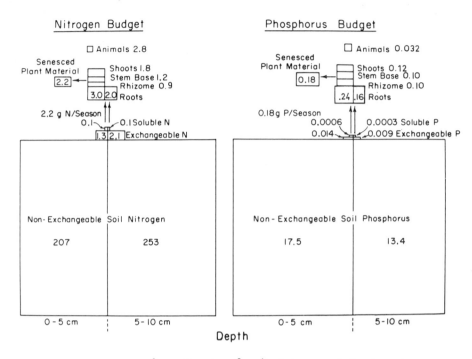

Figure 13. Standing crops (g m^{-2}) and flows (g m^{-2} yr^{-1}) of nitrogen and phosphorus in major components of the Barrow terrestrial ecosystem.

must "turn over" 11 times in the course of a growing season and soluble plus exchangeable phosphorus must be replenished 200 times a season or an average of 3 times per day. The soil does not store available nutrients and primary production is intimately dependent upon the release of nutrients by decomposition. In this latter respect the tundra ecosystem is more similar to tropical than to temperate ecosystems.

Given these constraints, it is not surprising that the Barrow ecosystem is conservative with nutrients. Most vascular plants show a strong internal cycle retaining and reincorporating these nutrients, particularly phosphorus, in other parts rather than relinquishing them to the decomposer cycle. In drier, better-aerated habitats mycorrhizae further facilitate phosphorus incorporation into vascular plants. Vascular plant production in wetter microsites varies several-fold and appears best correlated with plant and soil phosphorus contents. Despite variation in soil nutrient levels, nitrogen, calcium and potassium concentrations in vascular plants are remarkably similar from site to site, whereas phosphorus concentrations are highest in the most productive sites. These observations plus the general conservatism with which the plant treats phosphorus suggest that vascular primary production is more strongly limited by phosphorus than by other nutrients. Fertilization treatments corroborate this suggestion for they result in an increase in production and phosphorus concentration while other nutrients show no change in concentration levels.

Nutrient limitations to primary production are not mediated through altered photosynthetic rates. All leaves produced by an individual vascular plant have the same opti-

117

mal photosynthetic capacity regardless of the nutrient status of the plant. Plant nutrient levels, particularly phosphorus, apparently control the rate of production of new leaves and may also influence the rate at which nutrients are removed from older leaves to be reincorporated in new leaves. Thus, we do not expect and do not observe signs of nutrient deficiency in the vascular plants at Barrow. The effect of nutrient limitation is to lower general levels of primary production by limiting leaf area. Because activities of decomposer organisms are so intimately associated with both the generation of available nutrients (thus primary production) as well as organic matter degradation, the potential for positive feedback in the degradation or accumulation trends discussed above (Fig. 12) is enhanced.

Although much of the precipitation occurs in the summer, most of the run-off occurs in the spring when the soil is frozen. Thus, leaching is important primarily in the aboveground vegetative portion of the system and removal from the soil is minimal. However, leaching from the aboveground vascular pool may be important in determining the distribution of nutrients within the system. Significant amounts of nitrogen and potassium appear to be released into the soil as a pulse at the beginning of the growing season. The pulse results from 1) leaching by snow-melt of animal debris accumulated on the frozen soil during winter, 2) leaching of senescent plant material produced during the previous growing season, 3) the lysis of microbial cells by freeze-thaw action, and 4) the continuation of active decomposition before and after periods of active uptake by plants. Since 60 % of the live root biomass is located in the top 5 cm of soil, virtually all of this absorptive tissue is thawed and potentially active in nutrient absorption within 5 days of the beginning of snow-melt. Further, younger roots are most active in phosphate absorption at the beginning of the growing season. These observations indicate that both the distribution and absorptive capabilities of roots are such as to exploit maximally the early season influx of inorganic nutrients in the soil. The low levels of available soil phosphorus at Barrow (Fig. 13) are in the range where absorption by roots responds linearly to concentration. Thus, the seasonal course of phosphate absorption by plants closely follows phosphorus availability in the soil, further corroborating the close link between primary production and decomposer activity.

During the summer, vascular plants may lose a significant amount of potassium and perhaps phosphorus by leakage through the cuticle onto the leaf surface. These nutrients are subsequently washed off the leaves and may appear as pulses into the soil solution during periods of precipitation. The leaching of nutrients from live leaf surfaces and out of standing dead material appears to be the major source of input to the bryophytes. In many areas bryophytes form a continuous mat beneath the vascular canopy and appear to effectively absorb or adsorb many of the nutrients which would otherwise enter the soil. Once nutrients are incorporated into bryophyte tissue they are released slowly. The nutrient composition of green and brown bryophyte tissue is very similar and decomposition apparently proceeds slowly in the bryophyte layer. The bryophytes thus appear to be an important temporary nutrient sink, particularly for the microelements. To some extent nutrients within the bryophyte layer are recycled by lemming feeding activity, particularly in the winter. The winter shift in lemming feeding pressure towards bryophytes may be in response to the higher nutrient concentrations in bryophytes at this time.

Horizontal distribution of nutrients within the Barrow system also is partially controlled by lemming activities. Lemmings build their winter nests in polygon troughs and forage for food in the meadows, troughs, ridges and basins. Most defecation occurs in the troughs, thus nutrients are transported from many sites and concentrated in the polygon troughs. The concentration of lemming feces in the troughs may contribute to the generally higher levels of soil nutrients (particularly phosphorus) found in troughs, which in turn contribute to the high rates of production and decomposition found in these areas.

Nitrogen as an example

The overall nitrogen budget is shown in Fig. 14. The two major inputs are nitrogen fixation and, of less importance, precipitation. A very small proportion is lost to denitrification, a greater amount to runoff (primarily as dissolved inorganic nitrogen), and the difference, 59.2 mg m^{-2} represents storage by the system as in the case of the formation and burial of organic matter.

The system operates with a small nitrogen input compared to temperate latitudes, both in terms of precipitation and nitrogen fixation. Total losses, however, are also small and the Barrow terrestrial system presently stores an extremely high proportion of the gross input (at least 65 %). The nitrogen cycle thus illustrates the major points apparent in the general patterns of energy and nutrient flux: 1) the system is conservative of its nutrients, 2) there appears to be a general tendency towards accumulation in the terrestrial system and 3) the behavior of microorganisms (in this case free-living or phycobiont algae) is critical in governing flux rates and generating the structure of the system.

While the Barrow terrestrial ecosystem is relatively rich in terms of total nutrients and carbon stored, relatively little is available or circulates through the biota. Restriction of the activities of the decomposer organisms appears to regulate the system, despite the fact that of all floral and faunal groups, these show the greatest adaptation to cold temperatures and continue to function at $-7°C$.

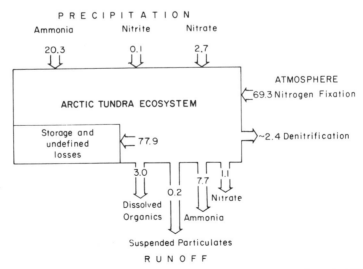

Figure 14. Nitrogen budget for the Barrow ecosystem (from Barsdate , Alexander, 1975).

INTERACTION BETWEEN TERRESTRIAL AND
AQUATIC COMMUNITIES

Principal land-water transfer of material is from the land to the water via surface run-off as channel and sheet flow over both ice- and snow-covered and snow-free tundra. During spring, runoff transfers of particulate and dissolved organic matter occur from higher relief positions on polygons into the interconnected trough system. Some litter material is redeposited as strand lines along streams and polygon troughs. The majority of runoff waters drain into nearby sloughs, lagoons, and the oceans. The remaining runoff is retained in or passes into polygon centers, or into ponds and onto the ice-covered larger lakes. Late summer rains occasionally result in additional runoff through polygon channels and soil water flows.

Nutrients, including phosphorus and nitrogen, are transferred mainly in the small amounts of soil water that move into tundra ponds. Smaller amounts of phosphorus and nitrogen enter the ponds during the spring runoff. At that time, although the quantity of water is large, nutrient concentrations are low and only small amounts remain in the ponds. Particulate and dissolved organic matter also enter the ponds during runoff but because the surrounding soils and the pond water itself are frozen during runoff, little is trapped in the ponds. Much of this particulate organic matter consists of bacteria and the bacteria which are found in high numbers in pond water immediately after melt originate from the surrounding soil. The reverse transfer of nutrients and energy from the pond to the land is principally through the feeding of phalaropes. These birds feed on insect larvae but have little effect on pond populations as over 6 000 larvae m^{-2} commonly are found. Phalarope densities are of the order of one pair per ha., and the birds are present on these ponds for a maximum of a few hours per day.

MAN'S INFLUENCE ON THE ECOSYSTEM

Principal impact or interactions of modern man upon the coastal tundra ecosystem involves disturbance due to permanent construction, transportation and exploration activities, plus activities related to water supply and waste disposal sites. Widespread modifications have resulted from off-road traffic both in winter and summer. During summer thaw, tracked vehicles exerting high ground pressure cause compression and shearing of the vegetation-organic layer; under intensive repetitive traffic, surface vegetation is removed, albedo is greatly reduced, and thermal erosion of the permafrost terrain occurs. Primary productivity and soil chemical and physical processes are modified in the vehicle tracks. Winter traffic is less disruptive; however, compaction of the snow cover and crushing and pressing of the standing dead vegetation results in green belts, a condition associated with increased microbial activity when dead vegetation is moved into a moister canopy layer. Winter roads constructed of compacted snow result in temporary impoundments during spring melt.

In specific cases, winter traffic across the IBP site some 20 years ago resulted in shifts from a complex mosaic of diverse plant communities associated with low-center polygons and their troughs to a simpler mosaic of less diverse communities of flat, better drained polygon centers and deeper thermokarsted troughs. This shift in diversity as a result of disturbance is also seen where temporary or permanent impoundments are created adjacent to road and gravel embankments across the flat coastal tundra. These shifts from a mixed vegetation to pure stands of monocotyledons give rise to higher primary productivity.

As the human population continues to expand there is a need to increase living and support facilities. This places increased demands on the land resource. The drier sites are preferred for these activities and the mining of gravel and sand deposits frequently occur on these drier sites. Increased combustion of fossil fuels for heating, generation of electricity, incineration and transportation increase the output of airborne pollution. However, adverse affects of these pollutants and dust are only conjectural at this time. Year-round water supply is commonly developed from water bodies deeper than winter freezing (> 2 m). In some winters abnormally thick ice encourages depletion of the small remaining amount of water, and in lakes containing fish such impacts may seriously alter long-term primary and secondary productivity. Hunting or trapping of fox, wolves, wolverine and caribou near population centers such as Barrow have undoubtedly influenced the composition of both the local fauna and flora.

The nature of man's interaction with the coastal tundra to date has been limited to narrow transportation strips and immediate town or industry complexes. These activities tend to have only local impacts on land, water and air resources. However, increasing recreational, industrial and population activities with greater year-round mobility over the tundra are likely to proliferate the specific animal-plant-soil interactions resulting in as yet unknown ecosystem perturbations.

ACKNOWLEDGEMENTS

This paper is based primarily upon the US Tundra Biome terrestrial synthesis which will appear in a separate volume under the auspices of the US IBP. Since much of this material has been derived from multiple sources and in many cases collated by the authors we have chosen not to use references in the text. Rather, in the reference section we indicate the key literature used. Sources of individual tables and figures are referenced in the appropriate captions since some are from copyrighted journals and books. A more complete list of US Tundra Biome publications is available separately and many substantiating results and citations will appear in the US IBP Tundra Synthesis Volume. The research was supported by a series of grants from the National Science Foundation under the Office of Polar Programs and the Ecosystem Analysis Section. Barrow field support was provided by the Naval Arctic Research Laboratory of the Office of Naval Research. We acknowledge collectively the many Biome participants who provided data, interpretation, ideas, and critique for this text.

SELECTED REFERENCES

Allessio, M.L. & Tieszen, L.L. 1974. Effect of leaf age on translocation rate and distribution of C14 photoassimilate in *Dupontia fischeri* at Barrow, Alaska. – Arctic and Alpine Res. 7: 3–12.

Alexander, V. & Schell, D.M. 1973. Seasonal and spatial variation of nitrogen fixation in the Barrow, Alaska tundra. – Arctic and Alpine Res. 5: 77–88.

Barsdate, R.J., Prentki, R.T. & Fenchel, T. 1974. The phosphorus cycle of model ecosystems. Significance for decomposer food chains and effect of bacterial grazers. – Oikos 25: 239–251.

Barsdate, R.J. & Alexander, V. 1975. The nitrogen balance of Arctic tundra: Pathways, rates and environmental implications. – J. Environmen. Qual. 4: 111–117.

Batzli, G.O. In press. Populations and energetics of small mammals in tundra ecosystems. – In: Moore, J.J. (ed.) Tundra: Comparative analysis of ecosystems. Cambridge University Press.

Batzli, G.O. In press. The role of small mammals in arctic ecosystems. – In: Petrusewicz, K., Golley, F. & Ryskowski, F. (eds.) Small mammals: Their population structure and impact on world ecosystems. Cambridge University Press.

Batzli, G.O., Stenseth, N.C. & Fitzgerald, B.M. 1974. Growth and survival of suckling brown lemmings (*Lemmus trimucronatus*). – J. Mammalogy 55: 828–831.

Bee, J.W. & Hall, E.R. 1956. Mammals of northern Alaska on the Arctic Slope. – Univ. Kansas Museum Nat. Hist., Misc. Publ. 8: 1–309.

Billings, W.D., Peterson, K.H., Shaver, G.R. & Trent, A.W. In press. Effect of temperature on root growth and respiration in a tundra ecosystem, Barrow, Alaska. – In: Proc. Symposium on the Belowground Ecosystem, Ft. Collins, Colo. Sept. 1973.

Brewer, M.C. 1958. Some results of geothermal investigations of permafrost in northern Alaska. – Trans. Am. Geophys. Union 39: 10–26.

Britton, M.E. 1957. Vegetation of the arctic tundra. – In: Hansen, H.P. (ed.) Arctic Biology, pp. 26–61. Corvallis: Oregon State University Press.

Brown, J. 1965. Radiocarbon dating, Barrow, Alaska. – Arctic 18: 36–48.

Brown, J. 1969. Soil properties developed on the complex tundra relief of northern Alaska. – Builetyn Peryglacjalny 18: 153–167.

Brown, J., Dingman, S.L. & Lewellen, R.I. 1968. Hydrology of a small drainage basin on the coastal plain of northern Alaska. – USA CRREL Research Report 240.

Brown, J., Coulombe, H. & Pitelka, F. 1970. Structure and function of the tundra ecosystem at Barrow, Alaska. – In: Fuller, W.A. & Kevan, P.G. Productivity and Conservation in Northern Circumpolar Lands, pp. 41–71. Morges, Switzerland: IUCN.

Brown, J. & Veum, A.K. 1974. Soil properties of the International Tundra Biome sites. – In: Holding, A.J., Heal, O.W., MacLean, S.F. & Flanagan, P.W. (eds.) Soil Organisms and Decomposition in Tundra, pp. 27–48. Stockholm: IBP Tundra Biome Steering Committee.

Brown, J., Bunnell, F.L., MacLean, S.F. Jr., Miller, P.C. & Tieszen, L.L. In prep. An Arctic Ecosystem: The Coastal Tundra of Northern Alaska.

Bunnell, F.L. 1973. Computer simulation of nutrient and lemming cycles in an arctic tundra wet meadow ecosystem. – Ph.D. dissertation, University of California, Berkeley. 312 pp.

Bunnell, F.L., Tait, D.E.N. & Flanagan, P.W. Submitted. Microbial respiration and substrate loss. II. A model of the influences of chemical composition. – Soil Biol. Biochem.

Caldwell, M.M., Tieszen, L.L. & Fareed, M. 1974. The canopy structure of tundra plant communities at Barrow, Alaska, and Niwot Ridge, Colorado. – Arctic and Alpine Res. 6: 151–159.

Challinor, J.L. & Gersper, P.L. 1975. Vehicle perturbation effects upon a tundra soil-plant system: II. Effects on the chemical regimes. – Proc. Soil Science Soc. Amer., 39 (in press).

Chapin, F.S. 1974. Phosphate absorption capacity and acclimation potential along a latitudinal gradient. – Science 183: 521–523.

Chapin, F.S. 1974. Morphological and physiological mechanisms of temperature compensation in phosphate absorption along a latitudinal gradient. – Ecology 55: 1180–1189.

Chapin, F.S. III, Van Cleve, K. & Tieszen, L.L. 1975. Seasonal nutrient dynamics of tundra vegetation at Barrow, Alaska. – Arctic and Alpine Res. 7 (in press).

Clebsch, E.E.C. & Shanks, R.E. 1968. Summer climatic gradients and vegetation near Barrow, Alaska. – Arctic 21: 161–171.

Coyne, P.I. & Kelley, J.J. 1974. Variations in carbon dioxide across an arctic snowpack in spring. – J. Geophys. Res. 79: 799–802.

Coyne, P.I. & Kelley, J.J. In press. Carbon dioxide exchange over the Alaskan arctic tundra: Meteorological assessment by an aerodynamic method. – J. Appl. Ecol.

Dennis, J.G. 1968. Growth of tundra vegetation in relation to arctic microclimates at Barrow, Alaska. – Ph.D. dissertation, Duke University. 288 pp.

Dennis J.G. In press. Patterns of belowground phytomass distribution in arctic tundra at Barrow, Alaska. – In: Proc. Symposium on the Belowground Ecosystem, Ft. Collins, Colo. Sept. 1973.

Douglas, L.A. & Tedrow, J.C.F. 1959. Organic matter decomposition rates in Arctic soils. – Soil Sci. 88: 305–312.

Drew, J.V. 1957. A pedologic study of Arctic Coastal Plain soils near Point Barrow, Alaska. – Ph.D. dissertation, Rutgers University, 117 pp.

Drew, J.V., Tedrow, J.C.F., Shanks, R.E. & Koranda, J.J. 1958. Rate and depth of thaw in arctic soils. – Trans. Amer. Geophys. Union 39: 697–701.

Drew, J.V. & Tedrow, J.C.F. 1962. Arctic soil classification and patterned groud. – Arctic 15: 109–116.

Ford, J.A. 1959. Eskimo prehistory in the vicinity of Point Barrow, Alaska. – Anthropol. Papers Amer. Mus. Nat. Hist. 47: 1–227.

Gersper, P.L. & Challinor, J.L. 1975. Vehicle perturbation upon a tundra soil-plant system. I. Effects on morphological and physical environmental properties of the soils. – Proc. Soil Science Soc. Amer. 39 (in press).

Hultén, E. 1968. Flora of Alaska and Neighboring Territories. Stanford University Press. 1008 pp.

Hussey, K.M. & Michelson, R.W. 1966. Tundra relief features near Point Barrow, Alaska. – Arctic 19: 162–184.

Johnson, P.L. & Tieszen, L.L. 1973. Vegetative research in arctic Alaska. – In: Britton, M.E. (ed.) Alaska Arctic Tundra. Arctic Inst. North America Tech. Paper 25: 169–198.

Lachenbruch, A.H. & Brewer, M.C. 1961. Geothermal evidence for recent climatic change near Barrow, Alaska. – Geol. Soc. Amer. Special Paper 68: 1–117.

MacLean, S.F., Jr. 1973. The life cycle and growth energetics of *Pedicia hannai antenatta* Alex. (Diptera: Tipulidae), an arctic crane fly. – Oikos 24: 436–443.

MacLean, S.F., Jr. 1974. Primary production, decomposition, and the activity of soil invertebrates in tundra ecosystems: A hypothesis. – In: Holding, A.J., Heal, O.W., MacLean, S.F. & Flanagan, P.W. (eds.) Soil Organisms and Decomposition in Tundra, pp. 197–206. Stockholm: Tundra Biome Steering Committee.

MacLean, S.F., Jr. 1974. Lemming bones as a source of calcium for Arctic sandpipers (*Calidris* spp.). – Ibis 116: 552–557.

MacLean, S.F., Jr. 1975. Ecological adaptations of tundra invertebrates. – In: Vernberg, J. (ed.) Physiological Adaptation to the Environment, pp. 269–300. New York: Intext Press.

MacLean, S.F., Jr., Fitzgerald, B.M. & Pitelka, F.A. 1974. Population cycles in arctic lemmings: winter reproduction and predation by weasels. – Arctic and Alpine Res. 6: 1–12.

McCown, B.H. 1975. Physiological responses of root systems to stress conditions. – In: Vernberg, F.J. (ed.) Physiological Adapdation to the Environment, pp. 225–237. New York: Intext Press.

Maykut, G.A. & Church, P.E. 1973. Radiation climate of Barrow, Alaska, 1962–66. – J. Appl. Meteorol. 12: 620–628.

Miller, P.C. & Tieszen, L.L. 1972. A preliminary model of processes affecting primary production in the arctic tundra. – Arctic and Alpine Res. 4: 1–18.

Miller, P.C., Collier, B.D. & Bunnell, F.L. 1975. Development of ecosystem modeling in the US IBP Tundra Biome. – In: Patten, B.C. (ed.) Systems Analysis and Simulation in Ecology Vol. 3.

Nakano, Y. & Brown, J. 1972. Mathematical modeling and validation of the thermal regimes in tundra soils, Barrow, Alaska. – Arctic and Alpine Res. 4: 19–38.

Norton, D.W. 1972. Incubation schedules of four species of calidridine sandpipers at Barrow, Alaska. – Condor 74: 164–176.

Norton, D.W. 1973. Ecological energetics of calidridine sandpipers breeding in northern Alaska. – Ph.D. dissertation, University of Alaska, 163 pp.

Pieper, R.D. 1963. Production and chemical composition of arctic tundra vegetation and their relation to the lemming cycle. – Ph.D. dissertation, University of California, Berkeley. 95 pp.

123

Pitelka, F.A. 1957. Some aspects of population structure in the short term cycle of the brown lemming in northern Alaska. – Cold Springs Harb. Symp. Quant. Biol. 22: 237–251.

Pitelka, F.A. 1973. Cyclic pattern in lemming populations near Barrow, Alaska. – In: Britton, M.E. (ed.) Alaska Arctic Tundra. Arctic Inst. North America Tech. Paper 25: 199–215.

Pitelka, F.A. 1974. An avifaunal review for the Barrow region and North Slope of arctic Alaska. – Arctic and Alpine Res. 6: 161–184.

Pitelka, F.A., Holmes, R.T. & MacLean, S.F. Jr., 1974. Ecology and evolution of social organization in arctic sandpipers. – American Zool. 14: 185–204.

Pitelka, F.A. & Schultz, A.M. 1964. The nutrient-recovery hypothesis for arctic microtine rodents. – In: Crisp, D. (ed.) Grazing in Terrestrial and Marine Environments, pp. 55–68. Oxford: Blackwell's.

Rastorfer, J.R. 1974. Element contents of three Alaskan-Arctic mosses. – Ohio J. Sci. 74: 55–59.

Reed, J.C. & Ronhovde, A.G. 1971. Arctic laboratory. – Arctic Institute of North America, 748 pp.

Rickard, W.E., Jr. & Brown, J. 1974. Effects of vehicles on Arctic tundra. – Environ. Cons. 1: 55–62.

Schell, D.M. & Alexander, V. 1973. Nitrogen fixation in arctic coastal tundra in relation to vegetation and micro-relief. – Arctic 26: 130–137.

Sellmann, P.V. & Brown, J. 1973. Stratigraphy and diagenesis of perennially frozen sediment in the Barrow, Alaska, region. – In: Permafrost: The North American Contribution to the Second International Conference, pp. 171–181. Washington, D.C.: National Academy of Sciences.

Shaver, G.R. & Billings, W.D. 1975. Root production and root turnover in a wet tundra ecosystem, Barrow, Alaska. – Ecol. 56: 401–409.

Smith, D.K. 1974. Floristic, ecologic, and phytogeographic studies of the bryophytes in the tundra around Barrow, Alaska. – Ph.D. dissertation, University of Tennessee. 191 pp.

Soil Survey Staff. 1974. Soil taxonomy of the National Cooperative Soil Survey. Soil Conservation Service, US Department of Agriculture.

Spetzman, L.A. 1959. Vegetation of the Arctic Slope of Alaska. – US Geological Survey Professional Paper 302–8: 19–58.

Stoner, W.A. & Miller, P.C. 1975. Water relations of plant species in the wet coastal tundra at Barrow, Alaska. – Arctic and Alpine Res. 7: 109–124.

Tedrow, J.C.F. & Cantlon, J.E. 1958. Concepts of soil formation and classification in arctic regions. – Arctic 11: 166–179.

Thompson, D.Q. 1955. The role of food and cover in population fluctuations of the brown lemming at Point Barrow, Alaska. – Trans. North American Wildlife Conf. 20: 166–174.

Tieszen, L.L. 1972. The seasonal course of aboveground production and chlorophyll distribution in a wet arctic tundra at Barrow, Alaska. – Arctic and Alpine Res. 4: 307–324.

Tieszen, L.L. 1974. Photosynthetic competence of the subnivean vegetation of an arctic tundra. – Arctic and Alpine Res. 6: 245–256.

Tieszen, L.L. & Sigurdson, D.C. 1973. Effect of temperature on carboxylase activity and stability in some Calvin cycle grasses from the arctic. – Arctic and Alpine Res. 5: 59–66.

Tieszen, L.L. & Wieland, N.K. 1975. Physiological ecology of arctic and alpine photosynthesis and respiration. – In: Vernberg, F.J. (ed.) Physiological Adaptation to the Environment, pp. 157–200. New York: Intext Press.

Van Cleve, K. 1967. Nutrient loss from organic matter placed in soil in different climatic regions. – Ph.D. dissertation, University of California. 290 pp.

Weller, G., Cubley, S., Parker, S., Trabant, D. & Benson, C. 1972. The tundra microclimate during snowmelt at Barrow, Alaska. – Arctic 25: 291–300.

Weller, G. & Holmgren, B. 1974. The microclimate of the arctic tundra. – J. Appl. Meteorol. 13: 854–862.

West, G. & Norton, D.W. 1975. Metabolic adaptations of tundra birds. – In: Vernberg, F.J. (ed.) Physiological Adaptation to the Environment, pp. 301–329. New York: Intext Press.

White, R.G. 1975. Some aspects of nutritional adaptations of Arctic herbivorous mammals. – In: Vernberg, F.J. (ed.) Physiological Adapdation to the Environment, pp. 239–268. New York: Intext Press.

Wiggins, J.R. & Thomas, J.H. 1962. A flora of the Alaskan arctic. Univ. Toronto Press. 425 pp.

Rosswall, T. & Heal, O.W. (eds.) 1975.
Structure and Function of Tundra Ecosystems.
Ecol. Bull. (Stockholm) 20: 125–139.

MT. PATSCHERKOFEL, AUSTRIA

W. LARCHER, A. CERNUSCA, L. SCHMIDT, G. GRABHERR,
E. NÖTZEL and N. SMEETS

INTRODUCTION

At Mt. Patscherkofel (47°13′N, 11°20′E), with an elevation of 2 247 m, three sample areas were selected for the IBP investigations.

1. Vaccinium heath, 1 980 m

The heath consists of *Vaccinium myrtillus* L. and *V. uliginosum* L. with abundant mosses interspersed with *Rhododendron ferrugineum* L. shrubs and dwarf larch tree groups. The heath is a plant community developed on a former forest ground and is the transition between the forest and the dwarf shrub heath.

2. Loiseleuria heath, 2 000 m

The sample area "*Loiseleuria* heath 2 000 m" is situated close to the tree line on a ridge where the *Vaccinium* spp. have been suppressed in their development by the microclimate of the habitat. *Loiseleuria procumbens* (L.) Desv. forms a continuous dense cover.

3. Loiseleurietum, 2 175 m

This sample area represents an open Loiseleurietum cetrariosum alectorietosum near the upper limit of the dwarf shrub zone on an extremely windswept west slope.

Mt. Patscherkofel consists of quartzphyllite (phyllonite) belonging to the Tuxer Voralpen. Only the summit which was rounded by glaciers during the glacial ages is built of biotite gneiss of the Ötztal-Stubai old crystalline basement. Well-aerated acid soils are developed on the stony-sandy weathered horizons. The Mt. Patscherkofel slopes are covered to a great extent by coniferous forests; the tree line is formed by *Pinus cembra* L. and *Larix decidua* Miller, on the northern slope up to 1 920–1 950 m, and on the southern slope up to 2 050 m; see vegetation map and profile (11). Above the tree line, which was almost entirely lowered by man for the last time in the early Middle Ages, when the forest was partly turned into grazing land, there is a dwarf shrub zone 150 m wide with transitions from a Rhododendretum to an open Loiseleurietum. The zone is followed by a lichen heath and Curvuletum fragments.

ENVIRONMENTAL CONDITIONS

Climate

Long-term climatic patterns

The macroclimate is characterized mainly by low average temperatures (Table 1). The annual mean temperature at 2 045 m is 1.3°C and at 2 247 m −0.5°C. At the lower limit of the dwarf shrub zone at 1 920 m the annual mean temperature is about 2.1°C. The air temperature rises above the freezing point only after the melting of snow at the beginning of May, then falling again below 0°C at the beginning of November.

The average annual precipitation is 951 mm, 61 % of which falls in summer. The snow-free period lasts from the beginning of May to the end of October. A continuous snow cover lasts for about 188 days but varies with the microclimate of the specific site. Windswept ridges, however, lack a snow cover for most of the winter, whereas snow lasts about a month longer on snow beds in spring. The possibility of summer snow-fall is a typical climatic feature of the dwarf shrub zone above the tree line.

Wind is an essential climatic factor for the dwarf shrub zone. A wind speed of 3 to 5 m s^{-1} occurs most frequently − the average being 4.1 m s^{-1}. Only 5 % of all days of the year are without wind. The winds are mostly southerly, their high frequency being due to the south föhn.

The degree of cloudiness averages 6/10. At the summit of Mt. Patscherkofel sun shines for 1 977 hours, i.e. 47 % of the possible local sunshine duration. The global radiation amounts to 493 kJ cm^{-2}; 288 kJ cm^{-2} (= 58 %) of it occurs during the period May through September. The area is screened by the summit of Mt. Patscherkofel and also by surrounding mountains. This obstruction reduces the duration of sunshine. In the *Loiseleuria* heath and the *Vaccinium* heath sun shines for 1 418 h (i.e. a loss of 29 %) and in the Loiseleurietum for 1 737 h (i.e a loss of 13 %). The global radiation is reduced by about 17 % in the *Loiseleuria* and the *Vaccinium* heath, and by 8 % in the Loiseleurietum.

Microclimate

The microclimate at mountain sites above the tree line differs remarkably from the macroclimate and exerts great influence on plant growth. The deviation is caused by the combined effect of radiation and wind. These two climatic factors are characterized not only by their intensity but also by their direction. They modify the macroclimate of mountainous sites and create a number of very different microclimates in a small area.

Fig. 1 shows air-temperature and soil-temperature profiles on a bright summer day and wind-speed profiles during föhn. The air temperature 2 m above the soil surface fluctuates diurnally only between 2.0°C and 11.5°C, but 10 cm above the plant cover it fluctuates between −2°C and 16.5°C; the highest temperatures (39.5°C) are found at the upper surface of the litter. The lowest temperatures (−3°C) are found in the early morning at the surface of the plant cover owing to a negative energy budget at night. The diurnal thermal fluctuation amounts to 42.5°C in the plant cover. In the soil a diurnal temperature fluctuation can be observed down to a depth of 20 to 30 cm.

It is significant that the wind profile is almost logarithmic in the range 6 cm − 2 m above the plant cover at low and high wind speeds. This phenomenon was also noticed

Table 1. Meteorological data from the observation station on the north slope at Mt. Patscherkofel (1951–1960). Long-term climate of the middle part of the dwarf shrub zone (*Loiseleuria* heath and *Vaccinium* heath). Compiled according to (14).

	J	F	M	A	M	J	J	A	S	O	N	D	Year
Global radiation (kJ cm^{-2})	17.8	25.1	42.8	50.1	57.8	64.2	64.0	57.2	44.3	34.2	19.6	16.3	493.4
Air temperature, 2 m ($^{\circ}$C)													
absolute maximum	8.1	10.8	13.0	14.7	19.8	22.4	26.7	22.9	20.3	17.9	14.0	9.4	26.7
average maximum	-3.2	-3.6	-0.4	1.9	7.1	10.9	13.3	12.9	10.6	6.1	1.3	-0.8	
monthly mean	-6.1	-6.3	-3.4	-1.1	3.5	6.9	9.1	8.9	6.8	2.7	-1.3	-3.5	1.3
average minimum	-8.8	-8.8	-5.9	-3.6	0.6	4.1	6.2	6.0	4.1	0.2	-3.7	-6.0	
absolute minimum	-23.1	-28.8	-18.7	-14.4	-11.7	-6.6	-2.7	-0.8	-7.5	-9.8	-16.4	-17.5	-28.8
Days with frost (min <0°C)	30.6	26.9	28.2	23.2	13.6	3.5	0.9	0.5	5.0	13.9	23.4	28.8	198.5
Ice days (max <0°C)	20.7	20.5	15.5	10.5	2.5	0.3	0.2	0.0	0.3	4.0	5.4	17.4	101.3
Wind speed (m s^{-1})	4.5	4.6	4.7	4.1	4.0	3.6	3.4	3.5	3.7	4.3	4.6	4.4	4.1
Precipitation (mm)	50	60	45	65	73	136	151	129	84	66	42	50	951

127

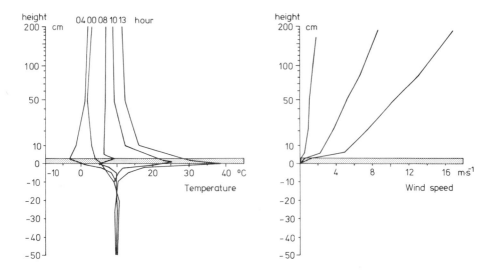

Figure 1. Left: Profile of the air and soil temperature of the sample area *Loiseleuria* heath 2 000 m on a hot summer day (1972−08−26). Right: Profile of wind speed during föhn at wind speeds of 16, 8 and 2 m s^{-1} (2 m above soil surface).

by Nägeli (10) in a *Rhododendron* community. This shows that prostrate vegetation hardly affects the winde profile in the air layer near the ground. The wind speed at the surface and middle of the plant cover are 9 % and 2.5 %, respectively, of the wind speed 2 m above the soil surface.

Based upon annual course of the air temperature and the temperature in the plant cover, Fig. 2 shows the differences in the microclimate of the *Loiseleuria* heath and the *Vaccinium* heath. The annual mean temperature of the *Vaccinium* heath lies 0.5°C, and that of the *Loiseleuria* heath 1.2°C, above the air temperature at 2 m above soil surface. The *Vaccinium* heath is protected from low temperatures by a snow cover·lasting all winter. In the *Vaccinium* heath the lowest temperatures therefore occur in the autumn and spring when the snow cover is absent due to cooling by long wave radiation on clear nights. The *Loiseleuria* heath growing on windswept habitats lacks a snow cover for a great part of the winter and is therefore exposed to low temperatures. In late winter and spring the temperature in the *Loiseleuria* heath canopy rises remarkably above that of the air at 2 m height because of the intensive irradiation. This increases the potential transpiration, which results in water stress (winter drought) as water-uptake by the roots is blocked because of the frozen soil (4, 5).

Soils

The soils of the study sites have developed on stony-sandy weathered horizons. They are well-aerated podsols low in nutrients and bases. The *Vaccinium* heath grows on deep iron podsol, the *Loiseleuria* heath on medium deep iron humus podsol, and the Loiseleurietum (2 175 m) on a thin layer of iron humus podsol. A narrow charcoal horizon

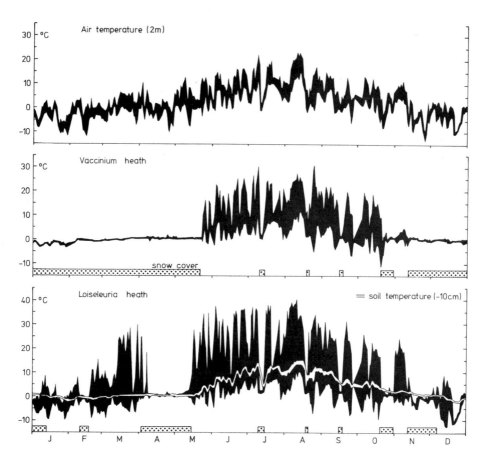

Figure 2. Annual course of temperature (1972) and snow cover for the *Loiseleuria* heath and the *Vaccinium* heath at the lower part of the dwarf shrub zone (1 950 m).

is found in the *Vaccinium* and *Loiseleuria* heaths, indicating that these soils have developed on former forested ground turned into grazing land in the Middle Ages. The iron humus podsol of the Loiseleurietum (2 175 m) was developed under the dwarf shrub heath. The soils are fresh to humid. The litter of all three plant communities consists of dead plant parts accumulated over several years. The litter layer is slowly decomposing, resulting in the accumulation of raw humus. The humus of the Loiseleurietum (2 175 m) is rich in fine sands, which were blown or washed out from the adjacent soils. The soils have a high potassium content, deriving from biotite gneiss. Nitrogen and phosphates are not readily available for the plants.

PRIMARY PRODUCTION

Community classification

The main representatives of the *Vaccinium* heath (1 980 m) are *Vaccinium myrtillus, Vaccinium uliginosum* and *Calluna vulgaris* (L.) Hull. The moss *Pleurozium schreberi* (Willd.) Mitt. invariably accompanied by *Cetraria islandica* (L.) Ach. predominates in the moss layer. The "Loiseleuria heath 2 000 m" is characterized by a small number of species. The growth of herbaceous plants is inhibited by *Loiseleuria procumbens* which forms a dense closed vegetation cover. Only isolated *Vaccinium* species and a number of lichens grow among the *Loiseleuria* plants. The "Loiseleurietum 2 175 m" is an "open" vegetation with a plant cover of only 75 to 80 %; it is rich in lichens. This sparse dwarf shrub heath consists mainly of *Loiseleuria procumbens*, various species of *Vaccinium* and herbs being sporadically interspersed. Numerous lichens are found among the prostrate plants which cover the dwarf shrubs being especially dense at exposed habitats.

Standing crop

The standing crop of the communities is presented in Table 2. The results indicate that the *Vaccinium* heath and the *Loiseleuria* heath are plant communities which do not expand. The dry weight of the total aboveground biomass of the *Vaccinium* heath fluctuates between 750 and 1 150 g m^{-2} (90 % phanerogams and 10 % cryptogams). In the *Loiseleuria* heath the biomass reaches values from 1 000 g m^{-2} to 1 250 g m^{-2} (90 % phanerogams and 10 % cryptogams), and in the "Loiseleurietum 2 175 m" the standing biomass amounts to an average value of 750 g m^{-2} (72 % phanerogams and 28 % cryptogams) at a coverage of 80 %. At a theoretical calculation for a 100 % coverage the biomass of this stand is still smaller than that of the *Loiseleuria* heath at the lower habitat. The smaller height of the plant cover is responsible for the lower values.

In the *Vaccinium* heath the relation between assimilating and non-assimilating parts of the phanerogams changes during the year, which is typical for a plant community where deciduous shrubs dominate. In winter, when the deciduous shrubs have no leaves, the dry matter of the non-assimilating parts is higher than that of the assimilating parts (1:0.8); at the time when all leaves are fully developed the ratio is 1:1.3. In the evergreen *Loiseleuria* heath, the ratio between green to nongreen parts does not change during the year. Here, compared with the *Vaccinium* heath, the high percentage of assimilating organs is remarkable. The biomass of the assimilating plant parts is twice as high as that of the non-assimilating plant parts.

The belowground biomass (especially belowground shoots and stolons, roots being of little importance) makes up the main part of the total biomass. In the *Vaccinium* heath and the *Loiseleuria* heath the belowground biomass fluctuates about an average of 2 200 g m^{-2}. The belowground biomass of the "Loiseleurietum 2 175 m" is significantly smaller (800 g m^{-2}) than that of the two other communities, due to the smaller coverage and production.

The average aboveground to belowground biomass ratio for the *Loiseleuria* heath and the *Vaccinium* heath is approximately 0.4 to 0.5:1; in the Loiseleurietum the ratio is 0.7:1. These values correspond to those of other arctic and alpine dwarf shrub communities.

Table 2. Standing crop and production (g m^{-2}) (average values)

	Vaccinium heath 1 980 m	Loiseleuria heath 2 000 m	Loiseleurietum 2 175 m
Community plant cover	100 %	100 %	80 %
Standing crop			
aboveground			
live			
Monocotyledons	7	0	11
Forbs	4	0	1
Woody green	557	748	} 562
nongreen	445	336	
Mosses	44	0	0
Lichens	22	136	205
dead (standing)			
Woody	255	139	61
Litter	861	1 117	699
belowground			
live	2 206	2 213	1 039
dead	1 272	553	48
Net production			
aboveground			
Monocotyledons	7	0	11
Forbs	5	0	4
Woody green	300	227	88
nongreen	110	50	15

n.d. = not determined

Production and production rates

The dry matter production of the new growth in the *Vaccinium* heath amounts on the average to 312 g m^{-2}, in the *Loiseleuria* heath to 227 g m^{-2}, and in the Loiseleurietum which is exposed to more severe climatic conditions only to 118 m^{-2}. The increase in dry matter of the woody stems was then determined as the difference in the dry matter at the beginning of the growth period and when the biomass was at its peak. Woody stems in the *Vaccinium* heath gained, on average, 110 g m^{-2} yr^{-1}, which is about 35 % of the increase in the assimilating parts. In the two evergreen *Loiseleuria* communities the dry matter of the woody stems increased by only about 25 % of the value for green parts, i.e. 50 g m^{-2} for the *Loiseleuria* heath, and 15 g m^{-2} for the "Loiseleurietum 2 175 m". These data correspond with determinations on *Dryas integrifolia* which stores about 20.6 % of the annual green production in woody stems (12).

The annual net production of the aboveground organs amounts to 422 g m^{-2} in the *Vaccinium* heath which corresponds to a 4.2 g m^{-2} · d^{-1} increase during the growing period of 100 days. The annual net production reaches a value of 317 g m^{-2} in the *Loiseleuria* heath — daily growth rates amounting to 2.2 g m^{-2} · d^{-1} during the grow-

ing season of 128 days. The Loiseleurietum near the summit of Mt. Patscherkofel, however, shows the smallest net production rates with only 107 g m^{-2} corresponding to a
daily increase of 0.9 g m$^{-2} \cdot$ d^{-1} during the growing season of 128 days. These data
match well with those from dwarf shrub communities in the tundra [13]. No values on
the net production could be obtained from the cryptogams and the belowground organs
as the individual values of the biomass showed large deviations (standard error up to
30 %).

Production processes

Gas exchange for *Loiseleuria procumbens*

Plants of the Loiseleurietum show a significantly lower photosynthetic capacity than
those of the *Loiseleuria* heath (Table 3). This is caused by a lower chlorophyll content
of the plants and by a higher respiratory loss.

Table 3. Maximal rates of photosynthesis measured in the laboratory
(T = 26°C, PhAR = 202 W m^{-2})

	Loiseleurietum 2 175 m	*Loiseleuria* heath 2 000 m
mg CO_2 g^{-1} h^{-1}	2.62	4.06
mg CO_2 dm^{-2} h^{-1}	5.46	9.81
mg CO_2 mg chlorophyll^{-1} h^{-1}	3.98	3.70
dark respiration (mg CO_2 g^{-1} h^{-1})	0.76	0.64

Fig. 3 shows the dependency of the net photosynthesis on light and temperature of
plants from the *Loiseleuria* heath 2 000 m. At strong radiation the temperature optimum lies around 30°C. This is an unusually high temperature for a plant of circumpolar distribution. Temperature courses of the plant cover during summer, however, show
that temperatures around 30°C occur frequently, caused by strong radiation. In weak
light the temperature optimum is shifted to a lower range, i.e. at 15°C. Thus the net
photosynthesis in the optimum temperature range shows a clear adaptability to the climatic conditions at the habitat. At optimal temperatures the net photosynthesis reaches
its light saturation between 79 and 119 W m^{-2} (PhAR). The light compensation point
lies somewhat below 5 W m^{-2}. A water potential less than -17 bar affects the CO_2 uptake. At -30 bar and somewhat below the CO_2 uptake is completely blocked.

132

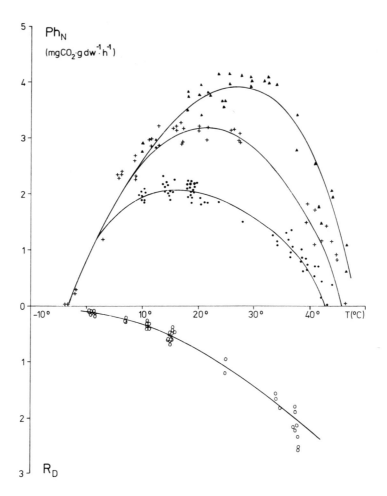

Figure 3. Dependence of net photosynthesis on temperature.
PhAR: $-\cdot-$ 39.7 W m^{-2}
  $-+-$ 79.5 W m^{-2}
  $-\blacktriangle-$ 198.7 W m^{-2}
  $-$ o $-$ dark respiration

Besides individual plants, vegetation blocks cut out of the plant cover were also studied. Compared with the individual plants the blocks with a dense *Loiseleuria* cover exhibit a change in the light dependency of CO_2-gas exchange. At a PhAR of 199 W m^{-2} the CO_2 uptake of the blocks decreases by 40 % at 15°C, 70 % at 25°C, and 86 % at 35°C. This shows that the *Loiseleuria* community is able to photosynthesize with gain even at temperatures around 35°C. The light compensation point of the net photosynthesis lies in the temperature optimum (= 25°C) at 40 W m^{-2}, at 35°C it is 119 W m^{-2}. The low absorption of only 57 % of the incident radiation by the assimilating organs, besides other factors, is a reason why the CO_2 uptake is strongly inhibited.

Effect of plant geometry

The effect of plant geometry upon the dry matter production was investigated primarily for *Loiseleuria procumbens*. Fig. 4 shows the vertical structure of *Loiseleuria* heath radiation profiles. The average height of the plants is 3 cm. 72 % of the total phytomass of 1 090 g m^{-2} consists of *Loiseleuria* leaves, 8 % of lichens, 9 % of shoots, and 11 % of dead leaves still attached to the plant. The highest density of the phytomass is found in the middle layer of the plant cover. The plant geometry is determined not only by the distribution of the phytomass and the leaf area but also by the inclination of the leaves. Whilst the leaves of the upper and the middle layer show a very characteristic main inclination, the lower third of the plant cover shows a relatively even distribution of the leaf inclination.

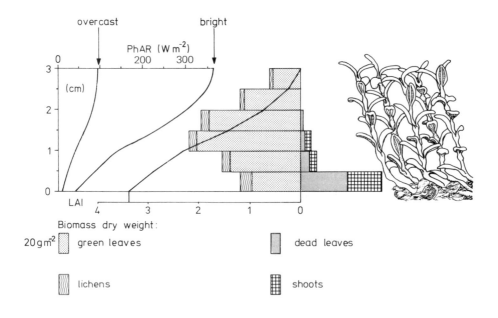

Figure 4. Vertical structure of the *Loiseleuria* heath and radiation profile. The instantaneous values of photosynthetically active radiation (W m^{-2}) are plotted against stand height for a bright day and for an overcast day.

Attenuation of the radiation in the uppermost third of the plant cover is lowest, while it reaches the highest rates in the middle layer. The equation used for evaluating the attenuation of radiation in the plant cover is:

$$I_x = I_o \cdot e^{-K \cdot F_x}$$

with F_x = LAI (leaf area index) leaves + LAI lichens + BAI (bark area index) shoots. F_x is the sum of the total leaf area index of leaves (living and dead), lichens and shoots in the layer above the measuring point x. The extinction coefficient is 0.2 in the uppermost layer, 0.6 in the middle layer, and 0.9 in the bottom layer, amounting to 0.66 for the entire plant cover. In the *Loiseleuria* heath the extinction coefficient equals that of a forest (9). Besides the leaves, shoots are also of essential importance for the absorption of radiation in the *Loiseleuria* heath, whereas they have less significance in other plant communities like grasslands and forests.

In order to calculate the efficiency of the primary production it is necessary to know the radiation absorbed by the photosynthetically active leaves. The plant cover and the soil reflect 16.6 % of the incident radiation; 76.6 % is absorbed by the plant cover. The remaining 6.7 % is absorbed by the soil surface. The radiation absorbed by the plant cover is distributed among the living leaves (i.e. photosynthetically active), dead leaves (attached to the plant), lichens, and shoots. Photosynthetically active leaves of *Loiseleuria* absorb 57 % of the PhAR recorded above the plant cover.

Plant constituents

The annual mineral incorporation and the deposit of organic substances in the "*Loiseleuria* heath 2 000 m" (Table 4 and 5) are based upon preliminary results of the analyses of *Loiseleuria procumbens* which constitutes almost 83 % of the phytomass of this plant community.

Relatively high nitrogen contents are characteristic of the *Loiseleuria* heath. Ca and K are present in almost equal amounts, 10 to 20 % of the ash, followed by P and Mg with 3 to 5 %, and Fe with 0.3 to 1.5 % depending on the organ and season. The *Loiseleuria* heath represents the N Ca/K-type which is typical for northern tundras (2).

Table 4 presents the mineral incorporation during the annual shoot growth and the dry matter production in the vegetation period. The *Loiseleuria* heath at Mt. Patscherkofel is poor in minerals. The mineral contents in this alpine plant community range near the lower limit of the values for arctic tundra plants (12). The amounts of phosphorus and potassium are remarkably low.

The amount of organic substances deposited per unit area (m^2) of the plant community can be calculated by multiplying the values of the chemical analyses with the phytomass of the *Loiseleuria* heath. The most striking result of that calculation is the enormous amount of lipids stored in this plant community. One hectare of dwarf shrub heath contains more than 2 tons of fat in summer, the amount being even higher in winter (7). Ericaceous dwarf shrubs represent a food source rich in energy for consumers of this ecosystem. The tundra might be considered as a potential source for raw materials in the future.

The chlorophyll content of the leaves of *Loiseleuria procumbens* averages 1.2 mg chlorophyll a + b g^{-1}. The chlorophyll content per m^2 cover corresponds approximately

135

Table 4. Average incorporation of mineral nutrients by a community of *Loiseleuria procumbens* at **2 000 m during the growing season (23 weeks)**

	Incorporation by current years shoots ☆ $g\ m^{-2}\ yr^{-1}$	Incorporation by annual dry matter production ☆☆ $g\ m^{-2}\ yr^{-1}$
Nitrogen	2.24	2.75
Phosphorus	0.16	0.19
Potassium	0.63	0.77
Calcium	0.91	1.11
Magnesium	0.20	0.24
Iron	0.02	0.02

☆ Calculated on the basis of 197 $g\ m^{-2}\ yr^{-1}$ shoot growth during the vegetation period.
☆☆ Calculated on the basis of 241 $g\ m^{-2}\ yr^{-1}$ net dry matter productivity.

Table 5. Phytomass constituents of a community of *Loiseleuria procumbens* at 2 000 m in summer (July, August). Average values in $g\ m^{-2}$

Plant constituents	Assimilating parts	Nonassimilating above-ground parts	Belowground parts	Total
Soluble carbohydrate [1]	47	9	75	131
Starch [1]	14.0	0.5	9.0	23.5
Crude fibre [1]	150	103	587	840
Raw protein [1]	33	11	52	96
Lipid [2]	73	34	113	220
Chlorophyll (a+b) [3]	0.9	–	–	0.9
Chlorophyll ratio (a/b) [3]	3.8/1	–	–	–
Carotenoids [3]	0.15	–	–	0.15
Ash [3]	12.6	3.5	20.3	36.4

Source of data: [1]E. Nötzel, [2]W. Larcher, [3]N. Smeets

to open tree stands of the same size; it is higher than that of grassland (1). The correlation between chlorophyll content and primary productivity of the *Loiseleuria* heath agrees fairly well with the empirical formula of Medina and Lieth (8).

Different calorific values are obtained for the individual parts of the investigated plants and the energy content also varies over the year. High energy values are obtained for the shrubs particularly in spring and autumn.

The evergreen shrubs have the highest energy contents. *Loiseleuria procumbens* shows the highest values due to a high fat content. This species shows generally higher energy values in the aboveground woody stems (seasonal mean: 24.7 kJ g^{-1}) than in assimilating parts (23.4 kJ g^{-1}) as well as in belowground organs (22.2 kJ g^{-1}). The deciduous shrubs show lower energy values than the evergreen ones. Here the values of the assimilating parts are higher (21.6 kJ g^{-1}) than those of the non-assimilating parts (21.3 kJ g^{-1}) and of the belowground organs (21.1 kJ g^{-1}). Mosses (18.5 kJ g^{-1}) and lichens (17.4 kJ g^{-1}) have significantly lower energy values which show no seasonal change.

Fauna

The number of consumers in the two heath populations is small, exerting more influence on the *Vaccinium* heath than on the *Loiseleuria* heath. In summer (end of June until beginning of September), cattle — mainly cows but also some sheep and goats — graze the *Vaccinium* heath, obviously despising the *Loiseleuria* probably because of the extremely bitter taste of the leaves. *Loiseleuria*, however, constitutes the food for the snow hare (*Lepus timidus varronis* Miller) and the ptarmigan (*Lagopus mutus* Montin) in winter, especially when the more desired *Vaccinium* heath is covered by a dense snow cover. Whether the chamois (*Rupicapra rupicapra* (L.)) feeds on the two plant communities is not known yet. Birds feeding on berries, e.g. the ring ouzel (*Turdus torquatus* L.), or on seeds, e.g. the snow finch (*Montifringilla nivalis* (L.)), are of some importance. Herbivory by arthropods is of minor importance. Caterpillars — including monophagous species — predominate among the arthropods on the *Vaccinium* heath, being absent from the *Loiseleuria*.

Carnivorous vertebrates can only seldom be observed because of lack of prey as well as anthropogenic influence (tourists).

Besides other arthropods, spiders, which occur frequently, play a certain role among insectivorous animals. Saprovorous animals are mainly represented by nematodes; collembola, dipteran larvae, and oribatid mites are of minor importance.

OVERVIEW OF THE ECOSYSTEM
AND MAN'S INFLUENCE ON IT

The alpine dwarf shrub heath at Mt. Patscherkofel is increasingly influenced by man. Mt. Patscherkofel is a well-known recreation area easily reached from Innsbruck and visited by numerous tourists all year around; it was also the site of the 1964 winter Olympic games. The stress upon the plant cover is mainly caused by the construction of hotels, ski-lifts, trails, and ski pistes. The latter represent a great stress factor. For long lasting ski pistes it is necessary to compress the snow cover by piste mobiles. Snow fences are set up on wind exposed sites which are supposed to protect the pistes from drifting snow. Along the pistes the natural snow distribution is completely disturbed, causing a change of the microclimate in the plant cover. The growing season is shortened on ski runs by the long lasting snow cover, resulting in a disturbed balance between individual plants and subsequently causing a change in the sequence of the ecological succession. The anthropogenic stress upon the dwarf shrub heath at Mt. Patscherkofel will be studied in more detail.

POSTSCRIPT

The aim of the IBP research program "Alpine dwarf shrub heath Mt. Patscherkofel" was to analyse primary production and its dependency on environmental conditions (microclimate and soil).

The project was directed by W. Larcher; investigations on macro- and microclimate were carried out by A. Cernusca; the effect of plant geometry and canopy structure was studied by A. Cernusca, J. Staud, W. Jaschke and E. Lanser; phytomass, productivity and energy content were measured by L. Schmidt; CO_2-gas exchange was studied by G. Grabherr; analyses of the various plant constituents were carried out by E. Nötzel (organic constituents) and N. Smeets (minerals, chlorophyll).

A detailed description of the research program and of the methods used is published in "Ökosystemforschung" (3, 6). Most of the data presented here are preliminary results. Details will be published in "Oecologia plantarum" and "Photosynthetica".

REFERENCES

1. Bray, R.J. 1960. The primary productivity of vegetation in central Minnesota, USA, and its relationship to chlorophyll content and albedo. – In: Lieth, H. (ed.) Die Stoffproduktion der Pflanzendecke, pp. 102–109. Stuttgart: Gustav Fischer Verlag.
2. Bazilevich, N.I., Rodin, L.Y. & Rozov, N.N. 1971. Geographical aspects of biological productivity. – Soviet Geography (Rev. & Translation). New York: American Geogr. Soc.
3. Cernusca, A. 1973. Einsatz mobiler Messeinrichtungen. – In: Ellenberg, H. (ed.) Ökosystemforschung, pp. 195–201. Berlin–Heidelberg–New York: Springer Verlag.
4. Larcher, W. 1957. Frosttrocknis an der Waldgrenze und in der alpinen Zwergstrauchheide auf dem Patscherkofel bei Innsbruck. – Veröff. Ferdinandeum Innsbruck 37: 49–81.
5. Larcher, W. 1972. Der Wasserhaushalt immergrüner Pflanzen im Winter. – Ber. Deutsch. Bot. Ges. 85: 315–327.
6. Larcher, W., Cernusca, A. & Schmidt, L. 1973. Stoffproduktion und Energiebilanz in Zwergstrauchbeständen auf dem Patscherkofel bei Innsbruck. – In: Ellenberg, H. (ed.) Ökosystemforschung, pp. 175–194. Berlin–Heidelberg–New York: Springer Verlag.
7. Larcher, W., Schmidt, L. & Tschager, A. 1973. Starke Fettspeicherung und hoher Kaloriengehalt bei Loiseleuria procumbens (L.). Desv. – Oecol. Plant. 8: 405–411.
8. Medina, E. & Lieth, H. 1964. Die Beziehungen zwischen Chlorophyllgehalt, assimilierender Fläche und Trockensubstanzproduktion in einiger Pflanzengemeinschaften. – Beitr. Biol. Pflanzen 40: 451–494.

9. Monsi, M. & Saeki, T. 1953. Über den Lichtfaktor in den Pflanzengesellschaften und seine Bedeutung für die Stoffproduktion. – Jap. J. Bot. 14: 22–52.

10. Nägeli, W. 1971. Der Wind als Standortsfaktor bei Aufforstungen in der subalpinen Stufe (Stillbergalp im Dischmatal, Kanton Graubünden). – Mitt. schweiz. Anst. forstl. Versuchswes. 47.

11. Pitschmann, H., Reisigl, H., Schiechtl, H.M. & Stern, R. 1970. Karte der aktuellen Vegetation von Tirol 1/100000. I. Teil: Blatt 6, Innsbruck-Stubaier Alpen. – In: Ozenda, P. (ed.) Documents pour la Carte de la Végétation des Alpes. VIII: 7–34.

12. Svoboda, J. 1973. Primary production of plant communities of the Truelove Lowland, Devon Island, Canada-beach ridges. – In: Bliss, L.C. & Wielgolaski, F.E. (eds.) Production and Production Processes, Tundra Biome, pp. 15–26. Edmonton: IBP Tundra Biome Steering Committee.

13. Wielgolaski, F.E. & Kjelvik, S. 1973. Production of plants (vascular plants and cryptogams) in alpine tundra, Hardangervidda. – In: Bliss, L.C. & Wielgolaski, F.E. (eds.) Primary Production and Production Processes, Tundra Biome, pp. 75–86. Edmonton: IBP Tundra Biome Steering Committee.

14. Winkler, E. 1963. Beiträge zur Klimatologie hochalpiner Lagen der Zentralalpen. – Ber. Naturwiss.-Med. Ver. Innsbruck 53: 209–223.

Rosswall, T. & Heal, O.W. (eds.) 1975.
Structure and Function of Tundra Ecosystems.
Ecol. Bull. (Stockholm) 20: 141–158.

AGAPA, USSR

V.D. VASSILJEVSKAJA, V.V. IVANOV, L.G. BOGATYREV,
E.B. POSPELOVA, N.M. SHALAEVA and L.A. GRISHINA

The Agapa station is situated on the east bank of the Pyasina river near the mouth of its west tributary, the Agapa river, in the Western Taimyr, at 71°25'N and 88°53'E.

The site occupies the Pyasina floodplain, the stream terraces and adjoining watershed. The absolute elevations range from 20 m (waterline) to 120 m a.s.l. (watershed) (Fig. 1).

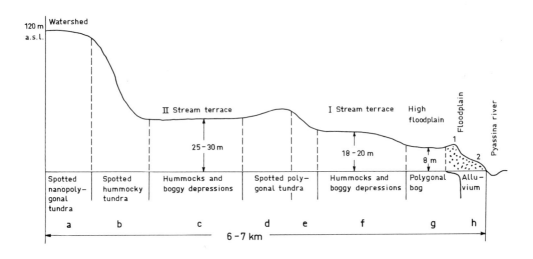

Figure 1. Cross-section of the Agapa (USSR) IBP study area.

ENVIRONMENTAL CONDITIONS

Geological structure and relief

The present Agapa river valley represented by the floodplain and high floodplain terrace (8 m high) is part of the more ancient preglacial valley. It has inherited two ancient stream terraces with relative heights of 18–20 m and 25–30 m. The Agapa station territory mainly occupies the second stream terrace.

The area is situated within the limits of the North Siberian Lowland developed as a result of marine transgression during the Quaternary period. The main part of the watershed areas and stream terraces consist of sandy loams and clays of marine origin mantled with glacial silt loam to a depth of 1–2 m on the watershed and with shallow (1–3 m) lacustrine-alluvial deposits of loamy-sandy texture on the stream terraces. Alluvial sandy and sandy deposits are found in the high floodplain and floodplain terraces to a depth of 8–10 m. On the watershed slopes marine clays are often exposed at the surface.

The clay material of all soils, including the alluvial floodplain, is obviously inherited from the previous phase of marine sediment accumulation, which is confirmed by its homogenous mineral composition, with 70–80 % being accountered for by the smectite group.

Owing to the intensive frost processes, various forms of microrelief caused by permafrost (polygonal ground, spots) are widely distributed over the Agapa station territory. Spotted, nanopolygonal tundras are developed on the high watershed areas. They consist of an alternation of bare spots and separating troughs with a total plant cover often amounting to only 20 % (cf. Fig. 2). Spotted hummocky tundras predominate on the slopes of the watershed. Here the microrelief consists of alternating hummocks, usually with a spot of bare mineral soil on the top, and depressions with a plant cover. The microrelief of the stream terraces is mostly formed by the alternation of low hummocks with a diameter of 1–3 m and boggy depressions. Spotted polygonal tundra is found on the more drained surfaces of the stream terraces; the surface consists of an alternation of convex, bare mineral spots surrounded by elevated vegetation borders and troughs with a plant cover. The polygonal bogs are typical of the high floodplain terrace. The surface here is characterized by the presence of frost-boil polygons, 8–10 m in diameter, with a concave boggy surface and a rim of 0.5–1 m height; the polygons are separated by narrow deep boggy depressions. As a rule, the permafrost microrelief is not pronounced on the lower flooded part of the floodplain.

Climate

According to the climatic division of the USSR, the Western Taimyr belongs to the subarctic zone, being situated at the junction between the Arctic and Atlantic continental regions (1). Air currents from moderate latitudes confer a more continental climate (warmer summers and colder winters) on the inner regions of the Taimyr peninsula than would otherwise be the case owing to the high latitude. Southerly winds prevail all the year round, particularly in summer. The amplitude of temperature between the warmest and coldest months is 60° at Kresty village situated 90 km south of the station (Table 1). Precipitation is highest in summer and the thickest snow cover is observed in April (3). Yearly precipitation amounts to 105–350 mm (4). Snow persists for up to 9–10 months

a Spotted nanopolygonal tundra

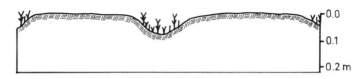

b Spotted hummocky tundra

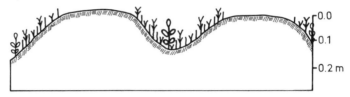

c,f Hummocks and boggy depressions

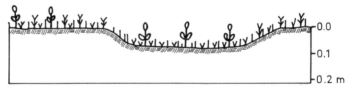

d—e Spotted polygonal tundra

g Polygonal bog

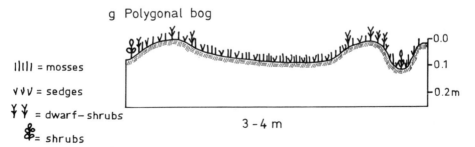

||||| = mosses

∨∨∨ = sedges

Ψ Ψ = dwarf—shrubs

  = shrubs

3 - 4 m

Fig. 2. Characteristic plant communities of the main biotopes of the Agapa station.

Table 1. Climatic conditions at the Agapa Station (Data from Kretsky village)

Variables		J	F	M	A	M	J	J	A	S	O	N	D	Year
Screen temperature (°C)														
min		-34.1	-31.8	-30.1	-23.2	-11.3	-1.0	7.0	4.6	-1.7	-14.3	-27.1	-29.6	-15.9
mean		-30.6	-27.9	-25.6	-18.3	-8.1	3.4	11.4	8.6	1.5	-10.6	-23.3	-28.3	-12.3
max		-10	-10	-6	0	4	18	26	23	14	3	-4	-7	27
Relative humidity (%)		79	79	78	80	84	82	72	79	85	86	81	79	80
Wind velocity (m s^{-1})		8.5	8.0	7.8	7.2	6.4	5.6	5.3	5.4	5.5	7.1	7.7	8.6	6.9
Precipitation (mm)		24	18	19	18	23	33	38	49	38	34	27	23	344
Snow depth (cm)		35	40	44	49	43	0	0	0	0	19	26	31	–
Sunshine duration (h)		0	28	131	214	236	244	326	206	72	33	2	0	1492
Soil moisture (% dw)														
0–10 cm	min	–	–	–	–	–	149	31	34	–	–	–	–	–
Dryas-moss	mean	–	–	–	–	–	170	47	35	–	–	–	–	–
tundra	max	–	–	–	–	–	190	58	39	–	–	–	–	–

and, owing to the lack of winter thawing, can reach a considerable depth, 65 cm on average.

In the region of study, mean daily temperatures above $0°C$ occur on some 65 days of the year. The annual temperature sums over $5°$ and $10°$, derived from mean daily temperatures at Kresty village, are $700°$ and $432°$ respectively.

The depth of permafrost ranges from 400 to 600 m; the depth of seasonal thawing does not exceed 35—70 cm.

Microclimatic observations were carried out at four sites during three growing seasons from June through the end of August. Air temperature was measured at a height of 1.5 m and soil temperature was measured at the surface of the plant cover, on bare spots and at various depths.

Air temperature at a height of 1.5 m is practically the same for the various community types. The change in average daily soil temperature coincides with that in the air but it always lags behind, on an average by $2—3°C$ under bare spots and by $3—5°$ under moss cover at 5—10 cm depth. A decrease in the air temperature is followed by a very sharp fall in the soil temperature which shows the dominating effect of permafrost upon the temperature regimes of the active layer. In spite of the relatively rapid heating of the surface, the soil temperature under moss cover is much lower than under bare spots at all depths. Thus during the growing season the temperature regime is more favourable on bare spots as compared with adjacent areas under vegetation cover. On the whole the soil heat regime of the hummocky tundra with a thick moss cover is the least favourable, and that of the sandy terraces the most favourable.

The temperature of the warmest month (July) is much higher in the Agapa territory than in other parts of the subarctic zone, while winters, by contrast, are characterized by low temperatures, which are close to those of the arctic zone — a result of the above-mentioned air circulation. Owing to this, the Agapa territory is characterized by the highest fluctuations of air temperature in the subarctic zone. The average annual temperature is close to that of the arctic zone.

Soils

The main processes in the tundra gley soils of the station territory are as follows: gleying, accumulation of raw humus, cryogenic moisture, mass exchange and eluviation in the above-permafrost horizons, mainly in the organogenic ones.

In spite of the fact that the organogenic horizon in the boggy soils, unlike the tundra gley ones, contains a considerable amount of fine earth admixture and looks like a peaty soil, gleying is well developed. Cryogenic moisture and mass exchange is less marked than in the tundra gley soils owing to heat insulation by a mossy-peaty cover and parent material of lighter texture. The tundra boggy soils are intermediate with regard to soil forming processes.

Alluvium continuously accumulates in the floodplain soils; sod formation with gleying in loamy alluvium is well developed.

The texture of the tundra gley soils is mainly clay loam. As a rule, only the humus accumulative horizons are of lighter texture. The pulverized state of all horizons should be noted.

The following minerals are found in the fine sandy fractions of the watershed soils:

quartz (58–75 %), feldspar (38–42 %); heavy minerals – epidote, ilmenite, garnet, amphibole, magnetite (total 3–5 %). In all soils more than 50 % of the clay fraction consists of minerals of the smectite group dervied from the sediment.

The texture of the boggy soils of the floodplain and high floodplain terraces is lighter than that of the watershed soils, which is related to lacustrine-alluvial genesis of the parent material. The upper organogenic horizons are rather poor in silt fraction.

The mineral part of the tundra gley soil profile is characterized by a weak differentiation into horizons, lack of podzolization, saturation by oxalate-soluble sesquioxides and mobile organic substances. Negligible acidity and high base saturation at a high cation exchange capacity are typical features of these soils (Table 2). These features are associated with the influence of parent material of marine genesis and with the mineralogy of the silt fraction, together with the bioclimatic conditions of the region. On the watershed these conditions favour the formation of soils with properties close to those of the typical tundra region. The upper humus-accumulative horizons differ markedly from the mineral layer both morphologically and chemically. These horizons are characterized by noticeable leaching, larger humus content and acidity; in some cases they are very poor in silt fraction due to intensive leaching and lateral eluviation.

The boggy tundra soils and boggy soils are characterized by greater acidity and less base saturation than the tundra gley soils (Table 2). However, the total amount of exchangeable cations remains fairly high.

The general features of organic substance in the station soils are as follows:

i.   all horizons are rich in semihumified residues
ii.   high content of nonspecific organic substance, including lipids
iii.   humus is rich in fulvate, with high mobility
iv.   organic substances seep through the active layer
v.   humus is generally retained above the permafrost.

The content of organic substance in a 0–50 cm layer amounts to 15 000 g m^{-2} in the watershed soils, 21 000 g m^{-2} in the slope soils, and 17 000 g m^{-2} in the terrace soils. The total content of organic substance in a 0–50 cm layer of boggy soil amounts to 32 000 g m^{-2}. The C/N ratio varies from 20 to 40.

Soil moisture and aeration in the station territory vary with the intensity of gleying. Highest porosity and low moisture are typical of the slightly gleyed soils on the spotted nanopolygonal tundras of the watersheds (air space 30–40 %). The gley soils of the hummocky spotted tundras are fully saturated. In the spotted polygonal ridgy tundras of the terraces, moisture by volume exceeds the value of general porosity, which is probably associated with thixotropy of the soil.

During the growing season the moisture in the mineral horizons changes little, which is related to full saturation of the majority of the soils. The content of ferric oxide increases from spring to summer – a result of the intensification of reducing microbiological processes as soil temperature rises and the thawing of the soil increases. The value of the Eh in soils of the region varies between 260 and 620 mV.

Hydrology

The station territory lies between the Pyasina river and its east tributary, the Lanka river. Within the limits of the station there are a few lakes of fluvioglacial and thermokarst

146

Table 2. Soil conditions at the Agapa Station (peak season values)

Soil parameter	Spotted tundra on watershed; tundra weakly gleyed soil					Floodplain terrace; bog (peaty-gley) soil			
	Bare spot, cm			Trough, cm		Rim, cm		Trough, cm	
	B_1 0–25	B_2 25–50	Bg 50–75	AB 5–20	B(g) 20–30	A_1/A_T 0–10	Bg 10–15	A_T/A_1 5–25	Bg 23–54
pH (H_2O)	6.6	6.3	7.2	6.3	7.0	5.5	6.1	6.1	6.6
Soil moisture (% dw)	18.4	18.8	–	33.9	25.3				
(% vol)	17.1	20.9	–	14.6	28.1				
Bulk density (g cm^{-3})	0.95	1.11	1.70	0.65	1.10	0.53	1.35	0.80	1.35
Maximum seasonal thaw (cm)			77		60		25		54
Redox potential (mV)	520	510	–	570	580				
Particle size (%, sand; 1–0.05 mm)	32.0	38.5	23.6	40.5	30.5				
(silt; 0.05–0.001)	44.7	38.5	60.2	38.7	52.9				
(clay; <0.001)	20.7	20.6	12.9	18.5	13.3				
Total organic carbon (% dw)	1.27	0.62	0.31	1.43	0.88				
Total nitrogen (% dw)	0.19	0.12	0.09	0.14	0.03				
Exchangeable cations:									
Calcium (meq 100 g^{-1})	16.4	15.6	17.6	17.6	19.0	7.6	7.2	7.2	6.8
(g m^{-2})	77.9	86.6	159.1	34.3	41.8	10.2	9.6	23.0	54.4
Magnesium (meq 100 g^{-1})	11.8	5.2	9.8	4.0	10.8	1.0	0.6	1.2	8.0
(g m^{-2})	33.6	17.3	50.0	4.7	14.3	0.6	0.5	2.3	38.4
Hydrogen (meq 100 g^{-1})	2.7	3.2	1.2	1.2	2.2	5.5	1.6	3.5	1.6
(g m^{-2})	0.6	0.9	0.9	0.1	0.2	0.3	0.1	0.6	0.6
Cation-exchange capacity (meq 100 g^{-1})	30.9	24.0	28.6	27.8	32.0	14.1	9.4	12.1	16.4
Soluble nutrients (ppm)									
P_2O_5	165	116	268	115	217				
K_2O	115	95	72	137	113				
FeO	114	97	–	377	410				
Soil temperature; mean °C for July at 5 cm	12.6	–	–	6.3	–				

Note: Ca, Mg, K_2O were determined in 1N CH_3COONH_4; H in 1N $BaCl_2$; P_2O_5 in 0.2 N HCl; FeO in 1N H_2SO_4.

147

origin and many streams draining the floodplain and high floodplain terraces. Snowmelt accounts for 60 % of the water in the Pyasina river, the rain and underground water each for 20 %. The minimum river runoff occurs in winter, the maximum in June. The frozen sediment, marked continental climate and high soil moisture with low evaporation are responsible for a high proportion of precipitation going into runoff (2). The average runoff of the Pyasina river basin amounts to 200–250 mm yr^{-1}.

The river water is slightly acid, with low mineral content. With the movement of suprapermafrost water through the system: soil layer − streams − rivers, there is a gradual fall in the mineral content: soil solution, 200–400; suprapermafrost water, 50–80; streams, 20–50; rivers, 20–35 mg l^{-1}. The station lakes, especially the watershed ones, have a lower mineral content. The mineral content of natural waters rises towards the end of the growing season.

PRIMARY PRODUCTION

Classification of plant communities

The station is situated at the border between the shrubby and typical tundras. Dwarf shrub, moss and lichen communities, peculiar to the typical tundra zone, are found on the windward hills. The *ernik* (*Betula nana* L.) tundra, sphagnum bogs and willow stands, i.e. the typical formations of the shrubby tundra of the southern tundra zone, are found on the flat surfaces of the terraces and floodplains.

The border situation of the station gives rise to a considerable variety of plant cover with plant communities peculiar to both the typical and shrubby tundras developing depending on the microrelief.

The vascular plants of the station accounting for 244 species in 107 genera and 40 families are typically arctic with some hypoarctic features.

Biomass and production

The phytomass (above- and belowground live and dead) of the vascular plant communities of the station varies from 1 830 g m^{-2} at the spotted tundra of the watershed hill tops to 5 470 g m^{-2} at the wet tundra community of the terraces. The values for the soddy tundras (2 400 g m^{-2}) are similar to those for the spotted–*Cassiope*–lichen–mossy tundras of the terrace slopes (2 560 g m^{-2}). The values for the spotted tundras of the terraces (3 580 g m^{-2}) are closer to those for the flat hummocky bogs (5 450 g m^{-2}). The phytomass of the vascular plants of meadows amounts to 4 020 g m^{-2}.

The aboveground biomass of vascular plants is the highest on the bogs (513 g m^{-2} on the flat hummocky bogs, site c, Table 3 and Fig. 1–2; and 439 g m^{-2} on the wet swampy communities, site f) followed by the spotted tundra communities of the terraces (site b; 234 g m^{-2}), soddy tundra communities (190 g m^{-2}) and *Cassiope*-lichen-mossy communities (site e; 167 g m^{-2}). The lowest values are found for vascular plants in the meadows (130 g m^{-2}) and for the spotted tundra community of the area between the rivers (sita a; 75 g m^{-2}).

Dwarf shrubs predominate in the spotted and soddy tundra communities (20–30 % plant cover), being less in the hummocky (15–20 %) and boggy (up to 19 %) commu-

Table 3. Aboveground biomass (g m^{-2}) at various sub-sites at Agapa. Location of subsites are given in Fig. 1 and microtopography of these sites in Fig. 2.

Site	Site name	Plant communities	Shrubs	Dwarf shrubs	Sedges and cotton grass	Grami-noids	Forbs	Total vascular plants	Mosses	Lichens
a	Spotted nanopolygonal tundra; area between rivers	Dryas-mossy tundra	28	41	5	1	<1	75	61	7
b	Spotted hummocky tundra	Cotton grass-dwarf shrub-sedge-mossy tundra	59	82	91	1	1	234	185	56
c	Hummocks and boggy depressions; hummocky bogs, wet swampy communities, boggy communities	shrub-cotton grass-sedge-mossy bog	262	124	123	3	1	513	380	8
d	Spotted polygonal tundra	Sedge-shrub-dwarf shrub mossy tundra	69	70	90	4	3	236	132	57
e	Spotted polygonal tundra	Cassiope-lichen mossy tundra	32	83	49	1	2	167	104	48
f	Hummocks and boggy depressions; wet tundra, boggy tundra, tundra-boggy complex	Dwarf shrub-shrub-sedge mossy wet tundra	232	134	69	3	1	439	207	47
g	Polygonal bog		n.d.	n.d.	n.d.	n.d.	n.d.	n.d.	n.d.	n.d.
h	Alluvium	1. Dry forb-dwarf shrub-lichen tundra 2. Arctophila fulva	n.d.	n.d.	n.d.	n.d.	n.d.	n.d.	n.d.	n.d.

n.d. = not determined

149

nities. The biomass values in the true tundra and bog communities are approximately equal; evergreen arcto-alpine species (*Cassiope tetragona* (L.) D. Don., *Dryas punctata* Juz.) are found in the true tundra communities, and deciduous-boreal species (*Vaccinium uliginosum* L.) on the bogs.

Shrubs comprise up to 30 % of the aboveground plant biomass on the bogs and shrubby meadows, that of the typical tundra communities amounting to 7–20 %. Shrub biomass is the largest in the swampy community. The shrubs include *Betula nana, Salix glauca* L., *S. pulchra* Cham., *S. reptans* Rupr., *S. lanata* L., *S. hastata* L. Net production of the predominant shrubs are given in Table 4.

The biomass of the sedge grasses (including cotton grass) is also highest on the bogs. *Carex stans* Drej.[*], *C. rariflora* (Wahlenb.) Sm., *Eriophorum medium* Ands., *E. scheuchzeri* Hoppe and *E. angustifolium* Honck. are typically found on the bogs; *Carex ensifolia* (Turcz. ex Gorodk.) V. Krecz. ssp. *arctisibirica* Jurtz.[**], *C. vaginata* Tausch. and *Eriophorum vaginatum* L. on the typical tundra communities. Their percentage of the aboveground plant biomass is equal for all communities (10–20 %), excepting meadows, where they are absent.

Graminoids and herbs are mainly found in the meadows, where their biomass is 4–8 times as high as in the tundra communities. They together make up 70 % of the aboveground biomass in the meadows, while in the tundra and swampy communities they vary between 0.5 % and 3 %.

Mosses account for 30–70 % of the aboveground phytomass. They prevail in the bogs and boggy tundras (200–380 g m^{-2}). The moss biomass in the soddy tundra communities amounts to 207 g m^{-2}, in the spotted tundra of the terraces to 132 g m^{-2}, in the spotted *Cassiope*–lichen–mossy tundra of the slopes to 104 g m^{-2}, and in the spotted tundra of the watershed territory to 61 g m^{-2}. There is no moss cover on the meadows.

The main moss species are *Tomenthypnum nitens* (Hedw.). Loeske, *Hylocomium splendens* (Hedw.) B.S.G. var. *alascanum* (Lesq. et James) Limpr. and *Aulacomnium turgidum* (Wahlenb.) Schwaegr. They are specific to all the tundra and bog communities, often being predominant. *Sphagnum* mosses (about 10 % of the biomass), *Drepanocladus* and *Calliergon* (up to 20 % of the moss biomass) are variably present in the bogs. There is considerable admixture of *Rhacomitrium lanuginosum* (Hedw.) Brid. and *Rhytidium rugosum* (Hedw.) Kindb. (10–15 % of the total mass of mosses) in the tundra.

The dead phytomass of mosses constitutes the main part of tundra litter, varying from 50–100 g m^{-2} (on spotted tundra between rivers) to 1 000–1 300 g m^{-2} (on bogs). The value for the spotted tundra on terraces and slopes and for the *Dryas* tundra is 500–600 g m^{-2}. Some other components – dead stems of shrubs, sedge and cotton grass (altogether up to 15 %) – are also found in the litter.

Lichens play a secondary role in the plant cover of the tundras and bogs of the station. They are found in considerable amount only on the elevations of the micro- and nano-relief and on the drained slopes of the terraces. The most common species are: *Cetraria cucullata* (Bell.) Ach., *C. nivalis* (L.) Ach., *Cladonia silvatica* (L.) Rab., *C. amaurocraea* (Flk.) Schaer., *C. mitis* (Sandst.) Hale & W. Culb., *Cetraria islandica* (L.) Ach. and

---

[*] = *Carex aquatilis* L. ssp. *stans* (Drej.) Hultén (editors' remark).
[**] = *Carex bigelowii* Torr ssp. *arctosibirica* (Yurtsev) Löve & Löve (editors' remark).

Table 4. Seasonal changes in plant biomass (g m^{-2}) at Agapa in 1970. Plant community type: Spotty sedge-shrub-dwarf shrub-moss tundra. Belowground parts were not measured.

Date	Aboveground plant parts				
	Live green Cur. yr.	Live nongreen Cur. yr.	Live nongreen Ear. yr.	Stand. dead Ear. yr.	Litter
Salix pulchra					
16.7	1.78	0.022	32.81	n.d.	n.d.
21.7	4.15	0.71	n.d.	n.d.	n.d.
26.7	7.02	0.73	n.d.	n.d.	n.d.
31.7	8.65	1.26	n.d.	n.d.	n.d.
6.8	9.15	1.56	n.d.	n.d.	n.d.
16.8	11.50	1.78	n.d.	n.d.	n.d.
21.8	7.91	1.91	33.88	n.d.	n.d.
per season	11.50	1.91	1.07	0.54	11.69

Aboveground net accumulation: 2.44 g m^{-2}

Salix glauca					
16.7	3.20	0.54	38.40	n.d.	n.d.
21.7	3.51	0.82	n.d.	n.d.	n.d.
26.7	5.26	0.87	n.d.	n.d.	n.d.
31.7	10.09	1.19	n.d.	n.d.	n.d.
6.8	10.82	1.47	n.d.	n.d.	n.d.
16.8	11.29	2.34	n.d.	n.d.	n.d.
21.8	10.96	2.34	40.19	n.d.	n.d.
per season	11.29	2.34	1.79	0.82	12.11

Aboveground net accumulation: 3.31 g m^{-2}

Betula nana					
16.7	10.09	n.d.	n.d.	n.d.	n.d.
21.7	14.81	0.08	128.68	n.d.	n.d.
26.7	19.25	0.25	n.d.	n.d.	n.d.
31.7	27.20	1.30	n.d.	n.d.	n.d.
6.8	33.15	1.38	n.d.	n.d.	n.d.
16.8	34.25	2.74	n.d.	n.d.	n.d.
21.8	31.15	2.71	132.84	n.d.	n.d.
per season	34.25	2.74	4.16	0.88	35.13

Aboveground net accumulation: 6.02 g m^{-2}

n.d. = not determined

Table 5. Mineral composition (mean % dw) of various plant parts at Agapa

Plants/Elements	N	P	S	K	Na	Ca	Mg	Al	Fe	Mn	Si	Sum without	Sum with N
Betula nana													
leaves	1.95	0.20	0.04	0.60	0.03	0.50	0.40	0.06	0.02	0.07	0.11	2.03	3.98
shoots	1.32	0.10	0.05	0.36	0.04	0.50	0.10	0.12	0.04	0.01	0.08	1.39	2.71
twigs	0.30	0.06	0.02	0.20	0.01	0.30	0.07	0.09	0.03	0.01	0.06	0.85	1.15
Salix glauca													
leaves	1.40	0.13	0.13	0.96	0.04	1.10	0.60	0.20	0.03	0.08	0.10	3.37	4.77
shoots	1.14	0.16	0.04	0.64	0.03	0.40	0.20	0.09	0.04	0.03	0.14	1.76	2.90
twigs	0.20	0.08	0.03	0.30	0.03	0.20	0.13	0.09	0.03	0.02	0.08	0.99	1.19
Salix pulchra													
leaves	1.30	0.12	0.20	0.80	0.02	0.60	0.40	0.03	0.02	0.09	0.06	2.34	3.64
shoots	1.00	0.12	0.09	0.60	0.01	0.60	0.20	0.05	0.02	0.04	0.07	1.80	2.80
twigs	0.20	0.04	0.05	0.30	0.02	0.60	0.12	0.02	0.02	0.03	0.04	1.24	1.44
Dwarf shrubs	0.70	0.08	0.08	0.40	0.04	0.50	0.20	0.20	0.07	0.06	0.03	1.93	2.63
Sedges	0.95	0.20	0.09	1.40	0.06	0.20	0.16	0.07	0.02	0.06	0.60	2.86	3.71
Forbes	0.98	0.20	0.25	1.30	0.20	0.80	0.30	0.04	0.02	0.02	0.35	3.48	4.46
Mosses	0.60	0.07	0.30	0.30	0.06	1.00	0.40	0.20	0.50	0.03	0.90	3.76	4.36
Lichens	0.22	0.05	0.25	0.25	0.05	0.20	0.06	0.30	0.01	0.01	0.20	1.37	1.59
Roots	1.00	0.08	0.20	0.10	0.04	0.80	0.30	0.70	1.20	0.07	0.70	4.23	5.23

Dactylina arctica (Hook.) Nyl. The spots of bare soil are occupied by *Toninia syncomista* (Flk.), *Lecanora epibryon* Ach., *Psoroma hypnorum* (Vahl.) S. Gray and some others.

True tundra communities are characterized by the largest biomass of lichens: 57 g m^{-2} for the spotted tundra on the terraces, 48 g m^{-2} for the spotted tundra on the slopes and 41 g m^{-2} for the soddy tundra. The values for the bog and tundra-boggy complex are 8 g m^{-2} and 47 g m^{-2} respectively. Thus lichens account for up to 20 % of the aboveground plant biomass of the tundras and 7 % of that of the bogs.

Mineral composition of plants

The ash content of plant roots of all tundra types is much higher (1.5–2 times) than that of aboveground parts. The following elements predominate in roots: nitrogen, calcium, aluminium, silicon and sometimes iron; nitrogen, potassium and calcium predominate in aboveground parts (Table 5).

The ash composition of plants varies considerably in different tundra types depending on ecological conditions. As a rule the total mineral content increases from accumulative landscape (terraces) to eluvial (watershed), being best illustrated in the aboveground parts of plants. This is obviously due to slighter acidity and gleyification of the watershed tundra gleyish soils as compared with the tundra gley and peaty gley soils of the terraces, and to more severe microclimatic conditions.

HERBIVORES

Lemmings play an important role in the biological cycle of substances. In three summer months about 280 kg ha^{-1} of excrement is deposited on the tundra soil surface for a lemming biomass of 3.8 kg ha^{-1} (a year of high density). This quantity of excrement contains about 15 kg ha^{-1} of ash elements. The total amount of organic substance consumed by the lemmings during this period amounts to 650 kg, of which ash elements account for 30 kg. The elemental composition of three different herbivore species is given in Table 6.

Table 6. **Important elements (mg 100 g^{-1} fw) of three herbivore species.**

Species	Ca	Mg	K	Na	P	S	Ash (% of fw)
Lemmus obensis Brants	126	115	285	138	513	30	3.0
Lagopus lagopus (L.)	544	146	330	120	466	40	3.1
Clangula hyemalis L.	434	55	315	126	304	32	4.0

153

For comparison the soils of most productive tundras of the second terrace receive about 30 kg ha^{-1} of ash elements with plant litter fall.

The data on the number and biomass of animals in the Western Taimyr were obtained by the staff of the Institute of Agriculture of the Extreme North (5). In the Western and Central Taimyr the biomass of wild reindeer *(Rangifer tarandus* (L.)) is 0.81 kg ha^{-1} with a density of 9 individuals per 1000 ha. In the region adjoining the station the number rises to 135 individuals per 1000 ha (12.1 kg ha^{-1}) at the end of July. The average annual production is 7 %.

The number of arctic fox (*Alopex lagopus* (L.) varies considerably depending on the number of lemmings, but averages 1.7–1.8 individuals per 1000 ha (0.004 kg ha^{-1}).

The number of birds fluctuates fairly considerably: willow ptarmigan (*Lagopus lagopus* (L.)) from 60–70 to 120–140 birds per 1000 ha, ptarmigan (*Lagopus mutus* (Montin)) from 10–20 to 30–40. The total number of waterfowl (Anseriformes, Gaviiformes) amounts to 80–100 birds per 1000 ha.

DECOMPOSITION AND SOIL PROCESSES

The investigation of soil microflora was conducted on a limited scale (Table 7). Out of all tundra types, the soils of depressions are the richest in mesophilic and psychrophilic bacteria. The higher proportion of psychrophiles compared with mesophiles is typical of these soils. A shallow thaw layer in depressions and permanent wetness are favourable factors for the selection of psychrophilic forms of bacteria. On the surface crust of the spot soils a considerable amount of mesophiles and psychrophiles is also found.

Collembola predominate among the different groups of soil invertebrates. The largest numbers of soil invertebrates are observed in the tundra boggy soils of the accumulative landscape of terraces (Table 8).

The annual plant litter decomposition (leaves of *Betula nana*, willow, sedge) varies between 7.4 and 29.8 %, while cellulose decomposes by 2–7 % (Table 9). During the same period excrement from lemmings loses 24 % in weight, and that from reindeer 89 %. Decomposition is most intensive on the soil surface of the terraces as a result of the larger number of invertebrates and greater moisture. The latter condition also favours leaching of water-soluble substances.

The determination of the degree of humification (6) showed that the greatest humification is in the soils of the spots of watershed tundra humus gleyish soils. The general level of humification of plant residues in the station soils is extremely low. Nonspecific substances amount to 40–60 % of the composition of soil organic substance.

NUTRIENTS

According to the scale applying to soddy-podzolic soils, the tundra and boggy soils of the station are sufficient in potassium (5 to 10 mg K_2O 100 g^{-1} of soil). The content

154

Table 7. Numbers of microorganisms ($\times 10^{10}$ m^{-2}) at peak of season in various subsites at Agapa. The method used was that of Zvyagintsev (7) for determination of microorganisms in soil on an area basis.

Subsite	Soil type	Subsite	Depth (cm)	Psychro-philes	Meso-philes	Myo-bacterium spp.
Watershed spotted tundra	Tundra weakly gleyed	Bare spot	0–20	7.0	16.5	0.9
			20–45	0.6	0.3	0.4
		Trough	0–20	39.3	28.3	0.1
Watershed hummock tundra with spots	Tundra gley	Bare spot	0–1	1.2	1.5	0.2
		Hummock	0–10	12.3	11.2	0.1
			10–20	1.0	0.2	0.2
Stream terrace	Tundra gley	Bare spot	0–6	1.1	5.5	5.9
			6–25	8.5	5.6	6.7
Polygonal tundra		Rim	0–20	n.d.	n.d.	35.8
Stream terrace	Bog-tundra gley	Trough	0–5	6.0	3.0	0.2
			5–15	22.5	32.5	0.1
Hummock bogged		Hummock	0–20	16.1	11.3	0.2
Floodplain terrace	Bog (peaty-gley)	Polygon	0–10	1.2	0.7	0.1
Polygonal bog			12–27	0.2	0.6	0.0

n.d. = not determined

Table 8. Numbers of invertebrates m^{-2} in the upper soil horizon of various types of tundra at Agapa

	Subsites	Annelida Lumbricidae	Annelida Enchytraeidae	Collembola	Insecta Diptera (larvae)	Insecta Colleoptera (larvae)	Arthropoda Araneida	Mollusca Gastropoda
Spotted *Dryas* sedge-moss tundra of watershed	Spot of bare soil	17	1 220	4 100	5	5	6	0
	Under vegetation cover	10	700	10 000	3	3	6	0
Shrub-sedge-moss tundra of stream terraces	Stream terrace II	15	1 000	10 200	10	6	30	0
	Stream terrace I	20	1 500	17 000	23	16	2	0
Polygonal bog of high floodplain	Ridge	5	156	10 200	18	7	15	0
	Polygon	0	300	5 500	11	6	12	2
Willow-shrubs		15	3 500	25 000	rare	rare	0	0

Table 9. Rates of decomposition (% weight loss in first year) of leaf litter and Borregaard cellulose on the surface of sites at Agapa.

	Dryas-moss tundra Bare spot	*Dryas*-moss tundra Moss	Shrub-sedge-moss tundra Sedge-moss in depression	Shrub-sedge-moss tundra *Hypnum* cover of hummocks
Betula nana	14.8	17.2	29.8	27.2
Salix pulchra	20.4	25.8	28.0	22.4
Carex ensifolia	7.4	20.0	27.4	24.6
Cellulose				
Surface	3.4	2.0	4.5	2.5
5 cm depth	n.d.	7.6	n.d.	5.9

n.d. = not determined

of readily soluble phosphates in the soils is rather low (5 mg P_2O_5 100 g^{-1} of soil). Considerably larger amounts of phosphorus are observed in the upper soil horizons of polar foxholes (10–20 mg 100 g^{-1}). The high content of phosphorus in the soil as well as the more favourable heat regime are probably responsible for the good development of graminoids and herbs at polar foxholes. The same can be applied to bird feeding sites.

About 40–50 kg ha^{-1} nitrogen accumulated in the aboveground phytomass of most typical shrub-cotton grass-moss spotted tundras of terraces. An annual uptake of nitrogen by plants (aboveground parts) accounts for 15 kg ha^{-1}, more than a half of this quantity is taken up by sedges and mosses. Annual uptake of ash elements and nitrogen by plants fluctuates from 59–167 kg ha^{-1}. A considerable part of elements (80–90 %) returns with annual litter-fall into the soil and to the soil surface. Every year accumulation of elements in different tundras make up 12–25 kg ha^{-1} (nitrogen 2–5), i.e. approximately 1/30–1/40 part from the total element reserve in the phytosenoses (Table 10).

REFERENCES

1. Alisov, B.P. 1956. Climate of the USSR. Moscow: Moscow University.
2. Arefieva, V.A. 1964. Waters. – In: Middle Siberia, pp. 132–188. Moscow: Nauka Publishing House.
3. Reference on the Climate of the USSR. 1967, 1969. Vol. 21, Nos. 1–4. Leningrad: Gydrometeoizdat Publishing House.
4. Sheveleva, N.S. & Khimichevskaya, L.S. 1967. Geocryological Conditions of the Northern Part of the Inisei River. Moscow: Nauka Publishing House.
5. Jakushkin, G.D., Pavlov, B.M., Zyrjanov, V.A., Kuksov, V.A. 1969. On biological productivity of the dominant species of hunting animals in the tundra region of Taimyr. – In: Gavrin, V.F. (ed.) Natural Productivity of Hunting Lands of the USSR. 2:7–10. Kirov.
6. Springer, U. 1943. Beitrag zur Fraktionierung der echten Humusstoffe. – Bodenk. Pflanzenernährung 32: 129–146.
7. Zvyagintsev, D.G. 1973. Relationship between Microorganisms and Solid Surfaces. Moscow: Moscow University.

Table 10. Reserves and cycling of ash elements and nitrogen (kg ha^{-1}) at Agapa

Tundra type	Annual primary production			Annual litter			Net productivity			Reserves in plant biomass		
	1	2	Sum	1	2	Sum	1	2	Sum	1	2	Sum
Dryas-moss, watershed	9.6	49.2	58.8	7.7	38.5	46.2	1.9	10.7	12.6	47.4	239.5	341.0
Shrub-sedge-moss, stream terrace	24.5	66.6	91.1	21.4	57.3	78.7	3.1	9.3	12.4	97.5	356.7	454.2
Shrub-sedge-cotton grass-moss, stream terrace	53.2	113.7	166.9	46.5	95.3	141.8	6.7	18.4	25.1	222.6	594.0	816.6

1 aboveground parts
2 belowground parts

Rosswall, T. & Heal, O.W. (eds.) 1975.
Structure and Function of Tundra Ecosystems.
Ecol. Bull. (Stockholm) 20: 159–181.

TAREYA, USSR

Yu.J. CHERNOV, E.V. DOROGOSTAISKAYA, T.V. GERASIMENKO,
I.V. IGNATENKO, N.V. MATVEYEVA, O.M. PARINKINA, T.G. POLOZOVA,
E.N. ROMANOVA, V.F. SCHAMURIN, N.V. SMIRNOVA, I.V. STEPANOVA,
B.A. TOMILIN, A.A. VINOKUROV and O.V. ZALENSKY

The intensive study site is on the east bank of the Pyasina river in Western Taimyr, near the mouth of its tributary, the Tareya river.

ENVIRONMENTAL CONDITIONS

Climate

The climate of the region is continental. Negative temperatures predominate in the annual cycle. The mean annual temperature is about $-14°C$, and the mean July and January temperatures are $10°C$ and $-32°C$ respectively (Table 1).

The Pyasina river is under ice for 8.5 months of the year, from October to the end of June. The summer temperature of the river water is about $10-15°C$. The duration of snow cover is 9 months – from the second half of September until the second half of June. Snow cover varies with relief, usually being about 40–60 cm in the level areas, 6–7 m in the creek valleys, while the most convex areas are snowless. Snow density ranges from 20 to 37 g cm^{-3}. Air humidity is about 80 %. Cloud cover is typical of this region, the number of clear days in summer being 4–5 per month. South-easterly and easterly winds prevail in winter and westerly and north-westerly winds in summer.

Six types of microclimate can be distinguished in the Tareya station territory (Table 3). The microclimate of the mossy *Dryas*-sedge hummocky tundra on the open flat surface was chosen for comparison with other subsites. The microclimate of the mossy *Dryas*-sedge spotted tundra is most similar to that of the mossy *Dryas*-sedge hummocky tundra. There are pronounced nanoclimatic differences within two sites due to the variety of nanorelief (Table 2). The microclimate of the swampy depressions is colder than that of the two above sites. Western and eastern slopes prevail in the study area because the creek valleys have meridional orientation; they receive more solar radiation than the

Table 1. Monthly means of temperature and precipitation at Tareya (mean values for 1962–1971)

	J	F	M	A	M	J	J	A	S	O	N	D	Year
Temperature (°C)	-32.2	-31.3	-28.8	-20.2	-11.4	0.2	9.8	7.4	0.7	-11.9	-23.7	-27.2	-14.1
Precipitation (mm)	25	25	17	19	15	20	39	33	30	21	25	26	295

Table 2. Soil temperature in different parts of medallion (spotted tundra) during one typical day in July:
1. surface; 2. 5 cm depth; 3. 20 cm depth.

Elements of nanocomplex		Time (hrs)											
		9	11	13	15	17	19	21	23	1	3	5	7
Raised border	1	21.3	23.0	21.5	20.2	17.0	13.5	9.4	5.5	3.7	5.7	9.9	13.4
	2	4.9	5.4	6.2	6.5	6.7	6.5	6.1	5.8	5.2	4.9	4.6	4.6
	3	3.5	3.5	3.6	3.8	4.0	4.2	4.2	4.2	4.1	4.0	3.9	3.7
Spot	1	14.9	17.0	18.4	16.3	13.2	10.5	7.7	5.1	4.0	4.7	6.6	10.0
	2	9.3	11.3	12.6	13.2	12.4	10.5	9.1	7.5	5.8	5.2	5.5	6.2
	3	4.3	4.6	5.2	5.7	6.2	6.3	6.1	5.9	5.3	4.8	4.4	4.2
Difference between	1	6.4	6.0	3.1	3.9	3.8	3.0	1.4	0.4	-0.3	1.0	3.3	3.4
raised border and	2	-4.4	-5.9	-6.4	-6.7	-5.7	-5.0	-3.0	-1.7	-0.6	-0.3	-0.9	-1.6
spot	3	-0.8	-0.9	-1.6	-1.9	-2.2	-2.1	-1.9	-1.7	-1.2	-0.8	-0.5	-0.5

Table 3. Microclimatic differences between sites at the Tareya station

Sites	S/S_p	V/V_p	t^{150}	t^0	t^{-5}	t^{-20}
Mossy *Dryas*-sedge spotted tundra on flat open surface	1.0	1.1	0	0	0	0
Mossy *Dryas*-sedge hummocky tundra	1.0	1.0	0	0	0	0
Swampy depressions occupied by polygonal bogs	1.0	0.9	d −1.0 n −0.5	−3 − −4 −1 − −2	−2 − −1 −2 − −1	−2 − −4 −2 − −4
Slopes of brook valleys facing west and east	1.4	0.7	d +0.5 n −1.0	+4 − +5 −2	+2 − +4 +1 − +2	+1 − +2 +1 − +2
Slopes of river valley	1.5	0.6− 0.8	d −1.0 n +1.0	+7 − +9 −1	+5 − +7 +3 − +5	+2 − −4 +2 − +4
Bottoms of brook valleys	0.9	0.6	d −1.5 n −2.0	−5 − −6 −2 − −3	−2 − −4 −2 − −3	−2 − −4 −2 − −4

S/S_p — solar radiation at the site (S) as a fraction of that in an adjacent level open area (Sp)

V/V_p — wind velocity at the site (V) as a fraction of that in an adjacent level open area (Vp)

$t^{150}, t^0, t^{-5}, t^{-20}$ are the differences in temperature between the site and the mossy *Dryas*-sedge spotted tundra on flat open surface, at 150, 0, −5 and −20 cm respectively.

d — day
n — night

Table 4. Physicochemical characteristics of soils of the Tareya station

Soil type	Sample depth cm	Fraction (% of dw) <0.001 mm	Fraction (% of dw) <0.01 mm	pH in KCl	Hydrolytic acidity (meq 100 g^{-1})	Exchangeable bases (meq 100 g^{-1}) Ca^{++}	Mg^{++}	Saturation degree (%)	Humus after Tjurin (%)	Nitrogen total (%)	Mobile forms (mg 100 g^{-1}) after Kyrsanov K_2O	P_2O_5	after Tamm Fe_2O_3	Al_2O_3	SiO_2
Dryas-sedge moss hummocky tundra															
Tundra-humus-gley soil (level surface)	0–5	–	–	4.2	–	–	–	–	88.2	–	131.3	34.8	–	–	–
	5–15	14.1	30.4	5.3	10.9	24.4	9.2	76	13.1	0.30	13.2	2.6	1 250	520	430
	16–25	17.7	28.7	5.1	2.8	10.3	7.4	86	2.1	0.09	18.2	3.6	700	490	360
	26–35	20.2	26.4	5.3	2.1	10.1	7.6	90	1.1	0.04	18.0	7.6	690	470	310
	38–50	19.5	22.7	6.0	1.4	11.3	6.5	93	2.3	–	14.4	10.3	570	420	280
	50–60	23.3	26.9	7.4	0.0	18.8	6.7	100	2.0	–	17.6	8.8	530	350	290
	70–80	22.9	34.8	7.8	0.0	20.3	7.0	100	0.8	–	15.0		480	270	190
Tundra-humus-gley soil (hummock)	0–5	–	–	4.1	–	36.4	14.1	–	96.0	–	147.4	42.0	–	–	–
	6–13	–	–	5.2	11.8	22.6	9.6	73	12.7	0.37	15.6	1.5	1 840	780	450
	13–22	–	–	5.5	3.0	12.1	7.6	88	2.4	0.12	17.6	3.5	750	560	370
	25–35	–	–	5.8	2.2	10.2	7.6	89	1.2	–	18.0	7.5	600	450	350
	37–49	–	–	6.2	0.6	16.7	6.9	97	2.5	–	17.0		570	390	290
Tundra-gley soil (trough)	0–4	–	–	4.3	–	–	–	–	87.6	–	115.0	36.0	–	–	–
	4–8	–	–	5.0	4.2	9.4	5.5	78	1.9	0.06	11.8	6.1	530	340	270
	8–17	–	–	4.8	3.6	9.1	6.5	81	1.5	–	8.6	6.6	530	370	290
	20–30	–	–	5.3	1.9	10.2	6.9	90	3.0	–	14.1	10.1	610	430	320
	40–50	–	–	6.2	0.9	11.6	7.7	95	2.4	–	16.6	5.4	590	460	320
	55–65	–	–	6.9	0.4	12.3	7.2	98	1.0	–	16.6	4.5	580	320	270
Dryas-sedge moss spotted tundra															
Tundra humus-gley soil of raised border	0–3	–	–	4.4	–	–	–	–	64.2	–	230.0	31.5	–	–	–
	3–8	17.9	30.2	4.9	7.3	16.5	12.3	80	5.8	0.24	21.6	2.6	800	490	390
	8–18	28.5	34.6	4.5	3.6	16.9	11.6	89	2.4	0.14	17.9	1.3	810	460	280
	22–29	16.1	27.1	4.4	2.7	14.6	9.9	90	1.9	0.12	12.6	3.0	960	470	360
	30–40	20.0	35.5	4.4	4.9	12.6	8.6	81	3.2	–	23.7	2.0	1 030	510	430
	45–53	28.7	37.4	4.9	3.3	13.9	9.3	88	2.8	–	20.8	2.0	1 020	490	350
Tundra residual-gley soil of spot	0–5	29.8	35.2	6.3	1.6	14.1	13.3	94	2.0	0.18	22.0	2.0	950	540	420
	5–15	31.0	38.5	6.0	2.1	12.6	11.1	92	1.7	0.13	20.7	3.0	1 090	630	380
	20–30	25.1	32.0	5.8	2.6	11.9	10.1	90	1.5	–	14.2	3.4	770	510	290
	40–50	22.2	28.6	5.6	2.6	10.4	7.7	87	3.5	–	13.1	1.9	920	460	310
	55–65	25.6	36.0	5.9	2.5	6.9	5.0	83	4.7	–	16.3	1.6	880	460	280

Soil / depth (cm)		pH				%							
Bog-tundra peaty-humus-gley soil of trough													
0–5	–	5.0	–	45.9	20.4	–	72.3	–	138.2	13.5	–	–	–
5–13	–	5.8	16.7	28.4	14.2	72	50.9	0.66	48.5	2.7	570	270	70
13–19	–	5.2	15.8	20.1	10.1	66	40.2	–	36.0	2.7	750	360	110
19–33	–	5.8	4.9	18.6	8.8	85	13.8	0.28	10.2	5.1	1 230	530	230
33–42	–	5.9	5.1	19.7	11.2	86	10.8	–	12.0	3.1	1 110	500	230
Polygonal bog													
Bog-tundra peaty-gley soil of raised borders													
0–3	–	4.6	–	32.4	11.5	–	78.3	–	462.4	41.3	–	–	–
3–15	–	5.5	24.3	12.5	3.6	64	48.4	1.03	186.9	2.5	2 500	950	480
15–23	–	6.8	0.5	10.8	5.4	97	2.9	0.06	7.0	5.0	1 340	370	260
23–35	–	7.0	0.6	10.8	5.4	97	1.3	0.04	8.0	6.1	950	350	230
40–50	–	7.4	0.1	13.7	6.7	100	0.7	–	7.3	6.1	670	280	180
Boggy permafrozen peaty-gley soil of troughs													
0–3	–	5.8	–	17.8	8.5	–	76.9	–	195.0	34.2	–	–	–
3–11	–	4.4	25.3	17.2	8.6	51	25.0	0.96	91.3	traces	–	–	–
11–26	–	4.4	38.2	14.4	8.9	40	52.3	0.67	13.8	20.8	–	–	–
26–38	–	4.1	11.2			68	4.3	0.09	5.2	2.6	–	–	–
Boggy permafrozen peaty-gley soil of polygon centres													
1–9	–	4.3	18.4	10.1	10.7	53	39.6	0.50	19.9	2.6	1 580	960	800
9–24	–	4.2	31.5	14.2	5.7	39	31.7	0.34	4.6	5.1	1 080	1 040	490
24–31	–	4.3	35.5	15.9	6.5	39	36.9	0.52	4.7	traces	1 100	920	420
31–41	–	3.9	29.0	13.9	9.0	44	23.6	–	3.7	traces	1 260	570	190
45–55	–	4.4	14.7	16.7	8.6	63	6.8	–	6.3	2.8	830	360	190

level areas: wind velocity is lower, and in spite of snow accumulation the thermal conditions are better here than in the open tundra. The microclimate of the southern slopes is the most favourable of all the above sites. The largest insolation occurs here as also the lowest velocities of northerly winds.

Soils

The study area is a plain where rolling hills alternate with lake depressions. Three geomorphological levels can be distinguished in the station territory. The upper one (40–50 m) is composed of dark marine deposits (clays and loams) of Sanchug and Kargin transgressions of the Polar Basin. The middle level (20–25 m) is the ancient river terrace; here marine clays and loams are covered by alluvial sandy-loams. The lower level (8–10 m), composed of modern alluvial and peat deposits, is the flood river terrace.

Permafrost underlies the entire area, the depth of active layer being 40–50 cm in automorphic loam soils, 20–45 cm in peat swampy soils, 60–75 cm in sandy and sandy-loam soils. Constant overwatering of soils and gley processes are due to permafrost.

A pronounced complexity is characteristic of the soil cover. The mosaic pattern is an expression of strong frost action in the ground. A trench method was therefore used to study the soils; trenches of 5–15 m were laid across the main elements of soil complexes. In the automorphic landscapes the complexity occurs in all varieties of tundra-gley and swampy-tundra soils. These soils are characterized by a shallow active layer above the permafrost, by a high content of exchangeable bases, by active potassium and oxalate-soluble forms of R_2O_3, by a low or moderately acid reaction, by a relatively low hydrolytic acidity and by a high humus content in all active soil horizons (Table 4).

In the semihydromorphic and hydromorphic conditions, the complex consists of the swampy-tundra and frozen-swampy types of soil, which differ in the moisture regime and the thickness of turf horizons. In chemical composition these soils have much in common: moderately or strongly acid reaction, considerable hydrolytic acidity, relative paucity of exchangeable bases and active forms of K_2O and P_2O_5 in peat horizons. The swampy soils differ from the swampy-tundra ones in a somewhat higher content of oxalate-soluble R_2O_3 and of exchangeable bases (Table 4).

Tundra-soddy soils under the *Dryas*-grass-herbaceous communities are characterized by the sod-forming process resulting in the formation of a humus-accumulation horizon and in a high content of exchangeable bases, humus, nitrogen and mineral nutrients.

PRIMARY PRODUCTION

Vegetation communities

The vascular flora consists of 240 species. More than half is accounted for by arctic (37.1 %) and arcto-alpine (28.5 %) species. There are 21.2 % hypoarctic and 10.2 % boreal and a very few high arctic (2.9 %) species in the flora of the region. Most boreal and hypoarctic species are found in the Pyasina valley along which they have migrated to the north. The cryptogam flora comprises 117 lichens, 141 higher fungi, 175 mosses and 46 liverworts.

The tundra communities are characterized by a rich floristic composition. Thus, in a single definite community 100–140 species, including flowering plants, mosses and lichens can be found. Lichen species are most numerous (40–50), followed by angiosperms (35–40) and last the leafy mosses and liverworts (30–40).

On the basis of phytocoenotic significance and with respect to measured cover and abundance, the mosses occupy first place; they dominate in biomass and cover the soil to 80–90 %. The lichens have a minimal coverage, but are characterized by a high frequency. Angiosperms occupy an intermediate position, with a projected cover in the aboveground layer not exceeding 30–40 %; a large part of the roots and rhizomes form a dense, cohesive network in the moss turf.

Intensive investigations were carried out in five different habitats:

Site 1. Mossy *Dryas*-sedge spotted tundra in the flat part of the high east bank of the Pyasina river.

The community contains 171 species, including 55 phanerogams, 56 lichens, 40 mosses and 10 liverworts. The dominant phanerogams are *Carex ensifolia* (Turcz. ex Gorodk.) V. Krecz. ssp. *arctisibirica* Jurtz. ☆ (10 % cover), *Dryas punctata* Juz. (10 %); important species are *Cassiope tetragona* (L.) D. Don., *Salix arctica* Pall., *S. polaris* Wahlenb., *Arctagrostis latifolia* (R. Br.) Griseb., *Luzula nivalis* (Laest.) Beurl., *Polygonum viviparum* L., *Parrya nudicaulis* (L.) Regel. Mosses are very abundant: *Hylocomium splendens* (Hedw.) B.S.G. var. *alaskanum* (Lesq. et James) Limpr. (25 %), *Tomenthypnum nitens* (Hedw.) Loeske (20 %), *Aulacomnium turgidum* (Wahlenb.) Schwaegr. (10 %), with a few *Phytidium rugosum* (Hedw.) Kindb., *Rhacomitrium lanuginosum* (Hedw.) Brid. and *Ditrichum flexicaule* (Schleich.) Hampe. The lichens are not abundant, being spread throughout the stand with high frequency (*Thamnolia vermicularis* (Sw.) Ach. ex Schaer., *Dactylina arctica* (Hook.) Nyl., *Cladonia mitis* Sandst., *C. rangiferina* (L.) Web., *C. amaurocraea* (Flk.) Schaer., *Cetraria cucullata* (Bell.) Ach., *Peltigera aphthosa* (L.) Willd., *Nephroma expallidum* (Nyl.) Nyl., *Psoroma hypnorum* (Vahl) Gray). Three microstands of vegetation correspond to three elements of nanorelief: spots of bare ground (30 %), hummocks around these spots (50 %) and troughs along the frosty cracks (20 %). Hummocks and troughs are completely covered by vegetation and spots form a series ranging from bare spots to almost overgrown ones. These are 32 spots per 100 m^2. Differences in vegetation between hummocks and troughs are more quantitative than qualitative: the same species occur with varying cover. A number of characteristic species are

---

☆ = *Carex bigelowii* Torr. ssp. *arctosibirica* (Yurtsev) Love & Love (editors' remark).

typical of spots: *Cerastium bialynickii* A. Tolm, *Juncus biglumis* L., *Sagina intermedia* Fenze, *Toninia syncomista* (Flk.) Th. Fr., *Lecanora epibryon* Ach., *L. verrucosa* Ach., *Rinodina roscida* (Smrft.) Arn., *Solorina spongiosa* (Sm.) Anzi, *Peltolepis grandis* (Sauter) K. Müll. The depth of the snow cover is 20 cm and the active soil layer is 65–70 cm.

Site 2. Mossy *Dryas*-sedge hummock tundra about 2 km distant from the river in the flat plain between the brooks.

This stand is floristically very close to the above-mentioned spotted tundra but is somewhat poorer with 128 species, including 39 phanerogams, 43 lichens, 40 mosses and 6 liverworts. The dominant phanerogams are *Dryas punctata* (10 %), and *Carex ensifolia* ssp. *arctisibirica* (15 %), but *Cassiope tetragona* and *Salix reptans* Rupr. are also abundant, with a few *Eriophorum angustifolium* Honck., *Ramischia obtusata* (Turcz.) Freyn ☆, *Polygonum viviparum*, *Arctagrostis latifolia* and *Salix polaris*. The moss layer is dominated by *Hylocomium splendens* var. *alaskanum* (25 %), *Aulacomnium turgidum* (20 %), *Tomenthypnum nitens* (20 %), *Ptilidium ciliare* (L.) Hampe. (20 %), and less abundant *Rhacomitrium lanuginosum* and *Ditrichum flexicaule*. The depth of the moss layer varies from 5 to 10 cm. Lichen species are distributed in small amounts throughout the stand; *Dactylina arctica*, *Peltigera aphthosa* (L.) Willd., *Cladonia elongata* (Jacq.) Hoffm., *C. amaurocraea*, *Thamnolia vermicularis*, *Cetraria laevigata* Rassad., *C. cucullata*, *Psoroma hypnorum*. The study area is covered by low isodiametric hummocks of 50 to 80 cm in diameter and a relative height of 10 to 20 cm. The hummocks are separated by a network of troughs that are 20–30 cm wide. A total of about 70 % of the surface consists of hummocks. The depth of snow cover is 40 cm, and the active soil layer is 50–60 cm.

Site 3. Polygonal mire in the lake depression. The surface is broken up into regular polygons with 7–10 m diameter.

The polygons are surrounded by ridges which are divided by ditches located along the frost cracks. The polygons and ditches are waterlogged throughout the summer and the ridges are dry. The vegetation in the polygons is very homogeneous and floristically poor. The polygons contain in decreasing order of occurrence *Carex stans* Drej. ☆☆, *C. chordorrhiza* Ehrh, *Eriophorum medium* Ands., *Hierochloe pauciflora* R. Br. and *Salix reptans*. Mosses are very abundant and cover the ground completely, the following species being common: *Drepanocladus revolvens* (Turn.) Warnst. and *Meesia triquetra* (Hook. et Tayl) Ångstr. Lichens are absent. The vegetation in ditches is similar to that on polygons but it is floristically poorer and the plant cover is reduced. The vegetation of ridges is similar to tundra vegetation and is dominated by *Dryas punctata*, *Carex stans*, *Salix reptans*, *Hylocomium splendens* var. *alaskanum*, *Aulacomnium turgidum* and *Tomenthypnum nitens*. The depth of snow cover is 60 cm and the active soil layer 50 cm.

☆ = *Orthilia (Pyrola) secunda* (L.) House ssp. *obtusata* (Turcz.) Hultén (editors' remark).
☆☆ = *Carex aquatilis* L. ssp. *stans* (Drej.) Hultén (editors' remark).

Site 4. Wet polygonal tundra in the upper reaches of a stream.

The frost cracks cut the surface into isodiametric polygons (d = 10 m). Some of these have a concave surface and are very wet during the summer period and are covered by bog vegetation. The other polygons are flat-convex without any ridges and are similar to typical tundra vegetation. Troughs form a network of winding waterways leading to a stream. As a whole the site is floristically poor: *Carex stans, Eriophorum angustifolium* and *Drepanocladus revolvens* occur in wet habitats and *Salix reptans, Betula nana* L., *Carex stans, Senecio atropurpureus* (Ledeb.) Fedtsch., *Dryas punctata, Tomenthypnum nitens, Aulacomnium turgidum* and *Polytrichum strictum* Sm. are found in polygons. Lichen species are very few. The active soil layer is 45—50 cm.

Site 5. *Dryas*-grass meadows on the steep bank of the Pyasina river.

The edge of the alluvial terrace slopes towards the river at an angle of 45—60°. The bank has a SSW aspect, so that it is warmer than other habitats and the active soil layer is 60—150 cm here. Thermocarst, water and snow erosion result in deep depressions being scarred in the bank and the snow stays in them until the middle of July. Snow cover is almost absent on the convex parts and 5—6 m in depressions. The microrelief is represented by flat hummocks (d = 40—70 cm) and frost cracks (20—25 cm depth) deepened by lemmings. The communities are floristically very rich. More than half of the vascular flora of the region is found here. The vegetation varies significantly along the complex habitat gradient. The vegetation heterogeneity is maximal; practically every hummock having its own microstands of plants. It is impossible to make clear distinctions between communities. Lichens are very few, the commonly occurring species belonging to the genera *Cetraria, Cornicullaria, Parmelia* and *Pertusaria*. Mosses are also not abundant and their composition is very diverse. The growing season is longer here than in other habitats as snow thaws rather early.

Production processes

The diurnal variations of photosynthesis in plants of the Western Taimyr (4, 6, 7) are similar to those reported for other arctic regions (1, 5). The capacity of the tundra plants for more prolonged photosynthesis during the continuous polar day is a dominating peculiarity in contrast with plants of other zones. The pattern of diurnal variations in photosynthesis is largely dependent on weather conditions and is determined by the dynamics of light and temperature. On foggy days and at total cloudiness the curve for diurnal variations displays a domelike pattern. In variable weather sharp changes in the intensity of photosynthesis occur and the curve for PIPh (potential intensity of photosynthesis) is marked by several peaks corresponding to the most illuminated daytime period. Due to the prevalence of cloudy weather in the Western Taimyr the PIPh in plants is essentially limited by the available light.

Diurnal variations in AIPh (actual intensity of photosynthesis) are also largely dependent upon the diurnal dynamics of light and temperature. On the whole, the daytime maxima of both the PIPh and AIPh occur at the same time. The major portion of the vegetation period in arctic plants coincides with the polar day. Consequently, the diurnal duration of the apparent photosynthesis in arctic plants is longer than that in plants of moderate latitudes (16—21 hrs). Only in the period from 10 p.m. to 3 a.m. is the AIPh close

167

to the compensation point while under bad weather conditions it is replaced by low rate CO_2 evolution. On infrequent clear, warm days a minor decrease in the AIPh (leaf temperature 24–28°C) is observed. This is evidently related to the increased proportion of respiration in the whole gas exchange process occurring with increase in temperature. This conclusion is supported by data on the temperature dependence on the AIPh in some plants, revealing a sharp decrease in the apparent photosynthesis at an ambient temperature above 25°C.

Values of the diurnal productivity of the AIPh vary considerably in different species. The range of these variations for plants of the Western Taimyr is rather wide (14 to 200 mg CO_2 dm^{-2} d^{-1}). In any botanical-geographical zone one can presumably find species characteristic of both low and high diurnal photosynthesis since the values of the index in question recorded for plants of other biomes fall within the indicated range. The mainly cloudy weather during the vegetation period — when the diurnal productivity of photosynthesis is low in arctic plants — results in lower photosynthesis during the polar day compared with plants of other zones. The continuous polar day allows the arctic plants to increase their level of diurnal productivity.

The temperature span within which the PIPh proceeds in arctic plants is rather wide: −3 to 48°C. Photosynthesis is possible at temperatures never normally observed at the plant habitat. The temperature optimum for the PIPh in the majority of the plants studied is 20–30°C.

The PIPh has a high light-dependence and the light-dependence curves, in the majority of the plants studied, reveal no light saturation at the full light daytime illuminance. At the same time, the light dependence curves for certain species level off at the saturation plateau at the illumination intensity of 20 000–50 000 lx. Light saturation for the apparent photosynthesis in the Taimyr plants is at the illumination intensity that constitutes 10–40 % of the full light daytime illuminance. Thus, arctic plants are able to assimilate CO_2 within a wide range of illumination.

The maximum values for PIPh and AIPh observed reveal that among arctic plants, as also among plants of other zones, some species assimilate CO_2 at a high rate provided optimal conditions are available. The maximum values of the AIPh vary from 6 to 30 mg CO_2 g^{-1} h^{-1} for the plants of the Western Taimyr while the PIPh varies from 21 to 193 mg CO_2 g^{-1} h^{-1}. Certain herbaceous perennial dicotyledonous plants assimilate at a high rate while comparatively low rates are characteristic of shrublets and of monocotyledonous plants.

FAUNA

Invertebrates

Most of the biomass of soil invertebrates consists of Lumbricidae (represented only by *Eisenia nordenskiöldi* Eis.), Enchytraeidae (the species composition is not yet determined), Nematoda (about 150 spp.), Collembola (about 70 spp.), Oribatei (about 30 spp.), Acarina and also the larvae of Tipulidae and other Diptera. All invertebrates, except the inhabitants of flooded sites, can be divided into 5 types (cf. Tables 5 and 6).

1. Animal populations of the watershed communities with continuous moss cover

(zonal type). Biomass reaches 7 g m^{-2} (wet weight), and O_2 consumption in July 2 ml m^{-2} h^{-1}. The bryobionts are very abundant, especially Collembola (2 g m^{-2} (ww), 0.8 ml O_2 m^{-2} h^{-1}). The pedobionts, Nematoda and Oligochaeta (Enchytraeidae and *Eisenia nordenskiöldi*), are less abundant here. On the whole, the saprophages are the dominant group. There are very few inhabitants in the grass layer, and pedobionts are almost absent.

2. Animal populations of bare ground spots at the different stages of succession. Pedobionts (Oligochaeta, Tipulidae, Lepyrus) account for the general abundance and the diversity of species. Zoomass reaches 12 g m^{-2} (ww), and O_2 consumption 4 ml m^{-2} h^{-1}. The different stages in plant succession on the spots are reflected in the structure of animal populations, the diversity increasing especially at the intermediate stages.

3. Animal populations of the wet mire. This type is characterized by rich species composition (Enchytraeidae, larvae of Tipulidae) and at the same time by comparatively low total biomass (6 g m^{-2} (ww), 1.5 ml O_2 m^{-2} h^{-1}).

4. Animal populations of xeromorphic dwarf (mainly *Dryas*) communities. This type is very rich in species and especially in typical pedobionts (Nematoda 7 g m^{-2} (ww), 7 000 000 ind m^{-2}, Oligochaeta 25 g m^{-2} (ww)). Several species and groups of species (*Xenylodes armatus* Axels.; Collembola), are abundant. The zoomass varies greatly and times reaches 40 g m^{-2}.

5. Animal populations of grass meadows in the snowy areas. The greatest number of typical pedobionts are found here (Nematoda 15 000 000 ind m^{-2}, Enchytraeidae 12 000, *Eisenia nordenskiöldi* 150, and Collembola, among which *Onychiurus* is dominating, 4 000) and also the maximal abundance and diversity of grass layer inhabitants. Total zoomass reaches 190 g m^{-2} (ww), and O_2 consumption 30 ml m^{-2} h^{-1} in July.

Variation in faunal composition and total quantity of the five types mentioned above reflects the differentiations of microbiotopes and of the successional stages.

MICROORGANISMS

Bacteria

The quantity of bacteria amounts to millions of cells per gramme soil (plate count), the direct count technique revealing figures hundreds and thousands of times greater (Table 7).

Significant variations in bacterial number occur not only between sites but also within sites. There were lower numbers of bacteria in habitats with low pH and temperature and there was also a decrease with depth. However, at some sites with sandy-loam tundra-sod soils on the steep river banks and under *Astragalus-Dryas* communities an increase in numbers of bacteria with depth was observed (Table 8).

Bacteria predominate in the microbial population of the tundra soils investigated. The quantity of microfungi was negligible in the total numbers of microorganisms, constituting from one tenth to several per cent of the total bacterial count. Actinomycetes were found in tundra-sod soils with pH close to neutral, with numbers 10–20 % of the total count. This group was not detected in the bog soils.

As the size of microbial population cannot be used as an index of microbial activity,

Table 5. Numbers m^{-2} of main soil invertebrates at Tareya (July, 1967–1971)

	Dryas-sedge mossy-hummocky tundra	Dryas-sedge mossy spotted tundra				Polygonal bog			
		Spots with lichen crust	Over-grown spots	Mossy ridges	Mossy troughs	Troughs	Dry mossy ridges	Herb-Dryas stands	Herb-grass stands
Nematoda (× 10⁶)	1.3 ☆	1.0 ☆☆	4.5	1.7	3.0	0.8	n.d.	7.0	10.0
Enchytraeidae (× 10³)	0.6	1.1	1.1	0.8	1.1	0.2	1.0	12.6	20.5
Lumbricidae	7	19	14	5	10	–	10	30	150
Lumbriculidae	–	–	–	–	–	90	–	–	–
Lithobiidae	–	–	–	–	–	–	–	32	120
Gamasoidea (× 10³)	3.0	1.3	2.7	3.2	2.5	0.5	3.2	4.0	8.0
Oribatei (× 10³)	4.5	1.3	2.8	4.4	1.2	0.1	4.0	20.0	5.0
Collembola (10³)	21.9	19.2	35.1	44.1	25.0	8.7	32.7	143.1	31.8
Staphylinidae	3	3	4	16	2	n.d.	10	9	32
Carabidae	4	18	39	6	–	2	40	70	64
Curculionidae	–	–	2	–	–	–	–	6	11
Tipulidae	2	7	20	2	1	29	5	50	29
Diptera	6	20	19	30	4	80	37	29	70

☆ – mean data – recalculation on two elements of nanorelief: hummock and troughs, taking into consideration per cent of areas (3.5 × 10⁶ on hummocks, 0.4 × 10⁶ – in troughs)

☆☆ – on bare spot without lichens about 0.1 × 10⁶

n.d. – not determined

Table 6. Zoomass (g ww m^{-2}) of dominating groups of soil invertebrates at Tareya (July 1968)

	Dryas-sedge mossy hummocky tundra	Dryas-sedge spotted tundra			Herb-Dryas stands	Herb-grass stands
		Spots with lichen	Overgrown spots	Mossy ridges		
Nematoda	1.20 ☆	0.78 ☆☆	2.70	1.02	4.20	7.70
Enchytraeidae	1.00	4.93	3.49	1.66	13.90	25.69
Lumbricidae	2.00	4.18	3.28	1.99	26.00	60.00
Lithobiidae	–	–	–	–	0.11	0.42
Gamasoidea	0.09	0.08	0.14	0.08	0.24	0.40
Oribatei	0.10	0.06	0.08	0.13	0.20	0.10
Collembola	1.53	0.35	0.86	1.86	2.36	2.22
Tipulidae	0.30	0.52	1.20	0.40	4.60	3.83

☆ – mean data (2.6 on hummock; 0.5 in troughs)

☆☆ – on bare spots without lichens – about 0.03

the estimation of bacterial production and growth rate was carried out in different soils of the Tareya station. As at the present time there are no methods for the direct determination of bacterial production and growth rate, these data were obtained indirectly from daily estimates of the number of bacteria using Winogradsky's technique as modified by Shulgina. The greatest fluctuations of bacterial numbers were detected in the biologically active horizons of tundra-sod soils and in the spot crust of *Dryas-Carex*-mossy frost-boil tundra. The lowest were observed in the peat horizon of the polygon of polygonal bog. The size and frequency of number fluctuations are a measure of the size of bacterial production, and data for different soils are found in Table 9. The highest values of bacterial production were observed in the biologically active spot crust layer and in tundra-sod soil under the meadow communities. The lowest were observed in the peat of the polygon of polygonal bog.

As the calculation of microbial biomass was carried out on the basis of the direct count of bacteria which includes both living and dead cells, it was necessary to make an assessment of the proportion of the viable and dead cells. The percentage of dead bacteria under natural conditions in different tundra soils was calculated by means of Peshkov's technique (3). The number of dead cells appeared to be connected with the level of biological activity of soils. The lowest numbers were observed in the biologically active horizons of *Astragalus-Dryas* tundra (< 6 %) and in the spot crust layer of *Dryas-Carex*-mossy frost-boil tundra (< 12 %). The highest percentage of dead cells was observed in the peat horizon of the polygon of polygonal bog (7–41 %). Thus, in most cases the number of dead cells was rather low in the soil, and the extent of bacterial production cannot be an overestimate resulting from the presence of dead bacteria. Moreover, the real values for production may be greater, since the amount of predation on bacteria is unknown and direct counts do not reveal the total number of microorganisms.

There are great differences in bacterial growth rates in tundra soils (Table 9). With high rates in the spot crust and tundra-sod soils, reflecting the high biological activity of these soils. The converse occurs in the peat horizon of the polygonal bog.

The qualitative composition of microflora under the different plant-soil conditions was studied in the soils of the Tareya station with the help of capillary pedoscopes (2). The microbial landscape reflects the specificity of the microflora habitat and can be considered as an index of the soil physicochemical conditions. All the soils investigated showed greatest development of the microbial landscape in the upper very narrow horizon of the soil profile. Biological activity decreased with depth, confirming the fact that with increasing latitude activity becomes more and more confined to the soil surface. The patterns of distribution of microorganisms throughout the profile showed that the number of life-limiting factors also increased with depth.

Fungi

The soil mycoflora was studied in the following communities: 1) *Dryas*-sedge-mossy hummocky tundra, 2) *Dryas*-sedge-mossy spotted tundra, 3) *Dryas*-mossy cracked-spotted tundra on an isolated hill, 4) Under *Betula nana* in the wet polygonal tundra complex, 5) Sedge-mossy polygonal bog, 6) *Dryas*-grass meadow on the steep bank of the Pyasina river. The number of soil microscopic fungi in the tundra soils was rather low (Table 10).

Table 7. Physicochemical and microbial characteristics of sites

Site	Depth (cm)	Moisture ☆ (% of dw)	Temperature (°C)	pH (KCl)	Humus (%)	N (total) (%)	P_2O_5 (mg $100\ g^{-1}$)	Ca (exchangeable) (meq $100\ g^{-1}$)	Numbers of bacteria × 10^6 (g^{-1}) plate	Numbers of bacteria × 10^6 (g^{-1}) direct
Dryas-Carex-mossy frost-boil tundra										
Spot crust	0–3	29	9.4	6.3	2.0	0.18	2.0	14.0	0.9–20.0	20–38 000
Border	5–10	59	4.7	4.9	5.8	0.24	2.6	16.9	1.0–8.8	6 000
Fissure	11–23	n.d.	2.0	4.8	7.8	0.28	1.3	16.5	0.02–0.8	1 700
Main surface	5–10	77	5.2	4.8	8.6	0.27	1.3	16.9	0.04–0.7	70– 8 900
Dryas-Carex-mossy hummocky tundra										
Hummock (A_0–A_1)	6–13	69	4.6	5.2	12.6	0.37	trace	22.6	1.5	100– 7 300
Trough (A_0–A_1)	4–8	127	n.d.	5.0	1.9	0.06	6.1	9.4	1.8	3– 4 700
Polygonal bog										
Polygon (A_T)	0–10	187	5.5	4.3	39.6☆☆	0.50	2.6	10.1	0.5–15.3	3 300–12 600
Border (A_T)	3–15	118	2.7	5.5	48.3☆☆	1.03	2.5	32.4	2.4–35.2	1 150– 7 800
Grassy meadow of the steep river banks (A_T)	2–10	21	8.5	5.9	3.4	0.16	3.8	9.1	0.3–49.8	100–32 000

☆ The mean for a summer month

☆☆ Loss on ignition

n.d. = not determined

Table 8. The viable bacterial population in profiles of tundra soils (numbers g^{-1})

Dryas-Carex-mossy frost-boil tundra						Polygonal border				Grass meadow of the steep river banks						Astrallagus-Dryas-tundra	
Spot		Border		Fissure		Polygon		Border		Southern slope		Northern slope		Top of the slope			
Dept (cm)	No. ×10⁶	Depth (cm)	No. ×10⁶	Depth (cm)	No. ×10⁶	Depth (cm)	No. ×10⁶	Depth (cm)	No. ×10⁶	Depth (cm)	No. ×10⁶	Depth (cm)	No. ×10⁶	Depth (cm)	No. ×10⁶	Dept. (cm)	No. ×10⁶
0–5	3.0	5–10	18.9	0–7	36.6	0–2	15.3	0–5	35.2	0–2	49.8	0–5	1.8	2–20	1.0	0–10	1.3
5–35	1.4	10–34	1.6	7–17	3.6	2–24	0.6	5–23	1.5	2–12	2.3	5–30	1.8	20–35	0.7	10–20	0.9
35–42	1.4			17–30	1.6	24–38	6.8	23–27	0.8	12–27	1.6	38–55	7.5	35–65	2.1	20–27	0.9
42–47	1.5			30–32	0.7					27–57	6.0					27–35	2.1
										57–80	23.6					60–70	37.2

Table 9. Bacterial production and growth rates in different tundra soils

Site	Depth (cm)	Bacterial production within a summer month g(ww) g⁻¹ (dw) soil	Bacterial production within a summer month % of soil weight (dw)	Average generation rate within summer month (h)	No. of generations within the summer months
Tundra-sod soil of grass meadow of the steep river banks	2–10	0.071	1.80	18.0	14.7
Dryas-Carex-mossy frost-boil tundra	0–3	0.054	1.45	22.3	12.0
Spot crust	0–3	0.054	1.45	22.3	12.0
Main surface (A_0A_1)	5–10	0.008	0.20	42.4	7.3
Dryas-Carex-mossy					
Hummock (A_0A_1)	6–13	0.05☆	0.10☆	27.4	9.4☆
Trough (A_0A_1)	4–8	0.03☆	0.08☆	36.0	6.0☆
Polygonal bog					
Polygon (A_T)	0–10	0.005	0.10	92.9	2.8
Border (A_T)	3–15	0.007☆	0.17☆	32.8	4.3☆

☆ data for a period of 17 days.

Table 10. Plate count data (Czapek-Dox agar) of fungi in various tundra types (July 1971) (x 10^3 g⁻¹)

Tundra type, elements of nanorelief	Depth to permafrost (cm)	Quantity of fungi spergulas — In the upper soil layer	Quantity of fungi spergulas — In the above-permafrost soil layer
Dryas-sedge-mossy spotted tundra			
Spot	50	0.05	<0.01
Ridge	42	0.16	0
Depression	13	3.10	0.09
Dryas-sedge-mossy hummocky tundra (1972 data)			
Hummock	38	0.13	0
Hollow	30	0.98	0
Dryas-mossy cracked-spotty tundra on isolated hill	57	0.52	0
Under birch bush in the wet polygonal tundra complex	18	5.01	0.13
Sedge-mossy polygonal bog trough	25	1.64	<0.01
Dryas-grass meadow on steep river banks	70	0.68	0.29

Table 11. Fungi (plate count on Czapek-Dox agar) in the rhizosphere
soil of some tundra plants ($\times 10^3$ g^{-1})

Dryas-sedge-mossy hummocky tundra	
Carex ensifolia ssp. arctisibirica	4.0
Dryas punctata	6.4
Eriophorum angustifolium	0.6
E. vaginatum	12.3
Dryas-sedge-mossy spotted tundra	
Carex ensifolia ssp. arctisibirica	16.4
Dryas punctata	1.3
Arctagrostis latifolia	4.4
Dryas-mossy meadow tundra	
Astragalus umbellatus	23.4
Hedysarum arcticum	117.2
Oxytropis adamsiana	39.1
O. middendorfii	21.2
O. nigrescens	17.4

Sixty species of soil microfungi were found in the Taimyr tundra soils. Spotted tundra proved to be richest in fungi (23 species), the lowest number of fungi were found in the *Dryas*-mossy cracked-spotty tundra (7 species). *Penicillium lanosum, P. cyclopium, Mucor hiemalis* and dark-coloured sterile mycelium were the most common forms. The most abundant species was *Penicillium lanosum*. Generally, *Penicillium* was the most common genus.

A study was made of microscopic fungi in the rhizosphere-root zone of five species of Leguminosae from the *Dryas*-mossy meadow tundra on the steep river banks and of several dominating flowering plants in other tundra communities as well as of the rhizosphere of two cotton grasses and one *Arctagrostis* sp., which are not so abundant in these tundras. Some fungal species are confined to the rhizosphere of certain plant species. The number of fungi spergulas in the rhizosphere-root zone of the plants are presented in Table 11. The most common fungi were *Penicillium lanosum, P. cyclopium* and *Mucor hiemalis*; the same species which are typical of the soils as a whole.

Of the phyllosphere fungi the most characteristic species for the spotty tundra were: *Pleospora islandica, Septoria polygonina, Melanoleuca cognata* and *Cystoderma amianthinum*; for the hummocky tundra: *Septosphaeria andromeda, Pleospora magnusiana, Pucciniastrum pirolae, Inocybe oreina* and *Russula delica*; for the polygonal bog complex: *Mollisia atrata, Leptosphaeria caricis, Myosphaerella capronii, Omphalina ericetorum, Lactarius glyciomus, Boletus scaber, Lactarius uvidus* and *Phlegmacium fabri*; for meadow tundra: *Leptosphaeria artemisia, Mycosphœrella primulae, Wettshteinina dryadis* and *Inocybe fastigiata*. Present in all types of tundra, although in different abundance, were: *Mycosphaerella trassiana, Leptosphaeria doliolum, Pleospora herbarum, Calvatia cretacea, Cortinarius alpinus, Sphacelotheca ustilaginea, Melampsora salicina, Puccinia polygoni-vivipari* and *P. saxifragae.*

Quantitative recording of rust and smut fungi (Tables 12, 13) and the influence of rust infection on the photosynthesis of flowering plants (Table 14) was examined using the radiometrical method elaborated in the Photosynthesis Laboratory of the Komarov Botanical Institute (6). During 1970–73 only isolated cases of infection were observed in the spotted tundra and, in 1970, 1972 and 1973 in the hummocky tundra and polygonal bog complex.

The biomass of macromycetes was also recorded in the main types of tundra (Table 15).

The decomposing ability of some species of soil micromycetes was studied using plant litter and cellulose. The most active cellulose decomposing fungi were *Phoma eupirena, Aspergillus versicolor, Penicillium* sp. and *P. natatum.*

Table 12. Infection of *Polygonum viviparum* **spikes by the fungus** *Sphacelotheca ustilaginea* **in the** *Dryas*-**grass meadow tundra in 1970–1973 (no m^{-2})**

	1970	1971	1972	1973
Total number of spikes	103	184	147	170
Numbers of infected spikes	65	82	84	56
Percentage of infection	63	45	57	33
Average number of bulbils per spike	28	30	29	28
Numbers of infected bulbils	25	26	26	27
Percentage of infection	88	87	90	98

Table 13. Infection of plants by rust fungi in 1970–1973 (s d = single damage)

Tundra types	Host plant	Infecting fungus	Total numbers of leaves m^{-2}				Numbers of infected leaves m^{-2}				% of infection			
			1970	1971	1972	1973	1970	1971	1972	1973	1970	1971	1972	1973
Dryas-grass meadow tundra	*Salix arctica*	*Melampsora arctica*	1 422	406	732	1 099	252	15	241	333	18	4	34	30
Dryas-sedge-mossy spotted tundra	*Salix pulchra*	*Melampsora salicina*	1 815	291	821	841	1 650	24	448	449	90	8	55	51
Dryas-sedge-mossy hummocky tundra	*Salix pulchra*	*Melampsora salicina*	2 224	552	507	613	2 115	58	229	164	95	11	59	27
Polygonal-bog-tundra complex	*Salix pulchra*	*Melampsora salicina*	2 560	351	1 425	833	2 520	69	965	218	98	17	68	27
Dryas-grass meadow tundra	*Saxifraga punctata*	*Puccinia saxifragae*	s d	s d	308	444	s d	s d	96	90	s d	s d	31	20
Dryas-grass meadow tundra	*Polygonum viviparum*	*Puccinia polygoni-vivipari*	974	s d	298	153	136	s d	98	28	14	s d	33	24

Table 14. The influence of rust infection on the intensity of photosynthesis in some flowering plants

Plant species	Condition of plant	Infection of leaves in units	Relative photosyn- thesis intensity	Photosynthesis of infected plants as per- centage of healthy plants
Astragalus umbellatus	healthy	–	137	47.4
	infected	10	65	
Salix arctica	healthy	–	41	43.9
	infected	6	18	
Polygonum viviparum	healthy	–	97	
	infected	8	11	11.3
Oxyria digyna	healthy	–	149	
	infected	7	54	36.2
Saxifraga punctata	healthy	–	95	
	infected	8	79	83.2

Table 15. Total production of pileate fungi (mushrooms) in the main types of tundra at the Tareya station in 1971–1973 (mg m^{-2})

	1971	1972	1973
Wet polygonal tundra complex			
Polygon	36.8	0.5	1.0
Trough	6.1	0.1	0.4
Dryas-grass meadows on the steep banks of Pyasina river			
Southern slope	4.7	0.06	1.0
Northern slope	1.8	0.04	0.6
Crest	1.9	0.2	0.3
Dryas-sedge mossy spotty tundra			
Spot	–	–	–
Ridge	1.5	0.07	0.2
Depression	0.8	0.02	0.1
Dryas-sedge-mossy hummocky tundra			
Hummock	0.2	–	0.3
Depression	0.2	–	0.2

THE ANTHROPOGENIC VEGETATION
OF THE TAREYA SETTLEMENT

The settlement is situated on the east bank of the Pyasina river, on a cape with a SSW aspect, bordered on one side by the river and on the other by a brook draining into the river. The Tareya settlement is a temporary one, utilized by fishermen during the fishing season. In 1968 the settlement consisted of five huts, a building for storing fishing tackle and one for the cold storage of fish. On the territory were clearly seen the remains of the previous geological expedition — half-rotted boats, heaps of coal, slag and debris.

In Tareya there are no anthropogenic associations in the sense of an association composed of plants introduced by man onto soil cleared by him of original vegetation. No agricultural experiments have been made here, and not one anthropochore has been found. The vegetation of the settlement, which we call anthropogenic, is just conditional and composed mainly of apophytes.

In the Far North the influence of man on the ground leads to drainage, better aeration, lowering of permafrost surface or to temporary loosening or compaction of the soil. Such changes give rise to a gradual disappearance not only of hydro- and hygrophytes — for example mosses, sedges and hydrophilous grasses — but also of tundra dwarf shrubs and prostrate willows, these being replaced mostly by grasses. On loose anthropogenic substrates some dicotyledons also take root.

The Tareya vegetation shows the following main associations:

1. Depressed and sparse *Alopecurus-Poa* associations are either completely trampled or the plants are in a depauperate state and of very low vigour. The thin moss cover consists of *Ceratodon purpureus* (Hedw.) Brid., *Bryum cirrhatum* Hoppe et. Hornsch., *B. nitidulum* Lindb. and *Funaria hygrometrica* Hedw.

2. The association of apophytes on loose, polluted soil, close to dwellings forms a rather constant set of apophytic-ruderal plants, most of which are frequent on the banks of ravines and on other loose and moist tundra substrates, e.g. *Descurainia sophioides* (Fisch.) O.E. Schulz, *Tripleurospermum phaeocephalum* (Rupr.) Pobed.

3. The associations with predominance of *Poa alpigena* (E. Fries) Lindm. on the slightly trampled and polluted slopes are close to the natural patches of *Poa* meadows and cover the biggest area in the Tareya settlement.

4. The associations with predominance of *Alopecurus alpinus* Sm. are characteristic of the wet and rather strongly polluted depressions of microrelief.

5. The associations with *Deschampsia sukatschewii* (Popl.) Roshev. occur mainly on the lower parts of slopes where there is brief flooding, flow of polluted water, trampling or pollution with waste matter. There is no moss cover, the ground being covered with dead and slightly decomposed leaves of *Deschampsia*.

REFERENCES

1. Mayo, J.M, Despain, D.G. & van Zinderen Bakker, E.M. 1973. CO_2 assimilation by *Dryas integrifolia* on Devon Island Northwest territories. – Can. J. Bot. 51:581–593.
2. Perfilev, B.V. & Gabe, D.R. 1969. Capillary Methods of Investigating Microorganisms. Edinburgh: Oliver & Boyd. 628 pp.
3. Peshkov, M.A. 1955. Cytology of Bacteria. Moscow – Leningrad: Akademia Nauk. 220 pp. (In Russian)
4. Shvetsova, V.M. & Voznesensky, V.L. 1970. Diurnal and seasonal variations in the rate of photosynthesis in some plants of Western Taimyr. – Bot. Zhurn. 55:66–76.
5. Tieszen, L.L. 1972. CO_2 exchange in the Alaskan arctic tundra – measured course of photosynthesis. U.S. Tundra Biome 29–35.
6. Voznesensky, V.L., Zalensky, O.V. & Semikhatova, O.A. 1965. Methods of Photosynthesis and Respiration Investigations. Moskow – Leningrad: "Science" Publ. House. (In Russian)
7. Zalensky, O.V., Shvetsova, V.M. & Voznesensky, V.L. 1972. Photosynthesis in some plants of Western Taimyr. – In: Wielgolaski, F.E. & Rosswall, T. (eds.) Proc. IV. International Meetings on the Biological Productivity of Tundra, pp. 182–186. Stockholm: IBP Tundra Biome Steering Committee.

The investigations of the Tareya station are being published in a series of volumes of which two have already appeared:

Tikhomirov, B.A. (ed.) 1971. Biogeocenoses of Taimyr Tundra and Their Productivity 1. Leningrad: Publishing House "Nauka". 240 pp. (In Russian with English summaries.)

Tikhomirov, B.A. (ed.) 1973. Biogeocenoses of Taimyr Tundra and Their Productivity 2. Leningrad: Publishing House "Nauka". 208 pp. (In Russian with English summaries.)

Rosswall, T. & Heal, O.W. (eds.) 1975.
Structure and Function of Tundra Ecosystems.
Ecol. Bull. (Stockholm) 20: 183–191.

ARY–MAS, USSR

B.N. NORIN, I.V. IGNATENKO

The Ary-Mas station is situated in the valley of the Novaya river (the western tributary of the Khatanga river) at a latitude of 72° 30′ N in the Taimyr peninsula.

The territory is composed of thick Quaternary deposits (loams and loamy sands). The Novaya river has four terraces, 30 to 150 m above sea level. Some problems of the Holocene history of Ary-Mas vegetation have been discussed elsewhere (4–8). The first data on Ary-Mas were published by Tolmachev (12) and Tjulina (13).

The territory is used nowadays for hunting and trapping in winter and the larch forest is partly used by the native population for various economic needs.

The climate of the district is continental. According to data from the nearest meteorological station in the Khatanga settlement the 25-year mean January and July temperatures are −33.8°C and 13.1°C respectively. Annual precipitation is 243 mm (Table 1).

Under the *redkolesja* (open larch woodland, Fig. 1) there are light-textured soils (loamy and sandy-loamy); forest-tundra cryogenic humus-slightly-gley on the plains and bog-tundra peaty-gley soils in the depressions.

The soil cover under the *redina* (very open woodland, Fig. 2) is complex in character and is composed of tundra residual-slightly-gley soils under the spot-ridges and bog-tundra peaty humus in depressions with frost cracks. Under the branches of semiprostrate and prostrate larch trees there are tundra turfy-slightly-gley soils (under the peripheral parts of tree clumps), and forest-tundra cryogenic humus-slightly-gley soils (in the centres of tree clumps).

The soil of the nanopolygonal frost-cracked spotted tundras has a complex character: i) the tundra residual-slightly-gley soils under the spots of bare ground; ii) tundra turfy-slightly-gley soils under ridges around spots; iii) bog-tundra peaty humus slightly-gley soils in cracks and depressions and iv) tundra turfy-gley soils under the level elements of nanorelief.

Chemical characteristics of *redkolesja* and tundra soils are shown in Tables 2 and 3. More detailed characteristics of soils may be found in Ignatenko (1).

The depth of permafrost thaw is closely correlated with the nano- and microrelief and vegetation patterns. In the larch *redkolesja* the depth of the maximum permafrost thaw (in the second half of August) is 50–70 cm; the mean thaw in depressions is 20 cm, under trees 30–50 cm and under the remaining surface 35–40 cm. In the nanopolygonal frost-cracked spotted tundra permafrost thaws down to 15–80 cm; the mean thaw in cracks and depressions is 40 cm and under bare spots and ridges 65 cm.

The general character of the flora is arctic and up to 259 species have been recorded of which 57.3 % comprise arctic and arcto-alpine elements, 25.9 % hypoarctic elements and 16.8 % boreal elements. The families with the biggest numbers of species are: Gramineae (35 species), Cyperaceae (23), Cruciferae (21), Ranunculaceae (21), Caryophyllaceae (20), Compositae (16), Salicaceae (12), Rosaceae (12), Saxifragaceae (12) and Scrophulariaceae (10).

The most abundant genera are: *Carex* (17 species), *Draba* (13), *Salix* (12), *Ranunculus* (12), *Saxifraga* (10), *Pedicularis* (10), *Poa* (7), *Juncus* (6), *Minuartia* (6) and *Eriophorum* (5).

The investigated area consists mainly of nanopolygonal frost-cracked spotted tundra, ridge polygonal mires, larch *redkolesja* and larch *redina* (9, 10). The larch (*Larix dahurica*, Turcz.) *redkolesja* covers an area 20 km long and 0.5–4 km broad on the third and fourth terraces of the Novaya river. Close to the river they are of maximal density (0.3–0.4) gradually thinning out towards the interfluve (0.2–0.1), where they already become *redina*. Tree height in the *redkolesja* is 4–7 m (up to 9–10 m in favourable conditions), and trunk diameter 8–14 cm (up to 25–30 cm). In some types of *redkolesja* there is a well-developed shrub layer of *Betula exilis* Sukatch., *Ledum decumbens* (Ait.) Lodd ex. Stend., *Salix reptans* Rupr. and *S. glauca* L. In the ground layers the dominant species are *Carex ensifolia* (Turcz. ex. Gorodk) V. Krecz. spp. *arctisibirica* Jurtz.[*], *Cassiope tetragona* (L.) D. Don., *Dryas punctata* Juz. and more rarely *Vaccinium uliginosum* L., *V. vitis-idaea* L. and *Empetrum hermaphroditum* Hagerup. The mosses *Ptilidium ciliare* (L.) Hampe, *Aulacomnium turgidum* (Wahlenb.) Schwaegr., *Hylocomium splendens* (Hedw.) B.S.G., *Tomenthypnum nitens* (Hedw.) Loeske are often present and sometimes also *Dicranum* species. The lichens, *Cetraria cucullata* (Bell.) Ach., *Cladonia silvatica* (L.) Rab., *C. rangiferina* (L.) Web. and *C. gracilis* (L.) Willd., occur occasionally in the moss layer. The main types of *redkolesja* are the following: 1) *Larix – Cassiope – Dryas*; 2) *Larix – Cassiope – Carex*; 3) *Larix – Betula exilis*; 4) *Larix – Salix*; 5) *Larix – Ledum*; 6) *Larix – Alnaster fruticosus* Ledeb.

The nanopolygonal frost-cracked spotted tundras cover all slopes on the third and especially the fourth terraces of the Novaya river, even extending onto the interfluve. A shrub layer is lacking in such tundras. *Dryas punctata*, *Cassiope tetragona*, *Carex ensifolia* and sometimes *Eriophorum vaginatum* L. predominate in the dwarf shrub layer. *Hylocomium splendens*, *Tomenthypnum nitens*, *Aulacomnium turgidum*, *Ptilidium ciliare* and *Dicranum* spp. are the most common mosses.

The ridge-polygonal bogs occupy nearly the entire surface of the second terrace of the Novaya river. Polygons attain a diameter of 10–15 m, and the surrounding ridges a height of 0.2–0.8 m. In the polygon troughs communities of *Carex stans* Drej. [**], *C. saxatilis* L., *C. vaginata* Tausch and *C. chordorhiza* Ehrh., develop with a thick moss cover of *Drepanocladus*, *Sphagnum*, *Mnium* and *Bryum* species. Distributed over the ridges are *Betula exilis*, *Salix* spp., *Vaccinium uliginosum*, *Eriophorum vaginatum*, *Aulacomnium turgidum*, *Tomenthypnum nitens* and *Hylocomium splendens*.

---

[*] = *Carex bigelowii* Torr. spp. *arctosibirica* (Yurtsev) Love & Love (editors' remark)

[**] = *Carex aquatilis* L. spp. *stans* (Drej.) Hulten (editors' remark)

Figure 1. *Redkolesja* (open larch woodland) with *Larix dahurica* at Ary-Mas.

Figure 2. *Redina* (very open larch woodlad) with *Larix dahurica* at Ary-Mas.

Table 1. 25-year mean monthly air temperatures (°C) and precipitation (mm) at Ary-Mas

J	F	M	A	M	J	J	A	S	O	N	D	Yearly mean	minimum	maximum
-33.8	-32.6	-27.5	-18.4	-7.7	-5.4	13.1	8.9	1.6	-12.2	-26.1	-29.2	-13.2	-53.6	33.6°C
9.9	9.4	10.0	9.9	13.2	30.3	40.5	35.3	27.1	22.1	17.9	17.3	243 mm		

Table 2. Soil characteristics in the larch *redkolesja*

| Subsite | Sample depth (cm) | Ignition loss (%) | Oxides in soil after ignition (%) | | | | | | | | | | | | |
			SiO_2	Al_2O_3	Fe_2O_3	TiO_2	P_2O_5	MnO	CaO	MgO	SO_3	K_2O	Na_2O	Sum
Forest-tundra	0–5	65.3	61.2	12.2	5.0	1.8	2.5	0.6	6.4	2.3	2.9	3.8	1.9	100.4
Humus-slightly gley	10–20	18.9	71.9	12.0	4.3	0.8	0.3	0.1	3.5	2.1	0.5	2.0	2.2	99.7
(under level surface)	20–28	4.4	73.4	11.5	5.3	0.8	0.2	0.1	2.3	2.2	0.5	2.2	1.9	100.3
	35–45	3.0	74.2	11.7	4.2	0.6	0.2	0.1	2.7	2.2	0.2	2.2	1.9	100.1
	55–65	2.8	73.9	11.5	4.6	0.6	0.2	0.1	2.5	2.0	0.3	2.3	1.9	99.7
Forest-tundra	0–4	85.8	59.1	11.6	4.5	2.1	2.3	0.7	8.9	2.4	3.0	3.8	1.9	100.3
Humus-gley	4–8	41.5	72.2	10.3	5.5	1.2	0.4	0.1	3.2	2.1	0.7	2.2	1.8	99.7
(under larch trees)	8–11	11.4	72.6	12.3	4.9	0.7	0.3	0.1	2.8	2.0	0.3	2.1	1.9	100.1
	12–22	3.3	73.7	11.6	5.1	0.9	0.2	0.1	2.4	1.9	0.4	2.2	1.9	100.2
	25–35	3.2	73.5	11.3	5.0	0.8	0.2	0.1	2.8	1.9	0.4	2.2	2.0	100.0
	45–55	3.2	73.4	10.9	4.9	0.8	0.2	0.1	3.5	1.9	0.3	2.3	2.0	100.2

Table 3. Soil characteristics of nanopolygonal frost-cracked spotted tundra

Subsite	Sample depth (cm)	Ignition loss (%)	Oxides in ignited soil (%)											Sum
			SiO_2	Al_2O_3	Fe_2O_3	TiO_2	P_2O_5	MnO	CaO	MgO	SO_3	K_2O	Na_2O	
Tundra peaty gley (level surface)	0–5	90.2	47.9	9.0	4.0	0.4	2.4	0.9	20.9	6.2	3.8	4.1	–	100.6
	5–9	8.2	72.7	12.8	5.4	0.5	0.2	0.1	2.5	1.7	0.3	2.0	1.7	100.0
	10–20	6.3	72.3	12.6	5.2	0.9	0.2	0.1	2.6	2.2	0.3	2.0	1.8	100.1
	20–30	6.0	72.4	12.7	5.3	0.8	0.2	0.1	2.6	2.2	0.2	2.0	1.8	100.2
	35–45	5.5	72.7	12.7	5.3	0.8	0.2	0.1	2.5	2.3	0.2	1.9	1.6	100.3
	50–60	7.1	72.5	11.6	5.8	0.9	0.2	0.1	2.6	2.4	0.2	2.0	1.8	100.1
Tundra slightly-gley turfy (spot ridge)	0–4	92.3	44.6	10.1	3.4	1.2	2.6	0.8	21.6	5.1	3.0	5.1	1.4	98.8
	4–13	6.1	75.7	11.2	5.6	0.4	0.1	0.1	2.0	1.2	0.2	2.3	1.3	100.0
	20–30	5.6	74.8	12.2	4.7	0.5	0.1	0.1	2.1	1.6	0.2	2.1	1.7	100.0
Tundra residual-slightly-gley (bare ground spot)	0–10	4.9	76.2	11.4	4.3	0.5	0.1	0.1	2.3	1.4	0.2	2.0	1.6	100.0
	10–20	3.6	77.5	11.0	4.3	0.3	0.1	0.1	1.9	1.3	0.3	2.1	1.2	99.9
	30–40	4.3	75.2	11.6	5.2	0.4	0.2	0.1	2.3	1.7	0.2	1.6	1.3	99.9
Bog-tundra peaty-gley (depression with frost-crack)	0–4	85.7	56.2	15.3	2.9	–	3.7	1.2	9.2	4.4	2.0	4.8	0.6	100.1
	4–16	52.3	66.6	11.2	4.7	0.6	0.4	0.1	4.3	4.1	0.7	3.9	3.7	100.2
	19–29	12.4	72.9	13.0	5.0	0.5	0.1	0.1	2.8	1.5	0.3	2.1	1.6	100.0
	31–41	5.3	72.5	12.5	5.3	0.7	0.2	0.1	2.5	2.3	0.2	1.9	1.7	99.9

Among the less widespread communities of the territory are willow communities on the floodplain terraces, *Betula exilis* communities in the drainage hollows, palsas in meso-relief depressions, and nival communities on places of long persisting snowdrifts.

The data on the total standing crop of phytomass and its distribution on the micro-relief elements and in the genetic horizons of soils have been published (2, 3). The total standing crop of phytomass (Tables 4 and 5) was determined in the following communities:

a. Larch *redkolesja: Larix dahurica, Ledum decumbens, Carex ensifolia* and *Ptilidium ciliare.* Density of canopy 0.2, average height 5 m, diameter 14 cm.

b. Larch *redina: Larix dahurica, Cassiope tetragona, Carex ensifolia* and *Hylocomium splendens.* Larch canopy density 0.1, the trees have a stunted or semistunted form and are situated as far as 15—30 m from each other.

c. Nanopolygonal frost-cracked spotted tundra: *Dryas punctata, Cassiope tetragona, Carex ensifolia* and *Hylocomium splendens.*

Table 4. Total standing crop of phytomass (g m^{-2})

	Larch *redkolesja*	Larch *redina*	Spotted tundra
Aboveground phytomass:	3 230	1 390	1 290
trees	670	120	0
shrubs, dwarf shrubs and herbs	650	330	480
mosses and lichens	1 490	660	600
organic residues	420	280	210
Belowground:	6 400	3 980	6 940
roots	2 870	1 890	2 340
organic residues	3 530	2 090	4 600
Total	9 630	5 370	8 230

Ash composition of plants was estimated in predominating species in *redkolesja* and tundras (Table 6).

Very little information is available on the processes of decomposition and nutrient circulation in the soils of Ary-Mas. However, samples of standard Borregaard cellulose (11) were placed on the surface and at 5 cm depth in subsites within the larch *redkolesja*, spotted tundra, polygonal mire and river bank. In most sites the per cent weight loss after one year was between 0 and 3 %. The most rapid rates were on the river bank with *Salix lanata* L. and *Drepanocladus* sp. where losses from four replicates were 5.2 ± 2.9 % (S.E.) at the surface and 7.5 ± 2.2 % at 5 cm depth. These rates are fairly typical of the Taimyr tundra sites with short, dry summers.

Table 5. Aboveground standing crop phytomass of tree layer (g m^{-2})

	Larch *redkolesja*	Larch *redina*
Stem wood	324	29
Branches:		
living	245	40
dry	56	31
Cones		
of present season	3	1
of previous seasons	14	7
Seasonal increment of sprouts	1	1
Needles	24	7
Total	667	116

Table 6. Ash contents of plants

	Insoluble admixtures (%)	Pure ash (%)	Oxides in the pure ash (%)											
			SiO$_2$	Al$_2$O$_3$	Fe$_2$O$_3$	TiO$_2$	P$_2$O$_5$	MnO	CaO	MgO	SO$_3$	K$_2$O	Na$_2$O	Sum
Betula exilis														
twigs	1.5	1.1	8.8	2.7	0	0	21.9	0.9	20.2	14.9	5.3	24.6	0	99.1
leaves	1.2	2.5	4.4	4.4	0.8	0	21.0	1.2	19.8	12.3	8.3	25.7	0.4	98.0
Salix glauca														
twigs	0.1	2.5	24.3	3.2	0.8	0	15.0	1.6	21.5	5.3	4.9	20.7	0.4	97.6
leaves	2.4	3.4	3.8	1.8	0	0	15.3	3.2	20.9	9.4	17.4	24.1	0.3	96.2
Ledum decumbens														
twigs	0.3	1.1	9.7	6.1	0	0	15.8	6.1	21.1	7.9	6.1	25.4	0.9	99.1
leaves	0.1	2.1	8.3	4.9	1.0	1.0	16.0	3.9	29.1	8.3	5.8	20.4	0.5	99.1
Cassiope tetragona														
stems with leaves	0.7	2.3	25.9	5.2	0.9	1.3	9.9	1.3	18.1	7.3	4.3	22.8	0.4	97.4
Dryas punctata														
stems	3.7	4.2	44.4	7.6	4.3	1.2	4.0	0.2	18.3	5.2	2.4	9.0	0.5	97.6
leaves	0.9	3.6	8.0	3.3	0	0	18.2	0.3	32.1	8.6	4.1	21.8	1.1	97.4
Carex ensifolia	0.9	7.2	68.3	1.1	0.4	0	4.7	0.8	5.8	1.3	2.9	10.0	0.1	95.6
Ptilidium ciliare	1.6	3.6	47.0	4.9	0.8	0	5.2	1.4	13.7	6.0	2.8	14.8	0.2	97.0
Aulacomnium turgidum	3.1	3.7	44.5	9.3	0.6	0	7.4	0.6	13.9	3.8	3.8	11.8	1.9	97.5
Tomenthypnum nitens	4.5	3.2	39.3	14.0	1.3	0	8.4	2.5	11.5	1.3	5.6	15.0	0.9	99.7
Hylocomium splendens	9.7	5.4	53.5	18.9	2.4	0	3.9	0.4	8.2	2.4	2.2	6.9	0.4	99.1

REFERENCES

1. Ignatenko, I.V. 1972. Soils of Ary-Mas forest-island. – In: Wielgolaski F.E. & Rosswall T. (eds.) Proceedings IV International Meeting on the Biological Productivity of Tundra, pp. 150–155. Stockholm: IBP Tundra Biome Steering Committee.

2. Ignatenko, I.V., Knorre, A.V., Lovelius, N.V. & Norin B.N. 1972. Standing crop in plant communities at the station Ary-Mas. – In: Wielgolaski F.E. & Rosswall T. (eds.) Proceedings IV International Meeting on the Biological Productivity of Tundra, pp. 140–149. Stockholm: IBP Tundra Biome Steering Committee.

3. Ignatenko, I.V., Knorre, A.V., Lovelius N.V. & Norin, B.N. 1973. Standing crop of phytomass in the typical plant communities of the forest-island Ary-Mas.– Ekologia 3:36–43.

4. Knorre, A.V., Lovelius, N.V. & Norin, B.N. 1971. Fluctuations of *Larix dahurica* Turcz. increment at the forest-island Ary-Mas (Taimyr). – Bot. Zhurnal 56(5):627–632.

5. Knorre, A.V., Lovelius, N.V. & Norin, B.N. 1971. Rhythmic fluctuations of wood increment in the trunks of *Larix dahurica* on its polar limits (Ary-Mas, Taimyr). – In: Shnitnikov, A.V. (ed.) Rhythmics in the Nature Phenomena. Readings in the Memory of Academician L.S. Berg, pp. 87–89. Leningrad.

6. Kultina, V.V., Lovelius, N.V. & Kostjukovich, V.V. 1974. The age of the "forest phase" in the Taimyr vegetation development. – Bot. Zhurnal 59(9):1310–1317.

7. Lovelius, N.V. 1972. Reconstruction of the course of meteorological processes on the basis of the annual tree rings along the northern and altitudinal forest boundaries. – In: Wielgolaski, F.E. & Rosswall, T. (eds.) Proceedings IV International Meeting on the Biological Productivity of Tundra, pp. 248–260. Stockholm: IBP Tundra Biome Steering Committee.

8. Lovelius, N.V., Norin, B.N. & Knorre, A.V. 1972. Rhythmic fluctuations of wood increment in the trunks of *Larix dahurica* Turcz. on its polar limits (Ary-Mas, Taimyr, $72°30'$ N) – Izv. Vsesojuznogo Geograficheskogo obtshestva 104(5):391–393.

9. Norin, B.N. 1972. The main ecological surveys at the station Ary-Mas. – In: Wielgolaski, F.E. & Rosswall, T. (eds.) Proceedings IV International Meeting on the Biological Productivity of Tundra, pp. 133–139. Stockholm: IBP Tundra Biome Steering Committee.

10. Norin, B.N., Ignatenko, I.V., Knorre, A.V. & Lovelius, N.V. 1971. Vegetation and soils of the forest-island Ary-Mas (Taimyr). – Bot. Zhurnal 56(9):1272–1283.

11. Rosswall, T. 1974. Cellulose decomposition on the tundra. – In: Holding, A.J., Heal, O.W., MacLean, S.F. & Flanagan, P.W. (eds.) Soil Organisms and Decomposition in Tundra, pp. 325–340. Stockholm: IBP Tundra Biome Steering Committee.

12. Tolmachev, A.I. 1931. On the distribution of trees and the northern forest limit in the region between Yenissei and Khatanga rivers. – Trudy Polarnoi komissii AN SSSR 5:1–29.

13. Tjulina, L.N. 1937. Forest vegetation of the Khatanga district at its northern limits. – Trudy Arkticheskogo instituta 63:83–180.

Rosswall, T. & Heal, O.W. (eds.) 1975.
Structure and Function of Tundra Ecosystems.
Ecol. Bull. (Stockholm) 20: 193–223.

KEVO, FINLAND

P. KALLIO

INTRODUCTION

The Finnish IBP Tundra programme has been conducted at the Kevo Subarctic Research Station (founded in 1956) of the University of Turku, in Inari Lapland, in northernmost Finland (69°45′N, 27°01′E, Fig. 1). The topography of the area features rounded mountains (ca 300 m) and river valleys, the relative height differences being ca 200 m. The geology is characterized by SiO_2-rich, acid Precambrian bedrock; however there is much variation, from the very acid and CaO-poor gneisses or granulites and mica schists to amphibolite.

The area was deglaciated early, 8 000 B.C., and the glaciofluvial matter deposited as kame terraces, esker-like chains and deltas. Rock cliffs with talus cones at their base present periglacial formations and on mountain slopes there are areas of patterned ground with different types of solifluction formations. Drumlins and other fluted moraine forms are common between the fells and some deflation formations occur.

Kevo is situated in the Fennoscandian birch forest zone, some 60 km north of the main coniferous forest, but close to small isolated pine forests in the deep valleys of Utsjoki and Kevojoki. The birch (*Betula tortuosa* Ledeb.) covers the land below 300–350 m, and above this spread low alpine heaths.

Human influence is slight in the area, with a population of below 0.3 persons km^{-2}. The main features of the geography and biogeography have been described by Kallio, Laine and Mäkinen (15).

Three IBP sites were chosen as representatives of the Kevo ecosystem (Fig. 2):

Pine forest (Fig. 3): This fenced site, 2 750 m^2, is on a glaciofluvial terrace at a height of 90 m. The dominant pines are 9–10 m in height with a density of 570 trees ha^{-1}. There are a few small birch bushes and the low field vegetation (7 cm in height) contains few species with a cover greater than 1 % (Table 1): *Vaccinium vitis-idaea* L., *Empetrum hermaphroditum* Hagerup, *Pleurozium schreberi* (Willd.) Mitt., *Dicranum fuscescens* Turn., *Ptilidium ciliare* (L.) Hampe., reindeer lichens and *Stereocaulon paschale* (L.) Hoffm., the last being the most important nitrogen fixer at the site. The moss cover is 17.0 %.

Birch forest: This site is situated close to the Station on a hillside inclined at 8° to

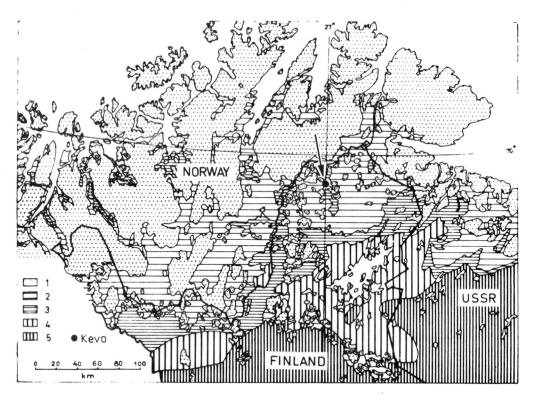

Figure 1. Location of Kevo and vegetation zones in northernmost Finland. 1 = barren fells, 2 = birch bushes and birch forests, 3 = birch forests and small pine groves, 4 = pine forest, 5 = coniferous forest (pine and spruce). Redrawn from the Atlas of Finland, 1960.

to NNE at a height of ca 130 m. The polycormic birches are ca 3 m in height, with a density of 1 400 ha^{-1}. The vegetation is more mesic than that of the pine forest, and the ground layer of vascular plants is higher (11 cm average): *Empetrum hermaphroditum, Vaccinium vitis-idaea, V. uliginosum* L., *Ledum palustre* L., *V. myrtillus* L. The amount of reindeer lichens is smaller than at the pine site and *Nephroma arcticum* (L.) Torss. is the most abundant nitrogen fixer. The total moss cover (*Pleurozium schreberi, Hylocomium splendens* (Hedw.) B.S.G., *Barbilophozia* and *Dicranum fuscescens*) is much higher than at the previous site (42.8 %). Small voles and lemmings are in certain years very important vertebrate consumers, and *Dineura* is the most important birch herbivore.

Low alpine heath (Fig. 4): The low alpine heath at 330 m is developed on a thin till with many outcrops of the bedrock. Sparse birch shrub covers about 15 % of the area. *Vaccinium vitis-idaea* and *Empetrum hermaphroditum* are the most abundant dwarf shrubs, but even *Arctostaphylos alpina* (L.) Spreng. and *V. uliginosum* have a cover value over 1 %. The height of the field layer is lower than at previous sites (4 cm). There are 30 lichen species, all having a low cover. *Oporinia autumnata* Bkh. defoliated the birches in 1965–1966, but basal shoot recovery has been effective at the IBP sites.

194

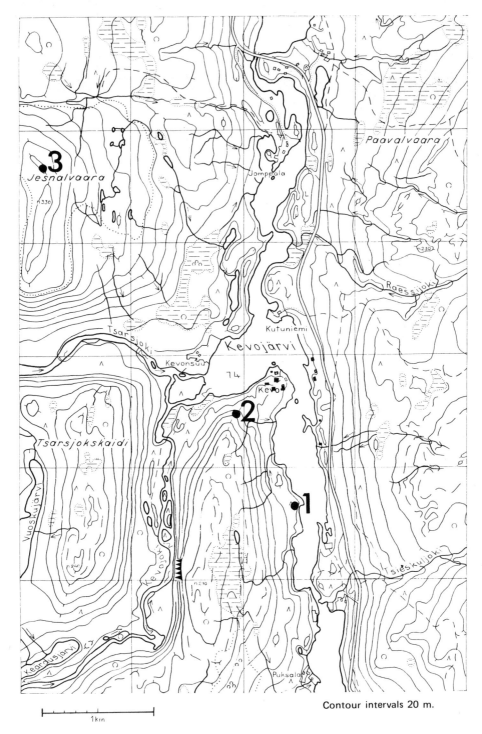

Figure 2. Location of the IBP sites at Kevo. 1 = pine forest, 2 = birch forest, and 3 = low alpine heath.

195

Figure 3. Pine forest IBP site.

Figure 4. Low alpine heath IBP site.

Table 1. Per cent frequency (1) and per cent cover (2) of ground vegetation on Kevo IBP sites (13). (– frequency = absent; – cover = no estimate; 0 cover = less than 0.01 %)

	Pine forest		Birch forest		Subalpine heath	
	(1)	(2)	(1)	(2)	(1)	(2)
Arctostaphylos alpina	–	–	1	0	13	1.02
A. uva-ursi	–	–	4	0.27	–	–
Calamagrostis	–	–	11	0.03	43	0.80
Deschampsia flexuosa	–	–	11	0.09	–	–
Empetrum hermaphroditum	45	4.42	100	20.18	82	16.98
Juncus trifidus	–	–	1	0.01	5	0.01
Ledum palustre	–	–	81	3.97	–	–
Linnaea borealis	2	0.04	20	0.36	–	–
Loiseleuria procumbens	–	–	–	–	2	0.04
Lycopodium annotinum	–	–	1	0.01	–	–
Pedicularis lapponica	–	–	3	–	–	–
Vaccinium myrtillus	–	–	30	1.35	–	–
V. uliginosum	2	0.11	66	4.43	51	1.12
V. vitis–idaea	100	13.50	97	6.71	89	3.85
Alectoria nigricans	–	–	–	–	49	–
A. ochroleuca	–	–	–	–	28	–
Cetraria crispa	–	–	–	–	36	–
C. cucullata	–	–	–	–	39	–
C. nivalis	2	0	12	0.04	84	2.08
Cladonia alpestris	84	1.11	21	0.13	30	0.08
C. alpicola	–	–	–	–	36	–
C. amaurocraea	2	0	4	0	77	–
C. bellidiflora	2	0	1	4.00	3	–
C. carneola	–	–	2	–	–	–
C. cenotea	1	0	2	0	–	–
C. chlorophaea coll.	29	0.10	1	0	30	–
C. coccifera	8	0.03	9	0.02	56	–
C. cornuta	9	0.02	7	0	3	–
C. crispata	43	0.34	31	0.09	34	–
C. deformis	12	0.05	–	–	11	–
C. degenerans	–	–	1	0	2	–
C. ecmocyna	4	0	3	0.01	–	–
C. furcata	–	–	2	0	–	–
C. gracilis	90	1.90	51	0.27	79	–
C. pyxidata	1	0	–	–	16	–
C. rangiferina	97	1.67	59	0.75	21	–
C. mitis	96	2.20	58	1.16	93	0.99
C. unicalis	79	0.71	39	0.36	56	–
C. verticillata	–	–	1	0	16	–
Cornicularia divergens	–	–	–	–	38	–
Nephroma arcticum	1	0.02	39	4.40	–	–
N. expallida	–	–	1	0.04	–	–
Ochrolechia frigida	–	–	2	0	28	–
Peltigera aphthosa	4	0.09	13	0.62	–	–
P. malacea	11	0.22	1	0.22	7	–
P. scabrosa	–	–	1	0.47	2	–
Sphaerophorus globosus	–	–	1	0.04	64	–
Stereocaulon alpinum	–	–	–	–	5	–
S. paschale	82	4.91	38	1.30	41	–
Chandonanthus setiformis	–	–	–	–	8	0.17
Barbilophozia	22	0.50	74	3.01	–	–
Ptilidium ciliare	82	8.08	32	0.82	43	1.32
Brachythecium salebrosum	–	–	12	0	–	–
Dicranum fuscescens	80	1.60	74	2.85	48	0.73
D. robustum	5	0.02	4	0	–	–
D. undulatum	1	0	1	0	–	–
Hylocomium splendens	–	–	21	3.18	–	–
Pleurozium schreberi	35	6.24	78	31.97	3	0.12
Pohlia nutans	33	0.28	35	0.09	21	0.03
Polytrichum commune	–	–	28	0.23	–	–
P. juniperinum	18	0.12	12	0	18	0.32
P. piliferum	–	–	–	–	30	0.43
Ptilium crista-castrensis	–	–	1	0.01	–	–

ENVIRONMENTAL CONDITIONS

Climate

The main climatic features are determined by the latitude, where the polar day lasts for 9 weeks, and by the moisture bearing west winds which are, however, affected by the Scandes Mountains west and northwest of the area. The warm Gulf Stream imparts a higher temperature to the entire area than is average for the 70° latitude.

The area is also exposed to the alternating influence of the Arctic Ocean, 50–100 km to the north, and of the continental climate from the south. Big temperature variations are common, and the area is more continental than the other Fennoscandian tundra study sites (41).

Large fluctuations, both periodical and aperiodical, have taken place after the glacial period (40). This is reflected, e.g. in the history of the northern forest limits. The permafrost, typical of the Subarctic, is absent, except in local palsa hummocks.

At the Kevo Meteorological Station at the centre of the IBP sites (ca 100 m a.s.l.) the macroclimate during IBP (1968–73) was roughly the same as the long-term average, even though there were great annual differences (Table 2). The year 1968 represented a cold extreme, and the first years of the 1970s were warmer than the average (Fig. 5). February is the coldest month (−16.9°C) and temperatures in June, July and August are above 10°C. The annual mean for 1962–1970 was −2.4 ± 0.3°C.

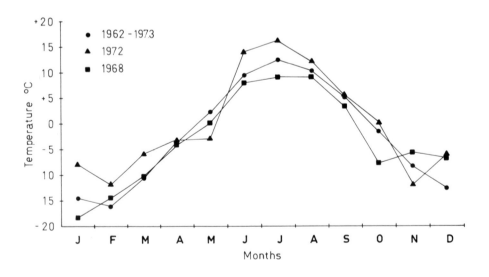

Figure 5. Variation of the mean temperatures in the period of 1962–1973 and in 1968 and 1972.

Table 2. Climate of the Kevo area for the years 1968–1973 measured at the Kevo Meteorological Station

Variables	J	F	M	A	M	J	J	A	S	O	N	D	Year
Total radiation 72–73 (kJ cm^{-2})	0.2	4.0	17.1	22.3	47.3	55.6	56.6	32.9	17.7	7.0	0.7	0	261.3
Screen temperature (°C)													
min	−18.9	−22.1	−15.3	−10.0	−1.9	5.3	8.4	6.3	0.9	−5.7	−14.8	−15.7	−7.0
mean	−13.5	−16.9	−9.4	−4.3	2.4	10.5	13.5	10.9	4.4	−2.3	−10.3	−10.4	−2.1
max	−8.7	−11.7	−4.2	0.4	6.1	15.8	19.0	15.8	8.2	0.8	−6.2	−5.9	2.5
Relative humidity air (%)	85	83	80	76	70	67	72	80	85	87	87	85	80
Wind velocity 72–73 (m s^{-1})	4.2	3.1	3.6	3.0	3.3	3.3	2.8	2.9	2.4	2.6	2.5	2.4	3.0
Precipitation (mm)	20.7	12.3	19.4	19.0	12.4	36.9	65.4	61.6	35.1	32.2	32.9	27.2	375
Evapotranspiration 72–73 (mm)						3.0	3.1	1.3					
Snow depth (cm)	40	54	57	54	32	0	0	0	0	12	23	26	
Sunshine duration 72–73 (h)	3	43	99	172	153	305	332	155	105	57	6	0	1 429

The total radiation is highest in June and July, i.e. the two months with a continuous polar day and the longest sunshine duration, although the cloudiness in these months is above the annual average. In some years maximum solar radiation occurs during the snow period, a considerable proportion of the yearly radiation therefore being received at a time when plants are not able to use it for production (30). In October—February, the low radiation is an important ecological factor limiting growth.

The annual precipitation during the IBP period was 375 mm which is slightly below the long-term mean. It is significant that the growth period is favoured by the highest monthly precipitation averages in July and August, 65 and 62 mm respectively, while the latter half of May and the whole of June are mostly dry. The low winter precipitation is seen in the rather low snow cover of the area. The birch site is the only place with a snow cover of more than 50 cm. The low alpine site does not have more than 25 cm, and there are always spots with a much thinner snow cover.

The growth period, in terms of days with a mean temperature above 0°C, is 160 days at the Meteorological Station and at the birch and pine sites. The temperature is above 5°C for about 115 days. The average thermal sum for 1962—70 was 577 degrees above 5°C but it varies considerably in different years and is also affected by topography (Table 3).

Table 3. Thermal sums: the sum of degree days above 5°C calculated from five-day means for the Kevo IBP sites

	1968	1969	1970
Met. Station	389.5	543.5	822.0
Pine forest	407.1	553.8	824.1
Birch forest	374.4	524.8	795.7
Low alpine heath	252.8	402.8	654.3

In the low alpine heath, in comparison with the other sites, the thermal sum is reduced by 20—30 %, the growth period is 15 days shorter, the mean summer temperature is 1.5°C lower and the summer maximum 2.0—3.5°C lower. In winter, thermal inversion often takes place, and the valley bottoms may be 10—15°C cooler than the mountain-tops, some 200 m higher. This may have an important ecological influence (16).

The temperature of the ground lichen stand is 5—20°C higher in direct sunshine than that in the meteorological screen, the highest values measured at the IBP sites being over 40°C, while in the litter layer of south-facing slopes the maxima can be over 50°C. During the night, the lichen temperatures are lower than the air temperature. The daily variation in the lichen layer and in the litter in summer is greatest in the open low alpine heath, the differences being smallest in the more closed birch forests.

The wind velocity, the yearly mean of which is 3.0 m s^{-1}, has a drying and cooling effect particularly in the summit habitats. Evaporation is much higher in the low alpine heath than at the other sites.

200

Soils

The area is in the centre of the great podzolic activity in the subarctic (8, 43). The podzolisation processes are facilitated by the acid parent material of the Precambrian rocks, the rather high summer temperature and the adequate drainage due to coarse glacial deposits. The removal of Fe from the A horizon and its precipitation in the B horizon is clearly manifest in the Kevo podzols, which are most typically developed in the birch and pine biotopes. The A_0 horizon is 7–10 cm thick at the birch site, but only 4-5 cm at the pine site. In the birch forest the humus is of fibrous mor type, while more greasy mor type prevails in the pine forest. The A_2 horizon is indicated distinctly by a whitish colour, and is 4 cm thick at the birch site and 3 cm at the pine site. The B horizon is 20–24 cm thick, dark brown, and has glacial till as parent material. The C horizon is grey in colour. It is distringuished from the B horizon by its texture, the latter being finer than that of the C horizon owing to more active weathering processes.

There are differences in the main structure between different sites, but the gravel, sand and fine material are almost equally distributed (Table 4). The very shallow soil and stones are typical of the low alpine heath, where the real podzol is confined under the birch bushes.

The soils are poor in available nutrients (Table 4). In the A_0 horizon, accumulation of exchangeable Ca, Mg and K is evident, but the underlying layers are poor in these elements. The poor availability of nitrogen to plants is indicated by a high C/N ratio, which is 36–48. The soils, except the A_0 horizon, are also poor in readily available P, because the phosphates in this soil are chiefly in the Fe-P and Al-P complexes.

The amounts of many micronutrients measured (8) are also lower than in southern Finland. This is partly due to the very acid soil, e.g. a copper content richer than average in some amphibolite streaks. Zn seems to be accumulated in the A horizon, although the values are rather low. On the other hand, Co is rather abundant and increases downward, owing to podzolisation. The big local variation is partly due to differences in the pH. However, the ultrabasic small outcrops are rich in Co in the Kevo area.

The peak values of Mn in humus layers are among the highest measured in Finnish soils. The values, however, show great variation. The Mo content in the A_0 horizon is rather high (e.g. for N_2 fixation). The deficiency of B in Lapland is well known, and was also confirmed by the IBP results at Kevo.

When the different Kevo IBP sites are compared, the birch site soil reveals a greater bioelement pool than the pine forest (Table 5). The organic layer is important in the nutrient pool because the mineral soil is mostly poor in colloids (8).

There are some small areas around Kevo with less acid bedrock and higher Ca content in the soil. These areas differ from the average in many respects including marked differences in vegetation and flora (15).

Soil moisture is controlled by the altitude, soil structure, inclination of the surface and the plant cover. The moisture percentage is higher in the birch forest than in the pine forest and lowest in the low alpine heath. The soil moisture retention in the C horizon at the three IBP sites is seen in Table 4 (30).

With the poor nutrient content of the soil, nutrient input through precipitation is important for the nutrient balance of the ecosystem (Table 6) (19), not only in ombrotrophic but also in other oligotrophic habitats.

Table 4. Soil profile analyses of the Kevo IBP sites. H$_2$O indicates the soil moisture retention (moisture expressed as % dry weight) at 15— bar suction (Poorly developed horizons indicated by inverted commas). All elements given as ppm except C and N in %.

Site and Horizon	Depth in cm:	Texture (%) mm 20–2	mm 2–0.2	mm 0.2–	H$_2$O	pH (H$_2$O)	Org. C	C/N	N tot.	Exchangeable in 1 N amm. acetate P	Ca	Mg	K	Mn	Fe	Fe	Mn	Ca	2 N HCl extractable Zn	Cu	Co	Mo	Hot water B
Pine																							
A$_0$	– 5	–	–	–		4.3	44.0	48.2	0.91	57.8	930	320	360	63	7.6	270	240	2 170	22	5.7	6.3	3.6	1.1
A$_2$	5– 8	13.2	48.2	38.6		4.2	0.4			2.3	5.6	3.5	9.2	0.4	20	390	14	1 100	1.0	4.3	7.7		
B$_{21}$	8–23	20.9	42.2	36.9		5.0	0.5			1.2	3.6	3.5	12	1.0	18	4 570	15	1 220	5.9	5.0	9.6		
B$_{22}$	23–32	12.9	45.7	41.4		5.0	0.3			1.1	4.1	1.6	11	1.5	9.5	3 130	16	820	5.2	5.2	5.0		
BC	32–60	0.0	45.0	55.0	1.8	5.0	0.2			0.8	9.3	1.2	6.7	0.1	1.6	680	42	1 610	2.3	6.5	7.6		
C	60–	0.9	38.7	60.4		5.0	0.2			0.2	37	2.3	7.9	0.1	1.6	620	10	1 980	1.8	5.8	8.9		
Birch																							
A$_0$+"A$_1$"	– 9	–	–	–		4.6	30.0	36.1	0.83	43.6	610	350	520	33	5.1	520	180	3 550	30	8.3	8.3	4.4	0.4
A$_2$	9–13	–	–	–		4.8	1.2			0.9	14	9.6	12	0.7	13	410	2	990	0.9	3.7	2.6		
B	13–35	32.8	30.2	37.0		5.2	1.9			1.6	7.6	6.0	10	0.4	31	5 630	16	1 060	7.4	8.1	6.4		
BC	35–55	46.0	32.2	21.8		5.2	2.0			1.9	30	5.2	9.6	0.1	17	3 300	17	1 360	5.0	8.5	4.6		
C	55–	39.7	36.5	23.8	5.8	5.3	0.6			0.8	16	3.2	7.6	0.0	12	3 120	19	1 760	15	10	11		
Alpine																							
A$_0$	– 3	–	–	–		4.0	47.5	36.8	1.29	104	540	400	270	6.6	1.4	150	280	3 920	84	9.4	10	11.0	1.0
"A$_2$"	3– 7	–	–	–		4.4	2.0			2.1	83	16	19	0.2	13	870	4	920	1.8	4.5	3.1		
"B"	7–24	48.8	31.8	19.4		5.3	2.6			1.5	63	7.5	15	0.0	13	5 650	9	1 280	7.4	7.1	8.4		
"C"	24–40	29.0	49.0	22.0		5.4	0.6			1.7	33	4.8	11	0.4	6.9	1 460	28	790	4.6	13	7.9		
"	40–60	30.6	38.5	30.9		6.1	0.2			1.9	41	6.1	14	1.0	5.3	2 540	45	920	5.9	13	6.0		
"	60–70	23.5	48.3	28.2	7.4	5.6	0.3			0.8	45	7.3	11	0.2	7.1	2 130	68	820	5.4	12	13		

Table 5. Bioelement pools in the soils of IBP sites at Kevo (g m^{-2} to 35 cm depth)

Site	Ca	Mg	K	P	Zn	Cu	Mn	Fe	Co	C
Pine	9.7	3.5	5.2	0.9	1.0	0.9	1.0	2.2	1.3	5.7
Birch	15.7	8.6	12.9	1.3	1.5	1.1	0.8	3.4	0.9	9.3
Low alpine heath	6.2	1.8	2.0	0.9	0.7	0.8	0.03	0.7	0.6	7.7

Table 6. Annual input of nutrients (g m^{-2}) in precipitation in the years 1971 and 1972. (Number of samples in brackets)

	Precipitation (mm)	SO$_4$	Cl	Org.C	Na	K	Ca	Mg	N Total	NO$_3$–N	NH$_4$–N	P Total	pH
1971	376	1.02 (8)	0.55 (8)	3.59 (8)	0.29 (9)	0.23 (6)	0.19 (7)	0.04 (7)	0.18 (10)	0.06 (10)	0.02 (7)	0.01 (8)	5.8 (10)
1972	404	1.27 (9)	0.80 (8)	3.78 (10)	0.25 (11)	0.13 (10)	0.35 (10)	0.06 (10)	0.16 (11)	0.05 (11)	0.02 (10)	0.01 (10)	5.6 (11)

The total nitrogen input of 0.17 g m^{-2} yr^{-1} must be significant in view of the low biological N$_2$ fixation in the area. In addition to nutrients, the aerosol contains different kinds of pollutants, of which sulphur compounds are most important. These originate partly from natural sources, partly from long-distance emission. The Kevo area is very slightly polluted in comparison with southern Fennoscandia, which is badly affected by the big European pollution centres (19). The sulphuric acid apparently has a slight effect on the pH of precipitation.

PRIMARY PRODUCTION

Kevo represents a poor type of vegetation in the subarctic (42). The total number of vascular plant species in the surroundings (Inari Lapland) is ca 500 and that of mosses 350 (excluding the hepatics), indicating a big choice of ecological niches. Lichens are an important component in the dry ecosystem, while the soil algae have only a minor role. Ericaceous plants and lichens are the two most important groups in the acid and xeric habitats (Table 1). This is also seen in the more mesic birch forest, which is the most common ecosystem north of the pine forest limit. Birch is superior in the area as regards biomass (about 60 %) and production. This plant is the main transmitter of energy for the ecosystem. The special role of the birch in the whole ecosystem is reflected very drastically in the enormous changes that took place in the 1960s, when thousands of square kilometres (Fig. 6) of birch forests were totally destroyed by caterpillars of the moth *Oporinia* (16). Since the birch also serves as reindeer forage, it has been one of the main objects of study in the Finnish tundra programme (6).

Figure 6. Damaged birch forest area near the Kevo Station.

The lichens, being an important part of the ecosystem, particularly in the most extreme climatic conditions, have a special role as winter forage for reindeer (3, 11, 24–27, 29), and lichens are also the main transmitters of nitrogen from the atmosphere to the ecosystem (10, 17, 20, 22, 23, 29, 32).

Among the ecological factors that limit production, particularly of vascular plants, is the low temperature. The low moisture content is another limiting factor not only for cryptogams, but also for trees (31). The long day may also be a restricting factor particularly for moss and lichen species (18). This ecological type of response is apparently possible only in such areas as Fennoscandia, where plants of the temperate boreal zone protrude to the north with the arctic light climate.

The very low number of species of vascular plants in the ground layer, particularly at the pine site (4 species), and the large number of lichens at all sites, are typical features of the primary producers (Table 1). The number of important species with cover values higher than 1 % is particularly small: 6 in the low alpine heath, 7 at the pine site and 9 at the birch site. The frequency of lichens in the low alpine heath is high, but the cover is very low. *Cetraria nivalis* (L.) Ach. is the only species with a cover value over 1 %. This results from excessive grazing pressure by the reindeer.

In biomass of primary producers at the Kevo research sites the pine forest represents favourable local conditions with the highest biomass which, however, depends totally on the pine (Table 7). The birch is the most important plant, representing ca 60 % of the biomass of the dominant birch forest ecosystem. Analysis of the standing crop of trees is seen in Table 8. In spite of the clear differences between the IBP sites in the total biomass, the variation in the ground vegetation is not significant. The biomass of vascular ground vegetation at the IBP birch site shows the dominance of ericaceous plants as a typical feature (Table 9).

Table 7. Biomass of primary producers at the Kevo IBP sites $(g\ m^{-2})$
Figures in brackets are approximations.

	Pine	Birch	Mountain
Pine	2 986	0	0
Birch	(40)	1 104	126
Other bushes	0	(20)	0
Ground vegetation, vascular	392	755	375
Ground vegetation, mosses	18	33	7
Ground vegetation, lichens	85	19	77
Total	3 521	1 931	585

Table 8. Detailed biomass analyses of pine and birch from their respective sites (g m^{-2} dw)

		Pine	Birch
Stem:	wood	1 191	353
	bark	165	159
Leaves:	live	188	60
	attached dead	36	0
Twigs:	attached dead	156	12
Branches:	live	748	178
	dead	121	9
Cones		60 ☆	0
Shoots:	dead basal	0	83
Roots		630	354 ☆☆
Total tree biomass		2 986	1 104
Total tree standing crop		3 295	1 208

☆   biomass varies greatly between years
☆☆   estimate

Estimation of primary production at the IBP sites (Table 10) indicates the differences between the sites and corresponds well with the differences in climatic and nutrient conditions. When compared with other Fennoscandian IBP sites, the values are rather low.

The significance of the birch is manifest considering that the biomass of birch leaves is about 60 g m^{-2}, which is higher than the yearly production of ground vegetation in the pine and heath areas.

CO_2 exchange experiments in the laboratory indicate that mosses and lichens are well adapted to the low temperatures (11, 14). As survival is the first vital necessity for an organism, adaptation to extremes of low temperature and desiccation is important in the Kevo area. This adaptation is seen in the typical net photosynthesis curve (Fig. 7) (11, 12). Activation after chilling takes place very rapidly.

Adaptation of the active phase to prevailing temperature is seen in the low optimum temperature for net photosynthesis, which is between 0°C and 15°C, and in the ability to have high activity values at 0°C. The activity range extends below 0°C, often down to −6°C and −10°C. The values of net assimilation by *Betula tortuosa*, the most important primary producer in the area, are clearly higher than in the southern Finnish provenances of the birch and are correlated with its high chlorophyll values (44).

Table 9. Vascular ground vegetation at the IBP birch forest site (g m^{-2} dw)

	Current year, leaves	Current year, stems	Earlier year, leaves	Earlier year, stems	Standing dead	Below-ground	Fruits	Total (live + standing dead)	Total (live)	Total (above-ground live)	Total (below-ground live)
Empetrum hermaphroditum	–	23.1 ☆	–	107.8	46.8	194.5	6.5	378.7	331.9	137.4	194.5
Vaccinium vitis-idaea	13.8	2.0	17.1	8.7	1.9	115.1	0.0	158.5	156.6	41.5	115.1
V. myrtillus	1.1	1.6	0.1	2.1	0.0	4.0	0.0	8.9	8.9	4.9	4.0
V. uliginosum	6.0	1.2	0.5	22.7	2.6	44.1	0.5	77.5	75.0	30.9	44.1
Ledum palustre	4.3	1.0	3.1	13.6	2.5	154.3	0.0	178.7	176.3	22.0	154.3
Linnaea borealis	0.2	0.0	2.1	0.1	0.0	0.1	0.0	2.7	2.6	2.5	0.1
Deschampsia flexuosa	0.1	0.0	0.0	0.0	0.0	0.0	0.0	0.1	0.1	0.1	0.0
Calamagrostis sp.	0.1	0.0	0.0	0.0	0.2	0.0	0.0	0.2	0.1	0.1	0.0
Juncus trifidus	0.1	0.3	0.0	0.0	1.5	2.5	0.0	4.4	3.0	0.4	2.6
Other forbs	0.0	0.0	0.0	0.0	0.0	0.0	0.0	0.0	0.0	0.0	0.0
Total	25.7	29.3	22.9	155.0	55.4	514.6	7.0	809.9	754.5	239.8	514.7

☆ Not separated into current year leaves and stems and earlier year leaves.

Table 10. Annual production of ground vegetation (g m^{-2} and %).
Note that the values do not include trees and shrubs.

		Birch site	Pine site	Low alpine heath
Vascular plants	(g m^{-2})	75	39	37
	(%)	88	78	82
Mosses	(g m^{-2})	7	2	1
	(%)	8	4	2
Lichens	(g m^{-2})	3	9	7
	(%)	4	18	16
Total	(g m^{-2})	85	50	45
	(%)	100	100	100

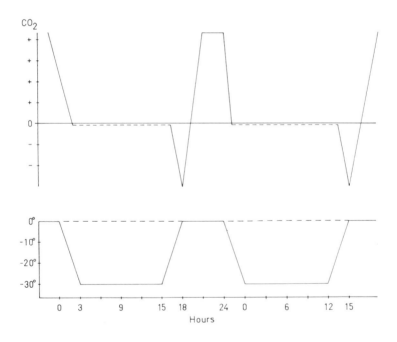

Figure 7. Dependence of CO_2 exchange on daily temperature variations (between $0°C$ and $-30°C$).
The lower curve indicated temperature ($°C$) and the upper one CO_2 exchange activity on a relative
scale. Schematic.

HERBIVORES

Birch, as the dominant primary producer, was a logical object for the herbivory studies. Accordingly, information on other aspects of herbivory is less detailed.

Great annual and long-term variations are typical of the herbivores in the area, both in vertebrates and invertebrates. The biomass of herbivores and the amount of material they consume are low in relation to the amount of available plant tissues.

Invertebrates

The dominant invertebrate herbivores in the birch foliage are larvae of sawflies (Hymenoptera) and Lepidoptera, Coleoptera adults and larvae, Diptera (Cecidomyiidae) larvae and sap-sucking Homoptera (34). Their average total biomass per 100 g dried leaves during the summer in 1971 and 1972 was 35 and 45 mg (34). Annual variations are considerable, an extreme example being the geometrid *Oporinia autumnata*, which defoliated vast areas of birch forests just before the IBP period (16): but also mining Lepidoptera, especially the genus *Eriocrania*, show a great deal of variation (33). In non-*Oporinia* years the species with the highest biomass is Cecidomyiidae.

In the field layer of the birch site, Symphyta larvae dominate in biomass but Homoptera in numbers. The same is true in the low alpine heath, while the field layer of the pine site is dominated by the Homoptera both in biomass and numbers (36).

Abundant microfaunal invertebrate groups in the soil are Acarina, Nematoda and Collembola; Araneae, Coleoptera and Diptera dominate among mesofaunal groups (Table 11).

Vertebrates

The reindeer is the only large herbivore in any appreciable numbers (Fig. 8), with a density of about 4 ind. km^{-2}. Hares (*Lepus timidus* L.) and small rodents (*Clethrionomys rufocanus* (Sund.)), *C. rutilus* Pall., *Microtus oeconomus* (Pall.) and *Lemmus lemmus* (L.) vary largely in number. The density of voles (*Clethrionomys rufocanus* and *C. rutilus*) has varied from nearly 0 (in 1972) to about 60 ind. ha^{-1} (in 1970). Lemmings were found in the IBP areas in 1970–1971, during the mass movements, but there was no effective way to quantify their density. Willow grouse (*Lagopus lagopus* (L.)) and redpoll (*Acanthis flammea* (L.)) are common among herbivorous birds (Table 12).

Functional effects

During the study years (1972 and 1973) a high consumption of birch leaves was caused by *Dineura virididorsata* (Retz.), about 0.66 g m^{-2} in 1971 (4). Cecidomyiidae larvae probably took nearly as much, and Homoptera a little less. Among Lepidoptera the mining *Eriocrania* spp. took about 0.2 g m^{-2} in 1973 (5, 35), and other Lepidoptera probably as much. The same applies to Coleoptera and reindeer (6). These figures refer to "normal", that is non-*Oporinia* years. During the outbreaks, *Oporinia* removes nearly 100 % of the leaves (7, 16).

Table 11. Numbers of some soil invertebrates (m^{-2} ± S.E. of the mean) from the three study sites, extracted by heating of wet funnels[1], dry funnels[2] or large dry funnels[3]. The number of samples is given in brackets and live weight biomass (g) in square brackets. Diptera were sampled in June 1973, Nematoda in July 1973, the remaining groups in August 1973 (37).

Group	Pine			Birch			Alpine		
	min	mean	max	min	mean	max	min	mean	max
Nematoda (×10³)[1]	7	42±11 (6)	76	44	114±38 (6)	276	13	33±9 (6)	66
Acarina (×10³)[1]	15	114±22 (17) [1.6±0.5]	331	66	211±21 (26) [2.8±0.7]	480	24	171+23 (18) [3.5±0.8]	339
Araneae[3]	64	120±12 (10)	192	48	221±23 (24)	464	16	116±30 (10)	352
Collembola (×10³)[2]	1	14±3 (17) [0.23±0.08]	49	4	39±5 (26) [0.40±0.15]	113	1	52±10 (18) [0.61±0.13]	119
Hemiptera[3]	0	43±9 (10)	80	0	67±12 (24)	240	0	13±3 (10)	32
Coleoptera adults[3]	0	37±8 (10)	64	0	69±11 (24)	240	0	18±6 (10)	48
larvae[3]	16	198±52 (10)	496	16	135±16 (24)	304	0	88±28 (10)	304
Diptera adults[3]	16	120±29 (6)	176	32	189±33 (12)	368	16	152±54 (6)	384
larvae[3]	80	296±117 (6)	784	0	101±24 (12)	304	0	161±59 (6)	326

Table 12. **Vertebrate species on the three IBP sites at Kevo.** The abbreviations are:

H – herbivores, H_g – granivores, C_i – carnivores on invertebrates, C_v – carnivores on vertebrates, O – omnivores; A – abundant, C – common, U – uncommon, R – rare; M – male, F – female; B – usually bredds, V – visitor.

The data for body weight, offsprings yr^{-1} and duration are taken from: v. Haartman, L., Hilden, O., Linkola, P., Suomalainen, P. & Tenovuo, R. 1969. Pohjolan linnut värikuvin (Birds of Finland) Vol. I–II. Helsinki and Siivonen, L. 1967. Pohjolan nisäkkäät (Mammals of Finland). Helsinki.

Species	Eco-system function	Density ha^{-1} Pine	Birch	Heath	Body wt (g ww)	Offspr. (no. yr^{-1})	Duration (days)
Rana temporaria	C_i		C		–		365 B
Lacerta vivipara	C_i	U	R		–	–	365 B
Aguila chrysaetus	C_v	R	R		3 500	1–2	365 B
Buteo lagopus	C_v	U	C	C	760	2–4	90 B
Accipiter gentilis	C_v	R			870	1–3	365 B
Circus cyaneus	C_v		R	R	390	4–5	– V
Pandion haliaetus	C_v	U	U		1 500	1–3	90 B
Falco rusticolus	C_v			R	1 500	3–4	90 B
Falco columbarius	C_v	C	U	R(?)	140	3–5	90 B
Falco tinnunculus	C_v	U			180	2–7	90 B
Lagopus lagopus	H_g/H	R	C	U	650	7–11	365 B
Lagopus mutus	H_g/H			U	550	7–11	365 B
Tetrao urogallus	H_g/H	U			M 4 000 F 1 850	6–8	365 B
Pluvialis apricaria	C_i			C	190	3–4	90 B
Eudromias morinellus	C_i			C	120	3	80 B
Numenius phaeopus	C_i		R(?)	U	320	4	80 B
Tringa glareola	C_i			R(?)	60	4	– V
Tringa nebularia	C_i		R(?)	R(?)	180	(3)–4	– V
Stercorarius longicaudus	C_v			C	240	2–(3)	80 B
Cuculus canorus	C_i		U		120	–	60 B
Surnia ulula	C_v	R(?)	U		M 250 F 320	4–8	365 B
Asio flammeus	C_v		R	R	250	4–7	– V
Dendrocopos major	C_i	R			90	5–7	365 B
Dendrocopos minor	C_i		R		24	4–8	365 B
Picoides tridacylus	C_i		R		70	3–6	365 B
Corvus corax	O	C	C	U	1 200	3–6	365 B
Perisoreus infaustus	O	C	U(?)		85	3–5	365 B
Parus major	C_i/O	C	C		19	6–12	365 B
Parus cinctus	C_i/O	C	C		13	5–11	365 B
Parus montanus	C_i/O	C	C		12	5–11	365 B
Turdus pilaris	O	C	C		110	3–7	90 B
Turdus philomelos	O	R(?)	R		65	2–6	90 B
Turdus iliacus	O	C(?)	A		55	5–6	90 B
Turdus torquatos	O			R	100(?)	–	– B
Turdus merula	O		R		100	–	– V
Oenanthe oenanthe	C_i			A	24	6–7	80 B

211

Table 12. cont.

Phoenicuros phoenicuros	C_i	C	C		15	6–7	80 B
Luscinia svecica	C_i		A		18	6–7	80 B
Erithacus rubecula	C_i		R		17	6–7	– B
Phylloscopus trochilus	C_i	C(?)	A		10	6–7	80 B
Phylloscopus borealis	C_i		R		–	6–(7)	– B
Muscicapa striata	C_i	C(?)	C		16	5	80 B
Ficedula hypoleuca	C_i	C(?)	C		13	6–7	80 B
Prunella modularis	C_i/H_g		C		18	4–6	90 B
Anthus pratensis	C_i		A	A	18	4–6	80 B
Anthus trivialis	C_i	C(?)	U		21	4–6	80 B
Anthus cervinus	C_i			U	20	5–6	80 B
Motacilla alba	C_i		C	C	22	5–6	80 B
Motacilla flava	C_i		C	C	20	5–6	80 B
Lanius excubitor	C_v		R		70	4–8	– V
Carduelis flammea	H_g/C_i	C(?)	A		14	5–6	365 B
Carduelis hornemannii	H_g/C_i		R		–	5–6	365 V
Pyrrhula pyrrhula	H_g	R			29	5–6	200 B
Pinicola enucleator	O	R	C		50	3–4	365 B
Fringilla montrifringilla	C_i/H_g	U	A		25	5–7	90 B
Emberiza schoeniclus	C_i		C		20	5–6	90 B
Calcarius lapponicus	C_i/H_g			A	25	5–6	80 B
Plectrophenax nivalis	O			C	35	5–(6)	80 B
Sorex araneus	C_i	U(?)	C	U(?)	10	3–30	365 B
Sorex caecutiens	C_i	U(?)	C	U(?)	6	2–22	365 B
Lepus timidus	H	C	C		2 000	9–40	365 B
Sciurus vulgaris	H_g/H	C			300	6–20	365 B
Lemmus lemmus	H	R–A	R–A	R–A	80	6–28	365 B
Clethrionomys rutilus	H		R–C	R–C	30	8–36	365 B
Clethrionomys rufocanus	H	R–C(?)	R–C	R–C	40	10–21	365 B
Microtus oeconomus	H		R–C	R–C	50	10–36	365 B
Vulpes vulpes	C_v	C	C	U(?)	5 500	3–8	365 B
Alopex lagopus	C_v		R	R	5 000	2–8	365 B
Mustela erminea	C_v	C	C		200	3–7	365 B
Mustela rixosa	C_v	C(?)	C		45	3–7	365 B
Gulo gulo	C_v	R	R	R	15 000	2–3	365 B
Alces alces	H	U	U		300 kg	1–2	365 B
Rangifer tarandus	H	C	A	A	100 kg	1–2	365 B

Figure 8. Typical view of the Kevo mountain area in spring.

About 4 % of the birch foliage was eaten by different herbivores in 1972. This figure, however, does not include losses caused by the reactions of the plant against herbivory. In the only case studied in detail, in *Eriocrania* miners, reactions of the plant were responsible for 5–20 times bigger losses of the plant material than actual consumption (5). Grazing by reindeer is also a significant factor in preventing the renewal of birch after defoliation.

Invertebrates evidently cause less damage to field layer shrubs than to *Betula tortuosa* (35). Lichen removal is severe and is caused by grazing and trampling by reindeer. Lemmings were also responsible for a large-scale destruction of mosses by consumption and burrowing activities during the peak years 1970–1971.

CARNIVORES

The information about carnivores and insectivores is scanty, and no quantitative estimations are available. The most important insectivores on birch foliage are spiders and parasitic Hymenoptera (34). Coccinellidae and Nitulidae (Coleoptera) were present, as well as ants and Neuroptera larvae. The biomass of spiders was about 8 % of the total mesofaunal biomass (34). The same groups dominated in the field layer (36).

Big predatory mammals are extinct in the Kevo region, with the exception of a few wolverines (*Gulo gulo* (L.)) which may be encountered near the IBP sites. Weasels (*Mustela erminea* L. and *M. rixosa* Bangs) were common during and after the rodent peaks. The same was true of foxes (*Vulpes vulpes* (L.)), including the arctic fox (*Alopex lagopus* (L.)). Shrews (*Sorex araneus* L. and *S. caecutiens* Lexmann) are not rare, but quantitative estimates are lacking. Falcons (*Falco columbarius aesalon* Tunstall and *F. rusticolus* L.) may visit all sites.

DECOMPOSITION

Biological activity in the soils at Kevo is low in comparison with other Fennoscandian areas. The annual rate of decomposition of cellulose in the pine forest is ca 15 % of that in central Finland (Table 13) (38), with winter activities particularly low compared with more southerly sites. Activity in the birch forest at Kevo is 2–3 times higher than that in the pine forest. Results from the cotton strip method correspond well with those from cellulose (1, 2, 38).

Low moisture is the main factor restricting decomposition of leaf litter on the surface of the soil (28), and the decomposition rate of lichens is low in comparison with that of leaves (Table 14). Activity appears to be highest in the birch forest and lowest in the low alpine heath. This is seen in soil respiration, the birch forest soil absorbing more oxygen per unit time (1) and it has also a higher enzymatic activity than the pine site. The difference may partly depend on the inhibiting effect of the conifer litter on

Table 13. Weight loss (% dw ± S.D.) of cellulose on the experimental plots at various depths of the soil at Kevo compared to values at Juupajoki, Central Finland (61°50′N; 24°20′E) (38).

	Depth cm	Kevo Birch site	Kevo Pine site	Juupajoki Pine site
During one year (1969−09−10−−1970−09−10)				
	0−1.5	23.0± 8.5	8.1± 5.2	93.2± 8.0
	1.5−3.0	41.0±12.2	21.1±10.2	96.1± 8.9
	3.0−4.5	38.9± 8.0	16.8± 9.7	96.8± 1.5
	4.5−6.0	37.8±11.1	17.5±10.2	96.7± 1.3
From fall to spring (1969−09−10−−1970−06−10)				
	0−1.5	14.5± 6.1	3.1± 3.0	89.0±12.6
	1.5−3.0	12.0± 5.4	2.2± 3.8	89.8±11.0
	3.0−4.5	9.7± 6.0	0.4± 0.6	87.5±12.2
	4.5−6.0	−	−	76.9±13.1

Table 14. Decomposition rates of plant litter at Kevo IBP sites. Measured values are given together with values (in italics) estimated from the measured ones assuming an exponential decomposition rate. S.E. is given and number of samples (n) (39)

Litter	One year loss (%)	Two years loss (%)	Three years loss (%)	Year of experiment, comments
Pine forest				
Pinus silvestris − wood	[5.0]	*6.9*	*8.3*	69/73 Litter surface [a]
Pinus silvestris − needles	18	*33*	*45*	68/69, 69/70 Litter surface [b]
Betula tortuosa − wood	[4.0]	*5.6*	*7.1*	69/73 Litter surface [a]
Cladonia alpestris	5.6 ±0.7 (3)	16.5±2.8 (3)	27.9±3.8 (3)	69/72 In plastic boxes
Birch forest				
Betula tortuosa − wood	[4.5]	*6.8*	*9.1*	69/73 Litter surface [a]
Betula tortuosa − leaves	27	*47*	*61*	68/69, 69/70 Litter surface [b]
Low alpine heath				
Betula tortuosa − wood	[5.0]	*6.9*	*8.3*	69/73 Litter surface [a]

a) Measured for four years and over first summer (in square brackets)

b) Mean for two first year observations

214

soil microbial activity, and the differences in the soil macro- and micronutrients may be additional factors. Dehydrogenase and invertase activity in the birch forest soil at Kevo are higher than in temperate zones (1).

ENERGY FLOW AND NUTRIENT CYCLING

The energy contents of some essential plant components of the ecosystem (Table 15) are higher than in more southern areas, which may be typical of the north and there is an analogous difference in birch from the birch and low alpine sites. The energy values of the dominant ericaceous plant, *Empetrum hermaphroditum*, are among the highest in the area. It is also seen that the energy values of the lichens are lower than in woody plants, and that the N_2-fixing lichens have a higher nitrogen (Table 16) and energy content.

Table 15. Energy values (kJ g^{-1} ± S.E. (n)) of plants from northern Finland. Sampling early June for lichens, mid-August for pine (needles of previous year), and July for birch (leaves of previous year) and *Empetrum* (shoots of previous year). (Kärenlampi, pers. comm.).

Pinus silvestris	22.41 ± 0.14(8)
Betula tortuosa (lowest elevation)	21.43 ± 0.12(7)
Betula tortuosa (low alpine heath)	21.37 ± 0.27(7)
Empetrum hermaphroditum	23.64 ± 0.36(7)
Non-nitrogen fixing lichens *Cladonia mitis*	18.21 ± 0.06(6)
Nitrogen fixing lichens *Peltigera aphthosa*	19.95 ± 0.21(6)
Nephroma arcticum	20.74 ± 0.10(8)

The energy reserves of the birch are an important source of energy for invertebrate and vertebrate consumers, and like the nutrients, are stored in the wood biomass. When these reserves are liberated in damage to the birch, as in an explosion, decomposition by fungi begins. Some 6 % decomposes annually during the first few years, but the tree may remain standing for at least 10 years, although its branches have fallen. The vegetation changes in the mesic birch forests after the liberation of nutrients and the change of light conditions. First there is an increase in the biomass of graminoids and forbs and a decrease in woody plants and cryptogams. After 5—8 years the area changes to a more xeric vegetation, and the biomass of ground vegetation decreases. It is probable that part of the nutrients have leached with the result that the grazing potential decreases.

In the nutrient dynamics of birch in the low alpine heath (Fig. 9) the buds and the young leaves are rich in nitrogen in the spring and the concentration in buds may be as high as in leguminous plants (*Astragalus alpinus* L.). This is the season when the birch is mainly consumed by reindeer. As the leaves grow, the nitrogen content declines, but

215

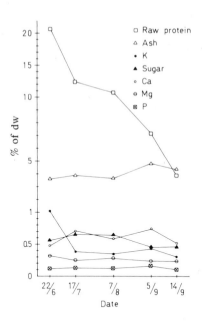

Figure 9. Nutrient contents of birch leaves through the growing season.

the ash content remains almost constant or increases. The ash content is always higher in the green parts of the plant, even though active roots may also have rather high values, particularly of nitrogen (Table 16).

Table 16. Macronutrient concentrations (% of dw) in various parts of birch

	Ash	N	P	K	Ca	Mg
Thin roots	2.10	0.83	0.07	0.29	0.28	0.11
Thick roots	1.04	0.30	0.05	0.19	0.16	0.05
Lower part stem (trunk)	0.95	0.24	0.04	0.11	0.14	0.04
Stem (trunk)	0.89	0.21	0.03	0.19	0.15	0.05
Branches	1.48	0.72	0.08	0.27	0.22	0.08
Buds	2.65	1.37	0.20	0.36	0.41	0.18
Leaves	3.20	1.74	0.14	0.53	0.55	0.29
Catkins	2.93	1.46	0.16	0.39	0.32	0.17

The total ash content is highest in *Equisetum* and lowest in some lichens, vascular plants being intermediate (45). Mushrooms form a special group with a high ash content and a higher total N content (up to 4.5 %) than in the native legumes (*Astragalus alpinus* and *A. frigidus* (L.) A. Gray).

216

The diversity of the mineral nitrogen and micronutrient concentrations influences the functioning of the ecosystem, in addition to the energy content of the biomass. The consumers, like *Dineura* and *Oporinia*, are highly specialized. This is also true of the reindeer which does not consume biomass at random, but selectively, probably in relation to its digestion physiology. In winter, particularly, it is adapted to eating lichens, but it eats them selectively, avoiding the common nitrogen fixing species despite their higher nitrogen, energy and mineral contents. On the other hand, reindeer are fond of mushrooms, which may have a special value in the ecosystem. Thus the function of an ecosystem is dependent not only on the energy content of the various components, but also depends on the qualitative differences in the composition of plants.

Nitrogen fixation

Lichens are the most important plant group responsible for atmospheric nitrogen fixation in the dry ecosystems of Kevo. Nitrogen fixation studies were carried out in 1972 and 1973, which were warmer than the average and had very dry midsummers. The lichen species studied were *Nephroma arcticum* and *Peltigera aphthosa* (L.) Willd. which are common species in the birch forests, *Stereocaulon paschale* in drier areas and *Solorina crocea* (L.) Ach. on sandy ground, especially in the solifluction areas of subarctic mountain slopes.

The environmental conditions in the birch forest area are more favourable for N_2 fixation than those at the pine and low alpine sites (22). On the basis of biomass, the annual amount of nitrogen fixed by lichens m^{-2} is highest in *Stereocaulon paschale* in the pine forest area and *Nephroma arcticum* in the birch forest (Table 17). Thus the N_2 input per unit area is dependent on the lichen species, on ecological factors, and particularly on the biomass. In the mesic birch forests the potential maximum nitrogen input would be about 4 g N_2 m^{-2} yr^{-1} for *Nephroma arcticum* and in the pine forests about 3 g N_2 m^{-2} yr^{-1} for *Sterecaulon paschale*, if the lichen cover is 100 % (22). The N_2 yield in precipitation is almost of the same magnitude as that of the biological nitrogen fixation by lichens.

Table 17. Comparison of the rate of nitrogen fixation under the environmental conditions on each site during summer 1972 (mg g^{-1} dw) and the annual yield of nitrogen per area (mg m^{-2} yr^{-1}) for the main lichen species

Site	*Nephroma arcticum*		*Stereocaulon paschale*	
	mg g^{-1} dw	mg m^{-2} yr^{-1}	mg g^{-1} dw	mg m^{-2} yr^{-1}
Pine	13.8	0	9.9	384
Birch	18.9	104	17.2	46
Low alpine	8.9	5	5.2	168

Temperatures above 0°C are needed to initiate N_2 fixation and the process does not seem to be adapted to sub-zero temperatures in contrast to the photosynthetic reactions of lichens (Fig. 10) (17).

Lichens need a relatively high moisture content for maximal nitrogen fixation compared with photosynthesis: about 250–300 % water of the dry weight of lichen thalli in *Nephroma arcticum* and *Peltigera aphthosa* (21), and above 500 % of the dry weight in *Stereocaulon paschale* (20). Consequently, the best times for nitrogen fixation by lichens are rainy periods, when temperatures are relatively high. Such periods are most common in August and early September – the main periods for lichen growth (26).

The example of the daily nitrogen fixation rates in *Nephroma arcticum* (Fig. 11) shows clearly that nitrogen fixation is at its minimum at noon, when the moisture conditions resulting from high temperature are lowest. Low light intensities do not limit nitrogenase activity between May and August, but after the first week of August, the nights become dark for some hours and the light intensity begins to have an effect on nitrogen fixation.

Drought also has a strong effect on microbial activity in the soil in the Kevo district. Nitrogen fixation (1.8 mg N_2 m^{-2} yr^{-1}) by free-living bacteria and blue-green algae is limited by dry soils and by low soil pH (3.5–4.5). Without these limitations, as in *Sphagnum*-layers in an eutrophic mire, nitrogen fixation by associated blue-green algae was about 130 mg N_2 m^{-2} yr^{-1}.

The importance of the N_2 fixing lichens in the Kevo ecosystems is based on their rather high total nitrogen content, but this nitrogen does not come immediately into circulation to higher trophic levels, because the main herbivores (reindeer) avoid eating these lichen species.

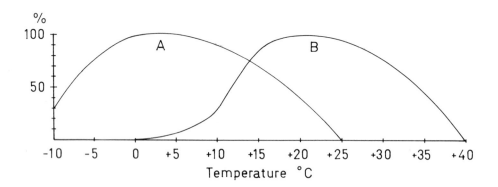

Figure 10. Typical differences in the response of net photosynthesis (A) and nitrogenase activity (B) to temperature in *Stereocaulon paschale*. Schematic.

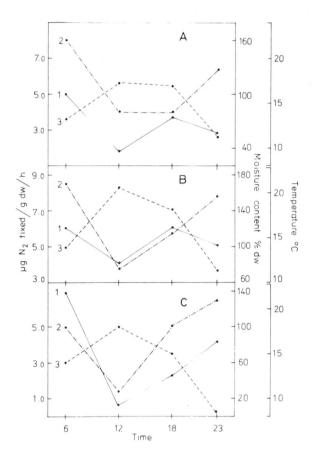

Figure 11. Diurnal nitrogen fixation (1), moisture contents (2) and temperatures (3) in *Nephroma arcticum* during the June–July period at the pine site (A), birch site (B) and low alpine site (C). Numbers of replicates (n) in each dot of the N_2 fixation curve (1) are 70–100, 70–130 and 60–140 respectively.

MAN'S INFLUENCE ON THE ECOSYSTEM

The only way for man to exploit the dry ecosystem of the Kevo area effectively is through herbivorous animals, chiefly reindeer. The reindeer is a native component in the functioning of the ecosystem, and a moderate grazing pressure may even increase the primary production, particularly that of lichens. When the area is overgrazed, disturbances in the ecosystem take place and the production decreases over wide areas. Overgrazing and the disturbing effect of snowmobiles are the most conspicuous signs of human influence outside the villages which are situated only in the main river valleys. Owing to hunting, human influence is also seen in the nearly total extinction of bigger carnivores. Even totally delichenized areas, however, are able to recover. This is seen for

219

example in the fenced areas at IBP sites where the surface of the experimental plots was cleared thoroughly and sown with fragments of *Cladonia alpestris* thalli. After a period of 5 years the lichen stand was renewed, the globular thalli being 1 cm in diameter. One way of preserving or relichenizing winter pasture areas would be to rotate pastures.

It is noteworthy that the birch, the most important component of primary producers, was "discovered" by local people only after the severe birch damage which affected the grazing. Until then it was considered to be outside the "economic forest limit" and was accordingly neglected. Recently there have been proposals of reafforestation of the damaged area (Fig. 12).

The IBP tundra programme has again revealed the sensitivity of the ecosystem and emphasized the necessity of protecting it for proper human use. The plans for widening the Kevo Nature Park, now 354 km^2, is one reflection of this endeavour. The need to activate ecological research and broaden the understanding of the functioning of the ecosystem from the viewpoint of man's natural economy was also a particular concern of the UNESCO meeting of Subarctic Ecology in 1966 (9). The significance of research work to human welfare became evident during the tundra IBP, and ecologists have received recognition as managers of the ecosystem in the development of the North.

Figure 12. Typical birch forest at Kevo.

ACKNOWLEDGEMENTS

The Kevo IBP work has been the joint effort of several scientists. Dr. Lauri Kärenlampi has throughout been responsible for the primary production, decomposition and many other studies, Dr. Erkki Haukioja has been in charge of secondary production, Dr. Sakari Hinneri has carried out soil studies, and Mrs. Sinikka Kallio, Ph.lic., has studied nitrogen fixation. The relevant sections of the present article are based on the work of these scientists, all of whom have had personal assistants. The author expresses his gratitude to all these persons, and particularly to Miss Heli Hurme, M.A., and Mr. Viljo Kohonen, Ph.lic., who have contributed to the preparation of this article.

REFERENCES

1. Baker, J.H. 1974. A comparison of the microbiology of four soils in Finnish Lapland. – Oikos 25: 209–215.
2. Berg, B., Kärenlampi, L. & Veum, A.K. 1975. Comparisons of decomposition rates measured by means of cellulose. – In: Wielgolaski, F.E. (ed.) Fennoscandian Tundra Ecosystems, Part 1, pp. 261–267. Berlin–Heidelberg–New York: Springer Verlag.
3. Bunnell, F., Kärenlampi, L. & Russel, D. 1973. A simulation model of the lichen-*Rangifer* interactions in Northern Finland. – Rep. Kevo Subarctic Res. Stat. 10: 1–8.
4. Haukioja, E. 1973. Weight development, consumption and egestion of *Dineura virididorsata* (Hym., Tenthredinidae) larvae. – Rep. Kevo Subarctic Res. Stat. 10: 9–13.
5. Haukioja, E. 1974. Measuring consumption in *Eriocrania* (Eriocraniidae, Lep.) miners with reference to interaction between the leaf and the miner. – Rep. Kevo Subarctic Res. Stat. 11: 16–21.
6. Haukioja, E. & Heino, J. 1974. Birch consumption by reindeer (*Rangifer tarandus*) in Finnish Lapland. – Rep. Kevo Subarctic Res. Stat. 11: 22–25.
7. Haukioja, E. & Niemelä, P. 1974. Growth and energy requirements of the larvae of *Dineura virididorsata* (Retz.) (Hym., Tenthredinidae) and *Oporinia autumnata* (Bkh.) (Lep., Geometridae) feeding on birch. – Ann. Zool. Fennici 11: 207–211.
8. Hinneri, S. 1974. Podzolic processes and bioelement pools in subarctic forest soils at the Kevo Station, Finnish Lapland. – Rep. Kevo Subarctic Res. Stat. 11: 26–34.
9. Kallio, P. 1970. General conclusions. – In: Ecology of the Subarctic Regions. Proc. of Helsinki Symposium, p. 362. Paris: UNESCO.
10. Kallio, P. 1974. Nitrogen fixation in subarctic lichens. – Oikos 25: 194–198.
11. Kallio, P. & Heinonen, S. 1971. Influence of short-term low temperature on the net photosynthesis in some subarctic lichens. – Rep. Kevo Subarctic Res. Stat. 8: 63–72.
12. Kallio, P. & Heinonen, S. 1973. Ecology of photosynthesis in *Rhacomitrium lanuginosum* (Hedw.) Brid. – Rep. Kevo Subarctic Res. Stat. 10: 43–54.
13. Kallio, P. & Kärenlampi, L. 1971. A review of the stage reached in the Kevo IBP in 1970. – In: Heal, O.W. (ed.) Proceedings of the Working Meeting on Analysis of Ecosystems: Tundra Biome Kevo Finland, p. 79–91. Stockholm: IBP Tundra Biome Steering Committee.
14. Kallio, P. & Kärenlampi, L. In press. The photosynthetic activity in mosses and lichens. – In: Cooper, J.P. (ed.) Photosynthesis and Productivity in Different Environments. Cambridge: Cambridge University Press.
15. Kallio, P., Laine, U. & Mäkinen, Y. 1969. Vascular flora of Inari Lapland. 1. Introduction and Lycopodiaceae – Polypodiaceae. – Rep. Kevo Subarctic Res. Stat. 5: 1–108.
16. Kallio, P. & Lehtonen, J. 1973. Birch forest damage caused by *Oporinia autumnata* (Bkh.) in 1965–66 in Utsjoki, N. Finland. – Rep. Kevo Subarctic Res. Stat. 10: 55–69.
17. Kallio, P., Suhonen, S. & Kallio, H. 1972. The ecology of nitrogen fixation in *Nephroma arcticum* and *Solorina crocea*. – Rep. Kevo Subarctic Res. Stat. 9: 7–14.
18. Kallio, P. & Valanne, N. 1975. On the effect of continuous light on photosynthesis in mosses. – In: Wielgolaski, F.E. (ed.) Fennoscandian Tundra Ecosystems, Part 1, pp. 149–162. Berlin–Heidelberg–New York: Springer Verlag.

19. Kallio, P. & Veum, A.K. 1975. Analyses of precipitation in Fennoscandian IBP-sites. – In: Wielgolaski, F.E. (ed.) Fennoscandian Tundra Ecosystems, Part 1, pp. 333–338. Berlin–Heidelberg–New York: Springer Verlag.

20. Kallio, S. 1973. The ecology of nitrogen fixation in *Stereocaulon paschale*. – Rep. Kevo Subarctic Res. Stat. 10: 34–42.

21. Kallio, S. & Alexander, V. In manuscript. Nitrogen fixation by *Peltigera aphthosa* in Alaska.

22. Kallio, S. & Kallio, P. 1975. Nitrogen fixation in lichens at Kevo, North Finland. – In: Wielgolaski, F.E. (ed.) Fennoscandian Tundra Ecosystems, Part 1, pp. 292–304. Berlin–Heidelberg–New York: Springer Verlag.

23. Kallio, S. & Varheenmaa, T. 1974. On the effect of air pollution on nitrogen fixation in lichens. – Rep. Kevo Subarctic Res. Stat. 11: 42–46.

24. Kärenlampi, L. 1970. Distribution of chlorophyll in the lichen *Cladonia alpestris*. – Kevo Subarctic Res. Stat. 7: 1–8.

25. Kärenlampi, L. 1970. Morphological analysis of the growth and productivity of the lichen *Cladonia alpestris*. – Rep. Kevo Subarctic Res. Stat. 7: 9–15.

26. Kärenlampi, L. 1971. Studies on the relative growth rate of some fruticose lichens. – Rep. Kevo Subarctic Res. Stat. 7: 33–39.

27. Kärenlampi, L. 1971. On methods for measuring and calculating the energy flow through lichens. – Rep. Kevo Subarctic Res. Stat. 7: 40–46.

28. Kärenlampi, L. 1971. Weight loss of leaf litter on forest soil surface in relation to weather at Kevo Station, Finnish Lapland. – Rep. Kevo Subarctic Res. Stat. 8: 101–103.

29. Kärenlampi, L. 1971. Food chain model of reindeer lichens. – In: Rosswall, T. (ed.) Systems Analysis in Northern Coniferous Forests. Bull. Ecol. Res. Comm. (Stockholm) 14: 83–85.

30. Kärenlampi, L. 1972. Comparisons between the microclimates of the Kevo ecosystem study sites and the Kevo Meteorological Station. – Rep. Kevo Subarctic Res. Stat. 9: 50–65.

31. Kärenlampi, L. 1972. On the relation of the Scots pine annual ring width and some climatic variables at the Kevo Subarctic Station. – Rep. Kevo Subarctic Res. Stat. 9: 78–81.

32. Kärenlampi, L., Tammisola, J. & Hurme, H. 1975. Weight increase of some lichens as related to carbon dioxide exchange and thallus moisture. – In: Wielgolaski, F.E. (ed.) Fennoscandian Tundra Ecosystems, Part 1, pp. 135–137. Berlin–Heidelberg–New York: Springer Verlag.

33. Koponen, S. 1973. On the mining insects of the mountain birch in northernmost Fennoscandia. – Rep. Kevo Subarctic Res. Stat. 10: 14–19.

34. Koponen, S. 1973. Herbivorous invertebrates of the mountain birch at Kevo, Finnish Lapland. – Rep. Kevo Subarctic Res. Stat. 10: 20–28.

35. Koponen, S. 1974. On the occurrence and ecology of *Eriocrania* spp. (Lep., Eriocraniidae) and other mining insects of the birch in northernmost Fennoscandia. – Rep. Kevo Subarctic Res. Stat. 11: 52–64.

36. Koponen, S. & Ojala, H. 1974. On the mesofauna of the field layer of three subarctic habitats. – Rep. Kevo Subarctic Res. Stat. 11: 65–71.

37. Koponen, S. & Ojala, M.-L. 1975. Quantitative study of invertebrate groups in the soil and ground layer of the IBP sites at Kevo, northern Finland. – Rep. Kevo Subarctic Res. Stat. 12 (in press).

38. Lähde, E. 1974. Rate of decomposition of cellulose in forest soils in various parts of the Nordic countries. – Rep. Kevo Subarctic Res. Stat. 11: 72–78.

39. Rosswall, T., Veum, A.K. & Kärenlampi, L. 1975. Plant litter decomposition at Fennoscandian tundra sites. – In: Wielgolaski, F.E. (ed.) Fennoscandian Tundra Ecosystems, Part 1, pp. 268–278. Berlin–Heidelberg–New York: Springer Verlag.

40. Sirén, G. & Hari, P. 1971. Coinciding periodicity in recent tree rings and glacial clay sediments. – Rep. Kevo Subarctic Res. Stat. 8: 155–157.

41. Skartveit, A., Rydén, B.E. & Kärenlampi, L. 1975. Climate and hydrology of some Fennoscandian tundra ecosystems. – In: Wielgolaski, F.E. (ed.) Fennoscandian Tundra Ecosystems, Part 1, pp. 41–53. Berlin–Heidelberg–New York: Springer Verlag.

42. Sonesson, M., Wielgolaski, F.E. & Kallio, P. 1975. An introduction to the Fennoscandian IBP Tundra sites. – In: Wielgolaski, F.E. (ed.) Analysis of Fennoscandian Tundra Ecosystems, Part 1, pp. 3–28. Berlin–Heidelberg–New York: Springer Verlag.

43. Tedrow, J.C.F. 1970. Soils of the subarctic regions. – In: Ecology of the Subarctic Regions. Proc. of Helsinki Symposium, pp. 180–195. Paris: UNESCO.
44. Vaarama, A. & Valanne, T. 1973. On the taxonomy, biology and origin of *Betula tortuosa* Ledeb. – Rep. Kevo Subarctic Res. Stat. 10: 70–84.
45. Wielgolaski, F.E., Kjelvik, S. & Kallio, P. 1975. Mineral content of tundra plants in Fennoscandia. – In: Wielgolaski, F.E. (ed.) Analysis of Fennoscandian Tundra Ecosystems, Part 1, pp. 316–332. Berlin–Heidelberg–New York: Springer Verlag.

Rosswall, T. & Heal, O.W. (eds.) 1975.
Structure and Function of Tundra Ecosystems.
Ecol. Bull. (Stockholm) 20: 225–264.

HARDANGERVIDDA, NORWAY

E. ØSTBYE (ed.), A. BERG, O. BLEHR, M. ESPELAND, E. GAARE, A. HAGEN,
O. HESJEDAL, S. HÅGVAR, S. KJELVIK, L. LIEN, I. MYSTERUD, A. SANDHAUG,
H.-J. SKAR, A. SKARTVEIT, O. SKRE, T. SKOGLAND, T. SOLHØY,
N.C. STENSETH and F.E. WIELGOLASKI

INTRODUCTION

Hardangervidda, in southern Norway, is the largest mountain plateau in Europe (Fig. 1). It is approximately 10 000 km^2 in area and lies mostly between 1 100 and 1 300 m a.s.l., with some peaks reaching a height of 1 800 to 1 900 m. Hardangerjøkulen, an active glacier of the Norwegian plateau type (78.2 km^2) – the sixth largest in Norway – lies in the northwestern part of the area. The central part, though slightly undulating, is flatter than the rest of the area. The topography and vegetational cover produce a strong mosaic pattern. The area is rich in water bodies – from small brooks to large rivers, and ponds to large lakes – and extensive peatlands.

For ecological reasons, our delimitation of Hardangervidda is more liberal than the official one (58). The northern part of this mountain plateau is bordered by mountain ridges running east-west (the Geilo-Hallingskarvet-Myrdal line). The steep gradient towards the west coast of Norway forms the western border (the Mjølfjell-Hardangerfjorden-Odda-Røldal line). Mountain valleys traversing other mountain areas (east-west orientated) make up the southern border (the Røldal-Haukelifjell-Rauland line). The eastern border is very difficult to define, but comprises small valleys with farmlands as well as mountain outlets running east to southeast (the Rauland-Rollag-Tunhovd-Geilo line).

The borders mostly follow natural dividing lines such as certain major water courses, and take in the area usually used by the Hardangervidda reindeer population. Adjacent farmlands are included when their inhabitants have traditionally used the mountain plateau in various ways. Historically, human impact on the area can be traced back approximately 9 000 years, to the time immediately after the melting of the large inland ice sheet.

Hardangervidda was chosen as a study area for the Norwegian IBP/PT–UM sections. Investigations were carried out at several sites, the most intensively studied being Finse (60° 36′N, 7°30′E) with several habitat plots on both north- and south-facing slopes (Fig. 2), where the High Mountain Ecology Research Station belonging to the Universities of Bergen and Oslo has been set up. Maurset (60°24′N, 7°17′E), a subalpine birch forest (Fig. 3) and Stigstuv (60°18′N, 7°41′E) a dry and wet meadow, a lichen heath and a willow thicket (Fig. 4) are other main sites. Fairly complete bibliographies of publications in the field of natural and cultural sciences from the Hardangervidda area and surrounding mountain areas, will increase the knowledge of this mountain plateau for any reader interested in more information than can be given in the present text (58, 65). Results from more recent investigations, mainly within IBP, are presented in several papers in two volumes titled "Fennoscandian tundra ecosystems" (87, 88). An overview of the results is given in (81).

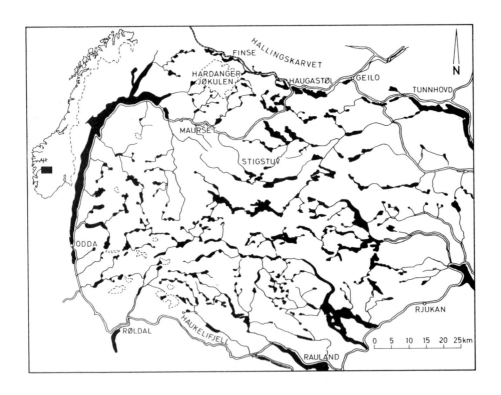

Figure 1. Simplified map of Hardangervidda, research sites marked.

Figure 2. The Finse area. The Hardangerjøkulen glacier in the background.

Figure 3. Subalpine birch forest at Maurset (from 81).

Figure 4. The Stigstuv area.

ENVIRONMENTAL CONDITIONS

Climate

Hardangervidda owes its rather variable weather and its relatively mild maritime climate (Tables 1, 2) to the prevailing warm, moisture-bearing westerlies and southwesterlies from the North Atlantic. This maritime influence causes the temperature to be much higher, especially in winter, than would otherwise be the case in view of the height and latitude. Locally, this zonal air flow is considerably influenced by the topography, elevation, and radiation balance of the earth's surface. All these factors lead to a pronounced climatic gradient from the western to the eastern parts of the plateau. There is a clear decrease in temperature and continentality with elevation and an increase in continentality eastwards.

Winter and late autumn are by far the stormiest seasons, with the most intense zonal circulation and cyclonic activity. The high mountain regions of western Norway have one of the heaviest cloud covers in the world, high frequency of fog, and high mean rel-

Table 1. Climatic features at meteorological station Haugastøl (60°31'N, 7°52'E, 988 m a.s.l.) Hardangervidda. Compiled from various sources (10, 11, 28, 41, 42)

Variables	J	F	M	A	M	J	J	A	S	O	N	D	Year
Screen temperature (°C)													
min	-13.9	-14.2	-11.9	-6.6	-1.2	3.4	7.5	6.6	2.7	-2.0	-6.2	-9.4	-3.8
mean	-9.6	-9.5	-7.0	-2.6	2.9	7.4	10.7	9.8	5.7	0.7	-3.4	-6.2	-0.1
max	-5.5	-4.9	-1.6	2.0	7.5	12.0	15.0	14.1	9.7	4.0	-0.6	-3.6	4.0
Relative humidity air (%)	83	82	78	78	74	73	75	77	79	82	85	85	79
Wind velocity (m s^{-1})	2.5	2.7	2.5	2.5	2.0	2.7	2.7	2.5	2.5	2.7	2.5	2.7	2.5
Precipitation (mm)	60	45	32	36	35	53	76	78	72	66	57	59	669
Fog (d)	2.4	1.7	1.7	1.2	2.6	1.5	1.1	2.1	2.6	2.7	2.3	2.3	24.2
Sunshine duration (h)	47	100	141	151	204	181	182	149	116	91	40	27	1 429

Table 2. Climatic features at meteorological station Slirå (60°37'N, 7°25'E, 1 300 m a.s.l.), Hardangervidda. Compiled from various sources (10, 11, 28, 41)

Variables	J	F	M	A	M	J	J	A	S	O	N	D	Year
Screen temperature (°C)													
min	-12.4	-12.9	-11.0	-7.6	-2.6	1.5	4.7	4.6	1.2	-3.4	-7.3	-9.9	-4.6
mean	-9.7	-10.0	-8.0	-4.8	0.2	4.1	7.3	7.0	3.3	-1.4	-5.0	-7.3	-2.0
max	-6.8	-6.9	-4.6	-1.2	3.5	7.7	11.1	10.1	6.1	1.0	-2.7	-4.9	1.0
Relative humidity air (%)	85	84	82	84	80	82	83	83	85	87	88	88	84
Wind velocity (m s^{-1})	4.5	4.7	4.3	4.3	4.1	3.9	3.8	3.9	4.7	4.7	4.5	4.7	
Precipitation (mm)	79	62	41	51	43	77	110	120	136	116	81	90	1 006
Fog (d)	6.6	6.2	8.1	7.8	7.5	8.3	8.6	6.0	7.7	9.6	9.0	7.6	93.0

ative humidity throughout the year. The leeward effect of the Scandinavian mountain chain markedly reduces cloud cover and precipitation on the eastern slopes. The climate of these leeward regions and to some extent the easternmost parts of Hardangervidda, is accordingly affected more by mesoscale radiation conditions than by large-scale advection.

The precipitation regime of Hardangervidda is to a great extent determined by the amount of water released from the westerlies and southwesterlies under topographical influence. The heaviest precipitation occurs on the western slopes and other western parts of the area. The season of maximum precipitation is September–October on the western slopes and July–August on the eastern slopes. The annual precipitation ranges from 1 500 mm and above in the western parts of Hardangervidda to 500 mm in the eastern parts. The mean annual potential evapotranspiration ranges from 200 mm to 250 mm and is accordingly lower than the mean annual precipitation in all sections of Hardangervidda (42).

Although considerable deviations from the standard normals are usual at Hardangervidda, these deviations are fairly uniform throughout the region. Thus the deviations from the monthly standard normals of the precipitation for 1931–60 and the air temperature at Haugastøl (eastern part of Hardangervidda) for 1969–72 (Fig. 5) are taken as typical of the corresponding deviations over the whole plateau. The figure also shows the month-

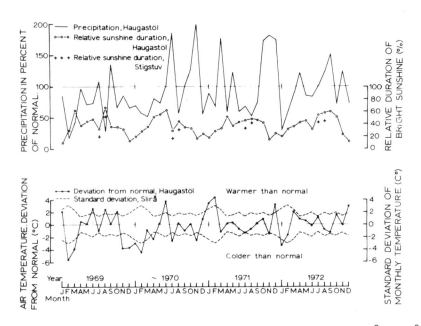

Figure 5. The variation of various elements at Haugastøl (meteorological station, 60°31′N, 7°52′E, 988 m a.s.l.) during the period 1969–1972: Monthly precipitation in per cent of the standard normal 1931–1960, duration of bright sunshine in per cent of possible duration, and the deviation of the mean monthly air temperature from the standard normal 1931–1960. Relative sunshine duration at Stigstuv (60°18′N, 7°41′E, 1 320 m a.s.l.) for the months of July and August, and the standard deviation of the mean monthly temperatures at Slirå (meteorological station, 60°25′N, 7°25′E, 1 300 m a.s.l.) during the period 1931–1960 are also included (10, 15, 16, 17, 18, 73).

ly duration of bright sunshine as a percentage of possible duration for a given period. Given the general westward increase in cloudiness, the Haugastøl data can be considered as providing an adequate picture of the month to month variation in cloud cover for all sections of Hardangervidda.

Soils

Although Hardangervidda is classified as tundra, there is no permafrost, one reason being that the snow cover is stable and relatively thick. Precambrian rocks predominate over most of the area, giving an acid, nutrient-poor parent material. Moraines are also common and stones are copious in many places. The low clay and silt content of many soils (9, 39) provides good drainage, which in combination with the climate and parent material has caused the development of podsolic profiles. Where drainage is impeded organic soils – sometimes with more than 30 cm of peat – have developed. The dominance of oligotrophic vegetation is associated with dry, nutrient-poor soils and primary production is correlated with soil nutrient content. Even in the eutrophic dry meadow site, fertilization increased aboveground productivity of plants four- to fivefold (89).

PRIMARY PRODUCTION

The Hardangervidda area is characterized by a mosaic of vegetation types caused mostly by the variation in abiotic factors. The vegetation consists mainly of perennial species with less than 10 % of therophytes (14). Vegetative propagation is normal. Approximately 130 species of vascular plants are represented in the low-medium alpine region of the area, hemicryptophytes above 50 %, phanerophytes 5 %, chamaephytes 10 %, geophytes 10 %, helophytes 10 % and hydrophytes 5 %.

The succession from barren ground after withdrawal of the ice is clearly demonstrated near the Hardangerjøkulen glacier, but the main part of the area is said to be close to climax communities. Peak diversity is reached 30–50 years after the withdrawal of the ice (19). Dispersal studies have shown that seed from the nearby plants is the most important form of new establishment. Only 13 % of the diaspores were dispersed more than 5 m. After peak diversity is reached, the more competitive species slowly displace the less competitive ones, leaving the first invaders restricted to areas such as riverbanks, solifluction slopes, small screes, etc. The result is a decrease in the number of species and an approach towards a mature vegetation.

Plant communities, standing crop and production

The development of plant communities at Hardangervidda depends greatly on climatic (74) and edaphic (39) factors. On a macro-scale, temperature is the most important factor limiting the alpine tree line by birch (*Betula pubescens* ssp. *tortuosa* (Led.) Nyman) at about 1 050 m (14) and also the upper border of woody plants, such as *Salix lapponum* L. (and related willows) and ericaceous plants. On a smaller scale, temperature is less important, as shown by the relatively small variation in maximum biomass from one year to the next in spite of temperature differences.

The snow cover, however, is very important for the various communities developed on a smaller scale. Often less than 50 cm maximum snow cover is found on windblown ridges. Only plants capable of withstanding the low winter temperatures under shallow snow cover will be found at these oligotrophic, often so called lichen heaths, e.g. *Empetrum hermaphroditum* Hagerup, *Vaccinium vitis-idaea* L., *Festuca ovina* L. and particularly lichens belonging to the genera *Cladonia* and *Cetraria* (91). Under somewhat thicker snow cover, plants such as *Vaccinium myrtillus* L. and *Betula nana* L. develop in low alpine areas and together with grass on chionophilous heaths. Most of these very important heath communities are oligotrophic at Hardangervidda (Table 3) (38) indicating the importance of the soil-nutrient factor on plant community development. The heath communities are generally dry, and soil moisture is one of the strongest growth limiting factors in these communities.

The total live biomass of vascular plants above- and belowground and cryptogam may be of the order of 300–700 g m^{-2} at the heaths – covering nearly half the total area at Hardangervidda (Table 3) – more than half being lichens at the driest and poorest types with shallow snow cover (cf. Table 4). The daily primary production at a typical lichen heath with some vascular plants is 2.0–2.5 g m^{-2} – less than 1 g m^{-2} being cryptogams (48) – when compensated for dieback and decomposition during the growing season, but not for consumption (89). It is obvious that the production to biomass ratio is lower for the lichens (about 0.2) than for the vascular plants. Lower production per m^2 may therefore be found at lichen heaths where vascular plants are absent. At the more chionophilous heaths, total primary production is estimated normally to be 2.0–3.5 g m^{-2} d^{-1}. The growing season on the windblown heaths may start in early June for vascular plants (92) or even earlier under extreme conditions and for cryptogams, and last until late September. The relatively long growing season compared with that in areas with thicker snow cover is favourable for the completion of life cycle of some plant species.

The number of vascular plant species is, however, higher in meadow-like areas with thicker snow cover (above ca 1 m) and less severe winter soil surface temperatures than in heath areas. Soil moisture is usually more favourable, particularly in spring after snow melt, but is still one of the most important plant growth-limiting factors. *Deschampsia flexuosa* (L.) Trin. is one of the most important species on the dominating oligotrophic moderate snow-bed meadow types at Hardangervidda (Table 3). In more eutrophic, moderate snow-beds, forbs are more abundant and grasses like *Anthoxanthum alpinum* (L.) and *Poa alpina* L. are common (91). These species have a higher mineral (94) and carbohydrate (76) content than the more oligotrophic species and are preferred by domestic animals, such as sheep (90).

The vascular plant biomass in particular is higher in the dry meadow (moderate snowbed) than in the heath communities, mainly because of the better soil moisture conditions. At the more eutrophic types with low C/N ratios (39), the total biomass is of the order 700–800 g m^{-2} (Table 4), but may be more than 200 g lower at the most oligotrophic types. The primary production at a relatively eutrophic meadow at Hardangervidda is about 5 g m^{-2} d^{-1}, about 2 g being aboveground vascular plant production (89). The aboveground production particularly of grasses and eutrophic forbs at this site is,

232

however, found to be increased 4–5 times by fertilization, showing that even the relatively eutrophic meadows are limited in production by lack of mineral nutrients. Due to a high percentage of herbaceous vascular plants at the Hardangervidda moderate snow-bed meadow communities, relatively higher production to biomass ratios are found than in most other communities; in vascular plants about 0.7 (91).

Table 3. Communities included in the 12 groups of vegetation types mapped at Hardangervidda. All formal names marked N are *sensu* Nordhagen, names marked G are *sensu* Gjaerevoll (22, 63)

Code	Name	Cover %	The vegetation types comprises associations belonging to:
	Oligothropic vegetation types		
O I	Chionophobous heaths	10	Loiseleurio-Arctostaphylion N and Juncion trifidi scandinavicum N.
O II	Chionophilous heaths	33	Phyllodoco-Vaccinion myrtilli N and Juncion trifidi scandinavicum N.
O III	Moderate snow beds	14	Deschampsio-Anthoxanthion G and Ranunculo-Anthoxanthion G.
O IV	Extreme snow beds	5	Herbaceon G, Stellaro-Oxyrion G and Polytrichion norwegici G.
O V	Birch forests	9	Phyllodoco-Vaccinion myrtilli N and wooded forms of Caricion canescentis-fuscae N.
O VI	Bogs and fens	12	Oxycocco-Empetrion hermaphroditi N, Leuco-Scheuchzerion N, Stygio-Caricion limosae N and Caricion canescentis-fuscae N.
	Eutrophic vegetation types		
E I	*Dryas* heath	<0.1	Kobresieto-Dryadion N.
E II	Tall herb meadows	3.3	Lactucion alpinae N.
E III	Moderate snow beds	0.7	Reticulato-Poion alpinae G, Ranunculo-Poion alpinae G and Potentilleto-Polygonion vivipari N.
E IV	Extreme snow beds	<0.1	Polarion G and Oppositifolio-Oxyrion G.
E V	Tall herb birch forests	2.3	Lactucion alpinae N and wooded forms of rich Caricion canescentis-fuscae N and Caricion atrofuscae-saxatilis N.
E VI	Fens	6	Rich Caricion canescentis fuscae N and Caricion atrofuscae-saxatilis N.

Table 4. Structure, biomass and primary production at Hardangervidda

Sites	Lichen heath	Wet meadow	Dry meadow	*Salix* shrub	*Betula* forest
Community plant cover (%)	100	150	115	160	115
Community LAI (live)	0.3	1.2	0.9	2.0	3.2
Standing crop (g m^{-2} at peak above ground)	910	3 240	1 245	2 640	4 900
Aboveground biomass					
Live					
Monocotyledons	8	94	34	40	22
Forbs	0	12	91	61	4
Woody – green	30	25	18	75	210
non-green	24	16	18	628	2 134
Mosses	7	175	31	307	61
Lichens	370	0	19	0	9
Algae	n.d.	n.d.	n.d.	n.d.	n.d.
Standing dead and litter					
Monocotyledons	35	216	39	66	43
Forbs	0	7	180	55	4
Woody	116	25	39	125	295
Belowground					
Live	191	1 316	545	1 305	1 768
Dead	125	1 345	184	47	206
Net production (g m^{-2} yr^{-1})	(understorey by harvesting and trees and shrubs by regression technique)				
Aboveground					
Monocotyledons	13	180	53	80	16
Forbs	0	18	155	125	5
Woody – green	62	49	27	70	314
non-green	13	7	6	110	216
Mosses	10	173	48	210	40
Lichens	78	0	(4)	0	0
Belowground	100	410	245	290	189

n.d. = not determined

The maximum snow cover in bogs and fens is of the order of 2 m (74) or more, and the growing season therefore usually lasts less than 100 days. These sites are most common in the western, most oceanic parts of Hardangervidda (91) and particularly in low alpine areas. As for the drier meadow types, about one quarter of the total Hardangervidda area is occupied by mires of different types, particularly relatively oligotrophic ones (Table 3). In typical bogs, *Rubus chamaemorus* L. and *Eriophorum vaginatum* L., for example, are abundant (91); in fens of varying richness *Carex* spp. predominate, in the richest low alpine areas willows and tall perennials are also common. Bryophytes are very important in these wet communities; several species predominate in the richer types (57), while, for example *Sphagnum* spp. are abundant in the poorer.

Soil moisture does not directly limit biomass and production in these communities, although stomata may be closed at midday (49), resulting, for example, in reduced photosynthesis. When lack of mineral nutrients is not strongly growth-limiting and the growing season not too short, these wet communities are very productive. It is found that the photosynthetic efficiency is nearly 2.5 % of the available radiation (400–700 nm) in eutrophic wet communities (93), compared with about 0.7 % in lichen heaths. The total biomass of the eutrophic mires is of the order of 1 500-2 500 g m^{-2}, often including 2–300 g m^{-2} bryophytes (Table 4). Considerably lower total biomass is, however, found in oligotrophic bogs –often below 1 000 g m^{-2}. The root biomass is often extremely high compared with that of tops in mires, and particularly in *Carex* fens; top to root ratios of 1:10 to 1:20 are common (95).

The high root biomass is caused, among other things, by slow decomposition in the anaerobic mire. In the upper, aerobic layers, however, almost 40 % may be decomposed in the first year after death of aboveground herbaceous vascular plant material in the favourable water conditions of the mire (69).

Primary production is also high at eutrophic mires if the snow cover is not too thick; 8–9 g m^{-2} d^{-1} is estimated as a total above- and belowground production (48, 89) including bryophytes (often about 2 g m^{-2} d^{-1}), but is considerably lower in oligotrophic bogs (e.g. 5 g m^{-2} d^{-1}). The production to biomass ratio is lower both at a *Carex* wet meadow and a low alpine willow thicket than at the drier, moderate snow-bed, meadow. For vascular plants, ratios of 0.3–0.4 are found, partly due to the presence of woody material in, for example, willows, but mostly to the high root biomass.

The area of extreme snow-beds is relatively small at Hardangervidda (Table 3). The snow cover may be several metres thick and the growing season from 0 to about 60 days. Only a few vascular plants (e.g. *Salix herbacea* L.) are able to develop, but some lichens and bryophytes may survive. The plant biomass and production will, of course, vary strongly with the snow cover, but the total biomass is usually lower than 500 g m^{-2} and the daily production is 0–2 g m^{-2}.

Due to higher temperatures in subalpine areas, as compared to alpine, both higher biomass and production are recorded in birch forests at Hardangervidda than in similar communities at greater elevations. At a relatively dry, oligotrophic birch forest dominated by ericaceous plants in the understorey, the total biomass is about 4 500 g m^{-2} including the birch trees (Table 4) and the daily total production about 6 g m^{-2} (48). This is higher than production at the eutrophic moderate snow-bed reported earlier, in spite of lower nutrient content. The production to biomass ratio is of course very low for vascular plants (0.2). In eutrophic birch forests with tall perennials in the understory considerably higher production is found – estimated to be up to 10 g m^{-2} d^{-1} in the growing season, which often exceeds four months.

The plant biomass and production results reported from different communities clearly show that the production processes are strongly influenced by both climatic and edaphic factors at Hardangervidda.

Production processes

Highest photosynthetic rates are found just after the leaves have reached their maximum growth, but before flowering (75). Optimum temperatures for net photosynthesis are in the range 10–20°C for most species, and are lowest for lichens from the lichen heath. Dark respiration seems to increase in leaves towards senescence and autumn. High temperatures seem to promote photosynthesis in most cases (64, 75, 76). The highest values (10–20 mg CO_2 g^{-1} h^{-1}) were found for deciduous shrubs, forbs and graminoids, while evergreen shrubs had much lower rates, down to 2.5 mg CO_2 g^{-1} h^{-1} in *Empetrum hermaphroditum*. Similar rates were also found in bryophytes, while lichens had very low rates of net photosynthesis (0.3–0.4 mg CO_2 g^{-1} h^{-1}). *Empetrum* and *Vaccinium* leaves from the birch forest, seem to be adapted to the lower light intensity and higher temperatures at this site when compared with similar species from other sites. Dark respiration at 15°C was usually about 1 mg CO_2 g^{-1} h^{-1}.

Root respiration measurements on single species in nutrient solution at 15°C give values between 0.5 and 1.5 mg CO_2 g^{-1} h^{-1}. Highest values are found in small forbs like *Ranunculus acris* L. while deciduous shrubs and grasses have lowest respiration rates. The highest translocation rate is recorded in the first hours after incorporation of $^{14}CO_2$ (4). More than 50 % of ^{14}C in the plants is found in belowground parts after two days. This figure increases in autumn because of carbohydrate storage and possibly also because of root growth.

The same general picture is true when the content of holocellulose is considered while the content of lignin increases throughout the whole season. The storage polysaccharides accumulate in roots and stem bases of forbs and graminoids, mostly in the stems of deciduous shrubs and in leaves of evergreens (2, 76). Highest amounts are usually found when the leaves are fully expanded but before reproduction and root growth. During spring there is a strong carbohydrate decrease in roots due to growth and translocation to shoots, while a downward movement seems to take place in deciduous species during leaf senescence in autumn. Some of this is probably used in root growth, causing a decrease in the total carbohydrate concentration.

Temperature and light appear to have an influence on the carbohydrate level and on the proportion of the different saccharides. Plants from the coldest sites have a higher level of ethanol-soluble sugars in their leaves than corresponding plants from the subalpine field. Highest leaf carbohydrate concentrations (25–30 %) are found in graminoids, while forbs with tuberous roots like *Alchemilla vulgaris* L. have very high starch concentrations in their roots (50 %). Xylan seems to be a more important storage compound than starch in shrubs and graminoids (76).

Maximum leaf area index (LAI), which is found in mid-August at all the sites, is highest (32) in the birch forest (Table 4) (3.) The LAI of the willow thicket is about two thirds of this, the wet and dry meadows about one third, and the lichen heath one tenth. The understorey vegetation at the willow thicket and birch forest is more than 20 cm high, at the wet meadow 16 cm, at the dry meadow 10 cm, and at the exposed lichen heath 4 cm (3). Leaf angles have the lowest values at the lichen heath and the highest for the protected vegetation of the birch forest.

Maximum chlorophyll per m^2 ground area is reached on about 1 August, while maximum chlorophyll content per g dry weight is measured about 14 days earlier (1). Chlorophyll con-

236

tent per unit nitrogen decreases with increase in height a.s.l. for the same species, while the chlorophyll a/b ratio increases. Chlorophyll content in relation to dry weight and nitrogen content was relatively constant from year to year in the species studied.

CONSUMERS

Invertebrates

The invertebrate taxa which have most successfully invaded the terrestrial niches on Hardangervidda are Enchytraeidae, Acarina, Araneae, Collembola, Heteroptera, Coleoptera, Diptera and to a certain extent some of the Hymenoptera taxa like Ichneumonidae and Tenthredinidae (43). About 300 species of invertebrates are known from the sites (excluding Protozoa, Nematoda, Crustacea and Acarina except Oribatei) (45, 66).

A characteristic feature of the invertebrate composition at the sites investigated is the absence of Isopoda, Diplopoda, Chilopoda and Formicidae, important in soil forming processes in the surrounding lowland. The scarcity of Lumbricidae and terrestrial Gastropoda (3 and 8 species respectively) is also noticeable compared with the adjacent lowlands of Hardanger where 8 lumbricid species and 55 gastropod species are found (84, Solhøy, unpublished). No species from these two groups are found in the snowbeds or on the lichen heath sites. The densities are also very low at the two eutrophic meadows investigated. The poor establishment of the groups mentioned is doubtless due to the harshness of the climate for they could easily have invaded Hardangervidda from lower altitudes after the last glacial period.

It is not always easy to judge whether a species of the more vagile taxa found, namely winged insects and spiders, are chance visitors or have established themselves permanently at Hardangervidda. There is a continual inflow of species from lower altitudes which may be especially extensive because of thermal winds from the Hardanger lowlands (23). According to present knowledge, 38 % of the Araneae species found at the sites can be classified as arctic-alpine, 11 % as subalpine and 51 % as lowland species (Kauri, pers. comm.).

Most of the invertebrate activity occurs in the litter layer and in the upper 1–3 cm of the soil (78). However, during drought periods a substantial part of the mite (Acari) springtail (Collembola) and enchytraeid populations migrate a few centimetres deeper. But even during such periods only a few percent penetrate lower than 6 cm, probably due to diminishing pore space.

All groups investigated exhibit aggregated distribution. Springtails are most aggregated on the dry lichen heath, intermediate on the dry meadow, and least on the wet meadow. Differences in soil moisture are alleged to be responsible for this (20). At the lichen heath the densities of adult oribatid mites are significantly higher below *Empetrum* mats than below lichen mats, which may be due to different microclimates or available food. It was found that the aphid *Acyrtosiphon malvae* (Mosley) was mostly bound to *Alchemilla alpina* L. and that the thrips *Anapothrips secticornis* Trybom aggregated on *Poa alpina* (47, 86). The web-spinning spiders showed a more even distribution probably due to inter- and intraspecific competition (46).

The abundance and biomass of some of the important taxa are given in Table 5 for

Table 5. The abundance (N = numbers m⁻²) and biomass (B = mg dw m⁻²) of some important invertebrate taxa at Hardangervidda. Snow bed data relate to Finse and other data to Stigstuv (24, 68)

Symbols: H = herbivore, C = carnivore, D = decomposer, $\star = N \cdot 10^3$.

Ecosystem component	function	Max Min Mean	Wet meadow N	B	Dry meadow N	B	Lichen heath N	B	Snow bed N	B
Hemiptera	H	1969	62	3.1	584	10.2	83	1.5	–	–
			6	0.3	280	4.9	76	1.4	–	–
			28	1.4	446	7.8	80	1.4	–	–
		1970	46	2.4	636	11.1	190	3.4	–	–
			3	0.2	160	2.8	44	0.8	–	–
			19	1.0	405	7.1	106	1.9	–	–
		1971	25	1.1	4 882	27.8	336	6.0	–	–
			4	0.2	234	1.3	45	0.8	–	–
			11	0.5	2 333	13.3	161	2.9	–	–
Lepidoptera (larvae)	H	1969	2	0.4	25	27.0	7	7.6	–	–
			0	–	3	3.2	4	4.0	–	–
			1	0.2	12	13.0	6	6.5	–	–
		1970	3	0.6	16	17.3	18	19.4	–	–
			0	–	4	4.3	6	6.5	–	–
			1	0.2	10	10.8	11	12.1	–	–
		1971	5	1.3	8	11.2	16	17.3	0.5	–
			0	–	6	8.4	4	4.3	0.2	–
			2	0.5	7	9.8	9	9.7	0.3	–
Coleoptera (adults total)	H+C	1969	52	–	11	–	16	–	–	–
			7	–	2	–	0	–	–	–
			27	–	3	–	8	–	–	–
		1970	16	–	12	–	6	–	–	–
			9	–	4	–	1	–	–	–
			13	–	6	–	4	–	–	–
		1971	12	–	10	–	8	–	1.4	–
			4	–	4	–	0	–	0.5	–
			8	–	8	–	4	–	1.0	–
Araneae	C	1969	82	4.9	56	4.5	40	3.2	–	–
			44	2.6	38	3.0	10	0.8	–	–
			62	3.7	46	3.7	25	2.0	–	–
		1970	128	23.3	88	7.0	69	5.5	–	–
			12	2.2	32	2.5	16	1.3	–	–
			52	9.5	54	4.3	43	3.4	–	–
		1971	69	10.8	94	8.5	65	5.2	5.5	–
			13	2.0	22	2.0	5	0.4	3.7	–
			35	5.5	46	4.4	32	2.5	4.6	–
Acari	C+D	$\star$ 1969	55.0	258	159.1	525	73.4	244	–	–
			11.3	53	33.4	110	37.3	124	–	–
			32.1	153	101.4	337	55.4	184	–	–
		$\star$ 1970	42.6	203	164.1	541	140.8	468	–	–
			18.3	87	46.3	153	56.1	186	–	–
			33.6	160	112.1	372	88.2	293	–	–
		$\star$ 1971	106.5	554	276.4	2 018	185.6	617	177.2	–
			20.8	108	22.4	163	59.1	196	119.9	–
			44.9	233	118.7	867	125.5	417	139.2	–

Table 5. cont.

Collembola	D	☆ 1969	63.3	342	121.7	301	31.5	78	–	–
			10.4	56	12.1	30	24.1	60	–	–
			39.4	214	68.2	168	27.8	69	–	–
		☆ 1970	71.7	389	123.2	407	75.1	186	–	–
			18.0	98	46.7	112	19.2	47	–	–
			52.8	287	79.6	197	36.3	90	–	–
		☆ 1971	72.1	373	105.7	349	73.0	181	57.0	–
			28.5	148	15.1	50	43.9	109	12.4	–
			44.2	229	64.8	214	54.7	135	42.2	–
Enchytraeidae	D	☆ 1970	39.0	1 123	11.3	401	–	–	–	–
			11.7	337	5.1	180	–	–	–	–
			29.7	857	8.8	313	–	–	–	–
		☆ 1971	48.4	1 103	36.8	567	–	–	–	–
			30.4	693	14.4	222	–	–	–	–
			39.0	891	20.0	308	–	–	–	–

each of the four sites investigated. As found for other arctic-alpine communities the most dominant groups are mites, springtails, enchytraeids and diptera larvae, all active in the decomposition process.

Invertebrate herbivores, represented chiefly by Lepidoptera larvae, sapsucking Hemiptera and chrysomelid beetles are of little importance at Hardangervidda. However, the chrysomelid beetle *Melasoma collaris* L. feeding on *Salix herbacea* may, along the edges of some snow-beds reach densities of more than 100 m^{-2} and remove a substantial part of the leaves (27).

Spiders, carabids, staphylinids and some chironomid larvae are the most important "macropredators", consuming a variety of other invertebrates from springtails and enchytraeids to large crane flies. The most prominent "micropredators" are chiefly mesostigmatid mites, some prostigmatid mites, and possibly also some freeliving nematodes. These "micropredators" prey chiefly on enchytraeids, springtails, mites and nematodes.

The fauna under stones — the hypolithion — is rather rich in all the habitats studied. Stone coverage is normally rather high, although it varies greatly from habitat to habitat (max. 30 %). Araneida, as a rule, always represent more than half the number of animals found. The high stone coverage creates suitable microhabitats for a great variety of invertebrate species, and is responsible for the rather high density of invertebrates found here (24).

The major part of invertebrate biomass (90 %) on Hardangervidda consists of decomposers utilizing dead organic matter and microorganisms. Five higher taxa are represented: Nematoda, Enchytraeidae, Acarina, Collembola and Diptera. Nothing is known about the distribution and densities of nematodes at Hardangervidda. The enchytraeids reach their highest densities and biomass in the wetter areas, a mean of 0.9 g m^{-2} (dw) being recorded from the wet meadow. Springtails and mites show highest densities in mesic and drier areas (Table 5). The biomass of Collembola is roughly equal in all areas but perhaps higher in the wetter areas owing to a greater percentage of larger species.

Few data are available on the abundance of dipterous larvae. In a tussock field at Finse 20–50 m^{-2} *Tipula excisa* Schum. were recorded and 300–800 m^{-2} Chironomidae from the wet meadow at Stigstuv (40, Solhøy, unpubl.).

The role of invertebrate decomposers in the mineral cycling at Hardangervidda is not well documented. Judging from biomass estimates, their direct contribution is of minor importance. They play a substantial indirect role, acting as "catalysts" for fungi and bacteria by promoting a physical change in the organic material ingested and enriching this material with nitrogenous compounds.

Data indicate that the invertebrates in these high mountain communities usually need one to several years to complete their life cycle, or the number of generations is reduced as in Aphididae (Table 6). With these comparatively long life cycles several instars coexist in the ground at the same time, a fact which can explain the relatively high abundance of some of the taxa.

Table 6. Estimated life cycles of some invertebrate taxa from Hardangervidda

Taxon	Duration of life cycle yr	Authority
Pardosa palustris (L.) (Araneae)	13	Steigen (unpublished)
Mitopus morio Fabr. (Opiliones)	1–2	Kauri (unpublished)
Oribatei	2–4	Solhøy (unpublished)
Collembola	1–2	(20)
Amara alpina Payk. (Coleoptera)	3	Solhøy (unpublished)
A. praetermissa Sahlb. (Coleoptera)	3	Solhøy (unpublished)
Melasoma collaris L. (Coleoptera)	1	(26)
Anapothrips secticornis Trybom (Thysanoptera)	1	(47)
Acyrthosiphon malvae (Mosley) (Aphididae)	1/3	(86)
Tipula excisa Schum. (Tipulidae)	2	(40)
Vitrina pellucida (Müll.) (Gastropoda)	3–5	Solhøy (unpublished)

Great fluctuations in abundance are found both intra- and interseasonally. In general, the lowest abundance is found in early summer just after snow melt, the populations being reduced during hibernation. The greatest abundance is found in August/September due to recruitment of the populations. Within this simple pattern, drought has a marked effect on the abundance in mesic and dry communities (78). During such periods the populations seem to be greatly diminished. This is especially well documented for enchytraeids (79).

However, analysis of the oribatid data from the dry lichen heath indicates that decreases in abundance during drought, earlier interpreted as mortality, are due to aestivation of a part of the population (80). Extraction by dynamic methods is not possible during aestivation.

The question of the existence of more long-term cyclic fluctuations cannot be answered at present as the observation series has not been carried out for long enough. It is, however, probable that the density of invertebrates changes with the lemming cycles, since these create variations in the vegetation cover and in the condition of the vegetation. The presence of nests, runways, excrement and dead lemmings also affects the habitat.

Vertebrates

The vertebrate fauna of Hardangervidda comprises both species with a distribution restricted to mountain areas, and species with a wider occurrence in other biomes such as alpine birch forests, coniferous forests, grassland and coastal areas. In addition to species which regularly inhabit and breed in these alpine environments, many pass through these areas, either on seasonal migrations or on occasional visits. Most members of the bird fauna which breed in the mountains, spend only the summer there, the colder part of the year being spent in lower areas in Fennoscandia or in warmer areas at southern latitudes. At Hardangervidda 148 species of vertebrates have been recorded (58, 67, 68). Of these only 88 can be regarded as breeders, while 31 must be characterized as migrants and 27 as visitors. Two introduced fish species do not spawn in the area. The number of species in each of these categories, organized into systematic groups, is shown in Table 7. The number of species usually breeding at Hardangervidda, together with indications of their functioning as components of a mountain ecosystem, and their relative abundance, is given in Table 8. Their function is expressed in terms of their trophic status. When reading this table, it should be kept in mind that it is very difficult — and often very inaccurate — to place an animal in a straight trophic level as, for example, it may be carnivorous for part of the year and omnivorous for the remainder. Some animals may be carnivores as juveniles and herbivores as adults, as ptarmigans, for instance.

Some species, here mentioned as synantropic, can only exist in connection with human settlements, for example, the magpie and house sparrow. The house martin nests in cliffs at some places on Hardangervidda.

Cyclic production in the vertebrate food chain

Hardangervidda lies within the large arctic and alpine circumpolar zone which is characterized by pronounced 3–4 year cycles in productivity of certain vertebrates, for instance small rodents (44). From Norwegian alpine mountains and adjacent northern coniferous forests, information on the cycling of rodent populations is available from as far back as 1848 (12, 13, 59, 60, 96, 97). Briefly, the degree of synchronism of rodent production is variable between different geographical areas in Scandinavia. During certain 3–4 year periods the rodent biomass production is in phase over large areas. During other periods, rodent production over smaller or larger areas displays a 1–2 year

241

Table 7. The number of vertebrate faunal elements at Hardangervidda

Systematic group	Total number number of species	Breeders	Number of Migrants	Visitors
Pisces	6 ☆	4	–	–
Amphibia	1	1	–	–
Reptilia	1	1	–	–
Aves	114	61	31	22
Mammalia	26	21	–	5
Total	148	88	31	27

☆ Two species introduced by man do not spawn in the area.

lag phase resulting in an asynchronous and complex productivity pattern, probably reflecting in part the high ecological diversity of Scandinavia (34, 59, 60, 61).

From analyses of the variability pattern in the Norwegian long-term data series, it is concluded that a certain directional regularity seems to exist in the phasic shifting and lag pattern development between different geographical areas during the cycles (34). The biomass peak of the individual cycle is normally reached first in the southwestern part of the alpine range, namely Hardangervidda and adjacent areas. The following year it is reached more or less markedly in the central alpine mountains, namely Dovre, Trøndelag-Nordland with adjacent parts of Sweden, and in the third year in the northeastern part (Troms-Finnmark) of the range (Fig. 6) (34, 60, 61).

Several other components of the vertebrate food chain exhibit density variations similar to those of cyclic rodents; whether through the same cause or other factors, however, is not agreed. Tetraonid birds, i.e. the willow grouse (*Lagopus lagopus*) and ptarmigan (*L. mutus*), and mammalian predators and raptors have pronounced biomass variation somewhat connected with the cyclic pulses in rodent productivity (33, 61). Preliminary data on passerine density from Hardangervidda indicate equivalent variation also in this component of the alpine food chain (54).

Herbivores

During the IBP period 1968–1974 peak populations of small rodents occurred in 1966/67, 1969/70 and 1973/74. All the rodent species increase in number in a peak year, but one or two species are usually predominant. In 1966/67 and 1973/74 the lemming (*Lemmus lemmus*) was the most abundant species, while in 1969/70 the root vole (*Microtus oeconomus*) topped the peak. Other rodent species on Hardangervidda are the bank vole (*Clethrionomys glareolus*), the grey sided vole (*C. rufocanus*) and the field vole (*M. agrestis*) (72, 96).

Trapping records from different sites and different phases of the population cycle

Table 8. The vertebrate species usually breeding at Hardangervidda

Symbols: H = herbivore; H/C_i = the adult is herbivorous, the juvenils carnivorous, taking invertebrates; H_h = grazers, browsers; C = carnivore; $C_{i,v}$ = carnivore, taking both invertebrates and vertebrates; C_v/C_i = the adult is carnivorous taking vertebrates, the juvenile carnivorous, taking invertebrates; $C_{i'}$ (O) = mainly carnivore taking invertebrates. There is however some plant material in its food, therefore (O); O = Omnivorous.
A=abundant, C=common, U=uncommon, R=rare.
The duration of stay in the area is based on judgement rather than actual observation.
Compiled from several sources (13, 29, 58, 67, 68, 71).

Ecosystem component	function	Relative abundance	Body wt. (g ww)	Offspring yr^{-1} (range)	Duration of stay (days)
Pisces					
Salmo trutta L.	$C_{i,v}$	A			365
Salvelinus alpinus (L.)	$C_{i,v}$	A			365
Coregonus lavaretus (L.)	C_i	R			365
Phoxinus phoxinus (L.)	C_i	R			365
Amphibia					
Rana temporaria L.	C_i	R			365
Reptilia					
Vipera berus (L.)	$C_{i,v}$	R			
Aves					
Gavia arctica (L.)	C_v/C_i	U	2 250–3 750	1–2 (3)	120
Anas platyrhynchos L.	H, (O)	U	♂ 840–1 380 ♀ 775–1 120	7–12 (15)	120
A. crecca L.	H, (O)	C	225– 355	7–8 (11)	120
Athya marila (L.)	C_i	C	750–1 372	6–11 (14)	120
Melanitta fusca (L.)	C_i	C	♂ 1 173–2 024 ♀ 1 040–1 857	7–10 (14)	120
M. nigra (L.)	C_i	C	♂ 780–1 450 ♀ 622–1 268	7–9	120
Mergus merganser L.	C_v	U	1 210–1 930	7–10 (14)	120
Aquila chrysaëtos (L.)	C_v	R	♂ 2 665–4 980 ♀ 3 240–6 670	(1) 2 (3)	
Buteo lagopus (Pontoppidan)	C_v	A[1]	♂ 717– 990 ♀ 810–1 247	3–4 (2–7)	150
Falco peregrinus Tunstall	C_v	R	♂ 510– 650 ♀ 860–1 400	3–4 (5)	
F. rusticolus L.	C_v	R	♂ 960–1 300 ♀ 1 330–1 690	3–4 (2–6)	365
F. columbarius aesalon Tunstall	C_v	U[1]	♂ 150– 185 ♀ 175– 243	4 (3–6)	120
F. tinnunculus L.	C_v	C[1]	♂ 135– 230 ♀ 170– 275	5 (3–6)	120
Lagopus lagopus (L.)	H/C_i	A[1]	♂ 584 (405–750) ♀ 517 (405–680)	8–12 (4–13)	365
L. mutus (Montin)	H/C_i	A[1]	♂ 519 ♀ 421 (243–586)	7–11	365
Grus grus (L.)	O	U	6 100	2 (1–3)	120
Vanellus vanellus (L.)	C_i	U	173– 264	4 (5)	135
Charadrius hiaticula L.	C_i	C	46–. 64	4 (3)	120

243

Table 8 cont.

Pluvialis apricaria (L.)	C_i	A	155– 185	4 (3–5)	120
Eudromias morinellus (L.)	C_i, (O)	A	ca 120	3 (2)	120
Gallinago gallinago (L.)	C_i, (O)	U	ca 111	4 (3–5)	120
G. media (Latham)	C_i, (O)	R	170– 265	4 (3)	?
Numenius phaeopus (L.)	O	R	♂ 76– 86 ♀ 80– 99	4 (3)	?
Tringa glareola L.	C_i	C	ca 61	4	120
T. totanus (L.)	C_i	C	102– 143	4	120
Actitis hypoleucos (L.)	C_i	C	41– 80	(3) 4 (5–6)	135
Calidris maritima (Brünnich)	C_i	C	50– 75	3–4	120
C. temminckii (Leisler)	C_i	C	ca 25	4 (3) × 2	120
C. alpina (L.)	C_i	C	46 (35–56)	4 (3)	120
Limicola falcinellus (Pontoppidan)	C_i	R	ca 33	4 (3)	?
Philomachus pugnax (L.)	C_i, (O)	U	♂198 (178–216) ♀115 (105–121)	4 (3)	?
Phalaropus lobatus (L.)	C_i	R	34– 43	4 (3)	120
Stercorarius longicaudus Vieillot	O, (C_v)	R[1]	ca 270	1–2 (3)	?
Larus canus L.	O	C	♂413 (325–475) ♀ 360 (300–480)	3 (4)	135
Cuculus canorus L.	C_i/O	C	♂ 100– 123 ♀ 98– 116	10–20 (26)	?
Nyctea scandiaca (L.)	C_v	R[1]	♂ 1–2 kg ♀ 1.5–2.6 kg	5–8 (3–10)	?
Asio flammeus (Pontoppidan)	C_v	C[1]	♂339(230–427) ♀419(350–505)	4–11 (2–14)	?
Alauda arvensis L.	O	R	22– 55	2–6	120
Eremophila alpestris flava (Gmelin)	C_i, (O)	C	♂ 32– 46 ♀ 26– 37	4 (3–7)	120
Delichon urbica (L.)	C_i	U	12– 20	3–6	120
Corvus corax L.	O	A	990–1 380	4–6 (3–7)	365
Pica pica (L.)	O	R[2]	♂236(185–253) ♀210(190–253)	6–8 (5–9)	0–365
Parus major L.	O	R[2]	♂ ca 19 ♀ ca 18	8–13 (7–14)	365
Cinclus cinclus (L.)	C_i, (O)	U	53– 72	5 (4–8)	135
Turdus pilaris L.	O	R	ca 103	5–6 (4–8)	120
T. philomelos Brehm	O	R	ca 70	4–5 (3–7)	120
T. iliacus L.	O	R	50– 88	4–6 (8)	120
T. torquatus L.	O	U	95– 120	4–5 (3–6)	120
T. merula L.	O	R	71– 130	4–5 (3–6)	120
Oenanthe oenanthe (L.)	C_i	A	♂ 24.1 ♀ 23.8	6–7 (5–8)	135
Luscinia suecica (L.)	C_i, (O)	U	♂ 20.3(17–22) ♀ 18.8(17–22)	6–7 (5–9)	120
Phylloscopus trochilus acre- *dula* (L.)	C_i	U	6.5–11.8	6–7 (5–8)	120
Anthus pratensis (L.)	C_i	A	18.8(15.2–21.8)	5–6 (3–7)×2(?)	135
Motacilla alba L.	C_i	C	19.6–23.6	5–6 (4–8)	135
Sturnus vulgaris L.	O	C[2]	♂ 81(52–108) ♀ 78(58–97)	5–6 (4–8)	135

Table 8 cont.

Carduelis flavirostris L.	H, (O)	C	14.5–17	5–6 (4–7)	120
C. flammea (L.)	H, (O)	U	ca 14.4	5–6 (3–8)	120
Emberiza schoeniclus (L.)	C_i, (O)	U	17.5–19	5–6 (2–7)	120
Calcarius lapponicus (L.)	O	C	23.8(18.5–29)	5–6 (2–7)	120
Plectrophenax nivalis (L.)	H, (O)	A_2	35.9(29.6–45)	5–6 (4–7)x2(?)	150
Passer domesticus (L.)	O	R^2	ca 30	4–5 (8)x2 (3)	365
Mammalia					
Sorex araneus L.	C_i	C^1	−18	4–8x2(?)	365
S. minutus L.	C_i	U^1	− 6	2–8	365
Neomys fodiens (Schreb.)	C_i	U	−25	4–10x1–2	365
Lepus timidus L.	H_h	A	− 4.7 kg	(2)3–5(8)x2	365
Castor fiber L.	H_h	U	12–15 (30) kg	1–3 (5)	365
Lemmus lemmus (L.)	H	A^1	−110	5–6(16)x4–5	365
Clethrionomys glareolus (Shreb.)	H	C^1	− 40	3–8x2–4	365
C. rufocanus (Sundevall)	H	A^1	− 60	5–12x2–3(4)	365
Microtus agrestis (L.)	H	U^1	− 85	5–6(11)x3–7	365
M. oeconomus (Pallas)	H	A^1	−100	5–6(10)x2–4	365
Arvicola terrestris (L.)	H	R	−235(400)	5–8x2–3	365
Vulpes vulpes (L.)	O	A^1 ♂5.8 ♀5.3	4–14 kg	3–8 (12)	365
Alopex lagopus (L.)	O	$U^{1,3}$	4.5–8 kg	2–8 (18)	365
Mustela vison Shreb.	C_v	U ♂0.53–1.7 kg ♀0.35–0.92 kg		5 (11)	365
M. erminea L.	C_v	C^1 ♂ −300 ♀ −200		4–6 (17)	365
M. nivalis L.	C_v	$C^{4,1}$	− 76	3–7 (12)	365
Gulo gulo (L.)	C_v	R	15–35 kg	2–3 (4)	0–365
Lynx lynx (L.)	C_v	R	18–38 kg	2–3 (7)	0–365
Alces alces (L.)	H_h	U^5 ♂ −300(600) kg ♀ −250(450) kg		1–2 (3)	0–365
Rangifer tarandus (L.)	H_h	A ♂ −150 kg ♀ −100 kg		1–2	365
Capreolus capreolus (L.)	H_h	R	15–35 kg	1–3	0–365

1) Cyclic, 2) Partly synantropic, 3) Population in slight increase
4) *M. nivalis* or *M. rixosa*, systematic position not clear
5) Extending its distribution area towards the western coast of Norway.

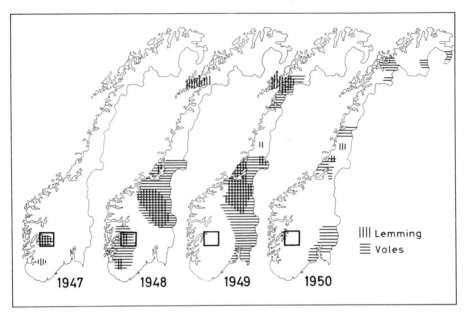

Figure 6. Geographical distribution of small rodent occurrence (peak years) at Hardangervidda (boxed), as an example of regional variability of production of rodent biomass in Norway during a 4 year cycle. Shaded areas indicate mass occurrence of lemmings and other microtines in the years 1947–50 (redrawn from (34)).

vary considerably. During a population minimum they vary between 0 and 3 animals ha^{-1}. In the year prior to a peak, growing populations with 0 to 50 animals ha^{-1} were recorded. In a peak year 25 to 330 animals ha^{-1} were trapped (number of animals trapped per ha during a six day period in September). Generally the sites with highest primary production and good shelter also have the highest rodent densities.

The main breeding season normally lasts from late May to October. However, lemmings may also breed during winter, while regular winter breeding is not observed in the other rodent species.

During summer the *Microtus* spp. usually inhabit wet places rich in grasses and herbs, while in winter a migration to drier habitats is assumed (30). *Clethrionomys* spp. inhabit the drier places rich in boulders and stones, while lemmings live in both wet and dry habitats (72).

During the trapping seasons of 1970 and 1974, the greatest numbers of lemmings were trapped in oligotrophic dry heath and pioneer communities. The main foods of *Microtus* spp. are grasses, sedges and forbs, *Salix herbacea* and roots; for lemmings: mosses, sedges and grasses; and for *Clethrionomys* spp.: herbs, ferns, roots and seeds and, to some extent, invertebrates. During a peak year a small rodent community (lemming excluded) may consume 146 kJ m^{-2} yr^{-1} or even more in years with very dense populations. However, this is probably less than 2 % of the primary production (30).

The role of small rodents in mineral cycling by consuming vegetation seems to be a minor one. However, with activities like clipping and browsing they also aid in mineral cycling, and are perhaps in this way an important element in this relatively simple eco-

246

system.

The arctic hare (*Lepus timidus*) is common up to the high alpine region, but can frequently be found there too. Its staple food consists of *Salix* spp., *Betula* spp., *Empetrum hermaphroditum* and *Juniperus communis* L.

The willow grouse breeds in the birch forest and in the low and mid-alpine region, while the ptarmigan breeds in the mid- and high alpine regions. Generally, the willow grouse inhabits the most flat and central part of Hardangervidda, while the ptarmigan is more common in the higher mountains to the west and north.

The willow grouse is mostly resident, living near its breeding places throughout the year (29). However, a winter migration from the alpine region down to the subalpine birch forest is not uncommon. Ptarmigans stay at the breeding places until autumn when they migrate to the highest and most exposed tops. When the snow comes they move down to the valleys and lower regions where large flocks of several hundred are seen.

Chicks of willow grouse, and obviously also ptarmigans, are insectivorous during their first month of life. They then change to a herbivorous diet (29). The most energy demanding period for ptarmigans is probably the breeding season, while they are able to increase their weight during autumn and winter.

Members of the deer family indigenous to Norway may occasionally — and even regularly — use lower parts of the alpine plateau, viz. the subalpine birch forest and low alpine region, but as part of the alpine ecosystem only reindeer (*Rangifer tarandus*) are of any importance. The reindeer has a very long history here — obviously going back to the Ice Age. Long term fluctuations seem to be an intrinsic part of the life of a reindeer population. At Hardangervidda a peak was registered in the 1890s, but in the first years of this century there as a sharp decline. The population was protected by law from 1902 to 1906, and attained a new peak in 1916, when it again declined. Population changes are based on hunting statistics and very little is known about the actual size of the population, except for the year 1911 when its numbers were estimated at 11 000. By about 1927 it may have sunk below 1 000, but from then on it grew and an estimate from 1947 gave 15 000, and in 1952 an air census gave 12 000. A new census in 1965 concluded that there were well over 25 000 animals and a reduction hunt pressed numbers down to 6 000 in 1971. A two year protection followed and an early summer census in 1974 recorded 14 200 animals.

Both wild and tame reindeer are considered as being the same species, *Rangifer tarandus tarandus* L. of the *Cylindricornis* group, and so the population has its ancestry in wild and tame animals.

Reindeer are of great economic importance, the yearly harvest being about $8 \cdot 10^4$ kg meat, about Nkr 1.2—1.5 millions (1974). Hides and antlers are of additional value.

The present wild reindeer management programme aims at a population varying between 10 000 in April (net population) to 13 400 just after fawning. Fig. 7 shows the population variation throughout a year. The year is divided into segments based on important social events, fawning and rut, as well as migration periods. The autumn population will be about 12 800 of which 2 300 is supposed shot during the hunting season.

The main seasonal habitats are represented as hatched areas on the map, Fig. 8, although outlying areas are also in use. Some bucks stay in the extreme western, and especially northwestern areas even during winter. They utilize small pockets in rain shadow

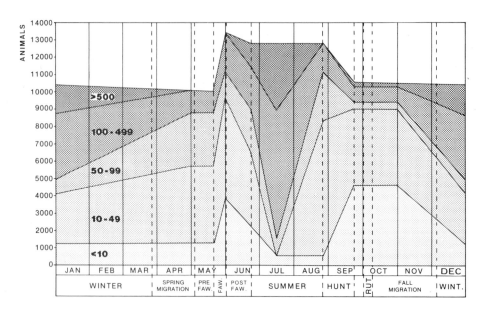

Figure 7. Band sizes and population size of reindeer throughout a year at Hardangervidda. Large bands, above 100 animals are usually integrated, while smaller ones may be buck bands, nursery groups etc.

in this extremely rugged terrain. In an average year the herd utilizes about 3 200 km², less than half of the total area. Whereas the density for the gross area is about 1.7 deer km⁻² in the autumn, it is 4.0 deer km⁻² for the net area. Density on the winter range is 6.4 deer km⁻².

Observations on vegetation utilization over three years (Fig. 9) show that in winter snow restricts the animals' choice to a minimum. The eastern winter ranges have least precipitation and the stands of Loiseleuro-Arctostaphylion are dominated by lichens, viz. *Cetraria nivalis* (L.) Ach., *Cladonia mitis* Sandst., and *Cl. alpestris* (L.) Wigg. being most important. For reindeer, lichens have a high digestibility, 69.6 % of dry matter, and reindeer are far better at utilizing their energy value than are, for instance, sheep. This must be viewed as an adaptation to this kind of food. Within the circumpolar reindeer distribution area, these lichens usually dominate the winter ranges in both tundra and taiga biomes, although important exceptions exist, for example Svalbard (Spitsbergen).

As spring progresses new plant stands of other alliances become available and reindeer show a preference for plants and development stages of high protein content (82). This causes the herds to seek south-exposed slopes in spring to early summer while northern exposures are favoured in late summer to autumn. In years with moist and warm weather, mushrooms may be very abundant in the low alpine-subalpine region and snow-bed grazing in late August becomes negligible. Instead the herds become scattered over large areas in the lowest parts of the mountains. Fig. 9, being a three year

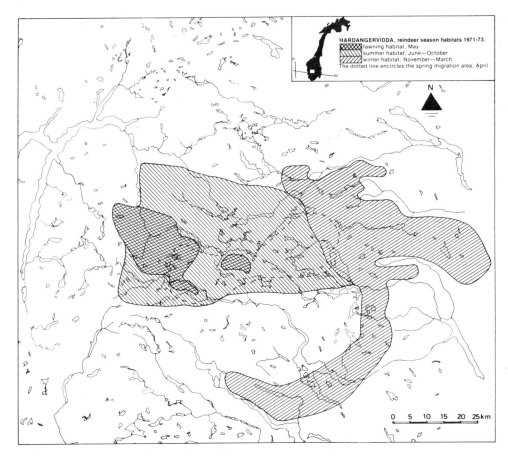

Figure 8. Reindeer seasonal habitats, Hardangervidda in 1971–1973. Areas shown where more than 60 % of the total herd was observed. In the autumn they may use most of the area.

average, partially hides this phenomenon.

Over a whole year nearly every plant species may endure grazing, but a preference is obvious even if it is not always easy to quantify. In the winter *Cladonia* spp. of the *Cladina* group (reindeer lichens) and yellow *Cetraria* spp. are taken, but graminoid and woody plants still make up about 40 % of the diet (21). Lichens are taken during the summer season too, but sedges and forbs together with leaves of shrubs, viz. *Betula na-na* L., *Salix* spp., especially *S. herbacea* are far more important. In relation to their frequency in the field, lichens are preferred. Species often found in rumen contents are *Cladonia mitis* and *Cetraria islandica s. lat.* The relative composition of the diet reflects the composition of the plant community although some species seem to be avoided, e.g. *Alectoria ochroleuca* (Hoffm.) Mass. and *Empetrum hermaphroditum.*

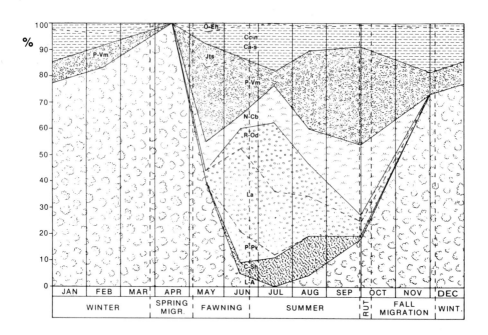

Figure 9. Reindeer use of plant alliances, Hardangervidda 1971–73, given as percent of time the alliances are used

Mires   O-Eh   Oxycocco-Empetrion hermaphroditi, ombrotrophous bog or bog hummocks.

             Cc-n   Caricion canescentis-nigrae, minerotrophous fen often with *Salix* shrubs.

             Ca-s   Caricion atrofuscae-saxatilis, minerotrophous rich fen.

Heaths   Jts   Juncion trifidi scandinavicum, oligotrophous and moderately chionophilous grass heath.

             P-Vm Phyllodoco-Vaccinion myrtilli, oligotrophous and moderately chionophilous dwarf-shrub heath.

             L-A   Loiseleuro-Arctostaphylion, oligotrophous, chionofobous dwarf shrub heath, often with dominating lichens.

             N-Cb Nardo-Caricion bigelowii, oligotrophous, chionophilous grass heath.

             C-Sh Cassiopo-Salicion herbaceae, oligotrophous, strongly chionophilous dwarf shrub heath.

Meadows R-Od Ranunculo-Oxyrion digynae, oligotrophous to eutrophous, strongly to very strongly chionophilous meadow.

             La   Lactucion alpinae, eutrophous, chionophilous tall herb meadow.

             P-Pv Potentillo-Polygonion vivipari, eutrophous, moderately chionophilous dry meadow.

250

Carnivores

Four large mammals were earlier of significance in the Hardangervidda food chain. Two of them, the brown bear (*Ursus arctos* L.) and lynx (*Lynx lynx*) are not true alpine animals — they have their main populations below the tree line and in the areas fringing the Hardangervidda. Earlier the bear used these mountains intermittently for hunting and feeding as reported from other alpine mountains in Scandinavia where the species has survived (37). The lynx is found in low populations in the fringing birch and coniferous forests, and is met as an occasional transient in the lower parts of the mountains. The wolverine (*Gulo gulo*) is still met in sparse populations while the wolf (*Canis lupus* (L.)), earlier the major carnivore and most important *Rangifer* predator, has been exterminated. In fact, only very few transient individuals have been reported from the whole of south Norway in latter years. No detailed estimates of population density and energy requisites are available on these species.

The arctic fox populations (*Alopex lagopus*) has, after long-term decrease and protection, reached a period of slight increase in population, and breeds more or less regularly in the peak rodent years. Investigations on this species have been carried out, but data are not yet available. The fox (*Vulpes vulpes*) is also a component of the mountain food chain and breeds over the whole range, in peak years in densities exceeding those of *Alopex*. The smallest mammalian carnivores occurring in the area are the short-tailed and the smallest of the weasels *(Mustela nivalis* ☆ and *M. erminea*). Their feeding ecology is highly adapted to rodents.

Within alpine ecosystems raptor population dynamics and movements are involved and change the structural composition of this food chain component from one cycle to the next. The major raptor species of Hardangervidda are the long-tailed jaeger (*Stercorarius longicaudus*), the snowy owl (*Nyctea scandiaca*), the short-eared owl (*Asio flammeus*), the rough-legged buzzard (*Buteo lagopus*), the kestrel (*Falco tinnunculus*) and a few other rodentivorous species which do not invade the mountains in the same density at each small mammal peak. The roughleg or one of the other species might even be completely lacking during some of the cyclic highs (61). The two rodentivorous owls so typical of tundras and alpine mountains have probably no fixed breeding and wintering ranges, their main populations being without racial subdivision — genetically homogeneous almost throughout their entire range of distribution.

Hypotheses have been presented to the effect that the movements and migrations of these owl populations are multiannual and have evolved through natural selection on the basis of the geographical variability pattern in rodent biomass production (61). Food habit studies have revealed that most species use small mammals as staple food, but can utilize a variety of food items from different trophic levels, changing with rodent abundance and ecological conditions in their habitats (33, 36).

In the Finse area, densities of 0.08 pairs km^{-2} have been observed for the rough-legged buzzard in a rodent peak year (1974). The distribution, however, is not even. The snowy owl breeds only within selected areas on Hardangervidda, mainly in undulating low mountain ranges. The last peak of invasion by a significant population was in 1959 when a density of 3.3 pairs km^{-2} (ecological density *sensu* Odum, not overall density) was recorded (35). No density estimate is available for *Asio* from Hardangervidda, but

---

☆ *Mustela nivalis* L. or *M. rixosa* Bangs., systematic position not clear (71).

during an 8 year raptor survey programme at Dovre, a peak density of 0.8 pair km^{-2} was found, and direct measurements between neighbouring pairs have varied between 0.5–1.5 km (33, 36).

Among the terrestrial birds, only adult grouse (*Lagopus lagopus*), ptarmigan (*L. mutus*), and certain migratory anatid ducks in aquatic systems such as the teal (*Anas crecca*), are dependent on fresh green plant material for most of the year. Invertebrates make up the staple food of most passerine birds, waders, plovers, and several duck species also utilize this food source. Passerine birds make up the bulk of the bird biomass during summer, and a large part of the energy is channelled through invertebrates. Densities of passerines may range from 24 to 100 breeding pairs km^{-2} (54).

An important group of birds numerically in semi-aquatic habitats is the plovers; ringed plover (*Charadrius hiaticula*), golden plover (*Pluvialis apricaria*), dotterel (*Eudromias morinellus*) and the scolopacine snipes, e.g. redshank (*Tringa totanus*), common sandpiper (*Actitis hypoleucos*), purple sandpiper (*Calidris maritima*), Temminck's stint (*C. temminckii*) and dunlin (*C. alpina*).

Of the reptiles, *Vipera berus* has been reported from selected localities, but is probably without any significance in the area as a whole. An anuran amphibian, the common frog (*Rana temporaria*), is found up to 1 220 m a.s.l. in the Finse area.

ENERGY FLOW

Primary production of Norwegian alpine tundras utilizes 0.7–2.4 % of the global radiation within the wave lengths 400–700 nm in lichens heaths and willow thickets. This gives an annual primary production of 4 200–16 700 kJ m^{-2} yr^{-1}, or a total of about 5 900·10^{10} kJ yr^{-1} for Hardangervidda (91). Considerably lower utilization is, however, found in snow-beds and under extreme conditions.

Table 9 gives examples of consumption and its further use by three primary consumers typical for Hardangervidda. As can be seen, the reindeer population consumes 42 kJ m^{-2} of the yearly primary production. This figure refers to the area actually used by the herd (Fig. 8). In addition, somewhat more than twice this amount is annually destroyed by trampling. Hence, altogether about 2.1 % of the total annual primary production is "destroyed" by the Hardangervidda reindeer population. This percentage may, however, rise to 10 % of the accessible food during winter. Table 9 also shows the energy budget of the root vole during a "high" in a dry meadow community at Finse. A primary consumption of 121 kJ m^{-2} yr^{-1} represents about 2 % of the total primary production in a typical dry meadow community. The chrysomelid beetle *Melasoma collaris* is used as an example of an invertebrate primary consumer from Finse; it feeds exclusively on *Salix herbacea*, the smallest of the willows.

In order to study the functional aspects of the Hardangervidda system, several models have been developed: (i) a total ecosystem energy flow model with the main emphasis on primary production (70); (ii) a total ecosystem model with the main emphasis on cyclic fluctuations of small rodents (32, 55) and (iii) a population dynamics model for the root vole based on an energy model for individual animals in the population (83). As any ecosystem is highly complex, it is believed that developing several models with

Table 9. Primary consumption $(kJ\ m^{-2}\ yr^{-1})$ estimated from field data

	Live biomass aboveground	belowground	Respira-tion	Excreta	Death and predation	Harvest by man
The reindeer *(Rangifer tarandus)* population at Hardangervidda	42	0	21	13	0.04	0.33
A root vole *(Microtus oeconomus)* population at Finse		121	84	34	3	0
A *Melasoma collaris* population at Finse	63	0	29	21	13	0

quite different approaches and emphasizing different aspects of the system may afford a better understanding of the processes under study than concentrating on developing a single model.

Only the results from the total energy flow model are summarized here. Details of the model structure and the simulation results are given in (70). The general structure of this model is the same for all trophic levels. A flow diagram of the primary production part, with solar radiation as the driving force, is given in Fig. 10. The primary production calculation is based on relationships defined by field and laboratory studies of death of plants, consumption of plant biomass by fauna, predation, respiration, and secondary production and excretion which are simulated by use of constant coefficients. Although the functional relationships seem to be satisfactory, several of the parameter values (especially those for the consumer section) are highly uncertain. Sensitivity analysis of the model is given in (70). Only simulation results for the average primary production of the system are therefore given in Table 10. These simulations fit closely with observations made at the study site at Stigstuv for which the model has been validated. One of the main conclusions from experimentation with the model is that early summer temperatures seem to be the most important factor influencing annual primary production.

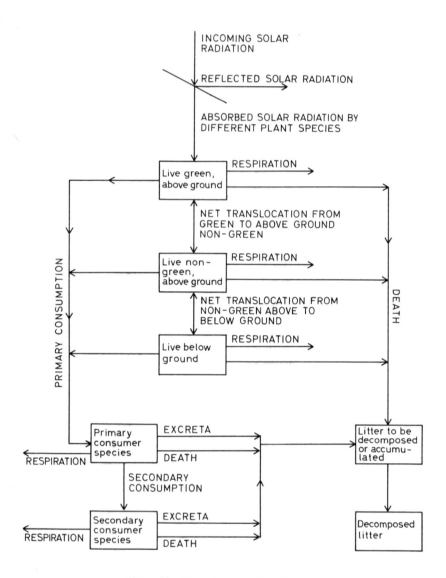

Figure 10. General energy flow diagram.

Table 10. Primary production (kJ m^{-2} yr^{-1}) estimated from the model shown in Fig. 10 (Wet meadow)

Variables	Mosses	Forbs	Grasses/ sedges	Woody plants
Respiration by				
green	50	192	1 335	197
non-green	33	33	724	59
belowground		71	2 160	268
Death of				
green	711	176	1 350	234
non-green	84	50	280	38
belowground		71	2 017	251
Translocation				
green to non-green	163	88	92	75
non-green to belowground		176	4 740	431

INTERACTION BETWEEN TERRESTRIAL AND AQUATIC COMMUNITIES

A characteristic feature of Hardangervidda, as for most of the tundra, is the large number of ponds, lakes, brooks and rivers. It is apparent from a large-scale map of the region that the distance between open waters is usually short, and the area covered by standing or running water is considerable. This mosaic of terrestrial and freshwater communities provides the basis for interactions between the two communities.

During the growing season the network of aquatic localities provides, to some extent, a water supply for terrestrial plants. Aquatic communities also influence the temperature of their surroundings. Because of the high specific heat and the high heat of fusion of water, they minimize the temperature changes which occur in the tundra.

On the other hand the biological production of freshwater communities is entirely dependent on the soluble biogenic salts from the terrestrial surroundings, the catchment areas. The aquatic communities are also continuously supplied with sand, gravel and stones of different sizes from the terrestrial surroundings, while in the northern part of Hardangervidda fine material from the glaciers is also washed into the freshwater systems. The glacier melt water usually contains quite a high percentage of nutrient salts, but aquatic production is restricted because of greatly reduced transparency and low temperatures (51, 52, 85).

The exchange of organic matter between the terrestrial and aquatic communities can be of importance for production in both communities. Significant amounts of leaves and stems are blown or washed into the aquatic systems each year (53). In slow-running or standing water this allochthonous material settles on the bottom, producing a characteristic type of substratum with a high density of freshwater invertebrates which use the allochthonous matter for shelter and food (F. Aarefjord, R. Borgstrom, A. Lillehammer, pers. comm., 7, 56). Several species of Plecoptera, Ephemeroptera, Trichoptera, Chironomidae, Crustacea and Oligochaeta, together with other groups, are found in these areas.

During the first period of ice-free water, considerable numbers of aquatic insects (Plecoptera, Ephemeroptera, Trichoptera and Diptera) emerge and enter the terrestrial communities. Some of the insects feed on allochthonous matter of terrestrial origin in their aquatic larval stage and many terrestrial animals, especially birds, feed on the emerging insects. Most of the bird species recorded on Hardangervidda are insect feeders, particularly the breeding species when rearing young (29, 54, 58, 67). The peak emergence of insects seems to coincide with the rearing of young birds.

Living organic matter of terrestrial origin provides, to some extent, food for aquatic animals. Trout and char feed on terrestrial invertebrates during certain periods of the year and even small mammals can be found in the stomachs of fish (50, 77).

Finally, many animals depend directly, for a variety of reasons, on both terrestrial and aquatic environments for existence; among mammals, the American mink (*Mustela vision*), beaver (*Castor fiber*) and water shrew (*Neomys fodiens* (Shreb.)), and among birds, gulls, and especially ducks and waders which occur in great numbers and are represented by many species on Hardangervidda (58, 67).

As can be seen, the aquatic fauna is dependent on the terrestrial production, and aquatic invertebrate production is especially utilized by birds. Considering the fauna directly dependent on both communities, interaction of the terrestrial and aquatic networks at Hardangervidda must strongly influence their dynamics.

OVERVIEW OF THE ECOSYSTEM AND MAN'S INFLUENCE ON IT

Several features of human activity have been significant for the ecosystem in the past or show increasing significance in the twentieth century. Most important are the disturbances connected with power plant construction, and atmospheric pollution from European industry (e.g. 8, 31). The general succession of selected cultural impacts are shown in Fig. 11.

Hunting and trapping of the all important game animal on Hardangervidda — the wild reindeer — must already have been quite important in prehistoric times. This conclusion can be drawn from the innumerable remnants of these activities still found. Most prominent on the one hand are the innumerable pitfalls usually found in pairs and strategically placed where the topography creates bottlenecks through which the animals must pass in their migrations over the mountain plateau; and, in addition, the large stone ruins with middens rich in reindeer bones found on the shores of some the lakes (5).

Recent research has shown that these ruins, as well as others less conspicuous today, were used in connection with reindeer drives (6). Across the lakes from the ruins are in fact found stone cairns making up drift fences which once served to intercept the animals and aid the hunters in driving them into the lakes where men in boats could, with ease, overtake them and make the kill. This hunting method, traditionally known throughout the circumpolar regions, was doubtless practiced at Hardangervidda back to the beginning of our calendar. It is probably even older, even if this is not yet known with certainty. As a method it lasted until the surrounding mountain communities were hit by the Black Death A.D. 1349).

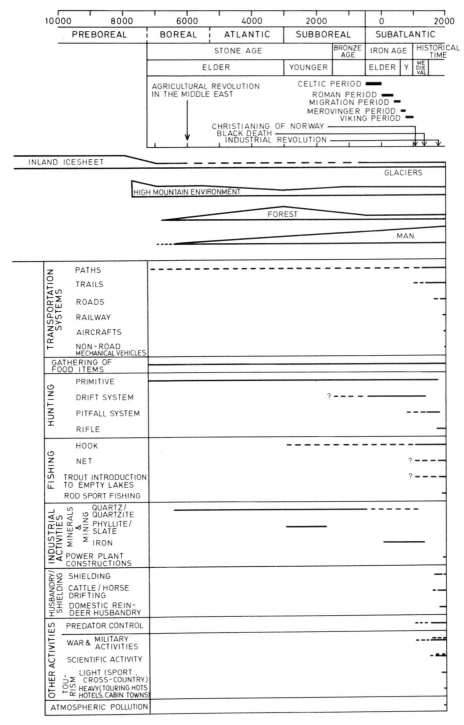

Figure 11. Cultural impacts on the Hardangervidda area in the post-glacial period. Compiled from different sources, mostly from (58).

When these communities were later resettled, reindeer drives were no longer feasible. This was probably due to social change making it impossible to recruit the complete hunting groups necessary for the success of the drive. Then the simpler method using pitfalls came into use. Judged by the local legends — for all have the motif of the heir, when faced by the choice, preferring the pitfalls belonging to the farm rather than the farm itself — this trapping method must have been rather successful. In spite of this, it had outlived itself when the gun, in the course of the seventeenth century replaced the bow and arrow in the lone hunt. The man with a gun could get the animals he wanted without having to depend on the use of pitfalls or other diversions.

Population growth in the mountain communities at this time led to an increase in the number of hunters. The ease with which these men with their guns could kill the desired number of reindeer as well as the development of the mountain farm system competed with reindeer. Important features of this system were cattle and sheep grazing in the alpine region in summer, and harvesting of lichens for winter cattle feed.

The wild reindeer population decreased so far that towards the end of the eighteenth century domestic reindeer were introduced. Reindeer husbandry in areas with wild herds has always proved difficult. Tame animals are lost to wild herds which grow large, and reindeer companies often choose to slaughter the remaining animals rather than lose all. Hunting combined with overgrazing again probably diminishes the wild reindeer population and the pattern may be repeated. About 1910 the wild population was estimated as being 11 000, while there were 12 000 tame beasts. The wild reindeer reached a low in the 1930s, then increased until the reduction hunt of the 1960s. After a long, difficult period the last tame reindeer company sold their herd to the government and they were set free. Today only wild reindeer exist, but their ancestors were probably mostly tame animals.

The projected harnessing of watercourses is bound to have significant impacts on the future of Hardangervidda (58, 62). The scientific interests affected raise a number of wide-ranging questions of principle. To carry out research work, scientists must have access to unviolated "models" of various ecosystems, and a research station which is to do basic research on systems ecology must accordingly be surrounded by representative unviolated systems.

The ecological research activity in general can best be understood if one takes as one's starting point the centre of Hardangerjøkulen (Fig. 1) — the active residue of ice which constantly frees new land for colonization by plant and animal communities. Regional research and studies along ecological gradients running out from this centre illustrate the evolution of the high-altitude mountain system from its glacier-covered origins to the stages governed by the type of climate now prevailing.

The whole of the Hardangervidda system may be divided into a cross with its axes intersecting at this centre, dividing the system into four sectors, differing in structure and productivity, a unified research programme with the ice residue as its centre could thus contribute greatly to our understanding of the ecological context in Scandinavian high-altitude mountain regions.

The vertical axis affords gradients through areas of very different structure, as regards topography, soil conditions and the effect of northward and southward inclined exposures on plant and animal life. Gradients in a southerly direction run through less elevated, more productive areas, richer in plant life than northerly gradients (Fig. 4). The latter traverse more broken mountain plateau areas, characterized by snow-patches and a rocky terrain of relatively low productivity (Fig. 2). The horizontal axis offers a gradient (climatically speaking) shifting from the oceanic in the western sector to the more typically continental type in the eastern sector. Within the various sectors studies could be carried out on many possible combinations of these basic types, each adding knowledge to the general understanding of Scandinavian diversity. With the rapid deterioration of our environment that is now under way, it will become steadily more obvious that Hardangervidda, in both the European and the global context, is unique.

The implemented and projected hydroelectric schemes would mean large representative areas which would cease to exist for large-scale ecological studies.

Our mountain regions, however hardy and robust they may seem, have shown themselves -- in common with every other arctic ecosystem which has been studied – to be extraordinarily sensitive to encroachments. It takes only a minor degree of outside influence to cause major changes.

It seems regrettable that arguments opposing the technical and economic plans for Hardangervidda are all too readily interpreted as prompted by narrow specialist interests. This misinterpretation hinders scientists and nature conservationists in making their voices heard. The conservation of Hardangervidda is therefore not just a dispute about petty local interests. Bearing in mind the global deterioration now taking place as a result of the general lack of ecological understanding, the question of the future administration of Hardangervidda assumes quite different proportions. In this connection it should be made plain that, on ecological grounds, we emphatically dissociate ourselves from the criteria and the poor ethical principles behind the present lopsided policy of economic growth, which in its destructive course is now wrecking Hardangervidda.

At the present time there is an increasing need for fundamental knowledge of the complicated functions of ecosystems, a need that grows in pace with the progressive destruction of man's environment. It is in this context that the conservation of Hardangervidda, with its simple and still comparatively unaffected biological systems, comes into its true perspective. Those characteristics which today make it one of the last unviolated parts of Europe will be drastically altered by the projected encroachments.

REFERENCES

1. Berg, A. 1975. Pigment structure of vascular plants and cryptogams at Hardangervidda, Norway. – In: Wielgolaski, F.E. (ed.) Fennoscandian Tundra Ecosystems. Part 1. Plants and microorganisms, pp. 216–224. Berlin–Heidelberg–New York: Springer Verlag.
2. Berg, A., Skre, O., Wielgolaski, F.E. & Kjelvik, S. 1973. Leaf areas and angles, chlorophyll and reserve carbon in alpine and subalpine plant communities, Hardangervidda, Norway. – In: Bliss, L.C. & Wielgolaski, F.E. (eds.) Primary Production and Production Processes, Tundra Biome, pp. 239–254. Edmonton: IBP Tundra Biome Steering Committee.
3. Berg, A., Kjelvik, S. & Wielgolaski, F.E. 1975. Measurement of leaf areas and leaf angles of plants at Hardangervidda, Norway. – In: Wielgolaski, F.E. (ed.) Fennoscandian Tundra Ecosystems. Part 1. Plants and microorganisms, pp. 103–110. Berlin–Heidelberg–New York: Springer Verlag.
4. Berg, A., Kjelvik, S. & Wielgolaski, F.E. 1975. Translocation of ^{14}C photosynthates in Norwegian alpine plants. – In: Wielgolaski, F.E. (ed.) Fennoscandian Tundra Ecosystems. Part 1. Plants and

microorganisms, pp. 208–215. Berlin–Heidelberg–New York: Springer Verlag.

5. Blehr, O. 1972. Hva dyregravene på Hardangervidda forteller om villreinfangst (What animal graves on Hardangervidda tell of reindeer slaughter). – Viking 1972: 115–130. (In Norwegian, English summary)

6. Blehr, O. 1973. Traditional reindeer hunting and social change in the local communities surrounding Hardangervidda. – Norw. Archaeol. Rev. 6: 102–112.

7. Brittain, J.E. 1974. Studies on the lentic Ephemeroptera and Plecoptera of Southern Norway. – Norsk Ent. Tidsskr. 21: 135–154.

8. Brosset, C. 1973. Air-borne acid. – Ambio 2: 2–9.

9. Brown, J. & Veum, A.K. 1974. Soil properties of the international tundra biome sites. – In: Holding, A.J., Heal, O.W., Maclean, S.F. & Flanagan, P.W. (eds.) Soil Organisms and Decomposition in Tundra, pp. 27–48. Stockholm: IBP Tundra Biome Steering Committee.

10. Bruun, I. 1967. Climatological summaries for Norway. Standard normals 1931–60 of the air temperature in Norway. Oslo: Det norske meteorologiske institutt. 270 pp.

11. Bruun, I. & Håland, L. 1970. Climatological summaries for Norway. Standard normals 1931–60 for number of days with various weather phenomena. Oslo: Det norske meteorologiske institutt. 193 pp.

12. Collett, R. 1895. *Myodes lemmus*: its habits in Norway. – Forh. Vidensk. Selsk. Krist. 3: 1–63.

13. Collett, R. 1911–12. Norges Pattedyr (Norwegian Mammals). Kristiania: Aschehoug. 744 pp. (In Norwegian)

14. Dahl, E. 1975. Flora and sociology in Fennoscandian tundra areas. – In: Wielgolaski, F.E. (ed.) Fennoscandian Tundra Ecosystems. Part 1. Plants and microorganisms, pp. 62–67. Berlin–Heidelberg–New York: Springer Verlag.

15. Det norske meteorologiske institutt. 1970. – Norsk met. Årb. 1969: 159 pp.

16. Det norske meteorologiske institutt. 1971. – Norsk met. Årb. 1970: 167 pp.

17. Det norske meteorologiske institutt. 1972. – Norsk met. Årb. 1971: 161 pp.

18. Det norske meteorologiske institutt. 1974. – Norsk met. Årb. 1972: 161 pp.

19. Elven, R. & Ryvarden, L. 1975. Dispersal and primary establishment of vegetation. – In: Wielgolaski, F.E. (ed.) Fennoscandian Tundra Ecosystems. Part 1. Plants and microorganisms, pp. 82–85. Berlin–Heidelberg–New York: Springer Verlag.

20. Fjellberg, A. 1975. Organization and dynamics of Collembola populations on Hardangervidda. – In: Wielgolaski, F.E. (ed.) Fennoscandian Tundra Ecosystems. Part 2. Animals and systems analysis. Berlin–Heidelberg–New York: Springer Verlag (in press).

21. Gaare, E. & Skogland, T. 1975. Wild reindeer food habits and range use at Hardangervidda. – In: Wielgolaski, F.E. (ed.) Fennoscandian Tundra Ecosystems. Part 2. Animals and systems analysis. Berlin–Heidelberg–New York: Springer Verlag (in press).

22. Gjaerevoll, O. 1956. The plant communities of the Scandinavian alpine snowbeds. – K. norske Vidensk. Selsk. Skr. 1956 (1): 1–405.

23. Greve, L. 1969. An aerial-drift of Neuroptera from Hardangervidda, Western Norway. – Årb. Univ. Bergen. Mat.-naturv. S. 1969: 1–15.

24. Hågvar, S. & Østbye, E. 1972. Quantitative and qualitative investigations of the invertebrate fauna under stones (the hypolithion) in some alpine habitats at Finse, South Norway. – Norsk Ent. Tidsskr. 19: 1–10.

25. Hågvar, S., Melåen, J. & Østbye, E. 1974. Quantitative studies of the invertebrate fauna in an alpine snow bed community at Finse, South Norway. – Norsk Ent. Tidsskr. 21: 45–51.

26. Hågvar, S. 1975. Studies on the ecology of *Melasoma collaris* L. (Col., Chrysomelidae) in alpine habitats at Finse, South Norway. – Norw. J. Ent. 22: 23–38.

27. Hågvar, S. 1975. Energy budget and growth during the development of *Melasoma collaris* L. (Coleoptera, Chrysomelidae). – Oikos (in press).

28. Håland, L. & Johannesen, T.W. 1969. Climatological summaries for Norway. Standard normals 1931–60 of the humidity of the air in Norway. – Det norske meteorologiske institutt, Oslo. 340 pp.

29. Haftorn, S. 1971. Norges fugler (Birds of Norway). Oslo–Bergen–Tromsø: Universitetsforlaget. 862 pp. (In Norwegian)

30. Hagen, A. 1973. Energibudsjett for en fjellrottepopulasjon (*Microtus oeconomus* (L.)) i den lav/ mellomalpine sone på Finse, Hardangervidda (Energy budget of a root vole population (*Microtus oeconomus* (L.)) in the low/mid-alpine zone at Finse, Hardangervidda). Unpublished thesis, University of Oslo. 48 pp. (In Norwegian)

31. Hagen, A. & Langeland, A. 1973. Polluted snow in southern Norway and the effect of the melt-water on freshwater and aquatic organisms. – Environ. Pollut. 5: 45–57.

32. Hagen, A., Kjelvik, S., Liestøl, K., Østbye, E., Skar, H.-J. & Swartzman, G. 1975. A simple ecosystem model with emphasis on small rodents. – Rapp. Høyfjellsøkol. Forsk. Stn., Finse, Norge 1975 (1) (in press).

33. Hagen, Y. 1952. Rovfuglene og viltpleien (Raptors and wildlife management). Oslo: Gyldendal. 603 pp. (In Norwegian)

34. Hagen, Y. 1956. The irruption of Hawk-owls (*Surnia ulula* (L.)) in Fennoscandia 1950–51. – Sterna, Opusc. Ser. zool. 24: 1–22.

35. Hagen, Y. 1960. Snøugla på Hardangervidda sommeren 1959 (The snowy owl, *Nyctea scandiaca* (L.) on Hardangervidda in the summer of 1959). – Meddr. St. viltunders. Ser 2 (7), 25 pp. (In Norwegian, English summary)

36. Hagen, Y. 1969. Norske undersøkelser over avkomproduksjonen hos rovfugler og ugler sett i relasjon til smågnager-bestandens vekslinger (Norwegian studies on the reproduction of birds of prey and owls in relation to micro-rodent population in fluctuations). – Fauna, Oslo 22: 73–126. (In Norwegian, English summary)

37. Haglund, B. 1968. De stora rovdjurens vintervanor II (Winter habits of the large carnivores II). – Viltrevy 5: 213–361. (In Swedish, English summary)

38. Hesjedal, O. 1975. Vegetation mapping at Hardangervidda. – In: Wielgolaski, F.E. (ed.) Fennoscandian Tundra Ecosystems. Part 1. Plants and microorganisms, pp. 74–81. Berlin–Heidelberg–New York: Springer Verlag.

39. Hinneri, S., Sonesson, M. & Veum, A.K. 1975. Geology and soil of some Fennoscandian tundra ecosystems. – In: Wielgolaski, F.E. (ed.) Fennoscandian Tundra Ecosystems. Part 1. Plants and microorganisms, pp. 31–40. Berlin–Heidelberg–New York: Springer Verlag.

40. Hofsvang, T. 1972. *Tipula excisa* Schum. (Diptera, Tipulidae), life cycle and population dynamics. – Norsk. Ent. Tidsskr. 19: 43–48.

41. Johannesen, T.W. & Håland, L. 1969. Climatological summaries for Norway. Standard normals 1931–60 of monthly wind summaries for Norway. Oslo: Det norske meteorologiske institutt. 217 pp.

42. Johannesen, T.W. 1970. The climate of Scandinavia. – In: Landsberg, H.E. (ed.) World Survey of Climatology. Vol. 5: 23–79. Amsterdam–London–New York: Elsevier Publ. Comp.

43. Jussila, R. 1975. Ichneumonidae from Hardangervidda. – Fauna of the Hardangervidda. – Zool. Mus., Univ. of Bergen 2: 50 pp.

44. Kalela, O. 1962. On the fluctuations in the numbers of arctic and boreal small rodents as a problem of production biology. – Ann. Acad. Sci. Fenn. Ser. A IV Biol. 66.

45. Kauri, H. 1971. List of animal species at Stigstuv Area, Hardangervidda, Norway. Evertebrata I. – Zoological Museum, Univ. of Bergen, mimeo. 14 pp.

46. Kauri, H. 1971. Notes on Turnbull-Nicholls' quick-trap method (summary). – Acta Ent. Fenn. 28: 106–107.

47. Kjellsen, E. 1975. Dynamics of Thysanoptera populations on Hardangervidda. – In: Wielgolaski, F.E. (ed.) Fennoscandian Tundra Ecosystems. Part 2. Animals and systems analysis. Berlin–Heidelberg–New York: Springer Verlag (in press).

48. Kjelvik, S. & Kärenlampi, L. 1975. Plant biomass and primary production of Fennoscandian subarctic and subalpine forests and of alpine willow and heath ecosystems. – In: Wielgolaski, F.E. (ed.) Fennoscandian Tundra Ecosystems. Part 1. Plants and microorganisms, pp. 111–120. Berlin–Heidelberg–New York: Springer Verlag.

49. Kjelvik, S., Wielgolaski, F.E. & Jahren, A. 1975. Photosynthesis and respiration of plants studied by field technique at Hardangervidda, Norway. – In: Wielgolaski, F.E. (ed.) Fennoscandian Tundra Ecosystems. Part 1. Plants and microorganisms, pp. 184–193. Berlin–Heidelberg–New York: Springer Verlag.

50. Klemetsen, A. & Østbye, E. 1967. Observasjoner over alder, kondisjon og ernæring hos røye fra Finsevatn (Observation on age, condition and food of char, *Salvelinus alpinus*, from Finsevatn, C. Norway). – Fauna, Oslo 20: 183–188. (In Norwegian, English summary)

51. Låg, J. & Bergseth, H. 1954. Studies on acidoid-basoid relationships of freshly formed material suspended in Norwegian glacial rivers. – Trans. Int. Congr. Soil Sci. 4: 53–57.

52. Låg, J. 1967. Noen forelopige resultater fra undersøkelser over kvartærgeologi- og jordbunnsproblemer ved Hardangerjøkelen (Preliminary results of investigations on quaternary geological and soil problems near Hardangerjøkelen glacier, Norway). – Meddr. Norske Skogfors. Ves. 23: 89–109. (In Norwegian, English summary)

53. Larsson, P. & Tangen, K. 1975. The input and significance of particulate terrestrial organic carbon in a subalpine freshwater ecosystem. – In: Wielgolaski, F.E. (ed.) Fennoscandian Tundra Ecosystems. Part 1. Plants and microorganisms, pp. 351–359. Berlin–Heidelberg–New York: Springer Verlag.

54. Lien, L., Østbye, E., Hogstad, O., Haande, K.M. Haande, P.S., Hagen, A., Skar, H.-J., Skartveit, A. & Svalastog, D. 1974. Bird surveys in the high mountain habitats of Finse and Stigstuv, Hardangervidda, South Norway, 1967–72. – Norw. J. Zool. 22: 1–14.

55. Liestøl, K., Østbye, E., Skar, H.-J. & Swartzman, G. 1975. A simulation model of a small rodent population. – In: Wielgolaski, F.E. (ed.) Fennoscandian Tundra Ecosystems. Part 2. Animals and systems analysis. Berlin–Heidelberg–New York: Springer Verlag (in press).

56. Lillehammer, A. 1974. Norwegian Stoneflies. II. Distribution and its relationship to the environment. – Norsk Ent. Tidsskr. 21: 195–250.

57. Lye, K.A. 1972. Vegetation of selected localities for IBP investigation in Hardangervidda, southern Norway. – IBP i Norden 8: 101–111.

58. Miljøverndepartementet. 1974. Hardangervidda. Natur-Kulturhistorie-Samfunnsliv (Hardangervidda. Nature-cultural history-community life). Norges offentlige utredninger 1974: 30A, 100 pp., 1974: 30B, 352 pp. & maps. Oslo: Universitetsforlaget. (In Norwegian)

59. Myrberget, S. 1965. Vekslinger i bestandstørrelsen hos norske smågnagene i årene 1946–60 (Changes in small rodent population levels in Norway 1946–60). – Meddr. St. viltunders. Ser. 2 (19): 54 pp. (In Norwegian, English summary)

60. Myrberget, S. 1973. Geographical synchronism of cycles of small rodents in Norway. – Oikos 24: 220–224.

61. Mysterud, I. 1970. Hypothesis concerning characteristics and causes of population movements in Tengmalm's Owl (*Aegolius funereus* (L.)). – Norw. J. Zool. 18: 49–74.

62. Mysterud, I. & Østbye, E. 1973. The future of Hardangervidda. Scientific interests and the harnessing of the watercourses on a Norwegian mountain plateau. – Research in Norway 1973: 59–68.

63. Nordhagen, R. 1943. Sikilsdalen og Norges fjellbeiter (Sikilsdalen and the mountain pastures of Norway). – Bergens Mus. Skr. 22: 1–607. (In Norwegian)

64. Nygaard, T. 1975. Acclimatization effect in photosynthesis and respiration. – In: Wielgolaski, F.E. (ed.) Fennoscandian Tundra Ecosystems. Part 1. Plants and microorganisms, pp. 163–167. Berlin–Heidelberg–New York: Springer Verlag.

65. Østbye, E., Mysterud, I. & Løkken, S. 1972. Bibliografi over naturvitenskapelig litteratur fra Hardangervidda og tilgrensense fjellstrøk. Preliminær utgave (Bibliography of the natural science literature dealing with Hardangervidda and the contiguous mountain areas in Southern Norway). – Rapp. Høyfjellsøkol. Forskn. Stn. Finse, Norge 1972 (1), 66 pp. (In Norwegian, English summary)

66. Østbye, E. & Hågvar, S. 1972. List of terrestrial invertebrates of the Finse area, Hardangervidda, South Norway. Preliminary list. – Rapp. Høyfjellsøkol. Forsk. Stn. Finse, Norge, 1972 (2), 21 pp.

67. Østbye, E., Hagen, A., Hogstad, O., Lien, L., Mysterud, I., Skar, H.-J. & Svalastog, D. 1972. List of vertebrates of the Finse area, Hardangervidda, South Norway. Preliminary edition. – Rapp. Høyfjellsøkol. Forsk. Stn. Finse. Norge 1972 (3), 17 pp.

68. Kauri, H., Solhøy, T., Østbye, E., Hagen, A., Lien, L., Skar, H.-J. 1975. Faunal structure of Hardangervidda. – In: Wielgolaski, F.E. (ed.) Fennoscandian Tundra Ecosystems. Part 2. Animals and systems analysis. Berlin–Heidelberg–New York: Springer Verlag (in press).

69. Rosswall, T., Veum, A.K. & Kärenlampi, L. 1975. Plant litter decomposition at Fennoscandian tundra sites. – In: Wielgolaski, F.E. (ed.) Fennoscandian Tundra Ecosystems. Part 1. Plants and microorganisms, pp. 268–278. Berlin–Heidelberg–New York: Springer Verlag.

70. Sandhaug, A., Kjelvik, S. & Wielgolaski, F.E. 1975. A mathematical simulation model for terrestrial tundra ecosystems. – In: Wielgolaski, F.E. (ed.) Fennoscandian Tundra Ecosystems. Part 2. Animals and systems analysis. Berlin–Heidelberg–New York: Springer Verlag (in press).

71. Siivonen, L. 1968. Nordeuropas däggdjur (Mammals of Northern Europe). Stockholm: Nordstedt & Söner. 183 pp. (In Swedish)

72. Skar, H.-J., Hagen, A. & Østbye, E. 1971. The bank vole (*Clethrionomys glareolus* (Schreber, 1780)) in South Norwegian mountain areas. – Norw. J. Zool. 19: 261–266.

73. Skartveit, A. 1974. Netto strålingsbalanse og energibalanse ved jordyta (Net radiation balance and energy balance at soil surface). – Unpublished thesis, University of Bergen. (In Norwegian)

74. Skartveit, A., Rydén, B.E. & Kärenlampi, L. 1975. Climate and hydrology of some Fennoscandian tundra ecosystems. – In: Wielgolaski, F.E. (ed.) Fennoscandian Tundra Ecosystems. Part 1. Plants and microorganisms, pp. 41–53. Berlin–Heidelberg–New York: Springer Verlag.

75. Skre, O. 1975. CO_2 exchange in Norwegian tundra plants studied by infrared gas analyzer technique. – In: Wielgolaski, F.E. (ed.) Fennoscandian Tundra Ecosystems. Part 1. Plants and microorganisms, pp. 183–186.. Berlin–Heidelberg–New York: Springer Verlag.

76. Skre, O., Berg, A. & Wielgolaski, F.E. 1975. Organic compunds in alpine plants. – In: Wielgolaski, F.E. (ed.) Fennoscandian Tundra Ecosystems. Part 1. Plants and microorganisms, pp. 183–186. Berlin–Heidelberg–New York: Springer Verlag.

77. Sømme, I.D. 1941. Ørretboka (The trout book). Oslo: J. Dybwad. 591 pp. (In Norwegian)

78. Solhøy, T. 1972. Quantitative invertebrate studies in mountain communities at Hardangervidda, South Norway. I. – Norsk Ent. Tidsskr. 19: 99–108.

79. Solhøy, T. 1975. Dynamics of Enchytraeidae populations on Hardangervidda. – In: Wielgolaski, F.E. (ed.) Fennoscandian Tundra Ecosystems. Part 2. Animals and systems analysis. Berlin–Heidelberg–New York: Springer Verlag (in press).

80. Solhøy, T. 1975. Dynamics of Oribatei populations on Hardangervidda. – In: Wielgolaski, F.E. (ed.) Fennoscandian Tundra Ecosystems. Part 2. Animals and systems analysis. Berlin–Heidelberg–New York: Springer Verlag (in press).

81. Sonesson, M., Wielgolaski, F.E. & Kallio, P. 1975. Description of Fennoscandian tundra ecosystems. – In: Wielgolaski, F.E. (ed.) Fennoscandian Tundra Ecosystems. Part 1. Plants and microorganisms, pp. 3–28. Berlin–Heidelberg–New York: Springer Verlag.

82. Steen, E. 1968. Some aspects of the nutrition of semi-domestic reindeer. – In: Crawford, M.A. (ed.) Comparative Nutrition of Wild Animals. Symp. Zool. Soc. Lond. 21: 117–128.

83. Stenseth, N.C. 1975. Energy model for individual small rodents and its significance for general population theory. – In: Wielgolaski, F.E. (ed.) Fennoscandian Tundra Ecosystems. Part 2. Animals and systems analysis. Berlin–Heidelberg–New York: Springer Verlag (in press).

84. Stop-Bowitz, C. 1969. A contribution to our knowledge of the systematics and zoogeography of Norwegian earthworms (Annelida Oligochaeta: Lumbricidae). – Nytt Mag. Zool. 17: 169–280.

85. Strøm, K.M. 1956. Changes in a glacier-fed lake. Finsevatn after 21 years. – Hydrobiologia 8: 293–297.

86. Thambs-Lyche, H. 1975. Dynamics of Aphididae populations on Hardangervidda. – In: Wielgolaski, F.E. (ed.) Fennoscandian Tundra Ecosystems. Part 2. Animals and systems analysis. Berlin–Heidelberg–New York: Springer Verlag (in press).

87. Wielgolaski, F.E. (ed.) 1975. Fennoscandian Tundra Ecosystems. Part 1. Plants and microoganisms. Berlin–Heidelberg–New York: Springer Verlag. 359 pp.

88. Wielgolaski, F.E. (ed.) 1975. Fennoscandian Tundra Ecosystems. Part 2. Animals and systems analysis. Berlin–Heidelberg–New York: Springer Verlag (in press).

89. Wielgolaski, F.E. 1975. Primary productivity of alpine meadow communities. – In: Wielgolaski, F.E. (ed.) Fennoscandian Tundra Ecosystems. Part 1. Plants and microorganisms, pp. 121–128. Berlin–Heidelberg–New York: Springer Verlag.

90. Wielgolaski, F.E. 1975. Comparison of plant structure on grazed and ungrazed tundra meadows. – In: Wielgolaski, F.E. (ed.) Fennoscandian Tundra Ecosystems. Part 1. Plants and microorganisms, pp. 86–93. Berlin–Heidelberg–New York: Springer Verlag.

91. Wielgolaski, F.E. 1975. Functioning of Fennoscandian tundra systems. – In: Wielgolaski, F.E. (ed.) Fennoscandian Tundra Ecosystems. Part 2. Animals and systems analysis. Berlin–Heidelberg–New York: Springer Verlag (in press).
92. Wielgolaski, F.E. & Kärenlampi, L. 1975. Plant phenology of Fennoscandian tundra areas. – In: Wielgolaski, F.E. (ed.) Fennoscandian Tundra Ecosystems. Part 1. Plants and microorganisms, pp. 94–102. Berlin–Heidelberg–New York: Springer Verlag.
93. Wielgolaski, F.E. & Kärenlampi, L. 1975. Energy content and use of solar radiation of Fennoscandian tundra plants. – In: Wielgolaski, F.E. (ed.) Fennoscandian Tundra Ecosystems. Part 1. Plants and microorganisms, pp. 201–207. Berlin–Heidelberg–New York: Springer Verlag.
94. Wielgolaski, F.E., Kjelvik, S. & Kallio, P. 1975. Mineral content of tundra and forest tundra plants in Fennoscandia. – In: Wielgolaski, F.E. (ed.) Fennoscandian Tundra Ecosystems. Part 1. Plants and microorganisms, pp. 316–332. Berlin–Heidelberg–New York: Springer Verlag.
95. Wielgolaski, F.E. & Kjelvik, S. 1975. Plant biomass at the Norwegian IBP sites at Hardangervidda 1969–1972. – In: Vik, R. (ed.) IBP in Norway. Methods and results. Sections PT-UM. Grazing project, Hardangervidda. Botanical investigations, pp. 1–88. Oslo: Norwegian National IBP Committee.
96. Wildhagen, Aa. 1952. Om vekslingene i bestanden av smågnagere i Norge 1871–1949 (On changes in small rodent populations in Norway 1871–1949). – Drammen: Statens viltundersøkelser. 192 pp. (In Norwegian, English summary)
97. Wildhagen, Aa. 1954. Einige Ergebnisse des phänologischen Kleinnagertierdienstes in Norwegen. – Säugetierk. Mitt. 2: 154–158.

Rosswall, T. & Heal, O.W. (eds.) 1975.
Structure and Function of Tundra Ecosystems.
Ecol. Bull. (Stockholm) 20: 265–294.

STORDALEN (ABISKO), SWEDEN

T. ROSSWALL, J.G.K. FLOWER-ELLIS, L.G. JOHANSSON, S. JONSSON,
B.E. RYDÉN and M. SONESSON

INTRODUCTION

The Swedish IBP tundra site is at Stordalen in the eastern part of the Torneträsk area (68°22′N, 19°03′E) ten kilometres east of Abisko (Fig. 1). The site is 351 m a.s.l. and 70 km from the sea; it is about one kilometre from and ten metres above Lake Torneträsk, which has an area of 322 km².

The Torneträsk area has an altitudinal range of 300 to 2 000 m. About 60 % of the area is in the Subalpine birch woodland belt of Fennoscandia (49); the rest is bare mountains. Stordalen occupies a narrow, level zone in the subalpine belt between Lake Torneträsk and the neighbouring Caledonian mountains (57). Archaean acid bedrock (granite) underlies the site.

The site is a 25 ha treeless, mainly oligotrophic mire (Fig. 2), made up of a complex of four major habitats: (i) elevated, nutrient-deficient (ombrotrophic) areas with a micro-relief pattern of usually low, but wide, hummocks and small shallow depressions; (ii) wet, nutrient-richer (minerotrophic) depressions; (iii) pools and (iv) brooks bringing water to and from the complex. The first habitat has permafrost near the surface throughout the growing season.

The mire is typical of the peatlands in the eastern continental parts of northern Fennoscandia with respect to the occurrence of permafrost and the composition of the plant cover. Peat formation began at least 5 000 years B.P. The elevated areas are on permafrost; since they are the most tundra-like, and make up the greater part of the mire, they were studied intensively and, unless otherwise stated, the following account applies to the elevated areas only.

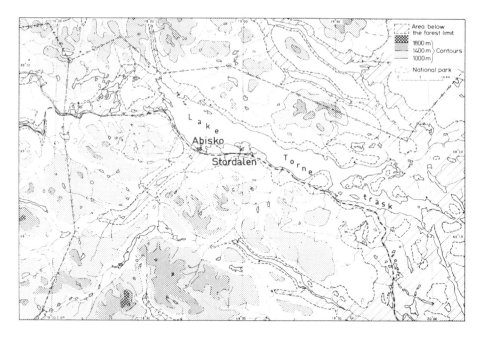

Figure 1. Map of the Torneträsk area showing the position of Stordalen and Abisko (52).

Figure 2. The Stordalen site from N showing the field laboratory and climatic station. In the background the railway line and the mountain range.

ENVIRONMENTAL CONDITIONS

Climate

From the beginning of the twentieth century until the 1940s the climate of Lappland was pronouncedly warmer than at present (67). Temperature and discharge trends since the 1930s indicate cooler summers, decreasing precipitation (30, 36) and a delay of the growing season towards the autumn. Winds in Lappland are predominantly westerly and they have probably been so since Late Glacial time (19, 25, 48).

Stordalen is within the continental part of an oceanic-continental climatic gradient running from west to east in the Torneträsk area. The proximity of the large Lake Torneträsk, and the position of the site in the valley bottom, combine to affect the local climate. Cool, moist air flow is frequent, and convective rain seldom occurs. The water divide between the Atlantic Ocean and the Gulf of Bothnia is 30–35 km west of Stordalen; mountains to the south, west, and north reach altitudes of 1 200–2 000 m. The annual precipitation at Abisko, sheltered from the western rain-bearing winds, is the lowest in Fennoscandia, about 300 mm; that at Stordalen is somewhat higher, since it is farther from the high mountains. Not more than 50 km west of Stordalen, i.e. on the Scandinavian water divide, the annual precipitation is 1 000 mm. The mean annual temperature is about $-0.5°C$, the warmest month being July, the coldest February, having monthly mean temperatures of 11.5 and $-11.7°C$, respectively (Table 1).

During the brief spring and autumn, environmental conditions at the site fluctuate markedly. The period of snowmelt and its associated processes cause large and rapid changes in the microclimate of the mire.

Yearly radiation income (global solar radiation) amounts to 200–300 kJ cm^{-2} (8, Table 1). Little is received outside the growing season because of the high albedo, 85 % or more, of the snow cover (47, 68). Only during May, June and July does the mire receive considerable radiation energy, i.e. when the sun is well above the mountains immediately south of the mire. The albedo drops rapidly during snowmelt (end of May – beginning of June) to values of about 15–20 % (51, 68).

During summer days with clear sky the bare ground surface reaches temperatures 10–15°C above screen temperature. These very large temperature gradients (Fig. 3) are caused by the high radiation intensity in combination with the low albedo of the snow-free tundra surface, the relatively low thermal conductivity of peat and an often negligible air turbulence close to the surface. Differences during the day in the rate of heating of the ground may be explained by an increase in albedo through the day (51). The energy loss to space is considerable, both during clear nights and during the polar day. Very intensive temperature variations are therefore created in the uppermost few centimetres of the peat, affecting dew formation and moisture movements through the canopy and litter layer (3). Upper soil temperatures vary widely, temperatures close to 30°C being observed in the moss-lichen covered surface in June. The insulating properties of peat (32) prevent the diurnal variations' reaching deeper than about 20 cm; annual variations are not observed deeper than 80 cm. However, during spring and early summer, diurnally repeated thawing and freezing occur to depths of 10 to 15 cm.

Air humidity tends to increase from two metres' height down to the ground. There is a tendency towards a diurnal, less pronounced gradient – sometimes close to isohumic – about the time for the temperature maximum, since turbulent mass exchange is

Table 1. Climatic data for Stordalen (S) and Abisko Scientific Research Station (A) (Means for 1971–1973)

	J	F	M	A	M	J	J	A	S	O	N	D	Year
Radiation (kJ cm^{-2}) (A)	0.9	6.1	18.8	30.1	40.7	34.3	32.5	23.3	11.3	6.6	1.2	1.7	208
Air temperature (°C) (A)													
max	4.1	3.0	5.0	9.3	17.2	27.4	30.0	22.4	20.5	11.2	4.2	7.3	30.0
mean	−9.5	−11.7	−10.3	−5.5	2.8	10.3	11.5	10.4	5.1	0.7	−7.4	−5.3	−0.7
min	−30.0	−29.5	−30.0	−23.2	−11.4	−1.7	0.5	−0.1	−5.8	−10.8	−23.5	−20.7	−30.0
Relative humidity air (%) (A)	87	83	81	81	74	69	72	79	76	75	86	87	
Precipitation (mm)													
(A) (1931–60)	22	19	18	14	15	30	45	43	33	21	18	22	300
(A) (1972–74)	n.d.	n.d.	n.d.	n.d.	8	25	57	49	34	n.d.	n.d.	n.d.	
(S) (1972–74)	n.d.	n.d.	n.d.	n.d.	10	42	69	57	47	n.d.	n.d.	n.d.	
Evapotranspiration ☆ (mm) (S)	n.d.	n.d.	n.d.	n.d.	n.d.	42	36	28	30	n.d.	n.d.	n.d.	
Snow depth (cm) (S)	6.9	8.7	7.6	13.6	1.5	0	0	0	0	3.4	9.7	11.9	

Growing season 1971: 135 days, 1972: 153 days, 1973: 146 days
(period with daily mean air temperature > 0 °C) (S)

☆ = measured using the evaporimeter of Andersson (1)

n.d. = not determined

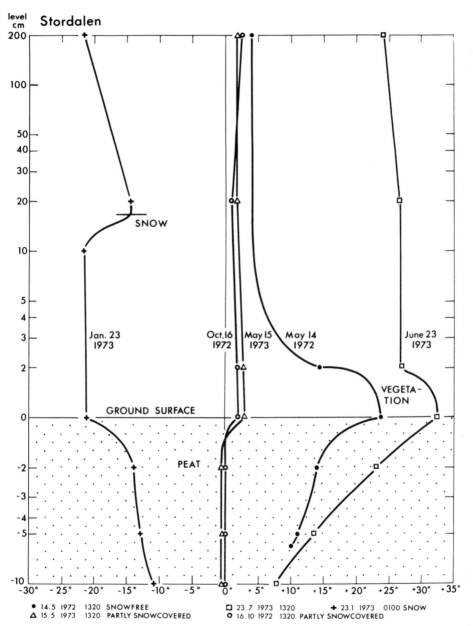

Figure 3. Typical temperature gradients in air, snow, vegetation and soil at Stordalen. The date **14 May 1972** represents a year with an early spring; the soil had thawed to 10–15 cm. The ground was warmed readily and the low vegetation stored heat. On **16 October 1972**, the ground was partly covered with snow to a depth of a few centimetres. The soil was not frozen. The date **23 January 1973** was a typical winter day as regards temperature gradients in snow and soil. However, the uppermost layer of the snow showed residual heat from a brief period of mild weather during the previous week. For **15 May 1973** the temperature conditions during snow-melt are shown. A "soil skin" a few centimetres deep had thawed, and the snow distribution was irregular. The date **23 June 1973** was typical for a summer day as regards soil and vegetation temperatures. – Note that all temperature profiles were recorded at midday, except 23 Jan 1973, which was at 01 00 hours.

269

greatest in daytime when the wind velocity and convection are strongest (15). Air humidity variations are greatest in the shallow vegetation layer.

The low winter temperature, the small precipitation and the uneven distribution of snow maintain permafrost conditions. The hummock summits have a snow cover of 0–10 cm, while the hummock slopes and the small depressions have 10–60 cm during late March and early April (cf. 53). The depth to permafrost during autumn is 30–50 cm in the hummocks and 40–80 cm in the depressions.

Hydrology

Small catchments in arctic areas have a short period of non-frozen conditions, during which the discharge is very pronounced, averaging two to three weeks of intensive snow-melt run-off, which yields about 80–90 % of the annual total (29, 47). At Stordalen the discharge period of about two weeks is more or less directly followed by summer conditions with negligible surface run-off.

Evapotranspiration at ground level is at a maximum (3 mm d^{-1}) during a short period after snowmelt, and decreases during July and August to about 1 mm d^{-1} (Table 1). The water exchange during the growing season is almost exclusively vertical, being a balance between precipitation, water released by the thawing of peat and evapotranspiration (46), averaging about 130 mm during the period of non-frozen conditions. Free water is mostly absent in the hummocks, but occur in the small depressions after snowmelt and after lasting rains (cf. 53).

The freeze-thaw cycle is important in the water budget of the mire. During snowmelt the frozen ground forces the melt-water to flow above the surface, regardless of whether the peat is fully recharged in the layers below or not. Thawing to an appreciable depth does not occur until after snowmelt; this gives rise to two different periods of water movement: horizontal until snowmelt is complete, vertical during the remainder of the summer. A remarkable feature of the freeze-thaw cycle at Stordalen is the entrapping of liquids and gases in unfrozen layers from October onwards. This continues until January–February; the latest time at which temperatures above freezing point are observed is February, at about 70 cm depth (Fig. 4).

Soils

The main surface soil of the mire is peat 0 to 3.0 m deep, overlying silt and/or sand. Granitic boulders or bedrock are also present locally. The boundary between the peat and the mineral soil follows approximately the surface topography (54). The topographic variation is about 0.3–1.0 m over the main area of the mire, increasing in the largest hummocks (palsas) to more than 2.5 m. The permafrost reaches unknown depths.

The great variation in peat types reflects both the diversity in peat-forming communities and the effects of soil processes (55). Regelation may be of importance in the development of the soil profile. Four main horizons can be recognised: (i) an undecomposed horizon of fresh or older debris: colour range dark brown to yellow, thickness 1–5 cm; (ii) a slightly decomposed horizon of more or less consolidated organic material: colour range dark brown to yellow, thickness 3–40 cm (the lightest colours occur either in the uppermost horizon or near the maximum depth of the active layer); (iii) transitional horizon with mixed organic and mineral matter: colours brown – dark grey, thickness

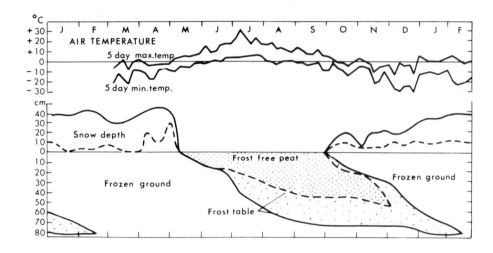

Figure 4. The freeze-thaw cycle of peat, illustrated with data on snow-cover and air temperature at 200 cm. Two curves are shown for snow depth and frost table representing hummocks (– ·· – – ··) and depressions (————) of elevated areas. Modified from (70).

3–10 cm; (iv) underlying stratum of silt or fine sand: colours grey or grey-black, depth unknown. The surface peat consists mainly of slightly decomposed bryophyte remains with bulk density of 0.08–0.10 g cm^{-3} (Table 2). Deeper peat strata may be highly decomposed and consolidated, with bulk densities of 0.30–0.40 g cm^{-3}. When sand or silt is present, density varies considerably, the homogeneous mineral soils having densities averaging 1.5 g cm^{-3}.

The water content of peat varies from 15 % to 95 % by volume. The underlying strata of mineral soil hold 10–40 % by volume. The capacity of peat to store water may be gradually changed by hysteresis and repeated effects of the freeze-thaw cycle. The peat is acid, pH (H$_2$O) about 4.0, and very poor in available nutrients (Table 2). The extractable cations (excl. H^{+}), as expressed along a profile of 10 cm-layers from the surface, have values of 23–26–28 g m^{-2}. The degree of humification according to the von Post scale amounts to 3–4.

PRIMARY PRODUCTION

Community classification and dynamics

According to common Scandinavian terminology (50), the Stordalen mire is a mixed mire, i.e. composed of ombrotrophic elevated areas forming complexes with minerotrophic areas. The former are bog sites, the latter fen sites in a restricted sense (10). Most of the plant cover is referable to "Oxycocco-Empetrion hermaphroditi" and "Leuco-Scheuchzerion" (7), which are true oligotrophic mire communities typical of northern Fennoscandia.

271

Table 2. Peat characteristics for Stordalen (± S.E. of the mean, numbers of samples analysed given in brackets)

Depth (cm)		0–10	10–20	20–30
pH_{H_2O}		4.0±0.1 (24)	4.1±0.1 (24)	4.2±0.2 (24)
Moisture (% of ww)		84±3 (24)	85±2 (24)	80±8 (24)
Bulk density (g cm^{-3})		0.084±0.013 (24)	0.103±0.014 (24)	0.102±0.019 (24)
Maximum thaw (cm)	30–80			
Total organic carbon (%)		44.6±0.7 (48)	45.8±0.9 (48)	43.8±2.1 (48)
Total nitrogen (%)		0.9±0.11 (48)	1.2±0.10 (48)	1.4±0.15 (48)
C/N		48	38	31
Total phosphorus (ppm)		590±100 (24)	525±100 (24)	530±100 (24)
Total ash (%)		2.4±0.5 (24)	2.8±0.6 (24)	3.7±1.0 (22)
Extractable cations [☆] (meq 100 g^{-1})				
Calcium		7.5±1.1 (20)	8.4±1.4 (19)	9.5±2.3 (19)
Magnesium		4.7±1.2 (24)	3.2±0.8 (19)	2.9±0.9 (21)
Sodium		0.5±0.1 (24)	0.3±0.1 (24)	0.3±0.1 (23)
Potassium		1.1±0.3 (22)	0.5±0.2 (20)	0.3±0.1 (19)
Temperatures (°C) (1971–74)				
July mean max		16.4	9.0	2.0
July mean		8.0	5.3	0.8
July mean min		4.0	4.2	0.0

☆ Cations were extracted with 1 M neutral NH$_4$Ac.

The main features of the vegetation (Table 3) at Stordalen are determined by the creeping (rhizomatous or prostrate-stemmed) growth habit of the dwarf shrubs and *Rubus chamaemorus* L. and by the low tussocks of *Eriophorum vaginatum* L. The vegetation is largely a mosaic of expanded clonal patches, some coherent, most dispersed. These patches range in size from a few dm^2 to several hundred m^2. Aboveground, the main factor affecting distribution and species composition on the elevated areas, hence also biomass and production, is exposure. This in its turn is related to microrelief. The depth and duration of snow cover at any point depend primarily on the surface con-

Table 3. Standing crop, primary production and community plant cover at the Stordalen mire. Estimated values within brackets

	Cover (%)	Standing crop (g m^{-2})	Net production (g m^{-2} yr^{-1})
Aboveground			
Dwarf shrubs Green	33	144	26
Non-green			(10)
Andromeda polifolia	12	25	7 ☆
Betula nana	2	32	5 ☆
Empetrum hermaphroditum	13	71	8 ☆
Vaccinium uliginosum	4	13	5 ☆
Others		3	1 ☆
Forbs	10	18	18
Rubus chamaemorus	10	18	18
Monocotyledons	23	18	(5)
Eriophorum vaginatum	20		
Lichens	20	12	(<3)
Cetraria spp	4		
Cladonia spp	12		
Crustose lichens	4		
Bryophytes	87	300	70
Dicranum elongatum	24	n.d.	16
Sphagnum balticum	23	n.d.	38
Sphagnum fuscum	13	n.d.	9
Other Musci	19	n.d.	7
Hepatics	8	n.d.	n.d.
Bare peat	11		
Belowground			
Live		(400)	24
Dead		(450)	

☆ = not including wood increment

n.d. = not determined

figuration, secondarily on the height of vegetation, which traps and retains snow. The vegetation is largely dependent on snow cover as a protection from desiccation and attrition by ice particles moving at considerable velocity along the snow surface. Hummocks are blown bare; plants on them are exposed and damaged, both by the weather and by grazing and trampling, principally by reindeer and rodents, especially hare. The longer growing season consequent upon exposure is more than offset by the severe and repeated destruction of growing points and the depletion of reserves. Production is reduced, biomass accretion prevented, and dead material removed from the hummock, reducing still further its ability to gather a protective snow cover.

Belowground, growth is not subject to this overriding influence, and production is probably closely related to soil temperature and moisture, the latter especially as regards its effect on aeration. The following account applies mainly to the dwarf shrubs, for which most results are available, and in particular to the aboveground standing crop, since the amount and distribution of belowground standing crop are incompletely known.

The microsite types recognised here are based primarily on the microtopography, and may be illustrated as follows (Fig. 5):

I. On the severely exposed hummock tops, grazed and eroded lichen communities prevail, in which *Cetraria nivalis* (L.) Ach., *C. cucullata* (Bell.) Ach., *Cladonia mitis* Sandst. and crustose lichens overgrow bryophytes and hamper their growth. The vascular plants are few, and depend for survival on the shelter of depressions a centimetre or two in depth and on the formation of small-scale "shelter complexes". The age of aerial shoots rarely exceeds ten years in *Andromeda polifolia* L. but may be 30—40 years in *Empetrum hermaphroditum* Hagerup. Few branch axes of *Andromeda* live longer than five to seven years, leaves uncommonly more than two seasons, whereas on the densely leafy shoots of *Empetrum* they may live for five or six seasons. Shoots of *Andromeda* and *Empetrum* extend 1—5 mm a year, but in *Vaccinium uliginosum* L. they may reach 10 mm. These longer shoots are repeatedly killed back to half their length. Abrasion by wind-borne ice particles scars and kills leaves and shoots, which are soon swept away. Although between one-third and half of the leaves and shoots die annually, little attached dead remains. For this reason, the production to biomass ratio is surprisingly high, $\geqslant 0.5$ for *Empetrum* and *Andromeda*.

Grazing and trampling of the brittle, frozen shoots by hare and reindeer in winter contribute further to the wastage of the hummock summits, which, once the surface is broken, may be eroded deeply by wind. The bare peat is recolonised in time by *Empetrum*, but usually first by *Rubus*, regenerating from abundant rhizomes. The low production per unit area of this microsite, combined with the continuous loss by wind action, prevents the accumulation of vascular plant biomass aboveground. Herbivore droppings accumulate locally, and are probably important in returning nutrients to a system which is otherwise characterised by nutrient and organic matter wastage.

II. On the more sheltered slopes of the drier hummocks and on the extensive level areas where *Dicranum elongatum* Schleich. and *Sphagnum fuscum* Klinggr. dominate the cryptogam layer, the population density of the vascular plants is greater and the number of species increases. *Rubus* forms dense populations, and has a high incidence of flowering and fruiting. *E. vaginatum* extends over large areas, mainly forming a mosaic with *Empetrum* and *Andromeda*, with *Rubus* throughout. Individuals of the dwarf-shrubs are both larger and longer-lived than those in site I. Production per unit area is therefore greater, much of it accumulating as perennial tissue. The leaves of the evergreen species live longer (three to four, occasionally five seasons in *Andromeda*, but still rarely more than six in *Empetrum*), and are larger. In the more open stands with much *Cladonia*, leaves and shoots of the dwarf shrubs may be quickly overgrown by lichens, often before they die. In the denser stands dominated by *Empetrum*, where *Empetrum* standing crop alone may reach 390 g m^{-2} and its current shoot production 43 g m^{-2}), dead leaves remain attached in large numbers, and retain their structure for many years. In this situation they are sheltered from precipitation and are not in contact with the moist substratum; decomposition is in consequence slow. Litter and attached dead therefore build up beneath these stands; not of *Empetrum* alone, the branching sys-

274

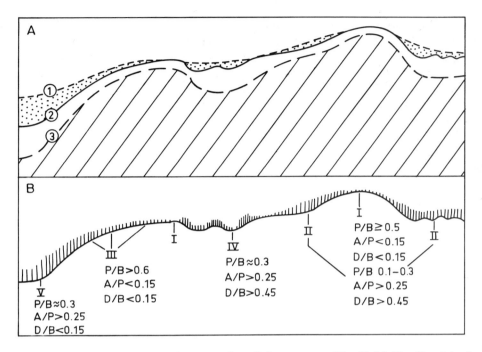

Figure 5 A. Schematic relationship between microrelief, snow cover (March) (cf. Fig. 4) and depth to permafrost table (August) for the elevated areas of the Stordalen mire. 1, snow surface; 2, ground surface; 3, permafrost surface (not to scale).
B. Schematic relationship between microrelief and standing crop of vascular plants (height of bars shows approximate relationship of height of vegetation between microsites). The microsites (see text) are a combination of topography and the vegetation types of Madsen & Widell (28). P/B = production/biomass; A/P = accumulation/production; D/B = attached dead/biomass, where P is current leaf + shoot + flower + wood increment; B is total weight of living plant material including P; A is P minus the loss by death of current year's production; and D is attached dead. Values in g m^{-2} or g m^{-2} yr^{-1}.

tems of which may attain a total length of 550 m m^{-2} of which attached dead is ca 28 % by length but only about 9 % by weight, but also of *Vaccinium vitis-idaea* L. and *Andromeda* which grow in its shelter. Even though production and litterfall are large, the rate of turnover is slow.

Betula nana L. occurs in shallow hollows in this site type, and in the lee of hummocks. It is prostrate and of slow growth, but longlived, with individual stems attaining an age of 40 years or more. Few long shoots are produced, most of the production being leaves on short shoots and diameter increment of the main stems. It makes only a locally significant contribution to biomass and production, the ratio of production to biomass being low, often ca 0.1. The rhizomes and creeping shoots of *V. uliginosum* grow throughout the lichen mat, generally away from the direction of exposure. Distal parts of the leafy shorter shoots are repeatedly killed, often by summer frosts, but new shoots arise from resting buds to produce closely matted clusters of stems. This site type as a whole is characterised by the accumulation of perennial tissue and attached dead giving a low ratio of production to biomass (0.1–0.3), and turnover is slow.

III. Where *Sphagnum fuscum* dominates the bryophyte layer, the growth, population density and turnover rate of the dwarf shrubs (principally *Andromeda*, *Empetrum* and *V. uliginosum*) and *Rubus* are closely related to the upward growth of the moss surface. A low mean tiller age is maintained, and a high ratio of production to biomass, which in extreme cases may reach unity. Both standing and attached dead are quickly overgrown by the *Sphagnum*. In *Andromeda* and to a lesser extent *V. uliginosum*, rhizome and secondary root growth seem to be stimulated by the moisture increase resulting from moss growth. The formation of new branches from basal buds, and the ingrowth of new tillers derived from superficial rhizomes, combine to give population densities of up to 8 000 individuals m^{-2} in *Andromeda*, although the greatest density normally attained on this microsite type is ca 4 000 m^{-2}.

With a production to biomass ratio of ca 0.50 (compared with ca 0.34 on the average), production is high, and more than 80 % is in the form of photosynthetic tissue. Since overgrowth by moss increases the rate of leaf replacement, plants are maintained in a high state of photosynthetic efficiency and the recycling of storage substances and mineral nutrients is rapid. Since, however, both leaves and twigs are still largely structurally intact at a depth of 10—15 cm in the peat, release of nutrients by decomposition may be slow. Reproduction by seed is also common, even though the abundant flowering (especially of *Andromeda*) on this microsite results in fewer ripe fruits than on the drier elevated areas. The population density, large production per individual, low longevity of tillers and rapid upward growth of the mosses combine to make this probably the most productive microsite of the elevated areas, even though the standing crop of vascular plants is not high.

IV. In the small depressions which dry up shortly after snowmelt, hepatics such as *Gymnocolea inflata* Huds. and *Ptilidium ciliare* L. and the lichens *Cetraria delisei* (Bory) Th. Fr. and *Ochrolechia frigida* (Sw.) Lynge dominate in the cryptogam layer. In this microsite *Andromeda* is the principal dwarf shrub and often the only vascular plant. Individuals attain both a considerable age (ca 30 years) and a large size, with woody tissues, including attached dead, sometimes amounting to more than half the weight of old individuals. The absolute production per individual to biomass ratio is generally close to the mean (ca 0.34) and may fall to 0.1 in old individuals.

These depressions receive much blown litter, mainly *Rubus* and *Betula* leaves, and other litter is washed into them during snowmelt. Small rodents, e.g. *Lemmus*, inhabit the slopes of the depressions, and their faeces periodically accumulate, but disappear within 2—3 years. Litter breaks down rapidly in the generally wet conditions of the floor of the depressions, but *Andromeda* leaves which accumulate on the small elevations (built up of *Andromeda* stems and rhizomes), represent at least ten years' litterfall. On the sides of the depressions, *V. uliginosum* is abundant. The effect of shelter is marked; current shoots on the slopes of the depressions are up to four times as long as those on the adjacent elevated areas. Production is about 0.3 of biomass, compared with 0.1—0.2 on exposed microsites. Growth and biomass of *Betula* are similarly increased on the slopes, and mean tiller age is substantially less than on the exposed areas.

V. In the wetter depressions dominated by *Sphagnum balticum* (Sw.) Lynge in the bryophyte layer, *Andromeda* and *Vaccinium microcarpum* (Rapv.) Hook. f. are usually the only dwarf shrubs present, although *E. vaginatum* and *Carex rotundata* Wahlenb. are at their most productive here. *Andromeda* forms sparse populations with large individuals and high production per individual. Mean age is also remarkably low (less than five years), and the rate of turnover high. The growth of *S. balticum* here stimulates rhizome and secondary root growth in *Andromeda* in the same way as does *S. fuscum*, but the result is markedly different: there are only 100–200 individuals m^{-2}, with a mean weight of 160 mg compared with ca 10–20 mg on the *S. fuscum* cushions. The large size is attained in two or three years by shoot increments of more than 50 mm yr^{-1} (compared with ca 5 mm). Decomposition seems to be more rapid here than on the *S. fuscum* cushions, although structurally intact leaves and shoots occur at some depth. *V. microcarpum* is locally abundant on this microsite, but both its production and biomass are insignificant.

Standing crop, production and production rates

Acrocarpous bryophytes are the principal contributors to the standing crop of the elevated areas, with a biomass (standing green) of about 300 g m^{-2} (Table 3). Although the green length of the shoots varies from approximately 5 mm on the hummock tops to 50 mm in the wetter depressions, the standing crop is fairly similar for all the microsites, owing to differences in weight/length relationships and spatial densities. Dwarf shrubs are the second principal plant group, with an aboveground standing crop of about 144 g m^{-2}. Monocotyledons, forbs and lichens contribute with ca 18, 18 and 12 g m^{-2}, respectively. The belowground biomass is approximately 400 g m^{-2}.

The total net mean production of bryophytes is 70 g m^{-2} yr^{-1}, ranging from zero on the hummock tops, 50-100 g on the slopes and level areas to about 150 g m^{-2} yr^{-1} in the wetter depressions. The lichen production is less than 3 g m^{-2} yr^{-1}, and the quantity produced equals that lost by consumption and wind drift. The aboveground vascular plant production is: dwarf shrubs 36 g, forbs 18 g and monocots 5 g m^{-2} yr^{-1}, and belowground production 24 g, making an annual total of 83 g m^{-2}.

Production processes

Owing to the uneven snow cover, the thaw is rapid during early spring when insolation becomes high. The temperatures in the vegetation are then sufficiently high to allow photosynthesis particularly for bryophytes and lichens of the hummock tops, which show positive photosynthesis as early as March, during bright days. Even the evergreen vascular plants, of which *Andromeda polifolia* and *Empetrum hermaphroditum* dominate the mire, benefit from the early thaw. In 1973, their photosynthetically active season began on about 10 May on the hummock tops and about a week later on the main parts of the mire (20). In many depressions the snow lay longer, but shoots of *Empetrum* under 0.5 m of snow in a snowbed, when exposed to ambient light and temperature, immediately reached a photosynthetic rate of 30–50 % of that of plants which had been snow-free for ten days or more.

The chlorophyll content in the leaves of evergreen plants is rather uniform from early May to late September. In 1973, the ranges for one-year-old (C+1) and current year's leaves (C) were 1.1–1.6 and 1.6–2.3 mg g^{-1} respectively for *Empetrum*, and 1.5–2.6 and 2.0–2.6 mg g^{-1}, respectively, for *Andromeda*. Chlorophyll is therefore not considered to limit the length of the growing season (21).

The deciduous plants studied (*Rubus chamaemorus* and *Betula nana*) do not develop their leaves until early June (20). By then the air and soil temperatures are high and the incoming solar radiation is near its maximum for the year. High rates of photosynthesis are therefore reached very soon after the leaves have appeared. In the later part of the growing season (July – September), the photosynthetic activity of the vascular plants decreases. In evergreens this is compensated by the development in late June of a new leaf generation which, when it is fully expanded, has a higher rate of photosynthesis (per leaf area or dry weight) than the one-year-old leaves. This gives the evergreen plants an extended late-season period of primary production (Table 4).

Senescence of the deciduous plants begins during August and is complete in mid-September, ending a growing season of about three months. Evergreens continue photosynthesis until late September or early October giving a five month growing season, at least in favourable years. The photosynthetic period of the cryptogams probably ends in mid-October, giving a growing season of about five months, plus intermittent periods of active photosynthesis earlier in the spring.

Lack of water is seldom a limiting factor for plants on a mire. However, plant water potentials between −15 and −20 bars have been recorded for vascular plants about midday on warm and dry days. Such low values probably cause closure of the stomata and thus affect photosynthesis. This water stress is probably due to the low water-conducting ability of the rhizomes, a hypothesis which is supported by anatomical studies showing that much of the vascular tissue in the older rhizomes is not functional.

Many evergreen tundra plants store organic compounds in their leaves, as well as in roots and rhizomes (4) and translocation studies on *A. polifolia* at Stordalen seem to confirm this (12, 22). Early in the season, before the new leaves develop, much of the assimilated carbon is distributed to belowground parts of the plant. During the warm summer period

Table 4. **Typical average midday rates of photosynthesis during the growing season. The values given are means of measurements made on 4–6 occasions per month at 10–12 a.m. Results are in mg CO_2 dm^{-2} h^{-1} for projected leaf area and mg CO_2 g^{-1} h^{-1} (in brackets) for leaf dry weight.**

Species	May	June	July	Aug.	Sept.
Rubus chamaemorus	n.d.	3.9(7.3)	4.9(6.6)	3.3(5.6)	n.d.
Betula nana	n.d.	5.1(10.9)	6.9(10.7)	5.6(8.7)	n.d.
Andromeda polifolia C [1]	n.d.	n.d.	4.6(4.6)	6.3(3.7)	3.8(2.2)
C+1 [2]	0.6(0.3)	5.0(2.8)	6.3(4.0)	3.7(2.0)	2.4(1.5)
Empetrum hermaphroditum C	n.d.	n.d.	n.d.(1.7)	n.d.(2.0)	n.d.(1.0)
C+1	n.d.(0.3)	n.d.(1.5)	n.d.(1.1)	n.d.(1.2)	n.d.(0.9)

1) C = current year's leaves
2) C+1 = one-year-old leaves
n.d. = not determined

278

(mid-June to late July) little assimilate is stored. Late in the season assimilates accumulate in aboveground as well as in belowground parts of the plant (Fig. 6). In deciduous plants, accumulation of assimilates in roots and rhizomes is small during the period of leaf extension growth but increases later in the season (22).

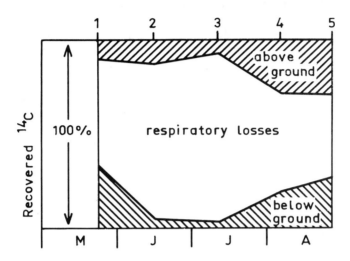

Figure 6. Distribution of assimilates in *Andromeda polifolia* during the growing season. The graph is based on five ^{14}C-labelling occasions (nos 1–5). The intercept on the vertical axis on each occasion shows the distribution of labelled assimilates three weeks after labelling.

HERBIVORES

The main sap-sucking insect groups present at the site are Cicadina, Psyllina, and Aphidina. Browsing insects (mainly Symphyta, Lepidoptera and Coleoptera) occur periodically. Especially important is the cyclic occurrence of *Oporinia autumnata* Bkh., which can completely defoliate large areas of birch woods, and such outbreaks have occurred regularly in the Torneträsk area (65). Plant feeding nematodes may make up about 30 % of the nematode fauna (24). Important vertebrate herbivores are reindeer (*Rangifer t. tarandus* L.), moose (*Alces a. alces* L.), hare (*Lepus timidus* L.), and rodents (*Lemmus lemmus* L., *Clethrionomys rufocanus* Sund., *C. rutilus* Pall.). Reindeer cross the site during migration and probably affect the vegetation more by trampling than by grazing. Moose are frequent in the adjacent birch woods but are rarely found on the site. Small rodents occur cyclically at high concentrations, when they have a considerable effect on parts of the ecosystem. Besides removing vegetation, they also cause local accumulation of nutrients around their holes and pathways.

Consumption of plant biomass rarely reaches levels of importance in years when rodent populations are low. Grazing is highly selective, current shoots and opening buds being preferred in early summer, persistent fruits especially in winter (*E. hermaphroditum*). Hares and willow grouse seem to have been responsible for most grazing during the period 1970–1974. Insect consumption is rarely appreciable, even when individual tillers are studied. Nevertheless, periodic outbreaks (e.g. *O. autumnata*) may completely defoliate even the dwarf shrubs (principally *V. uliginosum*).

Although willow grouse (*Lagopus l. lagopus* L.) and ducks (e.g. *Anas c. crecca* L.) consume far less of the vegetation than the rodents, they indirectly affect its structure, e.g. by eating buds and seeds. Many herbivores and omnivores contribute to the dispersal of seeds (18); seedlings of *E. hermaphroditum, V. uliginosum* and *R. chamaemorus* form clusters associated with hare and willow grouse faeces.

CARNIVORES

During the past 70 years man has increasingly affected the species composition and population level of predators. The drastic reduction of large predators, e.g. bear (*Ursus a. arctos* L.), wolf (*Canis l. lupus* L.) and wolverine (*Gulo gulo* L.), by hunting with modern weapons seems to be less important than the indirect reduction of these animals by changes in the environment through settlement and railway construction. The decrease of the original predator fauna has favoured periodic invasions by other predators, especially birds of prey, in phase with the mass occurrence of prey. As with most granivorous and insectivorous birds, several birds of prey are annual migrants, returning in May or late April, and staying for 3–4 months.

The number of warm-blooded predators is mainly associated with the rodent cycles, e.g. red fox (*Vulpes vulpes* L.), ermine (*Mustela erminea* L.), rough-legged buzzard (*Buteo l. lagopus* Pont.) and short-eared owl (*Asio f. flammeus* Pont.), or with mass outbreak of insects, e.g. willow warbler (*Phylloscopus trochilus acredula* L.), and meadow pipit (*Anthus p. pratensis* L.).

Wading birds, e.g. red-necked phalarope (*Phalaropus lobatus* L.), golden plover (*Pluvialis apricaria altifrons* Brehm), and whimbrel (*Numenius p. phaeopus* L.) occur regularly and nest on the site. Insects alternate with seeds as the staple food of fieldfare (*Turdus pilaris* L.), redwing (*T. i. iliacus* L.), redpoll (*Carduelis f. flammea* L.) and brambling (*Fringilla montifringilla* L.), which are the most abundant omnivorous birds on the site (23).

The numbers of invertebrate predators (mainly spiders, beetles, ants, and dragonflies) vary with food supply, climatic conditions (mainly temperature) or both. Gamasids and larval stages of several species of Diptera and Coleoptera act as soil-living predators. The omnivorous dorylaimoid nematodes seem to make up 40 % of the nematode biomass (24). Parasitic nematodes and insects are common on the invertebrates of the mire, e.g. on pollinators and browsing larvae. They seem to be as important as the insectivorous birds in the regulation of the insect populations. Culicids are the most important bloodsuckers on the vertebrates within the area.

DECOMPOSITION

The Stordalen site is not in a steady state, since the addition of organic matter through primary production exceeds the loss through decomposition by at least 70 g m^{-2} yr^{-1}.

Moisture seems to be the most important factor limiting decomposition rates. The moisture is in many cases too low, e.g. in surface litter, where wind increases evaporation and contributes to rapid drying of the litter. When aboveground litter is incorporated into the cryptogam and upper peat layers as a result of bryophyte growth and water movement, moisture conditions become optimal. In many areas high levels of peat moisture, especially in spring and autumn, probably retard decomposition of bryophyte and root litter as well as peat through development of anaerobic conditions. There is a fairly high temperature in the litter layer during the summer months (mean max. air temperature for July is 30°C, cf. Table 1 and Fig. 3) affecting decomposition, while the low temperatures resulting from the permafrost greatly decrease decomposition rates in the peat profile.

Microbial biomass and production

Penicillium is a frequently occurring fungal genus in standing dead (*Eriophorum vaginatum*) and litter (*E. vaginatum, Rubus chamaemorus, Empetrum hermaphroditum*); *Phoma exigua* Desm. is also a common litter fungus (16, 35). There is, however, a marked variation in occurrence of dominant species between years which probably to some extent reflects climatic conditions (17). Sterile mycelia are common. A high proportion of the first year's litter seems to be uncolonized by fungi (17). The fungal biomass of one-year-old *R. chamaemorus* leaf litter is 8 mg g^{-1} (35) and the bacterial biomass 0.4 mg g^{-1} (5, 37).

In the peat sterile mycelia are common (3–69 %); *Mortierella, Oidiodendron, Chrysosporium* and *Penicillium* are genera frequently found (17). The bacterial population consists of 45 % spore formers, and a large percentage of the bacteria are able to decompose cellulose, chitin, starch and proteins. Part of the bacterial flora is adapted to low temperatures, 20 % being able to grow well at 2°C (43).

The total fungal biomass is approximately 58 g m^{-2} (to 30 cm depth) (14), that of bacteria being 22 g m^{-2} (6). The fungal biomass is probably an overestimate, since only 10–30 % of the observed mycelia are considered to be alive. Dead bacteria are decomposed fairly rapidly (40), and of the bacterial numbers, as estimated by direct counts, approximately 90 % of the cells are alive (34). Numbers of fungi decrease rapidly down the peat profile (Fig. 7) with ca 2 % of the numbers of propagules g^{-1} at 20–30 cm depth, as compared to the numbers at 0.5 cm. Bacteria decrease only to ca 20 % of original numbers between the same two depths.

Anaerobic bacteria are numerous (Table 5), numbers usually increasing down the profile. As many as 10^6 anaerobes g^{-1} of peat have been observed, and viable counts are generally 10^4 g^{-1}. Anaerobic bacteria are responsible for prolific methane production especially in the minerotrophic depressions (59, 61, 63); sulphate reducing (60), anaerobic cellulose decomposing (62) and photosynthetic (*Rhodospirillum* spp.) (44) bacteria have also been isolated.

Table 5. Numbers of anaerobic bacteria in peat of different subsites of the Stordalen mire. The numbers were determined by the roll-tube method in half strength tryptone soya agar, 0.1 % ascorbic acid and 1 ppm resazurin under an atmosphere of N_2 and CO_2 (9:1) (62). n = 3

Subsite	Rubus chamaemorus-Dicranum elongatum-Eriophorum vaginatum community (1b-c ☆)			Rubus chamaemorus-Sphagnum fuscum community (1d)			Carex rotundata-Drepanocladus schulzei community (7a)			Eriophorum angustifolium-Carex rostrata community (7b-c)		
Depth (cm)	H_2O (% dw)	Nos.g^{-1} 10^{-4}	S.E. (%)	H_2O (% dw)	Nos.g^{-1} 10^{-4}	S.E. (%)	H_2O (% dw)	Nos.g^{-1} 10^{-4}	S.E. (%)	H_2O (% dw)	Nos.g^{-1} 10^{-4}	S.E. (%)
1–2	728	0.2	25	1 083	27.4	20	1 695	2.6	8	617	10.4	19
5–6	1 688	2.7	33	1 705	76.3	6	1 855	34.6	5	1 068	14.3	22
10–11	701	28.3	35	1 504	53.2	9	1 161	30.4	18	1 444[+]	11.8	19
19–20	501	0.2	50	810	102.1	19	955	31.6	19	n.d.	n.d.	n.d.

+ = 14–15 cm
☆ = community no (cf. Fig. 9 & 11)
n.d. = not determined

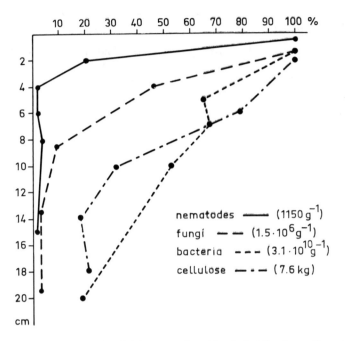

Figure 7. Numbers of nematodes, fungi (plate count) and bacteria (direct count) as well as cellulose decomposition (tensile strength of cotton strips after one year) in a peat profile in a *Rubus chamaemorus – Dicranum elongatum* community. Results are expressed as per cent of the value for the sample closest to the surface (6, 24, 35, 42).

Bacterial production is large (140 g m^{-2} yr^{-1}), especially in the upper layers which have a favourable temperature regime (6). The number of generations of bacteria during one season was estimated to be 9 in the 0–5 cm layer but only 3 in the lower layers (25–35 cm). No measurements were made on fungal production, but using the approximations of Hanssen & Goksøyr (14) a value of 81 g m^{-2} yr^{-1} is obtained giving a total microbial production of 220 g m^{-2} yr^{-1}, as compared with a total primary production of 156 g. However, microbial production is probably overestimated and primary production underestimated. The high turnover rates for soil bacteria are evident from the ratio of annual production to standing crop which is ca 6.3 while the value for vascular plants is only 0.2 (40).

Invertebrate biomass and production

A preliminary survey of soil invertebrates indicated that nematodes are the most abundant soil fauna group, with 4 000 000 m^{-2} (biomass 0.2 g); rotifers reach 900 000 m^{-2} (0.06 g), tardigrades 45 000 m^{-2} (0.003 g), mites 200 000 m^{-2} (biomass approx 0.08 g) and collemboles 76 000 (0.2 g) (24, 26). These numbers are equal to or higher than those found in other tundra areas (69). The enchytraeids, mainly *Cognettia lapponica* Nurminen, seem to have very low population numbers, for the most part less than 1 000 ind. m^{-2} (biomass 0.05 g) (27). The estimated annual production of soil invertebrates is less than one per cent of the microbial production.

Rates of decomposition

Rates of decomposition of aboveground vascular plant litter are high for tundra regions, with leaf litter from *R. chamaemorus* losing approximately 20 % of its weight during the first year and nearly 50 % after three years (38, 39) (Table 6), but even after this time the litter remains structurally fairly intact. Strong autumn winds sweep the litter into the small depressions, where moisture conditions, especially in autumn and spring, are favourable for microbial decomposition. The *R. chamaemorus* leaf litter decomposition is slow at less than 50 % moisture (% of dw), and reaches an optimum around 600 %, above which the rate declines somewhat until the litter reaches a moisture content corresponding to its maximum retentive capacity, which for *R. chamaemorus* litter is approximately 900 % (Fig. 8). Temperatures are probably never above optimal, with rates increasing up to 30°C with a $Q_{10} \approx 2$. Microbial respiration continues below 0°C and is measurable at −5°C (45).

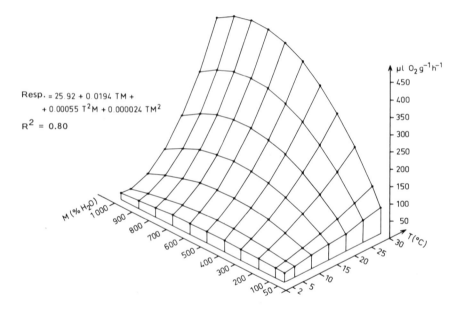

Figure 8. Regression surface for the dependence of respiration from *Rubus chamaemorus* leaf litter on temperature and moisture (n = 144) (41).

The rapid first-year weight loss of plant litter is due partly to leaching and partly to the rapid decomposition of certain substances, e.g. simple carbohydrates and protein, which are easily attacked by microorganisms. Leaching probably accounts for 50 % of the first year's weight loss (45). Decomposition occurs most rapidly in spring and autumn, and litter dries out during the summer although dew, and to a lesser extent rain, may provide sufficient moisture for decomposition.

First-year weight loss of aboveground litter of *Eriophorum vaginatum* is similar to that of *R. chamaemorus* litter (Table 6). Litter of dwarf shrubs decomposes more slowly, as determined by litter bag experiments; *Empetrum hermaphroditum* and *Andromeda*

Table 6. Decomposition of plant litter expressed as per cent weight loss (± S.E., number of samples in brackets) from litter bags or for *Betula nana* twigs from individually tagged samples (38, 39, 41, 45). Values are cumulative over the periods shown.

Species	Year out	1 yr	2 yr	3 yr
Rubus chamaemorus	1970	23.5±2.8	36.9±3.6	47.9±3.7
(leaves)		(10)	(10)	(10)
	1971	16.4±3.9	21.1±3.2	–
		(8)	(11)	
	1972	28.4±1.8	–	–
		(10)		
Empetrum hermaphroditum	1970	5.7±0.3	19.8±1.7	26.2±2.3
(aboveground parts)		(10)	(7)	(8)
Empetrum hermaphroditum	1972	28.7±1.4	–	–
(leaves, green)		(6)		
Eriophorum vaginatum	1972	37.0±1.0	56.6±1.3	–
(leaves)		(7)	(11)	
Betula nana	1971	20.9±1.2	28.2±1.1	36.5±1.0
(leaves)		(11)	(7)	(14)
Betula nana	1971	7.8±0.5	15.5±0.9	16.7±0.5
(twigs)		(9)	(10)	(8)
Andromeda polifolia	1971	15.0±0.9	24.7±1.4	28.6±0.7
(aboveground parts)		(9)	(7)	(10)
Sphagnum fuscum	1971	5.4	2.1	5.7
Sphagnum balticum	1972	4.3	7.8	–
Sphagnum lindbergii	1972	7.1	19.3	–
Dicranum elongatum	1972	7.1	4.3	–
Drepanocladus schulzei	1973	4.7	–	–

polifolia decomposing by only 6 % during the first year, but as their small leaves are more easily incorporated into the bryophyte layer under favourable moisture conditions these values may be an underestimate.

Dead bryophytes show a very low decomposition rate (Table 6) possibly because of microbial inhibitors which occur in several bryophytes (58). The slow decomposition results in accumulation of peat, the annual increment being greater than 1 mm in the moderately dry and mesic microsites (slopes of hummocks and level elevated areas) but probably higher in the wet microsites. Apart from bryophytes, only sheaths and roots of E. vaginatum make up a major proportion of the peat.

Anaerobic conditions probably dominate below 10 cm. Numbers of nematodes are already very low at 4 cm (Fig. 7), and numbers of fungi and cellulose decomposition rates are much lower at 10 cm than closer to the surface. Anaerobic decomposition is of major importance in the wetter, more nutrient-rich habitats. Methane, one end product of anaerobic decomposition, makes up 19 % of the total carbon loss from the mire (61) and can, in some microsites, account for 50 % of the loss (Fig. 9).

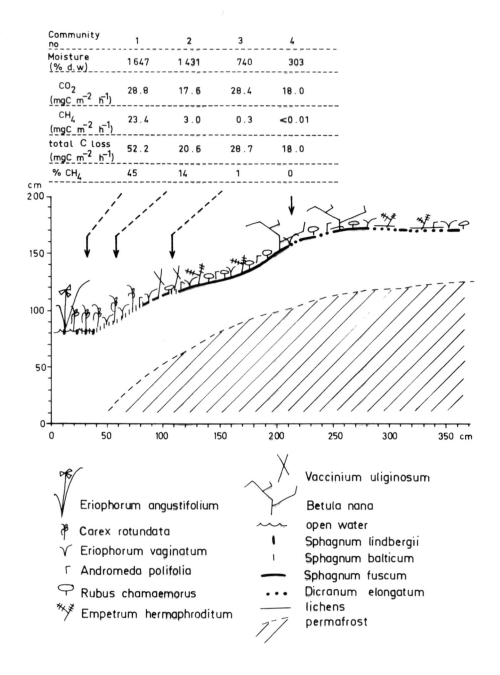

Community no	1	2	3	4
Moisture (% d.w)	1647	1431	740	303
CO_2 (mgC m^{-2} h^{-1})	28.8	17.6	28.4	18.0
CH_4 (mgC m^{-2} h^{-1})	23.4	3.0	0.3	<0.01
total C loss (mgC m^{-2} h^{-1})	52.2	20.6	28.7	18.0
% CH_4	45	14	1	0

Eriophorum angustifolium

Carex rotundata

Eriophorum vaginatum

Andromeda polifolia

Rubus chamaemorus

Empetrum hermaphroditum

Vaccinium uliginosum

Betula nana

open water

Sphagnum lindbergii

Sphagnum balticum

Sphagnum fuscum

Dicranum elongatum

lichens

permafrost

Figure 9. Carbon dioxide and methane released to the atmosphere from peat under four different plant communities (Nos 1–4) of the Stordalen mire. Data from July 1973 (60). Community numbers in brackets refer to the classification of Madsen & Widell (28). 1. *Eriophorum angustifolium* community (7 b). 2. *Carex rotundata – Drepanocladus schulzei* community (7 a). 3. *Rubus chamaemorus – Sphagnum fuscum* community (1 d). 4. *R. chamaemorus – Dicranum elongatum – Sphagnum fuscum* community (1 b–d).

A large proportion of the primary production passes directly to the decomposer chain, the herbivores being of small importance, with the exception of years when lemmings or defoliating insects are abundant. Only a minor part of the energy flow passes through the soil invertebrates (less than 1 %), while the rest passes through the soil microorganisms. It is possible that the large numbers of nematodes, by consuming bacteria and fungi, indirectly affect the energy flow through the microbial population, although the consumption of bacteria by nematodes is in the order of only 3 g m^{-2} yr^{-1} (24), i.e. a small part of the yearly bacterial production. Nematodes feeding on bacteria (microbial feeders) are more abundant in the wetter parts of the mire, while plant and fungal feeders are more important in the dry lichen communities (Fig. 10). Protozoa are probably also important in this respect, but their numbers are unknown.

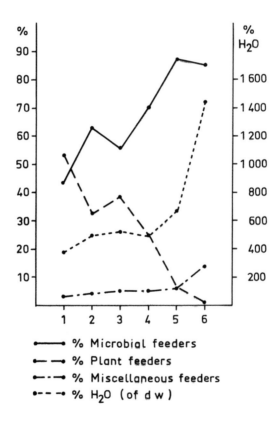

● % Microbial feeders
● — ● % Plant feeders
●—·—● % Miscellaneous feeders
●·— ·● % H$_2$O (of d w)

Figure 10. Distribution of feeding groups of nematodes along a moisture gradient at the Stordalen mire (from 24). 1. Lichen community (1a); 2. *Rubus chamaemorus – Dicranum elongatum* community (1b–c); 3. *R. chamaemorus – Sphagnum fuscum* community (1d); 4. *Eriophorum vaginatum* community (3); 5. *E. vaginatum – S. balticum* community (6); 6. *S. balticum* community (5). Numbers in brackets refer to the community classification of Madsen & Widell (28).

NUTRIENTS

The elevated areas of the mire are nutrient deficient (ombrotrophic), as there is a very limited input of nutrients other than through atmospheric sources (10) due to topography and permafrost. The supply of nutrients comes, with a few exceptions, from the atmosphere in the form of wet or dry deposition and nitrogen fixation.

The elevated ombrotrophic areas are approximately one to five metres above two medium sized lakes and a brook running along the western border of the mire. Since the areas are on permafrost, the hydrological connections to the water bodies are only temporary and unilateral; there is a superficial flow of meltwater in spring, carrying dissolved nutrients and organic matter via the wet minerotrophic depressions to the aquatic systems. Plant litter is blown into the small lakes surrounding the site during autumn storms, but the amount of nutrients lost in this way is probably insignificant and may be counterbalanced by the deposition of faeces from migratory animals (reindeer, hare and birds). There is also some input of insects to the mire after hatching in the lakes. The importance of these inputs/outputs is not known.

There is a nutritional gradient from the drier, elevated ombrotrophic areas to the minerotrophic wet depressions and lakes (Fig. 11), where the contact with mineral soil creates favourable nutrient conditions. These are also the subsites where there is an important nitrogen fixation (0.2–9 g nitrogen m^{-2} yr^{-1}) by blue-green algae living in close association with mosses, mainly as epiphytes (13). The nutritional gradient is shown by a marked change in floristic composition with minerotrophic plants (e.g. *Eriophorum angustifolium* Honck.) in the nutrient richer habitats (cf. Fig. 9).

Figure 11. Minerotrophic depression at the Stordalen mire with nitrogen fixation by blue-green algae growing in association with *Sphagnum riparium* (communities 7 a, b). The depression is surrounded by drier, ombrotrophic parts of the mire (communities 1 a–d). Cf. Fig. 9.

The site receives small but important amounts of nutrients in precipitation. Approximately 0.1 g m^{-2} yr^{-1} of nitrogen is added, approximately half as ammonium and half as nitrate (33); the content of organic nitrogen may be considerable (11), but has not been determined. Additions of other important nutrients are: Na 0.04 g, K 0.03 g, Ca 0.02 g, Mg 0.01 g m^{-2} yr^{-1} (33). Although the site is far removed from most industrial areas, the sulphur in rainfall reaches 150 mg m^{-2} yr^{-1}, but the addition of phosphorous is only of the order of 2 mg m^{-2} yr^{-1} (33).

The Stordalen mire is situated in the "nitrogen vegetation type" (2) as are most tundra areas. This vegetational zone is characterized by having a yearly nitrogen demand by the vegetation of $1-2$ g m^{-2}. The nitrogen budget for the Stordalen mire (Fig. 12) shows that ca 2 g of available nitrogen is needed for plant growth annually.

The input of nitrogen through nitrogen fixation is small in the ombrotrophic areas (0.18 g N m^{-2} yr^{-1}) (13), but this is nearly twice as much as the amount added through precipitation (0.10 g). The nitrogen is mainly fixed by aerobic bacteria, only 0.03 g m^{-2} yr^{-1} being fixed anaerobically (13).

Aboveground litter decomposition releases 0.2 g N m^{-2} yr^{-1}, but this is probably completely utilized by the moss cover; the nitrogen released from the litter layer is not available to the vascular plants. The latter are completely dependent on the amounts

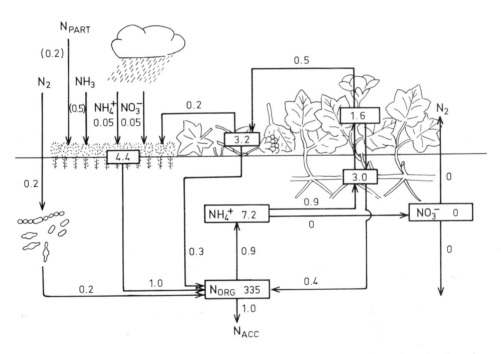

Figure 12. A preliminary nitrogen budget for the ombrotrophic parts of the Stordalen mire. Quantities expressed as g N m^{-2}, flows as g N m^{-2} yr^{-1}. The phytomass has been divided into aboveground parts of vascular plants, illustrated by *Rubus chamaemorus*, including lichens (1.6 g N m^{-2}), belowground parts of vascular plants (3.0 g N m^{-2}), aboveground litter (3.2 g N m^{-2}) and bryophytes (4.4 g N m^{-2}). N_{ORG} = organic nitrogen, N_{ACC} = nitrogen accumulated, N_{PART} = particulate nitrogen (dry deposition) (41).

Table 7. Distribution of roots at various peat depths at Stordalen

Depth cm	Shrubs[1] (%)	Herbs[2] (%)	Graminoids[3] (%)
0–5	53.7	40.0	38.2
5–10	30.9	26.7	24.1
10–15	12.8	13.9	12.0
15–20	2.4	6.4	7.3
20–25	0.1	4.5	11.6
25–30	+	3.2	3.5
30–35	+	2.4	1.9
35–40	+	1.6	1.2
40–45	+	1.3	0.2
45–50	0	+	+
>50	0	0	+

1) Shrubs: all woody vascular species
2) Herbs: mainly *Rubus*; *Pinguicula* negligible
3) *Eriophorum vaginatum* + *Carex rotundata*. The increase in graminoids at 20–25 cm was consistent in all samples
+ denotes a % less than the last figure shown. For shrubs, roots present below 20 cm are principally *Andromeda*.

mineralized from the peat, and as the decomposition of peat is retarded by low pH and low oxygen content, the vascular plants are probably nutrient-limited. Nitrogen mineralization in the peat is ca 0.5 g N m^{-2} yr^{-1} to 10 cm depth (41), where the majority of active plant roots are found (Table 7). The shrub and herb roots are mainly confined to the upper 15 cm, whereas graminoid roots, notably those of *Eriophorum vaginatum* are found at much greater depths. To meet the demands for nitrogen by plant roots, it is assumed that an additional 0.4 g N m^{-2} yr^{-1} is made available as a result of mineralization of organic matter at depths lower than 10 cm. The ammonium nitrogen produced is completely immobilized by plant roots and microorganisms, and no nitrate is formed, owing to the absence of nitrifying bacteria (44), which is probably a result of the low pH of the peat (9). Nitrate in precipitation is probably immediately taken up by the bryophytes and denitrification does not occur, even if bacteria capable of nitrate reduction are common (43).

The nitrogen budget for the site (Fig. 12) is not balanced, since it has been estimated that approximately 1.0 g N m^{-2} yr^{-1} is accumulated. The inputs accounted for by nitrogen fixation and precipitation are only ca 0.3 g. Apart from nitrogen input through rain, dry deposition is probably also important and could amount to twice that of wet deposition (55). Ammonium is probably also adsorbed directly from the atmosphere by the bryophyte layer (64).

OVERVIEW OF THE ECOSYSTEM AND MAN'S INFLUENCE ON IT

Direct influence on the site by man is slight, mainly for three reasons: (i) the sparse settlement of the area, (ii) the distance to the railway (1 km) and to the larger tourist tracks (10 km), (iii) the low commercial value of the ecosystem. However, cloudberry picking has probably been going on during early autumn for a very long time, resulting in an annual loss of energy and nutrients and in some trampling of the site. There are also fishermen's pathways crossing the site, and these tracks have a profound influence on the vegetation cover, which is easily destroyed with subsequent erosion and thawing of the permafrost. This trampling, together with the indirect human influence by reindeer grazing and trampling, may influence lichen productivity especially.

After the opening of the railway at the beginning of this century, the human impact on the ecosystem increased, when settlements other than the native Lappish ones were introduced. These settlements were, however, always placed in the close vicinity of the railway (54). During recent years, cross-country winter vehicles have increased in number, and are now regarded as the greatest potential threat to the ecosystem, the hummocks being only slightly covered with snow or totally bare during winter, when the plants are frozen and brittle, and therefore especially vulnerable. The impact of research activities on the site is also considerable, despite efforts to minimise it, and further developments in this direction may cause changes in plant distribution and species composition, even if erosion on the site of pathways can be avoided.

Air pollution is slight. The concentration of heavy metals in surface soils and plants is only about one-tenth of that recorded in south Sweden (31, 56, 66). Some transport of iron-ore dust and associated minerals may occur, but the high specific gravities involved should limit this form of pollution to the vicinity of the railway. Any future road development will cause a local increase in some air pollutants.

ACKNOWLEDGEMENTS

Many persons have been active in planning and research within the project. In this context we wish to express our appreciation to: U.-M. Andersson, K. Basilier, B. Berg, H. Bergman, K. Blomberg, M. Clarholm, Z. Dressie, U. Emanuelsson, H.-E. Engelbrekts, A. Flower-Ellis, L. Fors, S. Geidnert, U. Granhall, A.J. Hayes, S. Johansson, L. Karlqvist, S. Karlsson, S. Kjelleberg, L. Kostov, E. Kvillner, J. Lagerlöf, J. Larsson, O. Lindahl, U. Lohm, H. Lundkvist, I. Madsen, C. Magnusson, E. Mård, G. Nordin, T. Persson, P. Rheinberg, H. Selander, T. Sjöqvist, T.A. Stenström, B.G. Svensson, B.H. Svensson, H. Söderholm, M. Uno, B. Wessén and S. Widell.

Financial support has been received from the Bank of Sweden Tercentenary Fund, the Swedish Natural Science Research Council and the Royal Swedish Academy of Sciences which is gratefully acknowledged.

REFERENCES

1. Andersson, S. 1969. Markfysikaliska undersökningar i odlad jord. XVIII. Om en ny och enkel eva-porimeter (A new and simple evaporimeter). – Grundförbättring 22: 59–66. (In Swedish).
2. Bazilevich, N.I. & Rodin, L.Ye. 1971. Geographical regularities in productivity and the circulation of chemical elements in the earth's main vegetation types. – Soviet Geography 1971: 24–53.
3. Bjor, K. 1972. Micro-temperature profiles in the vegetation and soil surface layers. – Meddr. Norske Skogsfors. Ves. 30: 200–218.
4. Bliss, L.C. 1971. Arctic and alpine life cycles. – Ann. Rev. Ecol. Syst. 2: 405–438.
5. Clarholm, M. 1974. Direct counts of bacteria in tundra peat for estimating generation time and biomass production. – In: Flower-Ellis, J.G.K. (ed.) Progress Report 1973. IBP Swedish Tundra Biome Project Tech. Rep. 16: 43–55.
6. Clarholm, M., Lid-Torsvik, V. & Baker, J.H. 1975. Bacterial populations of some Fennoscandian tundra soils. – In: Wielgolaski, F.E. (ed.) Fennoscandian Tundra Ecosystems. Part 1: Plants and Microorganisms, pp. 251–260. Berlin–Heidelberg–New York: Springer Verlag.
7. Dahl, E., Kalliola, R., Marker, E. & Persson, Å. Fjällvegetation. 1971. Nordisk vegetationsklassificering för kartläggning. – IBP i Norden 7: 4–12. (In Swedish).
8. De Jong, B. 1973. Net radiation received by a horizontal surface at the earth. Rotterdam: Delft University Press.
9. Dunican, L.K. & Rosswall, T. 1974. Taxonomy and physiology of tundra bacteria in relation to site characteristics. – In: Holding, A.J., Heal, O.W., MacLean, S.F. & Flanagan, P.W. (eds.) Soil Organisms and Decomposition in Tundra, pp. 79–92. Stockholm: IBP Tundra Biome Steering Committee.
10. Du Rietz, G.E. 1954. Die Mineralbodenwasserzeigergrenze als Grundlage einer natürlichen Zweigliederung der Nord- und Mitteleuropäischen Moore. – Vegetatio 5–6: 571–585.
11. Eriksson, E. 1952. Composition of atmospheric precipitation. I. Nitrogen compounds. – Tellus 4: 215–232.
12. Flower-Ellis, J.G.K. 1975. Growth in populations of *Andromeda polifolia* on a subarctic mire. – In: Wielgolaski, F.E. (ed.) Fennoscandian Tundra Ecosystems. Part 1. Plants and Microogranisms, pp. 129–134: Berlin–Heidelberg–New York: Springer Verlag.
13. Granhall, U. & Selander, H. 1973. Nitrogen fixation in a subarctic mire. – Oikos 24: 8–15.
14. Hanssen, J.F. & Goksøyr, J. 1975. Biomass and production of soil and litter fungi at Scandinavian tundra sites. – In: Wielgolaski, F.E. (ed.) Fennoscandian Tundra Ecosystems. Part 1. Plants and Microorganisms, pp. 239–243. Berlin–Heidelberg–New York: Springer Verlag.
15. Haurwitz, B. & Austin, J.M. 1944. Climatology. McGraw-Hill Co., Inc.
16. Hayes, A.J. 1973. Studies on the microfungi occurring at Stordalen and Njulla 1972. – IBP Swedish Tundra Biome Project Tech. Rep. 15: 1–22.
17. Hayes, A.J. & Rheinberg, P. 1975. Microfungal populations of the Abisko area, northern Sweden. – In: Wielgolaski, F.E. (ed.) Fennoscandian Tundra Ecosystems. Part 1. Plants and Microorganisms, pp. 244–250. Berlin–Heidelberg–New York: Springer Verlag.
18. Heintze, A. 1915. Om endozoisk fröspridning genom skandinaviska däggdjur. – Bot. Notiser 6: 251–291 (In Swedish).
19. Hoppe, G. 1959. Glacial morphology and inland ice recession in Northern Sweden. – Geogr. Ann. 59: 193–212.
20. Johansson, L.G. 1974. Photosynthetic rates of some vascular plants on a subarctic mire at Stordalen. – In: Flower-Ellis, J.G.K. (ed.) Progress Report 1973. IBP Swedish Tundra Biome Project Tech. Rep. 16: 145–155.
21. Johansson, L.G. 1974. Chlorophyll content of four species of vascular plants at Stordalen. – In: Flower-Ellis, J.G.K. (ed.) Progress Report 1973. IBP Swedish Tundra Biome Project Tech. Rep. 16: 157–163.
22. Johansson, L.G. 1974. The distribution and fate of ^{14}C, photoassimilated by plants on a subarctic mire at Stordalen. – In: Flower-Ellis, J.G.K. (ed.) Progress Report 1973. IBP Swedish Tundra Biome Project Tech. Rep. 16: 165–172.
23. Jonsson, S. 1975. Vertebrate fauna of the Torneträsk area. – IBP Swedish Tundra Biome Project Tech. Rep. 5 (In press).

24. Lagerlöf, J., Magnusson, C. & Rosswall, T. 1975. Investigation of nematodes at the Stordalen site. – IBP Swedish Tundra Biome Project Tech. Rep. 18 (In press).
25. Liljequist, G.H. 1956. Meteorologiska synpunkter på istidsproblemet. – Ymer 76: 59–74. (In Swedish).
26. Lohm, U., Lundkvist, H. & Persson, T. 1973. Abundance and biomass of some soil animals at the Stordalen mire. – In: Sonesson, M. (ed.) Progress Report 1972. IBP Swedish Tundra Biome Project Tech. Rep. 14: 90–92.
27. Lundkvist, H. 1974. Occurrence of Enchytraeidae at Stordalen. – In: Flower-Ellis, J.G.K. (ed.) Progress Report 1973. IBP Swedish Tundra Biome Project Tech. Rep. 16: 29–34.
28. Madsen, I.L. & Widell, S. 1974. A vegetation map of the Stordalen site. – In: Flower-Ellis, J.G.K. (ed.) Progress Report 1973. IBP Swedish Tundra Biome Project Tech. Rep. 16: 3–15.
29. MacKay, D.K. & Løken, O.H. 1974. Arctic hydrology. – In: Ives, J.D. & Barry, R.G. (eds.) Arctic and Alpine Environments, pp. 111–132. London: Methuen & Co.
30. Melin, R. 1970. Hydrological regions in Scandinavia and Finland. – Nordic Hydrology 1: 5–37.
31. Modig, P. & Schuer, H. Unpublished data.
32. Nakano, Y. & Brown, J. 1972. Mathematical modelling and validation of the thermal regimes in tundra soils, Barrow, Alaska. – Arctic and Alpine Res. 4: 19–38.
33. Nihlgård, B. Unpublished data.
34. Parinkina, O.M. 1974. Bacterial production in tundra soils. – In: Holding, A.J., Heal, O.W., MacLean, S.F. & Flanagan, P.W. (eds.) Soil Organisms and Decomposition in Tundra, pp. 65–77. Stockholm: IBP Tundra Biome Steering Committee.
35. Rheinberg, P. 1975. Microfungal studies at Stordalen and Njulla 1973. – IBP Swedish Tundra Biome Project Tech. Rep. 17 (In press).
36. Rodhe, B. 1968. Studies on the effect of lake regulation on local climate. – SMHI Commun. Ser. B, No. 28: 61–77.
37. Rosswall, T. 1973. Aerobic bacterial populations at the Swedish tundra site. – In: Sonesson, M. (ed.) Progress Report 1972. IBP Swedish Tundra Biome Project Tech. Rep. 14: 93–98.
38. Rosswall, T. 1973. Plant litter decomposition studies at the Swedish tundra site. – In: Sonesson, M. (ed.) Progress Report 1972. IBP Swedish Tundra Biome Project Tech. Rep. 14: 124–138.
39. Rosswall, T. 1974. Decomposition of plant litter at Stordalen. A summary. – In: Flower-Ellis, J.G.K. (ed.) Progress Report 1973. IBP Swedish Tundra Biome Project Tech. Rep. 16: 207–212.
40. Rosswall, T. 1975. Decomposition. – In: Wielgolaski, F.E. (ed.) Fennoscandian Tundra Ecosystems. Part 1. Plants and Microorganisms, pp. 227–229. Berlin–Heidelberg–New York: Springer Verlag.
41. Rosswall, T. Unpublished data.
42. Rosswall, T., Berg, B. & Lundkvist, H. 1974. Use of cellulose in field decomposition experiments. – In: Flower-Ellis, J.G.K. (ed.) Progress Report 1973. IBP Swedish Tundra Biome Project Tech. Rep. 16: 109–121.
43. Rosswall, T. & Clarholm, M. 1974. Characteristics of tundra bacterial populations and a comparison with populations from forest and grassland soils. – In: Holding, A.J., Heal, O.W. MacLean, S.F. & Flanagan, P.W. (eds.) Soil Organisms and Decomposition in Tundra, pp. 93–108. Stockholm: IBP Tundra Biome Steering Committee.
44. Rosswall, T. & Svensson, B.H. 1974. Chemolithotrophic and photosynthetic bacteria at Stordalen. – In: Flower-Ellis, J.G.K. (ed.) Progress Report 1973. IBP Swedish Tundra Biome Project Tech. Rep. 16: 73–79.
45. Rosswall, T., Veum, A.K. & Kärenlampi, L. 1975. Plant litter decomposition at Fennoscandian tundra sites. – In: Wielgolaski, F.E. (ed.) Fennoscandian Tundra Ecosystems. Part 1. Plants and Microorganisms, pp. 268–278. Berlin–Heidelberg–New York: Springer Verlag.
46. Rydén, B.E. & Karlqvist, L. 1974. Water movement in tundra peat. – In: 24th Alaskan Science Conference Climate of the Arctic, Fairbanks, Alaska, USA, 1973.
47. Rydén, B.E. (In press.) Hydrology of the Truelove Lowland. – In: Bliss, L.C. (ed.) Truelove Lowland, Devon Island, Canada: A High Arctic Ecosystem. Edmonton: University of Alberta Press.
48. Sandberg, G. 1963. Växtvärlden i Abisko nationalpark. – In: Curry-Lindahl, K. (ed.) Natur i Lappland II: 885–909 (In Swedish).
49. Sjörs, H. 1963. Amphi-atlantic zonation. Nemoral to arctic. – In: Löve, A. & Löve, D. (eds.) North

Atlantic Biota and their History, pp. 109–125. Oxford: Pergamon Press.

50. Sjörs, H. 1965. Regional ecology of mire sites and vegetation. – In: Sjörs, H. (ed.) The Plant Cover of Sweden. Acta Phytogeographica Suecica 50: 180–188.
51. Skartveit, A. 1974. Netto strålningsbalanse og energibalanse ved jordyta (Net Radiation balance and energy balance at soil surface). – Unpublished thesis, University of Bergen, Norway. (In Norwegian).
52. Sonesson, M. 1967. Studies on mire vegetation in the Torneträsk area, northern Sweden. I. Regional aspects. – Bot. Notiser 120: 272–296.
53. Sonesson, M. 1968. Studies on mire vegetation in the Torneträsk area, northern Sweden. II. Winter conditions of the poor mires. – Bot. Notiser 122: 481–511.
54. Sonesson, M. 1970. Studies on mire vegetation in the Torneträsk area, northern Sweden. III. Communities of the poor mires. – Opera Botanica 26: 1–120.
55. Sonesson, M. 1970. Studies on mire vegetation in the Torneträsk area, northern Sweden. IV. Some habitat conditions of the poor mires. – Bot. Notiser 123: 67–111.
56. Sonesson, M. 1973. Some chemical characteristics of the Stordalen site. – In: Sonesson, M. (ed.) Progress Report 1972. IBP Swedish Tundra Biome Project Tech. Rep. 14: 31–43.
57. Sonesson, M., Wielgolaski, F.E. & Kallio, P. 1975. Description of Fennoscandian tundra ecosystems. – In: Wielgolaski, F.E. (ed.) Fennoscandian Tundra Ecosystems. Part 1. Plants and Microorganisms, pp. 3–28. Berlin–Heidelberg–New York: Springer Verlag.
58. Stenström, T.A. 1975. Bakterieinhibition och nedbrytning av några mossor i ett tundraekosystem (Bacterial inhibition and decomposition of some bryophytes in a tundra ecosystem). – Rapp. Inst. Mikrobiologi, Lantbrukshögskolan 4. (In Swedish).
59. Svensson, B.H. 1973. Methane production in a subarctic mire. – In: Sonesson, M. (ed.) Progress Report 1972. IBP Swedish Tundra Biome Project Tech. Rep. 14: 154–166.
60. Svensson, B.H. 1973. Anaerobic bacteria in a subarctic mire. – In: Sonesson, M. (ed.) Progress Report 1972. IBP Swedish Tundra Biome Project Tech. Rep. 14: 99–107.
61. Svensson, B.H. 1974. Production of methane and carbon dioxide from a subarctic mire. – In: Flower-Ellis, J.G.K. (ed.) Progress Report 1973. IBP Swedish Tundra Biome Project Tech. Rep. 16: 123–143.
62. Svensson, B.H. Unpublished data.
63. Svensson, B.H., Veum, A.K. & Kjelvik, S. 1975. Carbon losses from tundra soils. – In: Wielgolaski, F.E. (ed.) Fennoscandian Tundra Ecosystems. Part 1. Plants and Microorganisms, pp. 279–286. Berlin–Heidelberg–New York: Springer Verlag.
64. Tamm, C.O. 1953. Growth, yield and nutrition in carpets of a forest moss (*Hylocomium splendens*). – Medd. Statens Skogsforskningsinstitut 43(1): 1–140.
65. Tenow, O. 1972. The outbreaks of *Oporina autumnata* Bkh. and *Operophthera* spp. (Lep., Geometridae) in the Scandinavian mountain chain and northern Finland 1862–1968. – Zool. Bidr. Uppsala, Suppl. 2. 107 pp.
66. Tyler, G. 1972. Heavy metals pollute nature, may reduce productivity. – Ambio 1: 52–59.
67. Wallén, C.C. 1963. Klimat och klimatfenomen i Lappland. – In: Curry-Lindahl, K. (ed.) Natur i Lappland I: 145–157. (In Swedish).
68. Weller, G. & Holmgren, B. 1974. The microclimates of the arctic tundra. – J. Appl. Meteorol. 13: 854–862.
69. Whittaker, J.B. 1974. Interactions between fauna and microflora at tundra sites. – In: Holding, A.J., Heal, O.W., MacLean, S.F. & Flanagan, P.W. (eds.) Soil Organisms and Decomposition in Tundra, pp. 183–196. Stockholm: IBP Tundra Biome Steering Committee.
70. Skartveit, A., Rydén, B.E. & Kärenlampi, L. 1975. Climate and hydrology of some Fennoscandian tundra ecosystems. – In: Wielgolaski, F.E. (ed.) Fennoscandian Tundra Ecosystems. Part 1. Plants and Microorganisms, pp. 41–53. Berlin–Heidelberg–New York: Springer Verlag.

Rosswall, T. & Heal, O.W. (eds.) 1975.
Structure and Function of Tundra Ecosystems.
Ecol. Bull. (Stockholm) 20: 295–320.

MOOR HOUSE, UK

O.W. HEAL, H.E. JONES and J.B. WHITTAKER

INTRODUCTION

The Moor House National Nature Reserve (54°65'N, 2°45'W) is adjacent to Cross Fell — the highest point in the Pennine chain of hills (888 m). The rolling moorland of the 5 000 ha Reserve is representative of marginal agricultural land, close to or above the tree line (550 m), and is one of the most isolated parts of England. The present landscape and ecology are a product of the past — the geology, topography, climate and post glacial history of the area (33).

The underlying geology of thin, alternating, horizontal beds of carboniferous limestone, sandstone and shale gives a stepped topography superimposed on the basic topography left by the retreat of the ice sheets about 13 000 years B.C. (Fig. 1). Glacial drift covered the whole area and was subject to cryoturbation and solifluction, resulting in a thinner drift on the steep western scarp compared with the eastern dip slope. With continued climatic amelioration vegetation succession developed to a birch, willow, juniper scrub forest in late Boreal times.

The Boreal/Atlantic transition, at about 5 500 B.C., was marked by an increase in rainfall. The glacial drift, present as boulder clay, caused impeded drainage, and the resultant waterlogging led to widespread peat accumulation. The remains of the forest can be seen in the basal layers of this peat. Accumulation of peat has continued, at varying rates, since the Atlantic period, with *Sphagnum*, *Eriophorum* and *Calluna* as the main peat forming species. On the eastern side of the area, the blanket of peat up to 3 m deep is still almost continuous up to the summit ridge. Where streams have removed and redistributed the peat, shallow peaty podsols and peaty gley soils have developed or, in small areas where limestone outcrops are free of glacial drift, shallow mineral soils occur. Blanket peat becomes increasingly unstable as its depth increases and as a result of the action of wind and water, 10–15 % of the bog area is eroding. On the summit ridge and the steeper western scarp, most of the peat which developed during the Atlantic period has been removed by erosion. With outcropping of the bedrock of limestone, sandstone and shale through the thin glacial drift, a mosaic of mineral soils has developed in contrast to the predominantly organic soils on the east.

The mosaic of soils and vegetation which developed in the past 10 000 years has probably been fairly stable during the last few hundred years. The area has always been

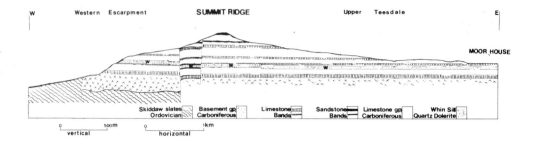

Figure 1. Generalized section across the Moor House Nature Reserve showing the geological formations and topography (33).

a marginal habitat for man. Mining for lead, silver and barytes has caused local disturbance through modified drainage, tracks and waste heaps, but this activity virtually ceased about 100 years ago. Sheep grazing (44), on a free-range system, has occurred for more than 500 years. About 8 500 sheep graze on the 5 000 ha of the Reserve from April to September, a three-fold increase over the last 200 years. The effect of the grazing has been to maintain or slightly extend the areas of grassland on mineral soils which can be regarded as man-induced climax communities. The blanket bog areas have been used for grouse during the last 150 years, but periodic burning of the *Calluna*, a normal grouse management practice, has been sporadic.

The IBP programme was developed from a wide range of previous and current basic and management research on the Reserve (11), but concentrated on an analysis of the blanket bog ecosystem. The objectives of the programme were to obtain estimates of primary and secondary production for the bog and to quantify the main pathways and rates of circulation of dry matter and nutrients through the ecosystem. The approach adopted for the programme was largely one of field measurement of the populations of plants and animals over time, plus a limited amount of field and laboratory experimentation. Field research centred on one bog site (Sike Hill), but to obtain estimates of variation in production on blanket bog at Moor House studies were extended to seven other bog sites. The analysis of the variation within and between bog sites, and the comparison of bog and grassland sites at Moor House has been used to provide insight into the factors controlling the distribution, abundance and activity of organisms at Moor House.

ENVIRONMENTAL CONDITIONS

Climate

The general climate (Table 1) is best described as cool, wet and windy. It is oceanic in type and is sub-arctic rather than temperate. The growing season is about 180 days but the highest mean monthly temperature (August) is usually only between 10–12°C.

Mean monthly temperatures only exceed 10°C for two months in the year, which

Table 1. Long term climatic averages at Moor House

	J	F	M	A	M	J	J	A	S	O	N	D	Year
Solar radiation (kJ cm^{-2}) 1972–1974	4.4	10.9	24.6	34.5	41.7	47.1	42.4	38.0	24.4	13.6	6.8	3.5	291.9
Screen temperature (°C) 1953–1972													
Mean max	2.1	1.6	3.9	7.1	10.8	13.8	14.7	14.4	12.7	9.7	5.1	3.3	8.3
Mean min	−2.9	−3.6	−1.7	−0.1	2.5	5.4	7.2	7.3	5.9	3.9	0.1	−1.7	1.9
1/2 (max + min)	−0.4	−1.0	1.1	3.5	6.7	9.6	11.0	10.8	9.3	6.8	2.6	0.8	5.1
Lowest grass min temp. (°C) 1957–1973	−13.9	−14.5	−10.9	−10.3	−7.7	−5.2	−2.9	−2.8	−5.6	−6.8	−11.5	−12.7	−9.5
Soil temp. at 30 cm, 09.00 GMT (°C) 1956–1972	1.6	1.4	2.1	3.7	7.0	9.9	11.5	11.7	10.4	7.9	4.4	2.7	6.2
Relative humidity at 09.00 GMT (%) 1953–1967	94.0	94.7	90.3	87.1	82.2	82.8	84.9	86.7	88.7	91.9	94.3	94.4	89.3
Rainfall (mm) 1953–1972	177.3	150.1	133.7	119.9	127.9	113.3	144.1	169.9	160.4	179.9	200.4	206.1	1 883.0
Number of days with rain 1953–1972	22.5	20.8	20.9	19.9	19.4	18.3	20.0	20.8	19.2	20.8	22.6	23.2	248.4
Number of days with snow lying at 09.00 GMT 1953–1972	16.5	17.4	11.6	4.0	0.6	0	0	0	0	0.2	6.0	10.4	66.7
Wind velocity (m s^{-1}) 1956–1972	8.1	8.0	8.0	6.7	6.3	5.9	5.9	5.9	6.4	7.4	7.5	8.2	7.0
Daily duration of bright sun (h) 1954–1972	1.0	1.7	2.6	4.0	5.2	5.8	4.6	4.2	3.4	2.5	1.3	0.9	3.1

probably explains the absence of trees at Moor House. The cool summer conditions are associated with frequent cloud cover and high rainfall (1 900 mm annual mean). Calculation of potential evaporation from mean monthly temperature and rainfall indicates that a moisture deficit would seldom occur. However, when calculations are based on shorter periods, e.g. pentades, moisture deficits appear to occur regularly in summer. In addition, periods of very low humidity (< 10 % RH) occur occasionally and may have a more marked effect on the biota than the general climatic regime. These low humidities contrast with the high frequency of days with rain (about 250 per year).

Winter conditions are mild compared with 'genuine' tundra sites. The mean monthly temperature for the coldest month, February, is $-1.0°C$ and the lowest minimum over a ten year period was $-18.3°C$. Snow cover is present for an average of 67 days per year between November and April, but the cover is irregular both in time and space. Average wind speed in February and March is about 8 m s^{-1}, with galeforce winds on 20–30 days in winter.

The climatic regime described above refers to the IBP study area in the vicinity of the meteorological station at 558 m, but the Moor House Reserve covers an altitudinal range from 300–600 m. The climatic variation over this range is indicated by the temperature in the litter layer. At the main study site (550 m), the mean annual temperature and the sum of degree days above $0°C$ are 5.0 and 2 $250°C$. These litter temperatures decline by 0.3 and $180°$ respectively for each 100 m increase in altitude (32). The lapse rate for air temperature on the east side of the Reserve is $0.4°C$ per 100 m, compared to a general figure of $0.7°C$ for northern Britain.

The main micro-habitat variations in climate are related to the vegetation canopy, topography and soil structure. On the bog the *Calluna vulgaris* (L.) Hull canopy, 30–40 cm in height, can reduce light intensity by 60 % of full daylight although the spectral composition varies little above and below the canopy (23). The main micro-habitat variation in temperature occurs in the surface litter of the bog. In tussocks of *Eriophorum vaginatum* L., maximum temperatures are usually $2–6°$ warmer, and minimum temperatures $0–2°$ colder, than in *Calluna* litter. This difference probably results from the tussock of *Eriophorum vaginatum* receiving more direct radiation than the horizontal shaded *Calluna* litter. *Sphagnum* lawn temperatures at -5 cm, i.e approximately where the *Sphagnum* litter begins, have a slightly narrower range than the maximum and minimum values at -1 cm in *Calluna* litter. The difference is probably related to the greater depth and evaporative cooling in the moist *Sphagnum* lawn (28). Absence of a *Calluna* canopy, for example through burning, causes an increase in the range of litter and peat surface temperatures (40). In *Sphagnum* communities pools are usually a few degrees warmer than hummocks, with lawns intermediate, but within a hummock temperature differences of up to $8°C$ result from aspect.

Differences in temperature regime between the different soil and vegetation types result from the extent of insulation by the vegetation, the surface reflectivity and the moisture content of the soil. At 1 cm in the litter, the sequence of mean temperatures for periods of approximately one month was blanket peat < brown earth < peaty gley < peaty podsol, with the average range in mean temperature over the series for any period being about $1°C$ (32).

Soils

Blanket peat covers about 80–85 % of the eastern part of the Reserve. In the past, with increasing depth and reduced contact with the underlying mineral soil, the developing peats were associated with a change in vegetation resulting from increased acidity, waterlogging and lack of nutrients. The development of this vegetation, consisting of *Calluna, Eriophorum* and *Sphagnum*, further increased amounts of peat because of the resistance of these species to decomposition. Variation in the vegetation, composition and production and in the conditions for decomposition, caused by minor climatic fluctuations, have produced bands of peat of varying degrees of humification. Topography has similarly affected the better-drained slope and summit sites producing more humified deposits than the wet sites.

Where the glacial clays and solifluction deposits were thin, peaty podsols and peaty gleys developed on the sandstone and shale rocks. Similar soils also occur along the stream margins where flood waters re-deposit eroded peat. Where the glacial drift was very thin or absent from the underlying limestone, especially along stream banks, well drained, nutrient rich, acid brown earths, brown calcareous and rendzina soils have developed (31, 33). The morphological and chemical characteristics of the soils are summarised in Table 2.

Table 2. Some physical and chemical characteristics of blanket peat at Moor House. Four depth zones are recognized by their colour

| | Horizon | | | |
	Litter	Black-brown	Green-brown	Rust
Mean thickness (cm)	3.8	6.0	8.7	9.3
Density (g cm^{-3})	0.03	0.07	0.09	0.10
pH (H$_2$O)	3.1–4.2	3.2–4.0	3.0–3.9	3.2–4.6
Moisture (% dw)	600–2000	500–1900	700–2400	500–1200
Ash (% dw)	1.8–2.9	2.9–4.3	2.4–3.8	2.7–4.5
Potassium (% dw)	0.06–0.10	0.06–0.09	0.02–0.04	0.02–0.03
Calcium (% dw)	0.12–0.22	0.19–0.27	0.17–0.31	0.24–0.31
Magnesium (% dw)	0.04–0.08	0.03–0.07	0.04–0.06	0.02–0.05
Phosphorus (% dw)	0.05–0.07	0.08–0.13	0.06–0.09	0.05–0.08
Nitrogen (% dw)	0.64–1.45	0.85–1.69	0.99–1.58	0.91–1.78
Cation exchange capacity (meq 100 g^{-1})	199	246	188	157

Although no marked seasonal variation in moisture is discernible from the monthly values there are considerable fluctuations resulting from short-term climatic changes. Litter samples also show diurnal variation in moisture with minimum and maximum values of, for example, 500 and 900 % in a 24 hour period (48).

On blanket bog the water table, indicated by the height of water in pits, is usually between 0 and 30 cm depending on micro- and local topography and drainage (18).

There are marked fluctuations in the height of the water table induced by climate. In dry conditions it may fall by 2 cm d^{-1}, though after prolonged dry spells when it has already fallen, the rate is much reduced. Rise in water table is rapid; thus after a period of a few days without rain, a 4 mm rainfall can produce a rise of 20 cm in a day. Because of the water holding capacity of the peat the difference in actual moisture content above and below the theoretical water table is usually small.

Associated with waterlogging the peat soils have low redox potentials, especially in very wet sites. Mean minimum Eh (corrected to pH 4.0) for a relatively dry and a waterlogged site were 336 ± 69 (SD) and 112 ± 38 mV at depths of 16.7 ± 6.1 and 18.4 ± 4.0 cm respectively. Results from four bog sites including two at Moor House show that redox potentials vary over the year, being mainly negatively correlated with temperature, the regression coefficient becoming progressively more negative with increasing depth. The potential shows complex variation within the peat profile but tends to decline with increasing depth, mean minimum values being at 15.5 ± 5.4 (SD) and 21.3 ± 6.5 cm for the two Moor House sites, based on three methods (51). The minimum redox values are associated with sulphide deposition and with maximum numbers of sulphate reducing bacteria (9). The peat profile often shows a greenish horizon between about 10 and 20 cm which darkens on exposure to air. Above and below this greenish horizon are usually dark-brown and red-brown horizons respectively (Table 2).

PRIMARY PRODUCTION

Community classification and dynamics

Most of the Moor House Reserve is above the present day tree line of about 550 m. Blanket bog dominates the east of the Reserve and grasslands the central ridge and west scarp (Table 3), these main vegetation communities (14, 18, 44) reflecting soil conditions. Blanket bog vegetation occurs on acid waterlogged peat with Calluneto-Eriophoretum as the main unit. *Calluna* is restricted altitudinally by low summer temperatures, and locally by sheep grazing. Under these conditions Calluneto-Eriophoretum is replaced by Eriophoretum (44). On very wet, usually flat, areas of the bog Trichophoro-Eriophoretum occurs. A short-term succession occurs after burning with rapid recovery and dominance of *Eriophorum vaginatum* followed by regeneration of *Calluna*, which regains co-dominance after 12–20 years.

On the shallow peaty gleys and peaty podsols, species-poor Nardetum sub-alpinum and Juncetum squarrosi sub-alpinum are the main communities, being replaced on the more mineral-rich alluvial and limestone soils by Festucetum and Agrosto-Festucetum. These four grassland vegetation units are maintained largely by sheep grazing, which when removed, allows the development, within a few years, of a deeper sward dominated by *Deschampsia flexuosa* (L.) Trin. (43), which at altitudes below about 550 m would develop into scrub or woodland.

The three main bog plants, *Calluna, Eriophorum vaginatum* and *Sphagnum* have characteristic growth forms and dynamics. In areas which have not been burned for 20 or more years, the age structure of the *Calluna* population is very wide, the modal age of stems emerging from the bog surface being about 8 years on the drier sites (Fig. 2).

300

Table 3. The extent of vegetation types on Moor House National Nature Reserve (43).
W = Western escarpment below 671 m, C = Central ridge above 671 m,
E = Eastern plateau below 671 m.

Vegetation types	Area (ha)			
	W	C	E	Total
Blanket bog				
Calluna-Eriophorum-Sphagnum	0	63	1 137	1 200
Trichophorum-Eriophorum				
recolonised peat	80	264	340	684
Eroding bog	2	104	217	323
Total	82	431	1 694	2 207
Grasslands				
Juncus squarrosus	121	239	17	377
Nardus stricta	255	266	94	615
Festuca	35	147	1	183
Agrostis-Festuca	85	28	37	150
Scree, made ground etc.	100	33	21	154
Pteridium (bracken)	34	0	0	34
Total	630	713	170	1 513
Poor fens and flushes				
Total	18	49	55	122
Totals	730	1 193	1 919	3 842

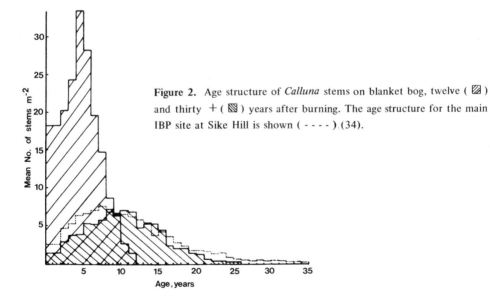

Figure 2. Age structure of *Calluna* stems on blanket bog, twelve (▨)
and thirty + (▧) years after burning. The age structure for the main
IBP site at Sike Hill is shown (- - - -) (34).

The low modal age is caused by wind and weight of snow forcing the older stems into a decumbent position in the litter layer, from which younger shoots emerge (18). The result is a steady state, with continual replacement of the younger age classes. This contrasts with many other *Calluna* dominated areas of Britain, characterised by relatively even-aged stands, the age depending on when the *Calluna* was last burnt. In the wetter areas, the modal age is considerably younger, because of rapid overgrowth by *Sphagnum*, but this is also a stable dynamic equilibrium, in contrast to the short-term seral state that results from burning.

Tussocks of *E. vaginatum* are co-dominant on the main study site. Although their basal area can be over 1 000 cm^2, over 50 % are less than 50 cm^2. Tussocks have a random distribution with respect to size, and there is no evidence of clumping or of budding of young tussocks nor, apparently, is there a relationship between age and size of tussock (17, 18).

The distribution and growth of *Sphagnum* species is closely related to moisture conditions and to shade (5). On the drier Calluneto-Eriophoretum, *Sphagnum* cover (mainly *S. rubellum* Wils.) may be less than 20 %, and the plants are often in an unhealthy condition (8).

Biomass and production

Production for the main study site on Sike Hill in 1968 was 635 ± 170 g m^{-2} yr^{-1} from a summer biomass of 2 450 ± 250 g m^{-2}, compared with an estimated mean total annual production on seven blanket bog sites of 659 ± 53 g m^{-2} yr^{-1}. There is a range of variation in production from a fairly recently burned and highly productive Eriophoretum (868 g m^{-2} yr^{-1}) to a wet site with a high cover of *Sphagnum* (491 g m^{-2} yr^{-1}). The higher productivity of the Eriophoretum and *Trichophorum cespitosum* (L.) Hartman, is attributed to the seral state of the vegetation (17, 18, 46).

Because biomass, on sites other than Eriophoretum and *Trichophorum cespitosum* does not increase from year to year, the vegetation is considered to be in a steady state. Seasonal increments of biomass are lost by death, so that each year the biomass input equals the output, and therefore seasonal production may be estimated from the measured losses. The annual transfers of biomass between compartments of the two main species are shown in Figs. 3 and 4 for the main study site (35).

Sphagnum production ranges from ca 45 g m^{-2} yr^{-1} on the drier sites to about 300 g m^{-2} yr^{-1} on a pool-lawn-hummock complex where four species are common. Each species has a higher production than other species in its own habitat, but all show increasing production with increasing wetness (Fig. 5) (7).

Production processes

The growing season is estimated to be about 180 days, and vascular plants convert about 1 % of photosynthetically active radiation (45 % of an input of 290 kJ cm^{-2} yr^{-1}) to primary production (17, 18), giving daily production of about 3.3 g m^{-2} on the main study site.

Management effects were not examined in detail during IBP, and present practices seem to have less effect on the vegetation than does the underlying geology. Burning

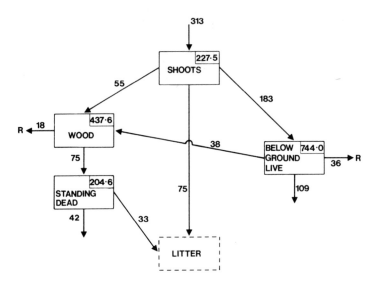

Figure 3. The standing crop and annual transfers of dry matter (g m^{-2}) in *Calluna* for the main study site, Sike Hill (35). R = respiration.

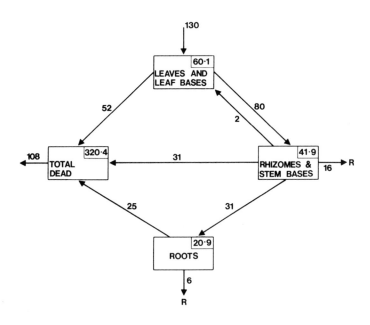

Figure 4. The standing crop and annual transfers of dry matter (g m^{-2}) in *Eriophorum vaginatum* for the main study site, Sike Hill (35). R = respiration.

303

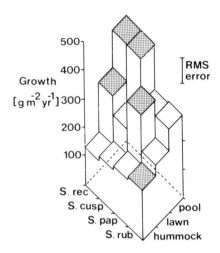

Figure 5. Production of *Sphagnum recurvum*, *S. cuspidatum*, *S. papillosum* and *S. rubellum* in pool, lawn and hummock habitats on blanket bog. Hatching shows the habitat(s) in which the species normally occurs (7).

kills old *Calluna* stems and encourages regeneration from seedlings. In the short term, about six years, *Eriophorum vaginatum* and *Rubus chamaemorus* L. cover increase at the expense of *Calluna*. Sheep grazing effects are very small but may reduce *Sphagnum* cover through trampling. Where grazing intensity has been increased on the blanket bog areas, *Calluna* cover has decreased and been partly replaced by *Juncus squarrosus* L. on the wetter sites, and *Deschampsia flexuosa* and *Festuca ovina* L. on the drier areas (45).

The blanket bog species respond differently to light and temperature. *Calluna* has an optimum rate of net photosynthesis (4 mg dm^{-2} h^{-1}) at 18°C and 325 J m^{-2} s^{-1}. The basic response surface (Fig. 6) was used, in conjunction with information on the influence of temperature prehistory, age and flowering, to simulate the seasonal growth of *Calluna* from data on biomass and microclimate. The predicted pattern is similar to the observed changes and falls well within the standard errors of the measured shoot standing crop. The sensitivity of the model to variations in environmental conditions indicates that production is influenced particularly by temperature changes in the second half of the growing season. Changes in solar radiation have relatively little effect on production (24).

In contrast to *Calluna*, *Rubus chamaemorus* shows a high maximum rate of net photosynthesis (18 mg dm^{-2} h^{-1}) at 12°C and 130 J m^{-2} s^{-1}. The low light saturation level helps to compensate for the shading effect of the *Calluna* canopy which can reduce radiation to 40 % of full daylight. However, under a *Calluna* canopy, carbon assimilation per unit leaf area is reduced to 78 % and per unit area of bog surface to 33 % of that where *Calluna* is absent. Major reduction of *Calluna* standing crop, especially through trampling, is closely followed by a large increase in *Rubus* cover. The temperature optimum for net photosynthesis in *Rubus* (12°C) reflects its arctic-alpine distribution and at Moor House daytime temperatures are often above optimum, e.g. 20 % of the days in the 1969 growing season. As a result, it is estimated that for *Rubus*, a reduction of 2°C in the aboveground temperature increases carbon assimilation by 5 %, and higher temperatures retard its performance (40).

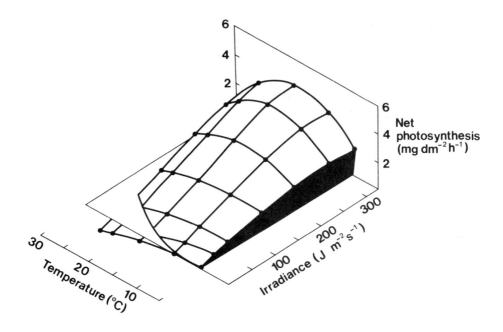

Figure 6. Response surface, derived from regression analysis, of net photosynthesis of *Calluna vulgaris* in relation to temperature and irradiance (22).

Net photosynthesis of *Sphagnum rubellum* is sensitive to water content of the capitulum, the maximum rate occurring at about 1 000–1 200 % moisture (21), within the usual range of field moisture content. *S. rubellum* has greater ability than other *Sphagnum* species to maintain its moisture content when the water table falls. This may be an important mechanism controlling species distribution, *S. rubellum* being the dominant species in hummocks (5). Photosynthetic rates of *S. rubellum* are only a fraction of those in *Calluna* when expressed on a leaf area basis. However, care should be taken in comparisons of this nature since the photosynthetic tissue present per unit area of leaf will be very different in the two species (22).

Reducing conditions attributable to waterlogging, acidity and low nutrient status of the peat and low temperatures severely restrict the number of species capable of growth and survival on the blanket bog at Moor House. The existing vegetation increased its production with added fertilisers and there is evidence that concentrations of P and K are limiting production of some species while N is limiting for others. However, the species occurring on the bog are adapted to, or selected for, growth under low nutrient conditions. Where nutrient concentrations are increased over long periods of time the species composition changes and, although there may not be greater production per unit area of surface, the concentration of nutrients in the vegetation is increased. This tentative hypothesis is derived from the comparison of blanket bog and limestone grassland at Moor House.

HERBIVORES

Man's interest in moorlands such as Moor House is particularly associated with two herbivores – sheep and grouse (*Lagopus lagopus scoticus* Lath.). Sheep grazing (44) is largely confined to the small area of grassland along stream banks where the present composition and structure of the vegetation is maintained largely by their activity. They have little effect on the bog where densities are usually 1 sheep per 10–50 ha. Where higher densities occur in the bog through heavier stocking of the grasslands, the effect of trampling changes the composition of the vegetation, with a marked reduction of *Calluna*. Grouse are largely restricted to the bog and they have no noticeable effect on the ecosystem. Management for grouse, by burning, is minimal above about 500 m in the north Pennines and causes a short term (20 year) vegetation succession. On the bog, herbivory by small mammals and invertebrates is low, probably because of the wet conditions and low chemical 'quality' of the vegetation. Thus there is a marked contrast between the bog where only about 1 % of the annual primary production is eaten by herbivores, and the grasslands, especially those dominated by *Festuca* and *Agrostis*, which can be regarded as grazed ecosystems with up to 40 % of the primary production consumed (10, 43).

Invertebrates

The psyllid *Strophingia ericae* (Curtis) (30) and the tipulid *Tipula subnodicornis* Zetterstedt (10) are the main invertebrate herbivores on the bog (Table 4), the former feeding on phloem of *Calluna*, the latter mainly on liverworts. Numbers of both species vary greatly from year to year; thus an understanding of factors influencing population size is of major importance in considering invertebrate productivity and their influence on the vegetation. *T. subnodicornis* crashed from densities of about 100 final instar larvae m^{-2} to local extinction as a result of dry conditions in early summer in one year. High survival occurred in a few, very wet, habitats which normally provided sub-optimal conditions. In other years there is more evidence for a density dependent mortality possibly related to interaction between larvae. *Molophilus ater* Meigen, another tipulid, is also well regulated on podsol sites, and over a period of eight years the population in spring has varied by a factor of 4 (10). *Strophingia* shows at least 10 fold variation in numbers between years.

The invertebrate herbivores of the grasslands, although consuming negligible quantities of dry matter, provide additional insight into invertebrate population regulation. Larvae of *Coleophora alticolella* Zell. (Lep.), the rush moth, feed on seeds of *Juncus squarrosus*. Its upper altitudinal limit fluctuates between about 500 and 650 m and is related to the fluctuation in seed-setting of *Juncus* which is under climatic control. In addition, parasitoids are virtually absent from populations on the Reserve, although they are an important cause of mortality at lower altitudes (ca 300 m), possibly regulating populations where food supplies are more stable (37). The homopteran *Neophilaenus lineatus* (L.) is also a lowland species near its altitudinal limit of about 800 m. This sapsucking, spittle bug, feeding on *Juncus squarrosus*, shows no obvious population regulation, suffering local extinction when low temperatures retard development and egg laying. At low altitudes in southern England, populations of *N. lineatus* are strongly regulated, probably by parasitism (52).

306

Table 4. A summary of the fauna populations on blanket bog at Moor House. Each group is tentatively placed into a trophic level; H = herbivore, C = carnivore, S = saprovore, M = microbivore. Total fauna estimates for Agrosto-Festucetum on brown earth and for Juncetum squarrosi on peaty podzol are also given. Results derived from (10). neg = negligible

	Numbers (m^{-2})	Biomass (g m^{-2})	Respiration (g m^{-2} yr^{-1})	Production (g m^{-2} yr^{-1})	Tentative trophic level
Lumbricidae	0.1	neg	0.01	neg	S
Enchytraeidae	80×10^3	2.160	13.60	3.00	S
Nematoda	1400×10^3	0.170	0.62	0.40	M
Collembola	80×10^3	0.100	0.34	0.28	S/M
Acarina	33×10^3	0.400	1.09	0.62	M/C
Tipulidae	700	0.580	3.14	1.30	H/S
Hemiptera	3.5×10^3	0.025	0.15	0.08	H
Lepidoptera	1	neg	neg	neg	H
Coleoptera (Carabidae)	1	0.002	0.01	0.01	C
Araneida	130	0.017	0.17	0.11	C
Grouse	0.00011	0.023	1.12	0.07	H
Sheep	0.00001	0.350	1.20	0.06	H
Small rodents	0.00001	neg	neg	neg	H
Total	–	3.8	18	7	
Agrosto-Festucetum	–	46.0	142	40	
Juncetum squarrosi	–	10.5	51	16	

This, and other evidence, suggests that parasitism and predation on invertebrate herbivores decrease with increasing altitude and are unimportant in population regulation at the Moor House study site. Species that are well within their climatic range show limited density dependent mortality while those that are near the edges of their ranges are poorly regulated, fluctuate widely in relation to climate, and suffer local extinction.

Vertebrates

To the casual observer, sheep are by far the most conspicuous animals at Moor House (44). They are driven onto the fells in spring after lambing and remain there until August or September. Although they graze all the main habitat types, limestone grasslands are preferred (approximately 5 sheep ha^{-1}) blanket bog being only rarely visited (1 sheep 10–50 ha^{-1}). The grazing intensity on limestone grassland is probably as much as can be supported and increased sheep populations would result in more grazing on the other, less preferred, vegetation types. Each ewe maintains a non-exclusive territory of about 100 ha which usually includes a number of vegetation types. Even on limestone grasslands, the average assimilation by sheeps is only about 1/3 of the total herbivore and decomposer assimilation, whereas on the blanket bog it is neglible.

Removal of minerals and nutrients from Moor House in the form of sheep fleeces and carcasses is probably only about 1 % of that lost by erosion and other causes (12). Trampling and selective grazing by sheep affect species composition usually increasing diversity. On the grasslands, close grazing produces a fine turf with a very different invertebrate fauna from that of ungrazed exclosures (3) whilst dung permits the presence of some Diptera and Coleoptera which would otherwise be absent.

Grouse, too, are conspicuous at Moor House but their actual density in the last 12 years has not exceeded 2 birds ha^{-1} (mean less than 1) in the spring and 6 ha^{-1} in the autumn (43). Fluctuations in density over this period have been about 10-fold. These densities compare favourably with other grouse moors but still imply assimilation of less than 1 % of the aboveground primary production on the bog. This feeding is, however, selective and, in the case of the chicks, green shoots or flower buds of *Calluna* (50 % by volume), capsules of *Polytrichum commune* Hedw. and invertebrates are eaten. Adult grouse also take considerable numbers of Tipulidae in addition to their normal diet of *Calluna* shoots (2).

Grouse and sheep may interact in the sense that heavy sheep grazing damages the bog by reducing the *Calluna* cover and encouraging *Empetrum nigrum* L. and *Eriophorum*. However, carefully controlled sheep grazing may, on this type of moor, improve *Calluna* shoot production and consequently grouse populations. On these high, wet moors, this type of management may be more important than burning (45).

CARNIVORES

Spiders, harvestmen, ground beetles, rove beetles and mites are the main invertebrate carnivores whereas frogs, meadow pipits (*Anthus pratensis* L.) and shrews are the most abundant vertebrate carnivores.

Secondary production on the Moor House grasslands is up to 5 times that on the blanket bog. Of great importance to carnivores is the emergence of soil and litter dwelling insects in the spring and summer. The pattern of emergence is quite different on the grasslands from that on the bog. On the grasslands, there is a ready supply of insects from May to October and many species contribute to this. On the blanket bog, emergence is largely restricted to June and this is almost entirely made up of ·Tipulidae. Thus carnivores on the bog have a readily available food supply only for a short period and need to be specialist feeders or mobile and able to feed off the bog to sustain themselves. One of the most important of these is the meadow pipit, but even this species ingests only about 1 % of the food available to it (10).

Although total carnivore production on the bog is less than that on the grasslands, the proportion of herbivore and decomposer production which is assimilated by the carnivores is very much higher on the bog (14 %) than on the limestone grassland (3 %). This may result from the herbivore production on the bog being largely invertebrate whilst most of that on the grassland is by sheep. The extra cover afforded by the *Calluna* canopy may also be important to the carnivores (10).

DECOMPOSITION AND SOIL PROCESSES

The large areas of acid waterlogged blanket peat adjacent to well drained base-rich mineral soils emphasise the key role which the control of decomposition plays in the structure and function of ecosystems. As mentioned earlier, the retarded rate of decomposition and the production of peat results initially from waterlogging of the soil, but once peat formation has begun there is a feedback effect resulting from change in the vegetation. In contrast, on the mineral soils the higher nutrient status and good aeration maintain relatively rapid decomposition and nutrient release. Hence a nutrient rich vegetation is maintained which is readily degradable on death.

Decomposition and soil processes are products of microbial and faunal activity. Weight loss and respiration of plant remains provide direct estimates of the combined activity of the populations. However, to obtain insight into the mechanisms involved, an analysis is necessary of the composition, distribution and abundance of the populations with experiments on their biochemical potential and factors influencing this potential.

Microflora

Microbial populations in the blanket bog (Table 5) are typical of temperate acid peats and are lower in numbers than on the adjacent base rich grassland soils (38). Numbers of bacteria and lengths of fungal mycelium decline slightly with depth, but these do not

Table 5. Estimates of the numbers of bacteria (numbers g^{-1}) and length of fungal hyphae ($m\ g^{-1}$) in four horizons of the blanket bog profile (9). See Table 2 for horizon characteristics

		Horizon		
	Litter	Black-brown	Green-brown	Red-brown
Dilution counts: bacteria				
Heterotrophic-aerobic (range)	$0.9-15.0 \times 10^6$	$0.5-6.2 \times 10^6$	$1.0-49.0 \times 10^6$	$1.6-23.0 \times 10^6$
Heterotrophic-facultative (")	$0.3-7.7 \times 10^6$	$2.3-13.8 \times 10^6$	$1.0-38.0 \times 10^6$	$2.7-21.0 \times 10^6$
Chitinolytic-aerobic	10.0×10^3	10.0×10^3	20.0×10^3	10.0×10^6
Chitinolytic-facultative	170.0×10^3	25.0×10^3	30.0×10^3	19.0×10^3
Cellulose decomposers	2.1×10^3	0.30×10^3	0.8×10^3	0.1×10^3
Sulphate reducers	2.4×10^3	4.6×10^3	6.5×10^3	1.6×10^3
Thiosulphate oxidisers	5.0×10^3	0.3×10^3	0.1×10^3	0.1×10^3
Denitrifiers	16.0×10^3	17.0×10^3	1.1×10^3	1.1×10^3
N-fixing, aerobic	4.7×10^6	3.1×10^6	2.6×10^6	1.1×10^6
N-fixing, anaerobic	4.8×10^6	3.1×10^6	3.0×10^6	1.3×10^6
Direct counts: bacteria	$11-41 \times 10^9$	$10-32 \times 10^9$	$15-38 \times 10^9$	12×10^9
: fungal hyphae	$3-11 \times 10^3$	$6-10 \times 10^3$	$2-9 \times 10^3$	1×10^3

adequately reflect the decline in activity indicated by measurements such as the percentage of washed particles colonised by fungi. This measure declines from 70 % in the litter to 2 % in the red-brown horizon (about 25 cm). Numbers of types of microorganisms isolated from peat are slightly lower than on *Juncus* and on *Festuca-Agrostis* grassland and populations of certain groups, e.g. denitrifying and cellulolytic bacteria, appear to be particularly limited. Fruiting bodies of basidiomycetes are low in biomass, possibly indicating a low potential for lignin decomposition.

The waterlogged conditions inhibit the distribution and activity of some species, especially fungi, but a high proportion of the bacterial isolates – the facultative anaerobes – are capable of growth under very reduced oxygen supply as well as aerobically. A major limitation to microbial activity is the chemical composition of substrates for decomposition. Most of the incoming organic matter is high in lignin and cellulose, low in soluble carbohydrate, protein and nutrients. In addition, because of the limited nitrogen cycle, only a small proportion of the nitrogen present in the peat (0.6–1.8 %) is in an available form. Numbers of bacteria and lengths of fungal mycelium on *Rubus chamaemorus* leaves are about double those on *Eriophorum* leaves and *Calluna* shoots, reflecting the differences in substrate quality. Also laboratory cultures on peat and field experiments have shown that bacterial numbers and respiration increase slightly with addition of glucose or certain nitrogen compounds but a much greater response occurs when glucose and nitrogen are added together, emphasising that it is both the carbon and nitrogen sources which are limiting activity in the peat. There is thus a strong impression that although anaerobic conditions inhibit microbial activity, the additional limitations of low availability of nitrogen and energy sources and low pH all combine to retard decomposition processes (9, 42).

Invertebrates

Populations of decomposer invertebrates on the bog (Table 4) are largely confined to the surface 3 cm of the peat and therefore only influence decomposition of a small proportion of the plant organic matter. In addition, most of the production and energy utilisation is by one species, the enchytraeid *Cognettia sphagnetorum* (Vejdovsky).

Cognettia sphagnetorum populations (49) are between 20 and 100 000 m^{-2} on the bog, the main seasonal variation being apparently related to death in winter. About 80 % of the population is usually within the top 3 cm of the bog and 95 % within the top 6 cm. There is some vertical migration related to short-term seasonal variation in soil moisture (48). Microclimate, plus food supply, probably account for the spatial variation in numbers on the bog, mean numbers in *Sphagnum* being significantly lower than in *Eriophorum vaginatum* tussocks and *Calluna* litter (27, 53 and 45 x 10^3 m^{-2} respectively) (50). In a preference experiment, *C. sphagnetorum* selected *Sphagnum*, *E. vaginatum*, *Calluna* and *Rubus* litters in the ratio of 1:2:4:7 and, in culture, it grew well on *Calluna* and *Eriophorum* litter, but poorly on *Sphagnum* (39). Like most invertebrates at Moor House, *C. sphagnetorum* has one generation per year but unlike most other animals, it reproduces asexually by fragmentation into two or three parts followed by regeneration and growth (47). It is not uncommon for invertebrates at Moor House to take more than one year to complete a generation (10).

On the bog, *C. sphagnetorum* accounts for 70–75 % of the total energy assimilated by the decomposer fauna. The total energy assimilated is equivalent to about 15 g of organic matter m^{-2} each year. Assuming that 5–10 % of the organic matter is digested during passage through the gut, this represents a turnover of 150–300 g m^{-2} yr^{-1}, i.e. about 10 % of the organic matter in the surface 3 cm. Thus the impact of the invertebrate fauna is small compared with that on the grasslands where assimilation is equivalent to about 125 g m^{-2} yr^{-1} and 1 250–2 500 g m^{-2} yr^{-1} is passed through decomposer guts, i.e. about 30 % of the total organic matter.

C. *sphagnetorum* is probably a decomposer rather than a microbial feeder (39) but its action in breaking down plant remains is also likely to stimulate general microbial activity. Decomposition of litter, as measured by weight loss, in the presence of C. *sphagnetorum* at field density, is about 1.35 times higher than decomposition in the absence of the enchytraeids. Only a small part of the difference is attributed to assimilation and respiration by the worms, so that most of the difference results from microbial stimulation (Standen, pers. comm., 53).

Decomposition of litter and soil organic matter

There is an annual input of surface and belowground litter from the vegetation of 500–800 g m^{-2} yr^{-1}. A high proportion of this input is of organic fractions resistant to decomposition (92 % is lignin or cellulose) and the nutrient content is low (5.2 g N in 500 g m^{-2} yr^{-1} input). Standing dead *Calluna* and *Eriophorum* may decompose for 2–3 years before it enters the litter layer. During the first few years, as standing dead or litter, weight losses range from about 8 % per year for *Calluna* stems to 35 % for *Rubus* leaves (Fig. 7). The rates appear to be related to the relative amounts of resistant (lig-

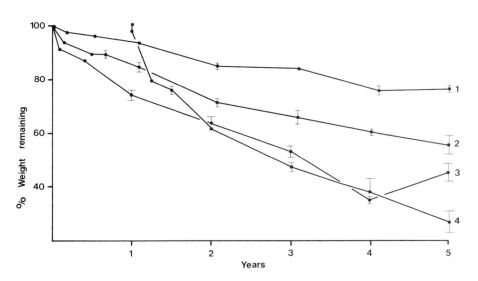

Figure 7. Decomposition of plant litters on blanket bog indicated by mean % weight remaining ± standard errors. 1. *Calluna* stems; 2. *Calluna* shoots. 3. *Eriophorum vaginatum* leaves; 4. *Rubus chamaemorus* leaves (25).

311

nin) and soluble (soluble carbohydrate) compounds, to mineral content and to the concentration of inhibitory substances such as tannins (25, 27).

Seasonal variation in decomposition is probably largely temperature controlled, and with microbial respiration ceasing at about $-5°C$, decomposition continues throughout most of the winter. In the litter, moisture levels below about 200 % inhibit microbial respiration (Fig. 8). Results for *Rubus* suggest that such inhibition occurs for about 10–20 % of the time mainly in summer. For the remainder of the year moisture is optimal for respiration. There is no evidence that high moisture levels in the surface layer inhibit decomposition and they probably contribute to initial losses, through leaching.

Rates of decomposition decline as the material decomposes, through an increase in the proportion of resistant compounds and probably through development of resistant complexes which lock up nutrients, especially nitrogen. Just below the surface, moisture conditions are probably optimal for decomposition but the high water table inhibits oxygen diffusion and as a result of microbial activity, reducing conditions develop below about 10 cm. This change in environmental conditions within the profile retards the decomposition (Fig. 9) of rhizomes and roots which die within the profile and also the surface litter which moves down the upper parts of the profile at about 0.5 to 1.0 cm yr^{-1}.

Loss rates of plant remains below the water table are very low, barely detectable by standard methods (4, 16, 25, 27). In the two computer models (6, 36) developed to simulate production, decomposition and accumulation, the rate at which decomposition

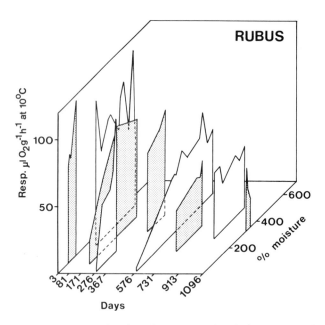

Figure 8. Respiration of leaf litter of *Rubus chamaemorus* in relation to age and moisture content. Individual sample readings are shown (27).

312

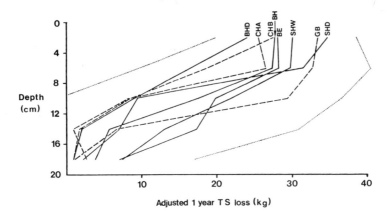

Figure 9. Decomposition of cotton strips, indicated by loss in tensile strength, at different depths in eight blanket bog sites (26). ..... = limits of standard deviation.

declines with depth markedly affects the amount of peat which accumulates. A constant fractional loss of 1×10^{-5} g g^{-1} yr^{-1} for *Sphagnum* in the anaerobic zone was estimated from measurements of methane loss from the bog surface, compared to best estimates, derived by the model, of 5×10^{-3} to 4×10^{-8} g g^{-1} yr^{-1} (6).

NUTRIENTS

Concentrations of nutrients such as N, P and K influence rates of production, consumption and decomposition of the vegetation. On the blanket bog, because the peat is frequently 1 m or more deep, the vegetation is divorced from the underlying mineral substratum. Thus the only input of nutrients to the system is from the atmosphere. The plants are therefore dependent on recirculation of nutrients from their decomposing remains and much of the nutrient capital is accumulated in an unavailable form in the peat. In addition losses in run-off, erosion and burning deplete the nutrient capital (12). The result is that the bog system is apparently in a delicately balanced state of nutrient poverty.

Bogs contrast with grasslands on mineral soils where there is a larger available nutrient capital and the nutrient constraint has been removed or reduced in many ecosystem processes.

The IBP programme has paid relatively little attention to studies of nutrient circulation, and its influence on productivity. Therefore much of our understanding of the involvement of nutrients in the dynamics of the bog system is derived from non-IBP studies and from interpretation of the distribution of nutrients within the system, i.e. not from experimental studies.

Nutrient limitations in ecosystem processes

The effect of low nutrient concentrations and availability is shown in all aspects of ecosystem functioning but there are three features which confuse the interpretation of results: 1. fertiliser experiments in the laboratory and field do not always produce results compatible with field observations, 2. different organisms respond differently to different nutrients and 3. the influence of nutrients is often shown by the absence of species rather than by the response of what is present.

On the bog there has been selection for plant and animal species capable of growth under low nutrient conditions, therefore an increase in nutrients could change species composition as well as productivity. There is no general pattern of plant response to fertiliser addition on the bog, e.g. *E. vaginatum* showed little or no response to Ca and P (39) but increased growth in response to an increase in all major nutrients (21), while *Rubus chamaemorus* showed no response to nutrients in the form of ash from burnt vegetation (41).

Most of the plants have low nutrient concentrations and this is probably partly responsible for the low level of herbivory, the low rate of decomposition and low level of invertebrate fauna production. Bacteria respond to N addition, especially when a readily utilisable carbon source is available (42) which probably explains the lack of response of *Sphagnum* decomposition to addition of nutrients. Unexceptional nutrient concentration in animal tissues (10—25 % N) implies that the decomposer invertebrates have developed some mechanism, e.g. selective assimilation and high throughput, to compensate for the low concentrations in decomposing plant remains (10).

Invertebrates have concentrations of P and N which are about ten times greater than those found in the peat or vegetation (2). For this reason their excreta and carcasses may be an important source of minerals to plants, particularly since they may circulate very rapidly. For example 77 % of all the production of a tipulid *Molophilus ater* is returned to the litter, as dead adults, in a period of 15 days in early June (10).

Nutrient cycling budget

The estimated inputs of major nutrients in rain are given in Table 6 (20). Nitrogen input through fixation is difficult to quantify on an annual basis, but may be up to 1 g N m^{-2} y^{-1} (42).

The standing crops of major nutrients within the vegetation, in other organisms and in peat when compared with the amounts utilised in production, show that the proportion of the nutrient capital in circulation increases over the series $N < P < K$. This implies an increasing possibility for nutrient limitation, but the nutrient concentrations give no indication of availability of the element and, as the sequence reflects the relative solubility of the elements, the interpretation must be treated with caution.

Some output from the system occurs in burning on moorlands. Most minerals are deposited in ash on the peat surface during burning and are leached and reabsorbed in the surface layers of the peat, so increasing the circulation rate. However, about 80 % of the N in the burnt vegetation goes up in smoke, and assuming a burn every 15—20 years, represents an annual loss of approximately 0.3 g N m^{-2}. As there is redeposition and condensation on adjacent areas, this estimate of the loss of N must be regarded as maximal (1, 15).

Table 6. Summary of the annual input and losses of five elements in a Moor House catchment. Data are in mg m^{-2} (12, 20)

		Sodium	Potassium	Calcium	Phosphorus	Nitrogen
Input in precipitation		2 554	307	898	46–69	820
Output	– stream water	4 524	896	5 375	40	294
	– peat	28	206	5	45	1 463
	– drift of fauna	0.1	0.5	0.1	0.5	5.7
	– sale of sheep and wool	0.2	0.5	0.2	1.2	5.3
	Total	4 552	1 104	5 860	86	1 767
Net loss		1 998	796	4 963	17–48	947

Nutrient output from the catchment (Table 6) in solution, peat and invertebrate drift in the streams, are losses from both bog and grasslands, but they probably give a true reflection of proportional losses from bog areas (12). The main features of importance are: 1) Nitrogen losses in solution represent about a third of the input in rainfall suggesting retention of the remainder (0.6 g m^{-2} yr^{-1}). 2) Losses in invertebrate drift are negligible, but there is a loss of nitrogen as peat – approximately 1.5 g N m^{-2} yr^{-1}. 3) For phosphorus between 60 and 90 % of the input in rain is lost in solution and again, when peat losses are considered there is a net loss of about 0.02–0.04 g P m^{-2} yr^{-1} compared with 1.0 g N m^{-2} yr^{-1}. 4) For other elements (K, Ca, Na), output in solution is greater than input in rain but this probably results from direct dissolution from the mineral soils or the stream bed rock. 5) Actual losses from the ombrogenous bog may be important relative to the small capital, especially for K. 6) Removal of sheep from the catchment in autumn results in a negligible loss of nutrients relative to the total nutrient capital and accounts for only about 0.1 % of the nutrients in annual primary production on grasslands.

Nutrients on the bog appear to be evenly balanced, the losses as peat representing the catastrophic loss of capital from eroding areas. Such losses are irrelevant to the long term nutrient economy of most of the bog which shows profiles undisturbed for centuries. However, the extent and rate to which nutrients become incorporated into the peat below the water table, and thus effectively outside the functional part of the ecosystem, is important. The maximal rate of incorporation of plant remains below the water table (at about 20 cm) is likely to be 100 g m^{-2} yr^{-1}, which represents about 1.0–2.0 g N, 0.06 g P and 0.02 g K m^{-2} yr^{-1}.

The data available do not allow an accurate assessment of the nutrient budgets for the bog, but it appears that inputs to, and losses from, the functional part of the ecosystem are approximately equal. However, the system is much too delicately balanced to be assessed by available techniques for the measurement of input, accumulation and losses. For example, on the data presented above, the net loss of 0.06 g P m^{-2} yr^{-1} from the functional part of the bog system implies that all the P in the surface 20 cm would be lost in a period of 200 years, yet within the errors of our estimates it can be calculated that this would not occur over much longer periods of time.

INTERACTIONS BETWEEN TERRESTRIAL AND
AQUATIC ECOSYSTEMS

The moorland consists of a mosaic of blanket bog, bordered by *Juncus* and *Festuca* grasslands, and dissected by streams (11). The terrestrial and aquatic systems are closely linked physically and ecologically.

About 75–80 % of the rainfall (1 500–2 000 mm) passes from land into the streams, the remainder being evaporated. The nutrient output in the streams (Table 6), represents loss from the soil, particularly as peat, plus dissolution of the stream bedrock, the latter contributing mainly to output of Ca, K and Na. Losses as drift of fauna are mainly terrestrial insects trapped on the surface film. About 50 kg are trapped annually from an 83 ha catchment, equivalent to about 0.06 g m^{-2} yr^{-1}. Annual production of brown trout (*Salmo trutta*) in a Moor House stream is of the order of 0.3–0.7 g m^{-2} of stream from a standing crop of about 1.15 g m^{-2}. This is similar to adjacent areas (13). Estimated food intake is 8.0–9.0 g m^{-2} yr^{-1} and about one third of this is of terrestrial origin. Thus although only a small proportion of the terrestrial input is utilised, it is an important source for stream fauna (12, 43).

Streams influence the terrestrial ecology: 1. through redistribution and redeposition of organic and mineral matter on the stream banks during flooding producing the alluvial grasslands which form an important sward for sheep and 2. through emergence of aquatic insects which provide a food supply for terrestrial carnivores. Tipulids are the major food for broods of meadow pipits (*Anthus pratensis*), with stream insects forming 11 and 33 % of the food for the first and second broods respectively (10). Aquatic insects constitute about 15 % of the prey caught in webs of the spider (*Araneus cornutus* Clerck.) (3). These represent a small fraction of the aquatic production but provide a valuable food source for terrestrial carnivores, particularly as the food supply from terrestrial sources is largely composed of adult tipulids belonging to two or three species and is markedly seasonal in occurrence.

ECOSYSTEM OVERVIEW

At Moor House although the catchment may be regarded as an ecosystem unit of organization, the various vegetation/soil complexes within the catchment also represent fairly discrete ecosystems – in the sense that primary production, decomposition and recirculation are largely contained within the limits of the system. The two extreme ecosystem types are the blanket bog and the *Festuca-Agrostis* grassland which differ in three main attributes: physical structure, organisation structure and rate of turnover (10, 11, 29, 43).

The blanket bog has a large scale structure, the main scale of variation – canopy, tussock, pool-hummock etc. – being in terms of 10s and 100s of centimetres. Numbers of species of flora, fauna and microflora are small compared with those of the grasslands and most plant and animal production occurs through only five species, *Calluna vulgaris, Eriophorum vaginatum, Sphagnum rubellum, Cognettia sphagnetorum* and *Tipula subnodicornis.* The species composition alters in different bog communities but the number of plant dominants is usually three.

The vegetation standing crop has an annual turnover of about 0.3 and only about 1 % of the production is consumed by herbivores. The remainder enters the decomposer cycle where, at most, 5 % is assimilated by decomposer fauna and 10 % passes below the water table. Thus about 85 % of the annual input is decomposed by microflora. However, rates of decomposition are slow and an index of the turnover rate of the system ($k = {}^1\!/X_{ss}$) indicates an overall fractional loss rate of about 0.001 which represents a 95 % turnover time of about 3 000 years. In the top 20 cm, k = ca 0.043 and the 95 % time is about 70 years. These are broad approximations and contain a number of assumptions, but the dates correspond reasonably with independent observations and represent the order of the rate of turnover of the system.

It appears that two major factors are responsible for the system features: 1. waterlogging which controls rooting depth, faunal and microbial distribution and the long term rate of decomposition, and 2. poor substrate quality which controls herbivore consumption and the rate of decomposition.

In particular the low availability and concentration of major nutrients influence most aspects of system functioning. Although about 14 % of the production of fauna is assimilated by predators (mites, spiders, meadow pipit), this is only about 1 g m^{-2} yr^{-1}, and secondary predators are rare. Thus the trophic pyramid is shallow. The low rate of predation and of parasitism is reflected in the lack of density dependent regulation of many of the fauna. Thus populations fluctuate widely between years — the range is often 10 fold — largely related to climatic conditions.

In contrast, the grassland on limestone is characterised by a smallscale physical structure (1–10 cm), with a much wider range of species. The aboveground primary production has a high turnover rate (ca 1) and up to 70 % of it is consumed by herbivores. Total primary production estimates are very approximate but 20–40 % may be assimilated by the fauna, and about 3 % of the fauna production is assimilated by carnivores. This low efficiency of transfer is probably related to the highly sporadic seasonal pattern of availability of prey, and is also reflected in the natural absence of top predators. The turnover of the organic matter (k = ca 0.01, 95 % turnover = ca 300 years) is much faster than in the bog.

The increased rates of herbivory and of decomposition and the higher turnover of the system relate to the high substrate quality (low lignin and cellulose, high nutrients) and to the well aerated soil. It appears that increased nutrient status has the effect of increasing the rate of turnover of the system and changing the trophic structure, but without necessarily increasing total production.

ACKNOWLEDGEMENTS

This paper has used data and ideas from many past and present research workers at Moor House. We are deeply indebted to them even though their work may not have been specifically acknowledged. The research was generously supported by the Nature Conservancy, the Nature Conservancy Council, the Natural Environment Research Council, the Institute of Terrestrial Ecology, the Royal Society and many university departments.

REFERENCES

1. Allen, S.E. 1964. Chemical aspects of heather burning. – J. Appl. Ecol. 1: 347–364.
2. Butterfield, J. & Coulson, J.C. 1975. Insect food of adult grouse *Lagopus lagopus scoticus* (Lath.) – J. Anim. Ecol. 14: 601–608.
3. Cherrett, J.M. 1964. The distribution of spiders on the Moor House National Nature Reserve, Westmorland. – J. Anim. Ecol. 33: 27–48.
4. Clymo, R.S. 1965. Experiments on breakdown of *Sphagnum* in two bogs. – J. Ecol. 53: 747–758.
5. Clymo, R.S. 1973. The growth of *Sphagnum*: some effects of environment. – J. Ecol. 61: 849–869.
6. Clymo, R.S. In press. A model of peat bog growth. – In: Heal, O.W. & Perkins, D.F. (eds.) The Ecology of Some British Moors and Montane Grasslands. Berlin–Heidelberg–New York: Springer Verlag.
7. Clymo, R.S. & Reddaway, E.J.F. 1972. Productivity of *Sphagnum* (bog-moss) and peat accumulation. – Hidrobiologia 12: 181–192. (Available as Moor House Occasional Paper 3.)
8. Clymo, R.S. & Reddaway, E.J.F. 1974. Growth rate of *Sphagnum rubellum* Wils. on Pennine blanket bog. – J. Ecol. 62: 191–196.
9. Collins, V.G., D'Sylva, B.T. & Latter, P.M. In press. Microbial populations in peat. – In: Heal, O.W. & Perkins, D.F. (eds.) The Ecology of Some British Moors and Montane Grasslands. Berlin–Heidelberg– New York: Springer Verlag.
10. Coulson, J.C. & Whittaker, J.B. In press. Ecology of moorland animals. – In: Heal, O.W. & Perkins, D.F. (eds.) The Ecology of Some British Moors and Montane Grasslands, Berlin–Heidelberg– New York: Springer Verlag.
11. Cragg, J.B. 1961. Some aspects of the ecology of moorland animals. – J. Anim. Ecol. 30: 205–223.
12. Crisp, D.T. 1966. Input and output of minerals for an area of Pennine moorland; the importance of precipitation, drainage, erosion and animals. – J. Appl. Ecol. 3: 327–348.
13. Crisp, D.T., Mann, R.H.K. & McCormack, J.C. 1974. The populations of fish at Cow Green, Upper Teesdale, before impoundment. – J. Appl. Ecol. 11: 969–996.
14. Eddy, A., Welch, D. & Rawes, M. 1969. The vegetation of the Moor House National Nature Reserve in the northern Pennines, England. – Vegetatio 16: 239–284.
15. Evans, C.C. & Allen, S.E. 1971. Nutrient losses in smoke produced during heather burning. – Oikos 22: 149–154.
16. Flanagan, P.W. & Veum, A.K. 1974. Relationships between respiration, weight loss, temperature and moisture in organic residues in tundra. – In: Holding, A.J., Heal, O.W., MacLean, S.F. & Flanagan, P.W. (eds.) Soil Organisms and Decomposition in Tundra, pp. 249–278. Stockholm: IBP Tundra Biome Steering Committee.
17. Forrest, G.I. 1971. Structure and production of north Pennine blanket bog vegetation. – J. Ecol. 59: 453–479.
18. Forrest, G.I. & Smith, R.A.H. 1975. The productivity of a range of blanket bog vegetation types in the northern Pennines. – J. Ecol. 63: 173–202.
19. Gore, A.J.P. 1961. Factors limiting plant growth on high-level blanket peat 1. Calcium and phosphate. – J. Ecol. 49: 399–402.
20. Gore, A.J.P. 1968. The supply of six elements by rain to an upland peat area. – J. Ecol. 56: 483–496.
21. Gore, A.J.P. & Urquhart, C. 1966. The effects of waterlogging on the growth of *Molinia caerulea* and *Eriophorum vaginatum*. – J. Ecol. 54: 617–633.
22. Grace, J. & Marks, T.C. In press. Physiological aspects of bog production at Moor House. – In: Heal, O.W. & Perkins, D.F. (eds.) The Ecology of Some British Moors and Montane Grasslands. Berlin–Heidelberg–New York: Springer Verlag.
23. Grace, J. & Woolhouse, H.W. 1973. A physiological and mathematical study of the growth and productivity of a *Calluna-Sphagnum* community II. Light interception and photosynthesis in *Calluna*. – J. Appl. Ecol. 10: 63–76.
24. Grace, J. & Woolhouse, H.W. 1974. A physiological and mathematical study of the growth and productivity of a *Calluna-Sphagnum* community IV. Model of *Calluna*. – J. Appl. Ecol. 11: 281–295.

25. Heal, O.W. & French, D.D. 1974. Decomposition of organic matter in tundra. – In: Holding, A.J., Heal, O.W., MacLean, S.F. & Flanagan, P.W. (eds.) Soil Organisms and Decomposition in Tundra, pp. 279–308. Stockholm: IBP Tundra Biome Steering Committee.

26. Heal, O.W., Howson, G., French, D.D. & Jeffers, J.N.R. 1974. Decomposition of cotton strips in tundra. – In: Holding, A.J., Heal, O.W., MacLean, S.F. & Flanagan, P.W. (eds.) Soil Organisms and Decomposition in Tundra, pp. 341–362. Stockholm: IBP Tundra Biome Steering Committee.

27. Heal, O.W., Latter, P.M. & Howson, G. In press. A study of the decomposition of organic matter. – In: Heal, O.W. & Perkins, D.F. (eds.) The Ecology of Some British Moors and Montane Grasslands. Berlin–Heidelberg–New York: Springer Verlag.

28. Heal, O.W. & Smith, R.A.H. In press. Introduction and site description. – In: Heal, O.W. & Perkins, D.F. (eds.) The Ecology of Some British Moors and Montane Grasslands. Berlin–Heidelberg–New York: Springer Verlag.

29. Heal, O.W. & Smith, R.A.H. In press. The distribution and transfer of dry matter and nutrients in the blanket bog ecosystem. – In: Heal, O.W. & Perkins, D.F. (eds.) The Ecology of Some British Moors and Montane Grasslands. Berlin–Heidelberg–New York: Springer Verlag.

30. Hodkinson, I.D. 1973. The population dynamics and host plant interactions of *Strophingia ericae* (Curt.) (Homoptera: Psylloidea). – J. Anim. Ecol. 42: 565–583.

31. Hornung, M. 1958. Soil morphology, mineralogy and genesis. – Ph.D. Thesis, University of Durham.

32. Horobin, J.C. 1971. Studies on the biology of moorland Tipulidae with particular reference to *Molophilus ater* Meigen. – Ph.D. Thesis, University of Durham.

33. Johnson, G.A.L. & Dunham, K.C. 1963. The geology of Moor House. – Monogr. Nat. Conserv. HMSO. 182 pp.

34. Jones, H.E., Forrest, G.I. & Gore, A.J.P. 1971. First stage of a model for the growth and decay of *Calluna vulgaris* at Moor House, U.K. – In: Heal, O.W. (ed.) Working meeting on Analysis of Ecosystems, Kevo, Finland, pp. 133–160. Stockholm: IBP Tundra Biome Steering Committee.

35. Jones, H.E. & Gore, A.J.P. In press. A simulation approach to primary production. – In: Moore, J.J. (ed.) Tundra: Comparative Analysis of Ecosystems. Cambridge University Press.

36. Jones, H.E. & Gore, A.J.P. In press. A simulation of production and decay in blanket bog. – In: Heal, O.W. & Perkins, D.F. (eds.) The Ecology of Some British Moors and Montane Grasslands. Berlin–Heidelberg–New York: Springer Verlag.

37. Jordan, A.M. 1962. *Coleophora alticolella* Zell (Lepidoptera) and its food plant *Juncus squarrosus* L. in the northern Pennines. – J. Anim. Ecol. 31: 293–304.

38. Latter, P.M., Cragg, J.B. & Heal, O.W. 1967. Comparative studies on the microbiology of four moorland soils in the northern Pennines. – J. Ecol. 55: 445–464.

39. Latter, P.M. & Howson, G. In prep. Studies on the microfauna of blanket bog with particular reference to Enchytraeidae 2. Growth and survival of *Cognettia sphagnetorum* on various substrates.

40. Marks, T.C. 1974. The effects of moorland management on the growth of *Rubus chamaemorus*. – Ph.D. Thesis, University of London.

41. Marks, T.C. & Taylor, K. 1972. The mineral nutrient status of *Rubus chamaemorus* L. in relation to burning and sheep grazing. – J. Appl. Ecol. 9: 501–511.

42. Martin, N.J. & Holding, A.J. In press. Nutrient availability and other factors limiting microbial activity in the blanket peat. – In: Heal, O.W. & Perkins, D.F. (eds.) The Ecology of Some British Moors and Montane Grasslands. Berlin–Heidelberg–New York: Springer Verlag.

43. Rawes, M. & Heal, O.W. In press. The blanket bog as part of a Pennine moorland. – In: Heal, O.W. & Perkins, D.F. (eds.) The Ecology of Some British Moors and Montane Grasslands. Berlin–Heidelberg–New York: Springer Verlag.

44. Rawes, M. & Welch, D. 1969. Upland productivity of vegetation and sheep at Moor House National Nature Reserve, Westmorland, England. – Oikos, Suppl. II, 72 pp.

45. Rawes, M. & Williams, R. 1973. Production and utilisation of *Calluna* and *Eriophorum*. – Potassium Institute Ltd., Colloquium Proceedings No. 3: 115–119.

46. Smith, R.A.H. & Forrest, G.I. In press. Field estimates of primary production. – In: Heal, O.W. & Perkins, D.F. (eds.) The Ecology of Some British Moors and Montane Grasslands. Berlin–Heidelberg–New York: Springer Verlag.

47. Springett, J.A. 1970. The distribution and life histories of some moorland Enchytraeidae (Oligochaeta). – J. Anim. Ecol. 39: 725–737.
48. Springett, J.A., Brittain, J.E. & Springett, B.P. 1970. Vertical movement of Enchytraeidae (Oligochaeta) in moorland soils. – Oikos 21: 16–21.
49. Standen, V. 1973. The production and respiration of an enchytraeid population in blanket bog. – J. Anim. Ecol. 42: 219–245.
50. Standen, V. & Latter, P.M. In prep. Distribution of a population of *Cognettia sphagnetorum* (Enchytraeidae) in relation to microhabitats on blanket bog.
51. Urquhart, C. & Gore, A.J.P. 1973. The redox characteristics of four peat profiles. – Soil Biol. Biochem. 5: 659–672.
52. Whittaker, J.B. 1971. Population changes in *Neophilaenus lineatus* (L.) (Homoptera: Cercopidae) in different parts of its range. – J. Anim. Ecol. 40: 425–444.
53. Whittaker, J.B. 1974. Interactions between fauna and microflora at tundra sites. – In: Holding, A.J., Heal, O.W., MacLean, S.F. & Flanagan, P.W. (eds.) Soil Organisms and Decomposition in Tundra, pp. 183–196. Stockholm: IBP Tundra Biome Steering Committee.

Rosswall, T. & Heal, O.W. (eds.) 1975.
Structure and Function of Tundra Ecosystems.
Ecol. Bull. (Stockholm) 20: 321–343.

GLENAMOY, IRELAND

J.J. MOORE, P. DOWDING and B. HEALY

INTRODUCTION

The Glenamoy IBP peatland sites are located (54°12′N, 9°45′W) on a low-lying, un-dulating plain on the west coast of Ireland which rises gradually to seacliffs of 200 m to the north and more abruptly to a range of 400 m to the east. The three main sampling sites are between 10 and 30 m above sea level.

This peat-covered landscape, usually referred to as western (atlantic, lowland) blanket bog (20, 35) is typical of the low-lying ground below 200 m with siliceous bedrock along the western atlantic coast of Ireland and it makes up about 3 % of the total area of Ireland. The sites are situated on the largest continuous area of this peatland type in the north-west of Co. Mayo.

Before the development of the peat a woodland dominated by *Pinus sylvestris* L. covered the area; oak (*Quercus petraea* (Mattuschka) Liebl.) occurred in the sheltered and more eutrophic areas such as river valleys. The woodland was drastically reduced, probably by fire, sometime after 5 000 B.C. and the already peaty ground of the flatter areas developed a peat layer of up to 50 cm. This was again colonised by *Pinus sylvestris*. Meanwhile Neolithic peoples, probably from Brittany (9), arrived some centuries before 3 000 B.C. and colonised the more fertile ground at the margins of the present peat-covered areas and some of their tombs (Megalithic Court Cairns) are now to be found with foundations on the mineral ground and buried under the peat. These tombs are confined to better drained areas on slopes and moraines.

Later, Bronze Age people laid out a complex field system and their dwelling sites have been unearthed under the peat. At about 2 300 B.C. a massive destruction of the second pine forest took place by burning; the woodland did not regenerate this time but instead a heathy grassland developed and eventually the peat cover encroached on-to the better drained ground and the whole area was abandoned in late Bronze Age times and remained uninhabited except for a narrow coastal strip (4).

Roads were built in the early 19th century (17) and settlements in the interior, mainly along rivers and on hillsides, increased during the Irish "population explosion" in the first half of the 19th century. The population in the area was drastically reduced by the Great Potato Famine (1846).

In 1955 the Irish Government acquired 400 ha of the bog as an experimental area to investigate the possibility of reclaiming the peatland for agriculture. Initial drainage was started and the area was taken over by the Agricultural Research Institute (An Foras Talúntais) in 1969. A research programme was designed to determine the most economical ways of reclaiming western blanket peat for human use. In an adjacent area of 1 000 ha the Forestry Division established experimental plantings of different species of exotic conifers (8, 26, 27).

Three intensive sites for the IBP work were chosen: undisturbed bog (often referred to as virgin bog) and two further sites where the peat had been drained and fertilised for the production of economically important crops. It was hoped thus to follow the changes in community structure and functioning arising from these manipulations. Neither of the manipulated areas differed greatly from the virgin bog site before reclamation started (11, 22).

Bog: the bog site is considered to be typical of the flatter atlantic blanket bog of western Ireland. It is unmanaged except for light grazing by sheep (Scottish Blackface) and cattle along the stream margins and the roadsides. Sporadic fires have been a regular feature since Neolithic times, as evidenced by charcoal fragments in the peat. The sampling area is 300 ha mainly confined to the catchment of a south-flowing stream. The area is bounded by a public road to the south from which it slopes northward for 200 m and then flattens out to form a flat pool-dotted plateau (11, 22, 24).

Grassland: four plots, managed as meadow were first drained in 1954 when the vegetation and topography closely resembled those of the present bog site. The area was rotivated in 1958 and received a dressing of 500 g lime and 2 g copper sulphate m^{-2}. Various crops of cereals or grass occupied the site from 1958 to 1964. Average fertiliser application during this period was about 25 g calcium ammonium nitrate, 38 g superphosphate and 13 g muriate of potash m^{-2} yr^{-1}. The present sward was sown in August 1965 with *Festuca arundinacea* Schreb., *Lolium perenne* L., *Trifolium pratense* L. and *T. repens* L. Clovers established poorly and in 1969 the sward was composed mainly of *Festuca arundinacea* and *Poa pratensis* L. The *Festuca* has receded in recent years with *Holcus lanatus* L. and *Ranunculus repens* L. becoming more important in the sward. No grazing occurs, except accidentally, and harvesting is for sileage or for hay.

Forest (Glenturk): this area, lying on the eastern shore of Carrowmore Lake, was drained by the Forestry Division in 1963. The bog was level and bore marks of having been previously drained over 100 years ago by drains 9 m apart which had completely filled in. This area is more sheltered than the other two sites with hills rising to the east and to the west; it is only 10–15 m above sea-level. The original vegetation had a greater proportion of the deciduous (nitrogen-fixing) dwarf shrub *Myrica gale* L. than the bog site. The drains cut in 1963 were either 3.6 or 1.8 m apart giving upturned ribbons of peat 1.8 m apart in both cases. On these strips were planted alternate *Picea sitchensis* (Bong.) Carr. (provenance, Forks, Wa., USA on the west slopes of the Olympic Mountains) and *Pinus contorta* Loud. (provenance, Newport, Oregon, USA on the Pacific coast) at 1.8 by 1.8 m spacing. The ground flora was sampled in 1969. In early 1970, the whole of the area was manured with ground phosphate (10 g m^{-2}), potassium sulphate (4 g m^{-2}), urea (2 g m^{-2}) and copper sulphate (0.5 g m^{-2}), applied broadcast. Four plots of 0.16 ha in the middle of the plantation were set aside for detailed study; they were hydrologically isolated from the surrounding peat and the outflow was measured with a recording V-notch. The treatments were: (1) Drains deepened; + manure. (2) Drains deepened; no manure. (3) Manure only. (4) Control — untreated.

In addition to the three intensive sites, some sampling has been carried out in a shelter-belt near the IBP grassland plots. Shelter-belts, mainly of *Pinus contorta* and *Picea sitchensis*, 30 m wide were planted in 1956 at 1.5 m spacing around the fields of the experimental station. This supplementary site supplies information on the further development of changes in the system as the trees approach maturity.

ENVIRONMENTAL CONDITIONS

Climate

The weather station at Glenamoy was established in 1959 and continuous records of the major macroclimatic parameters are available since that date. In addition, a major climatological station has been in existence at Belmullet, 15 km to the west since 1956 (Fig. 1).

The present climate is largely influenced by proximity to the west coast at the latitude where the majority of the atlantic cyclonic systems strike the mainland. The overall climate might be summarised as wet and windy with a mild temperature regime, no

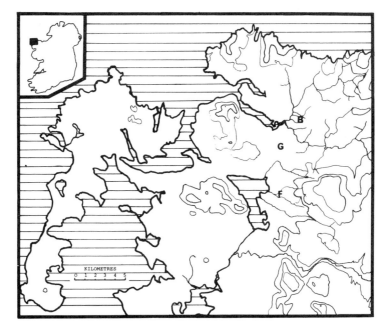

Figure 1. Map of N.W. Co. Mayo showing location of the three IBP sites: B = bog; G = grassland with shelter-belt nearby; F = forest at Glenturk. The 300, 600, 900 and 1 200 foot contours are shown (approx. 100, 200, 300 and 400 m).

323

Table 1. Long term climatic averages for Glenamoy. All figures refer to the 15 year period, 1959–1973, except for open pan evaporation which covers the years 1961–1973

	J	F	M	A	M	J	J	A	S	O	N	D	Year
Screen temp (°C)													
mean max	7.2	8.0	10.0	11.5	14.3	16.3	16.7	16.8	14.9	13.7	10.0	9.0	12.3
mean min	2.7	2.0	3.3	4.3	6.4	9.0	10.5	10.4	9.4	7.9	4.0	3.9	6.1
1/2 (max + min)	4.7	5.0	6.5	7.9	10.3	12.7	13.6	13.6	12.2	10.8	6.9	6.4	9.2
Soil temp (°C)													
10 cm 09.00 GMT	3.8	4.0	5.7	7.8	10.7	13.4	14.6	14.2	12.6	10.4	6.7	5.4	9.1
Relative humidity (%) 09.00 GMT	88.6	87.3	84.1	82.6	78.4	79.0	82.9	86.4	86.1	87.7	87.7	87.5	84.9
Rainfall (mm)	136.5	108.5	93.1	91.9	83.7	92.1	82.4	101.3	124.5	131.9	163.1	150.6	1 359.6
Number of days with rain	22.8	26.4	22.0	21.4	20.7	19.7	13.8	22.6	19.9	23.5	25.4	25.8	264.0
Daily duration (h) of bright sun	1.6	2.7	3.6	5.2	5.8	5.7	4.0	4.6	3.8	2.8	1.7	1.2	3.5
Evaporation (mm) open pan	16.5	22.4	41.1	60.1	86.9	98.1	84.2	72.4	50.9	34.6	17.8	18.1	602.9

month having a mean temperature below zero, and very little snow falling in any year. From the climatic point of view it thus stands at the wet, mild extreme of the Tundra Biome sites (13).

Table 1 summarises the macroclimatic parameters for Glenamoy.

The distribution of precipitation over time is an important parameter from the point of view of both the natural and manipulated systems. Even moderately long periods of drought cause profound changes in the system; the drop in the water table brings about an oxidising atmosphere in the previously anaerobic layers. This leads to increased biological activity on the part of the soil microbiota and to a considerable drop in pH. Parameters like 'number of rain-days' (over 0.2 mm precipitation per day) and 'number of dry periods' (3 days or more without precipitation) assume great importance. The values for the IBP years are given in Table 2.

The saturated peat has a low thermal conductivity and the temperature at 10 cm depth mirrors closely the screen mean with little diurnal variation. The absolute minimum temperature recorded so far at this depth was $0.9°C$ in the severe February of 1969 when screen minimum fell to $-11°C$. The sinusoidal mean temperature curve changes phase and amplitude as one descends in the peat; at 10 cm depth, the peak is in July and the annual amplitude is $11°C$, at 1.8 m the peak has shifted to October and the amplitude is reduced to $3°C$, at 5.4 m the maximum does not occur until March/April and the amplitude is reduced to $0.4°C$ with a mean of $10.3°C$ (27).

The mean temperature at 10 cm seems to be a good measure of the vigorous growing season (some growth in some species in all months of the year). In undrained peat, the mean temperature at this level does not reach $10°C$ until early May and it remains above this level until early November. This coincides with the peak growing season.

The climate of some of the IBP years departed considerably from the average. In 1969 the year when intensive sampling to determine primary production was carried out, the temperatures in January and February were much lower than usual with minimum screen temperatures below $-10°C$ on several days. 1970 was an abnormally wet year with precipitation exceeding open pan evaporation by almost 1 000 mm, 25 % more than the average surplus. The only spell when evaporation exceeded precipitation was late May and early June. 1971 had an abnormally dry summer with six dry periods extending from March to September. In 1972, the dry periods came late in the season in July, late August and late September.

Table 2. Rain and evaporation data for Glenamoy during the years of IBP investigations

	1969	1970	1971	1972
Days with rainfall	270	296	236	256
Dry periods (3 or more days without rain)	7	5	14	12
Total precipitation (mm)	1 248	1 445	1 114	1 163
Total evaporation (mm)	592	484	585	570

The winds average 4.5 m s^{-1} over the year and the open treeless bog is very exposed to North Atlantic gales which reach velocities of over 25 m s^{-1}. The microclimate of sheltered areas, either in stream depressions or close to the shelterbelts on the farm, departs considerably from that of the open bog, but no routine, long term measurements have been made.

Hydrology

Since one of the main research efforts of the Peatland Experimental Station at Glenamoy was the development of efficient drainage techniques, the hydrology of drained and undrained peat has been worked out in considerable detail (6, 7, 28).

Most of this work is applied in nature and aims at devising the most economical spacing of drains for reclamation. 4.5 m spacing has been found most satisfactory. The outflow from such drained areas is much more regular than from the undrained bog which acts as an impermeable surface. The outflow from undrained bog thus mirrors the irregularities of the rainfall very closely with a short time-lag, because of the small pore space. Since the peat has such a low permeability, no lowering of the water table occurs at more than 2 m from the drain edge. This impermeability is confirmed on the virgin bog where the water surface of adjacent pools no more than 2 m apart may differ by up to 50 cm. In some places on the virgin bog, the drainage water escapes by means of eroded tunnels under the peat to the sluggish streams running through the bog.

Table 3 gives the approximate average water balance and shows only a small surplus for the summer period. During the early part of the summer (May, June) there is usually a considerable withdrawal from the soil by evapotranspiration.

Table 3. Approximate average annual water budget for Glenamoy undrained bog

	Rainfall (mm)	Evapotranspiration (mm)	Surplus water (mm)
Annual	1 400	600	800
Oct–Mar	800	140	660
Apr–Sept	600	455	145

Soils

The soil at all the intensive sites (Table 4) is deep fibrous sedge peat up to 6 m deep on flat areas but thinner on the slopes. It is seldom less than 2 m deep except where the slope is over 15°. It is well decomposed except for the fibrous remains of roots and is waterlogged for most of the year when its pH is 4.6; when the water-table recedes during drought, the pH drops to about 3.5.

The underlying quartzitic drift (33, 34) is strongly podzolised with a narrow (1 cm) non-undulating iron humus hardpan about 50 cm below the peat/mineral interface.

326

Table 4. Some physical and chemical characteristics of the blanket peat at the Glenamoy IBP bog site. All figures refer to the top 5 cm (16) except columns 2 and 3 of soluble nutrients and total P. Nutrient concentrations are in ppm unless otherwise stated. S.D. and number of samples are given. Column 2 of soluble nutrients refer to the top 20 cm (36) and column 3 and total P to the top 2.5 cm (29)

pH	Moisture (% dw)	Bulk density (g cm^{-3} ww)	Total ash (%)	Total organic C (%)	Total N (%)	Total Mg	Total P
4.4±0.2(32)	90.4±3.9(79)	1.01	1.1±0.8(20)	46.8±1.5(10)	1.5±0.4(10)	1 652±335(18)	450(6)

	Soluble nutrients		
	in H$_2$O	in Morgan's solution	in 0.1 N H$_2$SO$_4$
P	0.24±0.18(66)	17	55
K	5.5 ±1.9(63)	190	1 067
Ca	3.0 ±2.3(69)	4	2 100
Mg	0.32±0.18(87)	–	–

The peat is composed of pure organic matter with a very low ash content, slightly over 1 % of dry matter. Moisture content of the upper layers varies considerably depending on the weather but averages 900 %. Bulk density varies little with depth at 1.01 g ww cm^{-3}. The soil may thus be classified as a histisol of fibrous sedge peat (2–6 m deep) over an aquod spodosol derived from quartzitic drift from a pre-Weichsel glaciation.

The total N is high but most of this is unavailable, locked up in complex organic residues. Both total and available phosphorous are very low and this element is probably the most important limiting factor for plant growth on the bog. Very spectacular improvement in growth has been obtained from small additions of phosphate fertilisers when trees are planted on the drained bog.

PRIMARY PRODUCTION

Community classification and dynamics

Most of the vegetation on the virgin bog belongs to the *Pleurozia purpurea – Erica tetralix* Association (5, 21). 94 species have been recorded on this vegetation type at Glenamoy with a mean species' number per quadrat of 1 m^2 of 24.

On the flat or gently sloping areas the general aspect of the vegetation is graminoid with *Molinia caerulea* (L.) Moench and *Schoenus nigricans* L. sharing dominance. The ground layer is a mosaic composed mainly of 4 *Sphagnum* species, a mucilaginous mass of algae in which 60 species have been identified, the mosses *Campylopus flexuosus* Brid.

and *C. atrovirens* DeNot. and the liverwort *Pleurozia purpurea* (Lightf.) Lindb. The two latter are particularly characteristic of this vegetation type. The ericoid shrubs, *Calluna vulgaris* (L.) Hull. and *Erica tetralix* L. are stunted and inconspicuous though very frequent. The dwarf shrub *Myrica gale* is present where there is slight seepage and thus a slightly more favourable nutrient supply; it is absent on the purely ombrotrophic domes (24).

On steeper slopes the microtopography becomes more hummocky, probably because of grazing by sheep, and the algal material is confined to the hollows between the irregular tussocks spaced about 1 m apart. Most of the hummocks are formed by the accumulated stem bases of *Molinia*, although some of them are hummocks of *Sphagnum rubellum* Wils. with a conspicuous overgrowth of *Rhacomitrium lanuginosum* Brid. to the SW, the direction of the prevailing wind.

Where drainage is improved, as along the natural drainage channels, *Scirpus cespitosus* L. first becomes more common and then on the steeper edges *Calluna vulgaris* becomes more vigorous forming a dark strip to each side of the stream. Similar enhancement of *Calluna* growth occurs where drainage is artificially increased by peat cutting or drains.

Under the drainage and fertilization regime practised in the forestry area there is a gradual elimination of the species of open bog with *Molinia caerulea* or *Calluna vulgaris* dominating depending on whether the area is more water-logged or well drained. On the very dry upturned sods several new species of lichen appear and in the drains the only species of *Sphagnum* is *S. apiculatum* Lindb., a species common in the drainage flushes running through the bog but not on the bog surface itself.

Although the grassland was sown with a seed mixture consisting of *Festuca arundinacea*, *Lolium perenne*, *Trifolium pratense* and *T. repens*, within a few years the botanical composition of the sward had changed radically; *Lolium* and *T. pratense* disappeared and *Holcus lanatus*, *Poa trivialis*, *Ranunculus repens*, *Stellaria alsine* Grimm. and *Epilobium palustre* L. had established themselves.

The shelter-belts and forestry plantations of different ages give a clear idea of the temporal succession following this manipulation. In the early stages most of the bog species survive but with growth of the conifers they gradually disappear and a number of species (mainly bryophytes) typical of Irish oakwoods on non-peaty soils appear (e.g. *Isothecium myosuroides* Brid., *Blechnum spicant* (L.) Roth, *Mnium hornum* L.).

The pools on the bog cover about 5 % of the flatter areas and vary from small, shallow hollows of about 2 m^2 dominated by *Sphagnum inundatum* Russ., *S. cuspidatum* Ehrh. ex Hoffm. and *Zygogonium* spp., to large deep pools, 150 m long and 2 m deep. The dominant plant growing on the peaty bottom of the pools is *Eriocaulon aquaticum* (Hill) Druce, which forms a dense mat which may float to the surface as oxygen accumulates in the air spaces in spring. *Lobelia dortmana* L., *Utricularia minor* L. and *Batrachospermum vagum* (Roth) Ag. are also common. The origin of the pools has not been elucidated satisfactorily. The smaller, *Sphagnum*-dominated pools are usually supersaturated with oxygen on bright days; this aerobic medium is in marked contrast to the anaerobic, water-logged peat where decomposition is arrested; it has been suggested (19) that accelerated decomposition under the pools may be responsible for their origin and persistence.

Standing crop and production

The total peak phytomass (including recognisable dead structures) on the virgin bog is over 1 600 g m^{-2}; of this, the aboveground vascular plants make up only 83 g while their belowground live parts amount to over 500 g, thus giving a "root/shoot" ratio of 16.5:1. The cryptogams, however, especially mosses and algae, form a very important component of the primary producers, their phytomass being 209 g m^{-2} and 360 g m^{-2} respectively. If these are added to the aboveground vascular component and allowance is made for dead algae, the revised ratio is approximately 1:1 (12).

The importance of the cryptogam component is even more apparent when one considers the production estimates. The production by the algal mat is 186 g m^{-2} yr^{-1} which is two thirds of the total vascular production (125 and 162 g m^{-2} yr^{-1} for above- and belowground). The bryophytes contribute a further 50 g m^{-2} yr^{-1} (12).

The improved meadow plots have a little over half the mean standing crops of the virgin bog. Production is however enhanced five-fold with a total production of 1 663 g m^{-2} yr^{-1} in 1969, 1 110 g of this being harvested in the form of three hay crops. This represents a 2.5 % utilisation of incoming photosynthetically active radiation. The maximum growth rate in early June of 17 g m^{-2} d^{-1} is higher than reported values for *F. arundinacea* grown on mineral soils under optimum conditions in England.

The trees growing on the reclaimed forestry plots had not reached their peak annual increment during the period of IBP. In one plot (drained and fertilised) tree production reached 1 500 g m^{-2} yr^{-1} in 1971; production in the ground flora was 980 g m^{-2} in 1969 and decreased by 1971. The overall energy conversion efficiency was thus even higher than on the grassland.

HERBIVORES

Vertebrates

The bog has few natural vertebrate grazers, the red grouse (*Lagopus lagopus* L.), the Irish hare (*Lepus timidus* L.) and *Apodemus sylvaticus* L., having a very low density on the virgin bog (3 pairs km^{-2}, 1 km^{-2} and 10 km^{-2} respectively) (18, 37). In addition, the area is grazed by sheep (Scottish Blackface) and a few cattle. The area is managed as commonage so that the density of domestic animals varies from season to season. On the IBP area, animals seldom venture onto the wetter 'pools' section and remain on the sloping ground, especially that bordering the drainage system. Grazing density in this area is about 10 km^{-2} but is considerably higher on the sloping hillsides nearby. Fencing an area to prevent sheep grazing and the application of fertiliser has led to a five-fold increase in grouse density and a three-fold increase in their breeding success (38).

Invertebrates

Poor vegetation cover on the bog and the exposed nature of the site limit the number of phytophagous insects such as Aphidae, Psyllidae, Cercopidae (Hemiptera) and Lepidoptera, all of which become more important wherever there is shelter from wind, as close to taller plants bordering the streams. The unpalatable nature of bog plant tissue may also be a factor limiting the diversity of herbivores.

On the grassland site mechanical harvesting prevents many invertebrate herbivores becoming established as the grass is cut before most Hemiptera and Orthoptera reach maturity (July–August). On uncut grass road verges these groups are fairly abundant. The most important herbivores on the grassland plots are probably Mollusca aboveground and tipulid larvae belowground.

At all sites, the total biomass of herbivores is small by comparison with other Irish habitats so that most of the plant tissue passes to the decomposers.

CARNIVORES

Among the aboveground carnivores on the bog the frogs (*Rana temporaria* L.) are probably the most important (3). Insect-feeding birds (*Anthus pratensis* L.) are present but in very low numbers, and may be less important than entomophagous plants, particularly the three *Drosera* spp. which are numerous especially in the wetter areas of the bog. Dipteran larvae, beetles and Acarina (Mesostigmata) are the dominant carnivores at and below the ground surface, both on the bog and on grassland. The presence of fox (*Vulpes vulpes* L.), the otter (*Lutra lutra* L.) and hooded crow (*Corvus corone cornix* L.) have been noted, but densities are extremely low.

DECOMPOSITION AND SOIL PROCESSES

In Glenamoy, as in other actively growing peatlands, the decomposition processes are inhibited, so that both incoming energy and nutrients are stored in the system. The flatter areas of bog have been accumulating uncompacted, anaerobic peat in recent centuries at a rate of 10 cm per century and a rate of 4 cm per century on the slopes (23). Drainage and initial addition of fertilisers release this inhibition of decomposition so that older conifer plantations seem to be self sufficient in regard to nutrient supplies.

Microflora

At all sites counts of viable aerobic bacteria in the top 5 cm were maximal in July/August, rising from March and falling sharply to a minimum in October (15). The greatest difference (20-fold) was on virgin peat, and the least (4-fold) at the pine site. Fungal counts were maximal at different times according to depth and generally followed the soil temperature maxima (Table 5). The minima were associated with both temperature minima and dryness in the surface layers. At all sites, surface drying in summer pushed the peak count to greater soil depths. Fungal mycelium (stained) at 2 cm (Table 6) reached maxima in May and September. The July minimum may be a result of consumption by microarthropods, with the plate counts representing spores produced by the maximal mycelium of the months before. A possible sequence for this depth

Table 5. Maximum and minimum numbers ($\times 10^5$ cm^{-3} peat) of fungal propagules, and time of occurrence, at various depths at the bog site, estimated by a dilution plate method

Depth (cm)	Max. count	Time	Min. count	Time
1	7.0	July	2.0	Mar., Jun., Sep.
2	4.0–5.0	Apr., Sep.	0.5	Feb., Jun.
5	3.0	Jan.	0.5	Apr., Jun.
10	3.0	Dec., Jan.	0.2	Feb., Mar.
20	3.5	Dec.	0.1	Mar., Jun.
50	1.0	Dec.	0.02	Jun.

Table 6. Lengths of stained and unstained mycelium (m g^{-1} dw) in virgin peat at 2 cm

	J	F	M	Months A	M	Jy	A	S	D
Stained	1 360	860	670	1 480	3 850	350	650	2 950	570
Unstained	2 300	2 810	1 491	3 220	2 340	1 500	1 730	1 310	3 580

may be: Spring-growth and sporulation; Summer-consumption by microarthropods and death due to drying; Autumn-growth spurt and sporulation.

The above analysis, however, neglects the contribution of different components of the fungal flora. Fungi normally found on leaf surfaces were the most frequent group in the surface layers during the summer; Penicillia were the most frequent component in the winter months. Mucorales and cellulolytic fungi showed no overall seasonal differences of importance but their absolute numbers relative to other groups were highest in winter.

Both pine and grassland areas had higher bacterial counts than the virgin peat site, the average increases being 10-fold and 100-fold respectively. Fungal counts were decreased 2–3 fold in the pine site, but increased 5-fold in the grassland site compared with the bog site. Part of the decrease at the pine site was due to the more prolonged summer 'drought' at this site (c.f. cellulose decay results). Fungal taxa also varied between sites, the differences being most marked in the 0–5 cm levels. At 50 cm few differences were detected between the three sites, showing that the effects of surface vegetation or of drainage and fertiliser did not penetrate very far into the peat.

The populations of organisms occurring on leaves and litter of higher plants have cosmopolitan and specific components. Between the sites there was no variation in the types of cosmopolitan fungi. Species-specific fungi occurred on their host irrespective of site. Site differences began to occur in older litter as soil conditions (micro-climate, drainage and fertilisation) became more important. Quantitatively, cosmopolitan species (especially *Cladosporium* spp. and Mucorales) were much more common (nos. cm^{-2} plant or litter surface) on the grassland site. This was associated with the 'softer' texture of *Festuca* leaves, as on the virgin site the density of *Cladosporium* on the 'soft' leaves of *Narthecium ossifragum* (L.) Huds. was as great as that on *Festuca*. On the pine site the prolonged, dry, standing dead phase in both *Calluna* and *Molinia* reduced all fungal counts.

Invertebrates

Invertebrates are involved in decomposition as saprovores (tipulids, enchytraeids and mites on the virgin bog; tipulids, enchytraeids and earthworms on grassland) and as fungivores and bacterial feeders (enchytraeids, mites, collembola and nemotodes on both sites). Most "decomposers" take a range of food which includes pollen grains, algae and amorphous peat, as well as dead plant material, fungi and bacteria. Different species consume these foods in different proportion (1).

At all sites, the fauna is concentrated in the top 6 cm, only nematodes extend in any numbers below this depth. Deeper penetration is limited principally by waterlogging of the lower layers of peat. Collembola are particularly vulnerable to flooding. In bog hol-

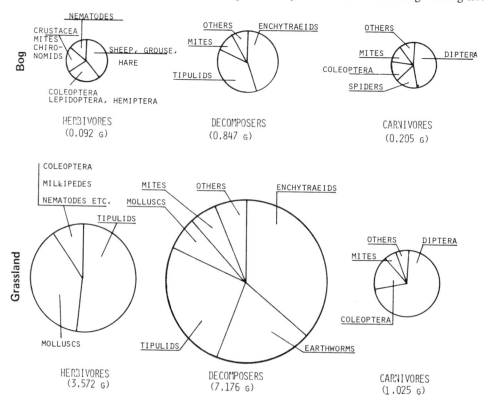

Figure 2. Biomass of the different categories of consumers and decomposers on the bog and grassland sites. The areas of each sector are proportional to the biomass (g dw m^{-2}) and the total biomass for each group is given in brackets.

lows and the wetter areas of grassland, they are restricted to the surface while in bog hummocks and drained peat they decrease in numbers to 3 cm. Three species of enchytraeid, which have red blood and may therefore be adapted to anaerobic conditions, are most abundant in the 4–6 cm layer.

Populations are subject to the usual fluctuations linked to cyclic or non-cyclic climatic changes but these fluctuations are not great and the community as a whole is relatively stable, having reached an equilibrium over a long period of time. The effects of manipulating this habitat are two-fold. Disturbance upsets the faunal equilibrium with consequent reduction of diversity and tendency to wide fluctuations in numbers. Drainage, resulting in aeration and release of nutrients, or dressings of artificial fertilisers bring about an increase in the total biomass of consumers (Fig. 2) and in the size of the dominant organisms. Except for the shelter belt, these derived habitats are unstable and fauna reverts to a bog type when management ceases.

Microflora-microfauna interactions

Microbial cells form an important food source for many soil arthropods. Arthropod activity breaks up plant remains and exposes new surfaces for colonisation. Spores of over 40 genera of fungi were found in guts of oribatid mites, including significant numbers of two genera not isolated by dilution plate procedures. Much of the hyphal material measured on Jones and Millison slides was in short fragments typical of faecal pellets. Most of the bacteria observed on these slides were growing on the outside of faecal pellets. Maximum densities of mites on the virgin site occur just after maximum amounts of mycelium. Enchytraeid populations are inversely related to hyphal populations, suggesting a similar pattern.

Comminution of litter during the later stages of decay and a parallel increased weight loss were observed on all sites. Microfaunal attack occurred earliest where the 'soft' nature of the litter allowed high microbial activity, so long as the environment was suitably moist. This attack appeared to occur in early and late summer, corresponding with peak densities of mites, collembola and enchytraeids. Surface drying during July and August drives the animals down into the peat.

Such descriptions are only circumstantial evidence of what is an extremely important qualitative interaction. The amounts of material assimilated by the microarthropods and their biomass are both very small in comparison to the amount of material they process. This processing is a vital stage in the decay of plant material, as it gives access for bacteria to previously unexposed areas. The demonstrated consumption of fungal spores by soil arthropods leads one to doubts of the validity of dilution plate counts.

Peat appears to consist of faecal pellets and fragments of plant remains. These fragments become progressively larger as their depth of origin increases and with their initial 'hardness'. Sclerotised roots are not readily broken down, and the brown leaf bases of the sedges persist apparently unchanged in the peat. The only aboveground fraction to escape thorough maceration are moss leaves, which also appear to be little colonised by microorganisms. Most plant production occurs belowground on the bog site, where decay processes are restricted, and it must contribute largely to the growth and stability of the peat. The aboveground production, thoroughly worked over by microorganisms and arthropods, provides the colloidal material with excessive water holding capacity and phenolic reducing substances. These ensure reduced decay rates, reduced mineral cycling and ultimately reduced plant production. It is possible that bog plants produce extra large root systems as a strategem to obtain more nutrients; the roots then become prisons for the nutrients as they cannot go through the normal decay and mineralisation processes when buried in the peat.

Decomposition

The counts of microbial propagules give little evidence of activity. Dilution plates estimate previous activity minus death and consumption; direct counts include large numbers of inactive, dead and digested cells as well as live, active ones. Few bacterial isolates could grow at 2°C or 48°C, but half grew at 5°C and 37°C. About 15 % possessed phosphatase and the same percent had protease. Tolerance to low pH decreased in the amended sites but the isolates from the grass site were more tolerant of high pH than other isolates. No cellulolytic bacteria were found on the grassland, nor were there any bacteria capable of growing without a nitrogen source at this site (31). However, both cellulolytic and lignin degrading fungi were frequent at all three sites and were distributed throughout the profile.

Cellulose decay, as measured by loss in weight of buried α-cellulose pads and by loss in tensile strength of cotton, showed distinct differences by depth and site (Table 7, Fig. 3) (14, 30). The increased rate at the grass site can be attributed to the combination of partial drainage and high nutrient levels. The effect of extra nutrients at the pine site is masked by the inhibition of decay caused by excessive drying in the summer months.

The decay of roots was not investigated directly, but roots of some of the sedges were sampled and divided into colour classes. A 25 % weight loss occurred between yellow roots and 'black' roots of *Schoenus nigricans*; the time over which this occurred was impossible to determine but is at least one year.

Table 7. Percent weight loss over six months of substrates in litter at Glenamoy

	Bog		Forest		Grassland	
	Winter	Summer	Winter	Summer	Winter	Summer
Cellulose	11 ± 8	n.d.	8 ± 1 (dry)	n.d.	52 ± 8	70 ± 9
			38 ± 2 (wet)			
Molinia leaves						
<1 yr dead	12	7	0☆	0☆	*Festuca* leaves	
1–2 yr dead	20	70	5	30	>100	>100
>2 yr dead	33	>50	60	n.d.		

☆ = standing dead

n.d. = not determined

334

The decay of leaf litter was measured in litter bags and by decrease in specific weight. The latter method was particularly useful for the dominant grass *Molinia* (Table 7). Summer drying, coupled with the exposed situation of litter less than one year old, results in low initial decay rates. The large summer loss of *Molinia* litter older than one year on the virgin site was attributable mainly to microfaunal activity. Litter bags gave different results because of prolonged exposure at or above the litter surface and because of exclusion of microfaunal activity.

Nitrogen and phosphorus losses followed a more typical decay curve, with the greatest loss in the first six months. It appears that the cosmopolitan leaf inhabitors and the specific fungi are more effective at mobilising nutrients than they are at removing carbohydrates.

In the laboratory, maximal respiration rates of litter were obtained at 27°C at between 200 % and 800 % water content. The litter of *Festuca arundinacea* showed a steady decline in respiratory rate from a moisture content of 200 % down to 25 % whereas *Molinia* litter showed a more gradual decline with dryness and had not reached zero at 25 % moisture. This corresponds with the production of *Festuca* litter below the sward in a damp environment whereas *Molinia* litter goes through a standing dead phase which, in the forest site, may be below 25 % moisture for several months.

The rate at which litter 'aged' was a function both of species and site. *Narthecium ossifragum* decays as quickly on the virgin peat as *Festuca* does on the grass site. *Molinia caerulea* decays faster on the forest site once it has reached the damper litter phase, than it does on the bog site (Table 7) (10). Species-specific fungi colonised leaves before death and reached maximal density in the autumn and spring after death. As soon as the dead

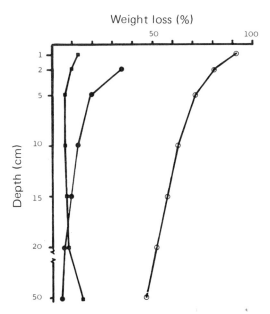

Figure 3. Percent decay of cellulose over 120 days at Glenamoy by depth. (● bog site; ■ forest site; ○ grass site).

leaves became colonised by cosmopolitan soil fungi (*Trichoderma,* Mucorales, *Penicillium*) the specific fungi disappeared. The specific group does not have a marked effect on weight loss (see decay results), since much more rapid rates of decay occur in older litter. It is possible that components of the soil microflora which were not isolated were responsible for much of the observed weight loss. For example pine mycorrhizal fungi were observed in the forest site in the litter of *Molinia* which was more than one year old.

NUTRIENTS

Most of the Glenamoy bog site is ombrotrophic, i.e. the only input of nutrients to the system is from rain and aeolian fallout since even the deepest roots are more than a meter above the mineral ground. It is thus relatively easy to construct a mineral budget for the whole area (Table 8) (16, 32).

The major output is in the drainage water since deep seepage in the waterlogged peat and migration of biota may be disregarded. It can be seen that the only elements being gained by the system are Mg and K which occur in high concentration in sea water.

A further loss in a system in which peat is actively accumulating occurs through nutrients being stored in the peat at depths below the rooting zone. O'Connell (23), using pollen analytical dating methods, estimated that the annual input of organic matter to anaerobic peat is 32 g m^{-2} yr^{-1}; combining this result with values for the nutrient content of the anaerobic peat (16, 36), an estimate of nutrients stored irretrievably is obtained (Table 8). It is thus obvious that the system is far from being in a steady state in regard to nutrients but is running down. This fits in with signs of incipient erosion which sug-

Table 8. Cumulative loss or gain of nutrients over the period February 1969 to January 1972 (mg m^{-2}) together with an estimate of nutrients stored irrecoverably in deep peat each year

Element	1969	1970	1971	Total	Stored
Ca	−525	−329	−1 207	−2 061	6 364
Mg	+429	+1 950	+964	+2 343	9 091
K	−52	+361	− 84	+225	4 546
NH$_4$	−567	−588	−537	−1 692	3 200
NO$_3$	−369	−427	−356	−752	
P	−5	−2	−13	−20	2 045
Fe	−201	−77	−94	−371	n.d.
Cu	+1	+5	−2	+4	n.d.

n.d. = not determined

gests that the present nutrient supply is not able to support a vegetation canopy sufficiently dense to protect the peat from erosion by torrential rain or hail.

Some idea of the limiting effects of nutrient deficiency on the productivity of the
vegetation may be obtained by comparing the early stages of the forestry plantation
with the virgin bogland. Forestry workers discovered that sustained tree growth was
impossible on the reclaimed peat unless phosphate was added at planting. Since many
of the bog species survive for several years in the forestry plantations, one can
observe the effects on nutrient levels of the small addition of phosphate and of the extra nutrients released from the peat by the enhanced decomposition processes.

Besides the enhanced growth of *Molinia* and *Calluna* which persists until competition
from the conifers depresses their yield, the actual concentration of key nutrients increases in the vegetation. The effect is most marked with phosphorous itself and with
nitrogen. The concentration of phosphorous in the shrub and graminoid species in the
ground layer of the forest is almost twice that on the undisturbed bog. The green leaves
of *Schoenus nigricans* are the only plant part analysed that showed a decline compared
with the values of plants on the bog, but since this species disappeared after two more
years, it was obviously already declining in vigour. Table 9 gives comparative nutrient
concentrations for bog and forestry ground flora and litter.

Evidence for accelerated nutrient cycling is even clearer in the comparative figures
for litter. The concentration of nutrients in the forestry litter is at least 30 % higher

Table 9. Comparison of the concentration of nutrients in the different components of
the vegetation at the Glenamoy bog and forest sites (excluding conifers).
Values (mg g^{-1} dw) are a mean of approximately 15 replicates for each of
seven samplings at 1 or 2 month intervals in 1969 (16)

		N	P	K	Mg	Ca
Photosynthetic tissue:						
Shrubs	Bog	16.8	0.54	2.12	2.03	2.16
	Forest	21.4	0.90	2.53	2.02	1.73
Molinia	Bog	26.4	0.76	5.68	0.94	0.21
	Forest	23.2	1.12	5.51	1.09	0.24
Schoenus	Bog	15.5	0.57	4.49	2.04	0.47
	Forest	15.6	0.43	2.69	1.94	0.51
Non-Photosynthetic, aboveground:						
Shrubs	Bog	15.5	0.39	1.14	0.96	0.92
	Forest	16.9	0.77	1.74	1.33	1.24
Molinia	Bog	10.4	0.34	1.61	0.83	0.39
	Forest	16.1	0.91	1.16	0.98	0.64
Schoenus	Bog	12.7	0.33	4.49	1.02	0.47
	Forest	14.7	0.79	2.69	0.83	0.51
Roots	Bog	11.7	0.41	1.83	0.99	0.49
	Forest	17.6	0.74	2.13	0.95	0.41
Litter	Bog	12.8	0.46	1.15	0.96	0.53
	Forest	15.2	0.58	1.38	0.95	0.80

than that on the bog with the exception of the two nutrients which are in good supply in the oceanic rain water (K and Mg). This, coupled with the fact that the amount of litter lying on the forest floor (mainly *Molinia* leaves) is three times that present on the bog, ensures a greatly enhanced return of nutrients to the forestry system. Leachate from the conifers also accelerates nutrient turnover (16, 25).

The grassland system bears little resemblence to either of the other systems since large additions of fertilisers are needed to maintain the high yield of grass. There is a high recovery rate of applied fertilisers, very little being lost in drainage water. In 1969, considerably more phosphorus and potassium were recovered in the first harvest than had been applied in fertiliser (Table 10). The extra nutrients presumably came from the breakdown of peat by the enhanced activity of the decomposer sub-system.

Table 10. Recovery of fertiliser and other nutrients from the Glenamoy grassland for the first harvest, 1969; units are g m^{-2}

Nutrient	Input in Fertiliser	Removal in Harvest	Recovery
N	34.7	17.9	52 %
P	1.9	2.5	132 %
K	7.5	12.0	160 %
Ca	19.7	1.3	7 %
Mg	0	1.0	--

THE AQUATIC COMMUNITIES AND THEIR INTERACTION WITH THE TERRESTRIAL ECOSYSTEM

A mosaic of shallow pools with peaty bottoms is characteristic of bogland on the level terrain of the Glenamoy district. This is in contrast to more recently glaciated areas with uneven terrain (e.g. Connemara, 100 km further south), where the bog is studded with lakelets with mineral bottoms. On the IBP site these peaty pools make up about 2 % of the area.

The water in the pools differs little in its dissolved nutrients from rainwater. It is slightly more acid (pH 4.4 ± 0.2 as against 5.9 for rain) and brownish in colour because of dissolved humic acids, but dissolved nutrients remain remarkably close to the concentration in rain (Table 11). This is reflected in the very similar total ionic concentration, 67 mg l^{-1} for pool water and 72 mg l^{-1} for rain. Nitrates and NH$_3$ are the only nutrients in higher concentration in the pools.

The phytomass in the pools is only about 7 % of that on the bog (67 g m^{-2}), the macrophytes contributing 21 g m^{-2}. Total annual production has been estimated at 177 g

Table 11. Comparison of the ionic concentration of the water of bog pools, small streams and of rain (measured at Belmullet, 15 km to the west). The collected rainwater was analysed monthly; 22 pools were sampled on six dates and the streams at three monthly intervals

Ion (mg l^{-1})	Cl	Na	Mg	Ca	K	SO$_4$	NH$_3$	NO$_3$
Rain (Belmullet, 1971–73)	36.5	22.1	2.8	1.7	1.3	7.8	0.20	0.19
Bog pools (1971–73)	36.4	20.2	2.7	1.2	0.8	5.7	0.64	0.17
Bog streams (1969–1970)	–	–	1.4	3.1	1.1	–	0.82	1.03

m^{-2} yr^{-1}, one third of that on the firmer bog. The benthic algae make the major contribution (130 g m^{-2} yr^{-1}), the plankton a relatively minor one of 15 g m^{-2} yr^{-1}.

Despite the low productivity, the pools support a large consumer component. This is because the pools act as traps for wind-blown litter in late autumn, especially for the deciduous leaves of *Molinia*, which retain about half their original nutrient content, and also for wind-borne pollen. Pollen grains have been found in the guts of chironomid larvae in spring and summer, but not in autumn or winter, which suggests selective feeding on the fresh pollen grains.

Transfer of material from the aquatic to the terrestrial system is mainly through the mature stages of insects which spend their larval stages in the pools (Chironomidae, Odonata). A further return of material takes place through the *Eriocaulon* plants which float to the surface because of dissolved oxygen building up in the air spaces in spring, and are then washed onto the rims of the pools in stormy weather.

The streams running through the bog usually have their bed on the mineral rock in their lower reaches. The vegetation along the banks is much more luxuriant than the bog and most of the grazing by cattle and sheep takes place along these stream courses.

ECOSYSTEM OVERVIEW

The Glenamoy project with its equal emphasis on reclaimed and on "natural" systems gives an opportunity of analysing the effects of man's impact. Admittedly the baseline ecosystem owes its origin, at least in part, to anthropogenic influences but since these date back to Neolithic times, the bog system has had several millennia to come to an equilibrium state.

The change in species' composition is easiest to follow: 158 species of seed plants and cryptogams have been recorded from the virgin bog site. About one-third of these persist in the early stages of forestry reclamation, but the main change that takes place in the ground flora is a striking increase in vigour of the stunted *Molinia* growing on the bog surface and the dominance in the drains of *Sphagnum apiculatum* Lindb., a species occurring only in the flushes on the bog. As the canopy closes most of the bog species disappear, leaving only a sparse cover of mosses such as *Isothecium myosuroides*, a species common in oakwoods, 20 km away.

In the grassland a few species occurring in the bog flushes remain (*Stellaria alsine, Epilobium palustre, Juncus effusus* L.) but the dominants are the planted species and grassland weeds like *Ranunculus repens*.

An indication of the consequential effects of drainage, fertilizing and planting is even more strikingly shown by changes in species' diversity within the invertebrate taxa studied. Differences in species diversity at the different sites can be explained by both habitat diversity and degree of disturbance; but differences in intensity of collecting should also be taken into account. Collembola, Coleoptera, Chironomidae, Acarina and Crustacea all show greatest diversity on the virgin bog, a long established habitat where available niches are exploited and where there has been little disturbance by man. Besides, there is a great range of microhabitats; the pools and flowing streams of the bog account for the presence of aquatic groups such as Lumbriculidae, Amphipoda, Ephemeroptera and Plecoptera which are absent from other sites. The aquatic fauna of small water bodies and water-logged peat, however, is similar at all sites where these aquatic habitats occur.

For all the groups studied, fewest species are recorded from Glenturk forest site where recent disturbance has upset the equilibrium of the faunal community and destroyed many niches. Grassland has also been subjected to recent disturbance but a significant rise in nutrient levels has allowed a new faunal component, usually associated with eutrophic soils, to become established. Enchytraeidae, Crustacea, Chironomidae and Coleoptera all show higher diversity than at Glenturk or at the shelter belt. Acarina and Collembola however have fewest species on grassland, perhaps because grassland species have not yet become established.

A comparison of the species lists provides clues to the nature of changes which result from the manipulation of bog habitats. Characteristic bog species are partly replaced by species characteristic of coniferous litter in the shelter belt or by species associated with wet pastures on mineral soils in the case of grassland. More than half the bog species of Acarina, Collembola, Chironomidae and Crustacea persist in the grassland site, about 45 % of Coleoptera and about 30 % of Enchytraeidae. The number of species unique to grassland is highest for Enchytraeidae for which nutrient levels are important and lowest for Collembola which are linked to plant species and therefore affected by a reduction in floral diversity (2). Few species of beetle or enchytraeid are confined to the shelter belt but Acarina and Collembola are represented here by a coniferous litter component not present at other sites. Glenturk has very few species which are not also found at the other sites (no Enchytraeidae or Crustacea, only 2 % of all beetles and 25 % of all Chironomidae). Nematode species are the same on all sites — only the proportions of species vary.

That the tenure of the new faunal elements is insecure is demonstrated by the ease with which the shift from bog to grassland fauna can be reversed. Within two years after fertilizer applications were discontinued on one grassland plot, many grassland species of Coleoptera and Enchytraeidae had disappeared and bog species were returning.

Just as plant production increased in the manipulated habitats, so did densities of

Nematoda, Enchytraeidae, Lumbricidae, Mollusca and Chironomidae. They are therefore highest on grassland and lowest on the virgin bog. Collembola and mites on the other hand have smaller populations on grassland. Mites reach their greatest numbers on the virgin bog and Collembola in the coniferous litter of the shelter belt. Collembola are probably inhibited on grassland by the wetness of the peat and the absence of appropriate plants (2).

Different groups have population peaks at different times, only enchytraeids and possibly insect larvae reach a peak in summer. Grassland populations although larger, are unstable and subject to greater fluctuations than on other sites.

The total biomass of consumers on grassland is similarly about ten times that of the virgin bog (Fig. 2). This also may be attributed to higher nutrient levels on grassland as well as to the deeper "active layer" above the water-table. Besides, grassland species of invertebrate, as well as having higher population densities, are also generally larger than bog species. The proportions of the different consumer levels are the same, however, at both sites although, as mentioned, the proportion of herbivores would probably be higher on grassland if the vegetation were not harvested.

One of the factors that determined that Glenamoy be included with tundra sites in the strict sense of the word was the superficial resemblance of the vegetation to several of the tundra sites with dominant graminoids or with a peaty layer. The IBP studies have confirmed that several resemblances exist: the layer of partly aerated peat above the water-table is analogous to the active layer of genuine tundra soils; the limiting effect of the low nutrient supply simulates the limiting effect of cold climate.

These similarities should not blind one to the major differences between the structure of the Glenamoy virgin bog and the true tundra. The long growing season with plant growth in some species at all periods of the year is the most striking difference. The absence of a microtene rodent or similar animal is another major difference, even though the deciduous habit of the grass *Molinia* produces a similar mass of litter as the winter grazing of the lemmings.

Although the root/shoot ratios at Glenamoy are close to those reported from true tundra sites, the significance of this adaptation seems to be connected with rapid recovery from burning of the vegetation. Thus instead of annual destruction of the aboveground parts by frost and snow cover as in true tundra, the mainly evergreen vegetation at Glenamoy is destroyed by fire at irregular intervals of 5 to 20 years but regenerates rapidly from belowground perennating organs. The high biomass of the algal mat is characteristic of the Glenamoy bog site.

One part of the definition of tundra is its lack of trees; trees once grew at Glenamoy but the main species (*Pinus sylvestris*) has since become extinct in Ireland. Exotic conifers, once established by draining and fertilising of the peat, cause a dramatic further drop in the water-table (28); this in turn enhances the soil decomposition subsystem, thus reversing the tundra-like characteristics towards the original post-glacial ecosystem type, a coniferous woodland.

REFERENCES

1. Behan, V. 1973. Gut content analysis of Oribatid mites from Glenamoy, Co. Mayo. – Report to IBP Tundra Biome Working Group meeting, Fairbanks, Alaska.
2. Blackith, R.E. & Speight, M.C.D. 1974. Food and feeding habits of the frog *Rana temporaria* in B: 203–226.
3. Blackith, R.M. & Speigh, M.C.D. 1974. Food and feeding habits of the frog *Rana temporaria* in bogland habitats in the West of Ireland. – J. Zool., Lond. 172: 67–79.
4. Bourke, D. 1972. Pollen analysis from Belderg, north-west Mayo. – Student Thesis, Univ. Coll. Dublin.
5. Braun-Blanquet, J. & Tüxen, R. 1952. Irische Pflanzengesellschaften. – Veröff. geobot. Inst. Rübel 25: 224–415.
6. Burke, W. 1961. Drainage investigation on bogland. The effect of drain spacing on ground water levels. – Irish J. Agric. Res. 1: 31.
7. Burke, W. 1969. Drainage of blanket peat at Glenamoy. – In: Robertson, R.A. (ed.) 2nd Int. Peat Congr. Leningrad 1963, 11: 809–817. London: HMSO.
8. Collins, D.P. & O'Toole, M. 1962. Burning of native vegetation for surface seeding. – Irish J. Agric Res. 1: 165–171.
9. DeValera, R. 1965. Transeptal court cairns. – J. Roy. Soc. Ant. Irel. 95: 5–37.
10. Dowding, P. 1972. Decay patterns and processes on the IBP site at Glenamoy, Ireland. – In: Proc. 1972 U.S. Tundra Biome Symposium Lake Wilderness, Washington, pp. 128–131.
11. Dowding, P. & Moore, J.J. (eds.) 1971. International Biological Programme; Irish contribution – Interim report 1971. Dublin: Royal Irish Academy.
12. Doyle, G.J. 1973. Primary production estimates of native blanket bog and meadow vegetation growing on reclaimed peat at Glenamoy, Ireland. – In: Bliss, L.C. & Wielgolaski, F.E. (eds.) Primary Production and Production Processes, Tundra Biome, pp. 141–151. Edmonton: IBP Tundra Biome Steering Committee.
13. French, D.D. 1974. Classification of IBP Tundra Biome sites based on climatic and soil properties. – In: Holding, A.J., Heal, O.W., MacLean, S.F. & Flanagan, P.W. (eds.) Soil Organisms and Decomposition in Tundra, pp. 3–25. Stockholm: IBP Tundra Biome Steering Committee.
14. Heal, O.W., Howson, G., French, D.D. & Jeffers, J.N.R. 1974. Decomposition of cotton strips in Tundra. – In: Holding, A.J., Heal, O.W., MacLean, S.F. & Flanagan, P.W. (eds.) Soil Organisms and Decomposition in Tundra, pp. 341–373. Stockholm: IBP Tundra Biome Steering Committee.
15. Holding, A.J., Collins, V.G., French, D.D., D'Sylva, B.T. & Baker, J.H. 1974. Relationship between viable bacterial counts and site characteristics in tundra. – In: Holding, A.J., Heal, O.W., MacLean, S.F. & Flanagan, P.W. (eds.) Soil Organisms and Decomposition in Tundra, pp. 49–64. Stockholm: IBP Tundra Biome Steering Committee.
16. Kilfeather, P. 1973. Nutrient circulation in relation to primary productivity of western blanket bog in Ireland. – Ph.D. Thesis, National Univ. of Ireland.
17. Knight, P. 1836. Erris in the Irish Highlands. Dublin.
18. Lance, A.N. 1973. Numbers of woodmice (*Apodemus sylvaticus*) on improved and unimproved blanket bog. – J. Zool., Lond. 172: 471–473.
19. Moore, P.D. & Bellamy, D.J. 1973. Peatlands. London Elek Science: 221 pp.
20. Moore, J.J. 1964. Die regionale Verteilung der Moore Irlands. – Ber. 8. Int. Kong. Torfforsch. Bremen.
21. Moore, J.J. 1968. A classification of the bogs and wet heaths of north-west Europe. – In: Tüxen, R. (ed.) Pflanzensoziologische systematik, pp. 306–320. Den Haag.
22. Moore, J.J. 1971. Report on the Glenamoy (Ireland) IBP ecosystem study. – In: Heal, O.W. (ed.) Proceedings of the Tundra Biome working meeting on analysis of ecosystems, Kevo, Finland, pp. 92–100. Stockholm: IBP Tundra Biome Steering Committee.
23. O'Connell, M. 1971. An investigation into rates of peat accumulation in a western blanket bog at Glenamoy, Co. Mayo. – Student thesis, Univ. Coll. Dublin.
24. O'Hare, P.J. 1959. An ecological study on certain blanket bogs in Co. Mayo. – M. Agr. Sc. Thesis, Nat. Univ. of Ireland.

25. O'Hare, P.J. 1967. The leaching of nutrients by rainwater from forest trees – a preliminary study. – In: Proceedings of the Colloquium on Forest Fertilization Jyväskylä, Finland. pp. 122–130.
26. O'Hare, P.J. 1968. Reclaiming peatlands for agriculture. – Span. 11: 3.
27. O'Hare, P.J. 1970. Glenamoy; Peatland Experimental Station Guide. – Dublin: Agricultural Institute.
28. O'Hare, P.J. 1970. A comparison of the effect of young forest and grassland on the water table of blanket peat. – In: An Aberystwyth Symposium: Research Papers in Forest Meteorology. Taylor, J.A. (ed.) 12: 126–133.
29. O'Hare, P.J. & Fleming, G.A. 1959. The chemical composition of peat supporting *Schoenus nigricans* in north Mayo. – In: Production and the use of grass. Dublin: Society of Chemistry in Industry.
30. Rosswall, T. 1974. Cellulose decomposition studies on the tundra. – In: Holding, A.J., Heal, O.W., MacLean, S.F. & Flanagan, P.W. (eds.) Soil Organisms and Decomposition in Tundra, pp. 325–340. Stockholm: IBP Tundra Biome Steering Committee.
31. Rosswall, T. & Clarholm, H. 1974. Characteristics of tundra bacterial populations and a comparison with populations from forest and grassland soils. – In: Holding, A.J., Heal, O.W., MacLean, S.F. & Flanagan, P.W. (eds.) Soil Organisms and Decomposition in Tundra, pp. 93–108. Stockholm: IBP Tundra Biome Steering Committee.
32. Sparling, J.H. 1967. The occurrence of *Schoenus nigricans* in blanket bogs. I. Environmental conditions. – J. Ecol. 55: 1–13.
33. Synge, F.M. 1968. The glaciation of West Mayo. – Irish Geography 5: 372–386.
34. Trendall, A.F. & Elwell, R.W.D. 1963. The metamorphic rocks of north west Mayo. – Proc. Roy Irish Acad. 62: 217–247.
35. Tansley, A.G. 1949. The British Islands and Their Vegetation. – Cambridge.
36. Walsh, T. & Barry, T.A. 1958. Chemical composition of some Irish peats. – Proc. Roy Irish Acad. 59B: 305–328.
37. Watson, A. & Hewson, R. 1973. Population densities of mountain hares (*Lepus timidus*) on western Scottish and Irish moors and on Scottish hills. – J. Zool., Lond. 170: 151–159.
38. Watson, A. & O'Hare, P.J. 1972. Research on Irish Red Grouse. – Newsletter No. 1 Grouse Research, Glenamoy, Co. Mayo.

Rosswall, T. & Heal, O.W. (eds.) 1975.
Structure and Function of Tundra Ecosystems.
Ecol. Bull. (Stockholm) 20: 345–374.

SIGNY ISLAND, MARITIME ANTARCTIC

N.J. COLLINS, J.H. BAKER and P.J. TILBROOK

INTRODUCTION

Signy Island is a member of the South Orkney Islands (60°S, 45°W) (Fig. 1). The nearest land mass is the Antarctic Peninsula (640 km), although the nearest major sources of immigrant organisms lie to the northeast at South Georgia (900 km) and northwest at Tierra del Fuego (1 440 km). Signy Island falls within the maritime Antarctic region (35), experiencing a cold oceanic climate and having a vegetation representative of that found elsewhere in the region (4, 28, 45, 47, 61, 63).

It is not known when extensive areas of ground became snow-free after the last glaciation but a radiocarbon date of about 1 840 years B.P. for the base of a moss peat bank is a minimum (30). Raised beaches occur at heights of up to 30 m in the South Orkney Islands (1) and it is on these that the most extensive stands of closed vegetation have developed. The topography is generally rugged; there are a number of freshwater lakes and a restricted ice cap with two main glacier outlets, to the south and east (34, 37). A British Antarctic Survey station was established on the island in 1947, followed by a biological laboratory complex in 1964 (36) (Fig. 2). A variety of sites have been used in terrestrial studies, but because of the occurrence of several well-defined habitats and communities (61) much of the information collected is directly interrelated. The following account draws mainly on information collected since 1964 and, rather than treating restricted sites, deals with the whole terrestrial ecosystem. Seabirds and marine mammals are only considered where they interact directly with the terrestrial ecosystem. Since 1970 much of the regular sampling has been concentrated on two specific sites where a long term programme of microclimate monitoring has been initiated (68).

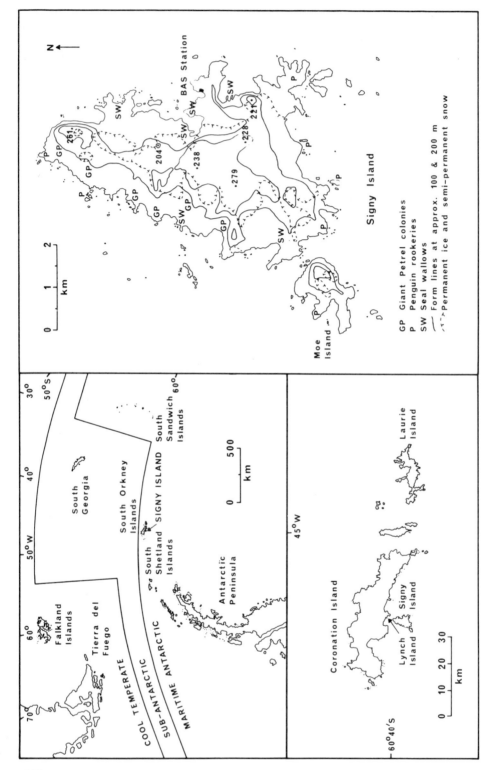

Figure 1. Maps of Signy Island showing the location in the maritime Antarctic region.

Figure 2. The British Antarctic Survey station on the shore of Factory Cove, Signy Island. There was a small shore-based whaling station on this site from 1920–30. In the foreground there is a shallow carpet of the moss *Drepanocladus uncinatus*, and a moss turf of *Polytrichum alpestre* covers two parts of the slope left of centre. Cape pigeons (*Daption capensis*) nest on the cliff ledges and patches of the grass *Deschampsia antarctica* grow on the scree below. In the background is one of the highest points of the main ice cap, which rises to 238 m.

ENVIRONMENTAL CONDITIONS

Climate

Meteorological records were maintained on Signy Island between 1947 and 1970, closely matching those for nearby Laurie Island (Fig. 1) which were begun in 1903 (18). Hence a reasonable prediction of the mean annual temperature for Signy Island can be made from this early date, with a particularly cold decade commencing in 1925. In recent years the cover of persistent snow and ice has decreased (14).

The oceanic influence on the climate of Signy Island is shown by the relatively small amplitude of the mean monthly temperatures (Table 1). In the warmest month, usually January or February, the mean temperature is above $0°C$, while in winter the mean temperature for the coldest month is $-9°C$. The extensive ice- and snow-free areas partly reflect the fact that the island is relatively low-lying. Although cloud cover is 60–80 % in winter and may exceed an average of 80 % in summer, the cloud base is often above the high ground on Signy Island, whereas Coronation Island, lying to the north (Fig. 1), has the catchment areas for its lowland glaciers on the peaks and plateaux (900–1 200 m) in rime-forming cloud for about 200 days of the year. Although precipitation is frequent

Table 1. Mean daily climatological data for Signy Island (1960–1969) (44)

	J	F	M	A	M	J	J	A	S	O	N	D	Year
Screen temperature (°C)													
Mean max	3.2	3.1	2.3	-0.2	-2.6	-4.7	-5.4	-5.3	-2.1	-0.4	0.8	1.9	-0.8
Mean	1.3	1.2	0.3	-2.1	-5.5	-7.8	-9.0	-8.9	-4.9	-2.8	-1.4	0.1	-3.3
Mean min	-0.2	-0.5	-1.5	-3.9	-8.0	-10.8	-12.7	-12.6	-8.2	-5.2	-3.2	-1.3	-5.7
Relative humidity (%)	86	86	85	85	88	87	86	85	85	84	85	85	86
Wind velocity (m s⁻¹)	5.8	6.9	7.5	6.9	6.4	6.5	6.5	6.7	8.1	8.2	7.5	5.7	6.9
Average number of days with:													
Fog[1]	4	3	2	2	3	2	3	3	2	2	1	2	29
Rain[2]	12	12	15	9	6	6	3	3	6	7	7	9	95
Snow[2]	19	18	22	23	27	23	26	25	25	26	25	22	281
Snow depth (cm)	Occasional snow fall		(20)	30	50	50, but drifting as sea ice forms				Partial thaws	Main melt		
Duration of sunshine													
Total (h)[3]	61.9	46.3	42.3	28.7	16.9	9.4	21.8	52.1	55.4	59.9	59.6	63.4	517.7
% of max. possible	12.6	12.5	12.7	12.0	9.7	7.3	13.8	22.1	18.1	15.0	13.2	12.4	13.5
Total cloud amount (oktas)	7.3	7.3	7.2	7.0	6.8	6.4	6.1	6.0	6.7	7.1	7.3	7.4	6.9

1 Water and ice fogs
2 Rain and snow may be recorded on the same day. Drizzle has not been included. The intensity of rain and snow varies from slight showers to continuous heavy precipitation
3 Determined after allowing for instrumental defects and topographical shading.

the water equivalent is usually small. However, because of the high humidity and general cloudiness most of this water is available. Since 1947 two freak summer rainstorms have occurred, in which about 30 mm of rain fell in one day. Because of the proximity of Coronation Island, winds from the northern quarter lead to föhn effects, with air temperatures soaring to 8°C or more for short periods (40).

Permafrost is present in most areas, although the active layer is often very thick. The most marked temperature fluctuations occur in the upper 25 cm of the active layer (12) but especially in the top 5 cm. The deeper parts of the active layer fall within the freezing boundary (temperatures between −0.5°C and +0.5°C) for the greater part of the year. Thus at a depth of 120 cm, although temperatures never become consistently positive, they remain within this boundary for about 7 months of the year. During midsummer, with air temperatures of 4°C, mineral soil temperatures can reach 10°C for much of the day, even at depths of 10 cm. Where a moss cover has developed the frequency of freeze-thaw cycles and the depth of the active layer are considerably reduced.

In summer diurnal temperature fluctuations may exceed 30°C within the vegetation, influenced particularly by sudden changes in intensity of incident radiation. During midsummer, when the peat beneath moss turves may become dry, the lower layers are cooler than in early or late summer, because of the difference in the thermal conductivity of water and air (59).

Winter snow cover is very variable and extensive drifting may not occur until after the sea ice forms around the island. The greatest diurnal temperature fluctuations in winter occur in the top 30 cm of the snow, and once depths greater than this accumulate, the vegetation beneath may remain slightly below 0°C for much of the winter (20, 40, 49, 51). Many grass swards and other vegetated areas are covered by less than 30 cm of snow and so are poorly insulated. However, in such situations the snow melts more quickly at the onset of summer, so that the potential growing season is longer than in the better insulated sites, although this potential may not be realised because the supply of melt water is often limited. The annual cycle of mean weekly temperatures in the surface of a moss carpet and a moss turf are given in Fig. 3, with the diurnal course of temperature and total radiation on sunny days on three occasions in the summer.

Soils

A range of rock types, including schists, amphibolites and marbles, with their differing responses to mechanical and chemical weathering, have provided a variety of substrates for soil formation (2, 40). The marine influence is considerable, most nutrients necessary for plant growth being available from sea spray or from seabirds. Many areas are covered by mineral debris, ranging from boulder scree to fine lithosols. As a result of solifluction and cryoturbation, stone stripes and small sorted polygons are common and because of the intermixing of marble fragments the pH is often high. Leaching often causes an increase in extractable nutrients with depth. Incorporation of clearly visible organic matter occurs mainly as a result of relatively catastrophic events, such as solifluction over vegetated areas.

The development of a vegetation cover dominated by cryptogams may be largely dependent on, but also partly the cause of, substrate stability. The type of plant cover then determines the amount of accumulation of organic matter. In areas permeated

349

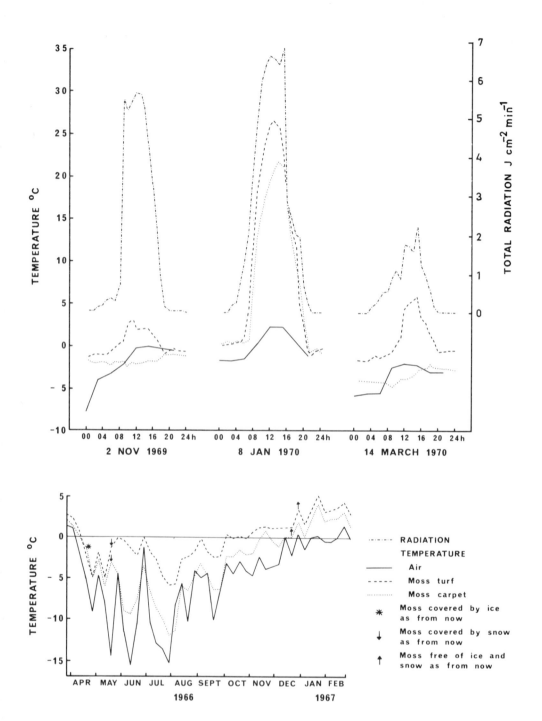

Figure 3. Diurnal (73) and annual (62) temperatures and radiation receipt for moss carpets and moss turves.

with ground water throughout the summer, thin organic layers (2—10 cm) accumulate beneath the living layer of moss carpets and moss hummocks. Due to the weight of winter snow, the partial or complete submergence by melt water in the spring and relatively rapid decomposition, the erect moss shoots collapse to form the shallow organic layer. Disruption may occur as a result of changing melt flow patterns and solifluction, so that some mixing may occur with the mineral soil beneath. In consequence the mineral content of the lower part of the moss carpet may be quite high.

Where more stable and drier conditions occur, two turf-forming mosses, *Chorisodontium aciphyllum* (Hook f. et Wils.) Broth and *Polytrichum alpestre* Hoppe., are able to grow and — because decomposition is extremely slow — banks of organic matter up to 2 m deep may develop above the general ground level. As a result many banks are semiombrogenous. There is relatively little compaction or compression, although some distortion may occur. Distinction between live and dead shoots below the surface is difficult and a permafrost exists below about 25 cm in the deeper banks, at which depth decomposition becomes negligible. Limited mixing with the mineral substrate beneath the banks may occur but loss on ignition is generally high throughout the profile. The nutrient content is usually highest in the surface layers of the banks and decreases down the profile, although N and P tend to accumulate just below the green shoots.

Most soils under grass swards are waterlogged at the time of the spring melt, drying later in the season (20). These loamy soils, which may be up to 15 cm deep, approximate to brown earths (20, 40) and the C/N ratio of about 12 indicates an active population of soil organisms (3).

A reducing mud of excrement mixed with moribund vegetation and mineral material develops around penguin rookeries and seal wallows (for locations see Fig. 1) containing exceedingly high N and P levels (40). A summary of the relationship between soils and vegetation and their extent on Signy Island is given in Table 2 and a summary of some soil properties in Table 3.

Table 2. The extent of soil types and plant communities on snow-free ground on Signy Island (modified from (67), who prepared the list from a sketch map of the vegetation by M.W. Holdgate)

Soil	Plant community	Approximate area (km^2)	% of total snow-free surface	
Mineral soils				
Soils of moraines and in areas of marked solifluction, frost heaving and low vegetation	Bare rock and mineral soil, with or without crustose lichens	4.25	26	
	Fruticose lichen and moss cushion subformation, often with an understorey of crustose lichens			
Soil over stable schist outcrop	continuous cover (> 50 %)	3.5	21	51
Soil over stable marble outcrop	sparse cover (< 50 %, often < 10 %)	5.0	30	
Organic soils				
Protoranker developing under moss carpets	Moss hummock subformation and moss carpet subformation			
	continuous cover (> 50 %)	1.25	7.5	12
	sparse cover (< 50 %, often < 10 %)	0.75	4.5	
Organic matter underlying moss turves	Moss turf subformation	1.0	6	
Brown earths	Grass and cushion chamaephyte subformation	0.0001	–	
Ornithogenic soils	Algal subformation often present	0.65	4	
	Penguin nests and seal wallows	0.1	0.6	
	Other birds' nests	0.0005		

Table 3. Properties of Signy Island soils (samples collected during February)

	Moraine	Mineral soils — Marble outcrop	Mineral soils — Schist. outcrop	Organic soils (peat) — Moss carpet (Peat)	Moss carpet (Soil)	Moss turf (Peat)	Moss turf (Soil)	Brown earth — Grass	Ornithogenic soil — Penguin rookery	Seal wallow (algal)
Main Bryophyte species		*Tortula* sp. *Grimmia* sp.	*Andraea* spp. *Dicranoweisia* sp.	*Drepanocladus* sp. *Brachythecium* sp. *Calliergon* sp. *Calliergidium* sp.		*Polytrichum alpestre Chorisodentium aciphyllum*		*Deschampsia antarctica*		*(Prasiola crispa)*
1. Horizon	Soil	Soil	Soil	Peat	Soil	Peat	Soil	Soil	Soil	Soil
2. Depth (cm)	0–5	0–8	0–10	2–8	8–25	2–15(200)	15–25	0–15	0–5	0–5
3. pH (H$_2$O)	7.1	7.9	5.4	4.9	4.9	4.7	5.0	5.4	6.1	6.7
4. Moisture (% dw)	19	56	61	613	–	473	–	183	–	–
5. Maximum thaw (cm)		100 cm				30 cm				
6. Silt (%)	18	7	5	–	14	–	–	10	9	–
7. Clay (%)	9	2	2	–	3	–	–	8	6	–
8. Total organic carbon (%)	0.4	2	2.3	30.9	9	43.6	23.4	13.8	10	30
9. Total nitrogen (%)	0.07	0.26	0.27	1.83	0.61	1.36	1.29	1.11	1.8	3.58
10. C/N	5.7	7.7	8.5	16.9	14.7	32.1	18.1	12.4	5.5	8.4
11. Total phosphorus (%)	0.13	0.18	0.18	0.52	1.11	0.13	0.25	0.47	3.39	0.74
12. Loss on ignition (%)	1.8	5.5	6.3	63.2	18.2	90.2	41.4	27.7	22.1	62.2
Soluble (available) nutrients (mg 100 g^{-1})										
13. Ammonia-N	0.28	0.3	0.4	1.5	0.3	1.1	1.6	0.6	136.9	489.7
14. Nitrate-N	0.12	0.6	0.19	3.24	1.95	1.83	2.38	1.5	9	4.3
15. Phosphorus	12	8	4	26.7	14	3	6	8	460	66
16. Potassium	8	5	7	17.3	6	17	9	16	73	100
17. Sodium	15	24	13	42.8	12	102	39	47	69	199
18. Calcium	71	596	95	75.3	25	213	130	96	106	220
19. Magnesium	13	17	28	35.3	13	196	72	58	68	134
20. January mean °C (depth–cm)		+3.1 °C (2.5 cm in soil)		+4.1 °C (2.5 cm in moss peat)				–	–	–
21. July mean °C (depth–cm)		−5.6 °C (2.5 cm in soil)		−3.4 °C (2.5 cm in moss peat)				–	–	–
22. Frequency of freeze-thaw cycles		25 in 2 years		13 in 2 years						
Sample size unless otherwise indicated in brackets	9 (4=4)	6 (4=25)	5 (4=92)	10 (4=55, 13=9, 15–19=6)	6 (6–7=3)	11 (4=89, 15–19=4)	5	7 (4=42, 6–7=2)	6 (6–7=4)	3

Source: Data compiled from (40), except for moisture and temperatures from (12)

PRIMARY PRODUCTION

Community classification and dynamics

The macrovegetation is predominantly cryptogamic, comprising approximately 200 species of lichen, 75 mosses, 12 liverworts and only 2 vascular plants, the extent of the main communities (61) being given in Table 2. Of a total area of 19.4 km^2, approximately 13 km^2 is snow-free in summer. Typical locations of the different communities and their relationships to nutrient availability are shown diagrammatically in Fig. 4 and 5.

The most extensive closed stands of vegetation have developed in the more stable areas of scree slopes and particularly on rocky ridges and headlands. However, more open communities occur in areas subject to disturbance by frost shattering or solifluction, formed by suitably adapted species either having rapid turnover and efficient sexual or vegetative reproduction, or else an ability to maintain cohesion when solifluction occurs in the underlying mineral soil.

Most exposed rock surfaces are colonized by lichens. Coastal rocks directly influenced by sea spray are commonly colonized by species of *Caloplaca, Verrucaria* and *Xanthoria*, while cliffs below bird colonies are dominated by nitrophilous species of *Biatorella, Buellia, Haematomma, Lecidea, Rinodina* and *Xanthoria*. Inland rocks support stands of nitrophobous species of *Lecidea, Lecanora, Ochrolechia, Pertusaria, Placopsis* and *Rhizocarpon*, which form a more or less ubiquitous layer over rock surfaces remaining free of other vegetation. Growth rates of ca 16 mm diametric increase per century for one crustose species, *Rhizocarpon geographicum* (L.) DC, are similar to those observed at Disko Island, Greenland, another cold oceanic site (46).

On the more stable lithosols, often in dry exposed situations, and on rock surfaces a range of communities occurs dominated by fruticose lichens, particularly species of *Himantormia* and *Usnea*, and cushion-forming mosses including species of *Andreaea, Grimmia* and *Dicranoweisia*. The mosses usually predominate where there is greatest stability and a regular water supply. The majority of mosses on Signy Island reproduce and establish vegetatively and only 13 of the 17 species known to produce sporophytes do so regularly; of these only 8 are widely distributed. Most of these mosses grow in unstable habitats and, with annual length increments of 3–5 mm (17, 71), it is apparent that there may be rapid turnover amongst such species, since large cushions are rarely found. Such species normally occupy temporary stable microhabitats within unstable areas, although cushions sometimes coalesce to form a continuous mat floating over the unstable mineral soil.

A similar growth strategy is shown by species of *Calliergon, Calliergidium* and *Drepanocladus*, which grow in permanently wet depressions and around melt streams or in areas where sheet water flow occurs on gentle slopes. Cohesion is maintained by the intertwining of shoots, which is particularly marked in *Drepanocladus uncinatus* (Hedw.) Warnst. Lichens are usually absent in these areas, as also in the flushed areas influenced by basic rocks that are dominated by moss hummocks formed by species of *Bryum* and *Brachythecium*. Rapid turnover is shown by *Brachythecium austro-salebrosum* (C. Muell.) Par. Although the annual length increments of shoots can be up to 4 cm (13), colonies of more than twice that height are seldom formed. Most shoots collapse during the two

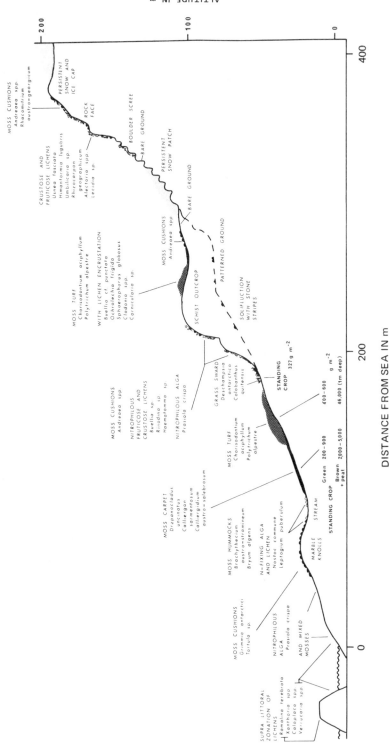

Figure 4. Diagrammatic profile of the coast of Signy Island showing the distribution of vegetation. Standing crop for mosses (13) and a grass sward (24) are included.

355

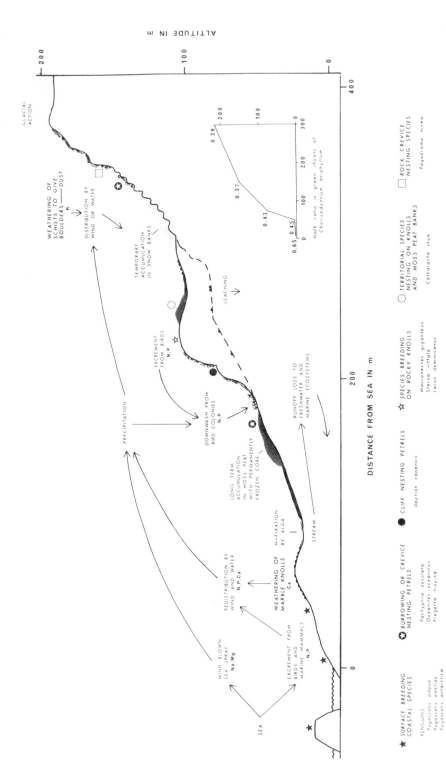

Figure 5. Diagrammatic profile of the coast of Signy Island showing the distribution of birds and seals as well as nutrient cycling, with the Na/K ratio in green shoots of *Chorisodontium aciphyllum* inserted (62).

seasons following initial growth, often to be removed by melt water, so that the plants never grow out of the environment to which they are irrevocably tied by their inability to conserve water (29). No emergent aquatic plants occur in the lakes, although there are several aquatic mosses, most of which are forms of species normally occurring in the wetter terrestrial habitats (43).

Against a background of secular changes and oscillations in persistent snow cover, the supply of melt water to a given area varies. Concurrently the development of carpets or loose turves formed from coalesced cushions will also alter the water regime. Colonization by more mesic turf-forming mosses is then often possible, sometimes directly onto the surface of the carpet or amongst cushions, sometimes onto areas where slight elevations are caused by the underlying rocks or by cryoturbation (Fig. 6). *Chorisodontium aciphyllum* colonizes moss carpets, *Polytrichum alpestre* favours drier conditions and may colonize boulder scree directly, along with cushion-forming species. *Polytrichum alpinum* occurs on more disturbed ground, forming loose turves.

Figure 6. The colonization of a moss carpet of *Drepanocladus uncinatus* on the left by the turf-forming moss *Chorisondontium aciphyllum*. The large outlying colonies in the foreground are between 10 and 15 cm high.

Because of the low decomposition rate, considerable vertical accumulation can occur and the bank surfaces become more exposed, receiving less winter snow cover. They may then be colonized by a variety of epiphytic lichens. Exposure also changes as climate and snow cover fluctuate between years. Many of the communities recognized on

357

the surfaces of banks represent phases of cyclic change and, even when the surface vegetation is apparently stable and comprises only two mosses, there is considerable variation in the small-scale distribution of shoots from season to season (15). In moss peat banks occurring up to the margins of large persistent snow fields, horizons are apparent which represent surfaces buried when the snow fields were more extensive and recolonized when the snow field receded (14). Such peat banks, 1 m thick, also occur beneath 3–4 m of persistent ice (25).

In addition to areas of ground covered mainly by mosses and lichens the green alga, *Prasiola crispa* (Lightf.) Menegh., is locally abundant on permanently wet ground and in pools enriched by seal excrement or around penguin colonies, particularly when biotic pressure is low (60, 61). *Nostoc commune* Vauch. is also locally abundant, particularly on bare, wet solifluction slopes influenced by basic rocks and supplied with melt water at pH 8–9 (41). During mid- to late summer the surface of firn snow is often coloured red, green or yellow by unicellular snow algae, mostly species of *Chlamydomonas, Raphidonema* and *Ochromonas*, the relatively sudden appearance of the patches probably being due to concentration of cells as the volume of snow in which they are contained decreases (26).

Both of the vascular plants, *Deschampsia antarctica* Desv. and *Colobanthus quitensis* (Kunth) Bartl., occur on well-drained, north-facing slopes in the coastal zone, often below cliffs with nesting birds. The grass is more common and occurs in a wider range of habitats (20, 61). Although a closed community is sometimes formed, both species usually grow as isolated tufts or cushions and are associated with a variety of mosses. The more widespread distribution of *D. antarctica* may be due to its ability to survive uprooting by frost and wind action and then re-establish itself. Both species are increasing in abundance on the island and successful transplants indicate that many suitable sites are available (20). Natural spread has been slow because mature seed of the grass has been recorded only 4 times since 1944 and at approximately 3 year intervals in *Colobanthus* (22). Seedling survival in both species is very low, much less than 50 % for *Colobanthus* over the first winter (24). Variation in performance (measured by leaf size) with age of plants (estimated from cushion diameters) has been demonstrated in *Colobanthus*, as well as a well-defined, small-scale pattern of distribution, associated with restricted dissemination of seed and fragmentation of older cushions (23).

Standing crop, production and production rates

Most of the mosses have clear innate markers of growth. Annual length increments vary greatly, being as high as 5 cm in some species, and net annual production ranges from 200–900 g m^{-2} (13). Direct comparisons of production levels are suspect, since there are considerable interspecific differences in growth forms and patterns of growth, susceptibility to decomposition, water relations and ability to recover normal metabolic activity after periods of desiccation or freezing. Species forming hummocks and carpets in wet habitats are analogous in their pattern of growth to annual species. Little tissue persists between seasons and new growth usually occurs from a sub-apical position. There is relatively limited accumulation (2, 6), even though annual production may reach 893 g m^{-2}, a value attained in a carpet of *Calliergidium* cf. *austro-stramineum* (C. Muell.) Bartr. (13). Only 35 m away, at the margin of a persistent snow patch, production fell to 275 g m^{-2}. Some growth had occurred in both instances before the snow had melted. Production rates of 3.3 g m^{-2} d^{-1} were attained between mid-December and early February but fell to 0.7 g m^{-2} d^{-1} towards the end of February.

Some species such as *Polytrichum alpestre*, exhibit a more complex pattern of growth and in many ways there are similarities to the growth patterns of perennial vascular plants (11, 15). Clear delimitation of each successive season's growth, by variations in leaf lengths, and the slow rate of decomposition allow past changes in shoot populations to be followed with ease. Growth can be continuous for a number of seasons but eventually the apex dies, to be replaced by new branches formed deeper in the turf. Variation in the spatial density of shoots of *P. alpestre* from 30–110 shoots cm^{-2} had little effect on yield of current growth segments per unit area ($\equiv$ net production), although the weight of annual increments of individual shoots varied greatly. Significant differences have occurred between two consecutive seasons in a more or less pure turf of this species (660 g m^{-2} and 430 g m^{-2}) (15). Within one season higher levels of production have been measured much further south in the Argentine Islands (65°15′S), of 404 g m^{-2} compared with 342 g m^{-2} at Signy Island, probably reflecting greater mean daily sunshine duration and higher plant temperatures at the more southerly station (48). Pure stands of *C. aciphyllum* attain similar levels of production, e.g. 436 g m^{-2} (8) and 551 g m^{-2} (13).

The biomass of the principal N-fixing blue-green alga *Nostoc commune* and the lichen in which it occurs as a symbiont, *Leptogium puberulum* Hue, amounts to 5.78 g m^{-2} and 0.48 g m^{-2} respectively in the nutrient-rich sites. The average annual increase in biomass is 2.25 % and 1.02 % respectively (41). Carbon fixation in the snow algae communities amounts to 10 mg C m^{-2} of snow surface d^{-1} (26); this low value implies a doubling time of about 23 days.

Annual above- and belowground production of the only grass, *Deschampsia antarctica*, amounts to about 390 g m^{-2} in a closed sward (21). The largest increase in green shoots was recorded in the warmest summer months of January and February. By March, as the season ended, the total standing crop was 327 g m^{-2}, about 2.5 times that in early spring. New roots could be clearly distinguished from older ones, root production representing approximately one third of annual production. No significant change occurred in the weight of old roots in the closed sward, although in an open community there was a progressive decrease in proportion throughout the season. New root biomass reached a peak in December and January at both sites but declined as new tillers and inflorescences were produced. The aboveground to belowground ratio remained fairly constant at 1:3 throughout the season in the closed sward. For the open sward the relative growth rate for roots was calculated from both field measurements and standard growth analysis methods to be 0.014 g g^{-1} d^{-1}.

Production processes

Material of *Colobanthus quitensis* and *Deschampsia antarctica*, grown under controlled conditions in the U.K., had temperature optima for net photosynthesis of 14–19°C and 13°C respectively (24), with maximum rates of ca 7 mg CO$_2$ g^{-1} h^{-1} for *Deschampsia* and slightly less for *Colobanthus*. At 0°C both species still exhibited high rates of net photosynthesis, being 40 % of maximum in *D. antarctica* and 30 % of maximum in *C. quitensis*. In both species the compensation point was at very low light intensities, with *C. quitensis*, a cushion-forming species, showing little sign of saturation at the light intensities used. This is also true of *Polytrichum alpestre*, a moss with a very dense growth form. Lack of saturation is probably a reflection of the shading of lower portions of the shoots. Neither species of vascular plant is normally exposed to severe water stress, as both occur in flushed sites and, in common with the mosses with dense growth forms, diffusive fluxes are reduced by the cushion forming habit of *C. quitensis*. The temperature optimum for net photosynthesis for *Polytrichum alpestre* is 5°C when grown at temperature regimes equivalent to those experienced in the field but 15°C for *Drepanocladus uncinatus*. The latter species has a much broader response curve than *P. alpestre*. When grown at higher temperatures, the response curve to light and temperature for *D. uncinatus* is little changed, but *P. alpestre* has a new optimum at 15°C. High rates are maintained in both species at 0°C (16). There is a good correlation between the habitat occupied by a particular moss and its ability to make use of available water, to conserve it and recover quickly if growing in a habitat normally prone to extreme water stress (29, 52). In midsummer severe drought may occur in some areas. Most mosses are unable to tolerate permanent alterations in their usual habitats, so that against a background of changing climate, snow cover and hence water availability, changes in vegetation cover are inevitable.

Between the beginning and end of season energy contents of the attached and lying dead components of a grass sward declined considerably, although values for dead roots and aerial tissue remained fairly steady (24). Values ranged from 20.40 kJ g^{-1} for live inflorescences to 19.32 kJ g^{-1} for live roots, and from 20.36 to 18.64 kJ g^{-1} for lying and attached dead respectively. An associated moss, *Brachythecium austrosalebrosum*, had a value of 16.90 kJ g^{-1} at mid season.

HERBIVORY

No vertebrate herbivores are present on Signy Island and invertebrate herbivory appears to be rare. Some mites feed on crustose lichen, but microscopic examination of moss and grass leaves has not revealed any conspicuous evidence of grazing, although this does not eliminate the possibility of some organisms feeding off cell contents by piercing the walls.

CARNIVORES

With the exception of two birds, the skua (*Catharacta skua lönnbergi* (Mathews)) and the sheathbill (*Chionis alba* (Gmelin)) which scavenge, take eggs and occasionally kill young birds, there are no vertebrate carnivores. Carnivorous invertebrates, with a predacious habit, are dealt with under the next section.

DECOMPOSITION AND SOIL PROCESSES

The disappearance of organic matter may be due to decomposition (biosynthesized $C \to CO_2$) or to physical removal, either in solution (leaching) or in particulate form. For approximately eight months of the year the organic matter is frozen and it is assumed that only limited changes in quantity or quality occur during this period. Although summer levels of precipitation are relatively low, leaching may occur where the vegetation is saturated throughout the summer. Loss of particulate organic matter occurs through the agencies of wind, water and solifluction. Although removal by water is generally restricted to the period of the major annual snow melt, occasional catastrophic summer storms can result in considerable erosion, particularly in the more unstable habitats (40). Many macroscopic plant fragments can be seen in run-off water, although the amount has not been quantified. Where vegetation dries out, as occurs in the more exposed and better drained habitats, wind erosion may occur.

The rate of decomposition of the moss, *Chorisodontium aciphyllum*, is extremely slow (8). However, it is clear that the general climatic conditions alone cannot account for the low rate because litter does not accumulate under *Deschampsia antarctica*, despite its relatively high production rate and the total absence of lumbricids and myriapods. In mosses and lichens it is difficult to separate living from dead tissue and apparently moribund moss tissue from several centimetres depth of peat is capable of regeneration. Mosses may sometimes be killed by fungal attack (50), although the plants often regenerate from underlying tissue.

The microorganisms which appear to be responsible for organic matter decomposition are distinguished both by the presence and the absence of certain groups. Thus the existence of a large yeast population in the peat is remarkable (6, 7) and the apparent absence of *Penicillium* spp., normally regarded as ubiquitous, is unexplained. Other anomalies are the absence of *Trichoderma* moulds (31) and the scarcity of *Bacillus* spp. amongst the bacteria (10). *Mucor* has been reported as absent (31) but an obligately psychrophilic mucoraceous fungus has been isolated (9). Any comments on these observations must be speculative, but it may be significant that the unusual presence of a large yeast population is coincident with the unusual absence of *Penicillium* and *Trichoderma* and both of these groups show similar substrate affinities in laboratory culture.

Very little is known about the feeding habits of the invertebrate groups and consequently it is difficult to categorise accurately the trophic level of most species. It appears that the majority are microbial or detritus feeders and so are considered under decomposition and soil processes. In addition three species are known to be carnivorous.

Microbial biomass and production

Mean values for biomass of various microbial and protozoan groups are given in Table 4. The most noticeable features are the high biomass of moulds in the moss turf peat and the high biomass of bacteria in the brown earths. For more detailed accounts the reader is referred to other authors (6, 7, 31, 58, 59, 60). In addition to the values given in Table 4 there is a very small number of ciliates in the peat under moss turves and carpets, but naked amoebae have not been detected (58).

Table 4. Biomass of microorganisms in various soils (μg wet weight g^{-1} dw of soil) ☆

| Microbial group | Mineral soils | | Organic soils | | Brown earths |
	Young moraine	Old moraine	Peat under moss turf	Peat under moss carpet	under grass
Bacteria	2	3	2	–	12
Yeasts	–	–	179	–	–
Moulds	32	665	40 600	–	2 610
Flagellates	–	–	3	–	–
Testates	–	–	115	150	59

☆ Bacteria, yeasts and flagellates estimated by viable counts, moulds and testates by direct counting. Data derived from various authors (5, 7, 31, 58) assuming:
1. Fresh wt. of a bacterium is 1.5 x 10^{-12} g
2. Fungal hyphae have a uniform diameter of 3 μm
3. Flagellate and testate protozoa are spheres of radii 5 and 10 μm respectively
4. Fungi and protozoa have a specific gravity of 1.1.

The productivity of microorganisms is more difficult to assess than that of plants or metazoans and it is not possible to measure assimilation and respiration rates of individuals. However, it is possible to compute minimum turnover rates in terms of the number of generations occurring in a given time (56). For example, from the increase in bacterial numbers observed in the 1–2 cm depth of peat during the month of a spring thaw (7) the number of generations was estimated to be 2.2. A similar calculation for the dominant testate protozoan, *Corythion dubium* Taranek, also in a peat under a moss turf (59), gives 2.65 generations for the same period. Assuming that bacteria contain 75 % water, a growth rate of 2.2 generations in a month is equivalent to the production of 1.8 mg dry weight m^{-2} at the 1–2 cm depth. Bacterial numbers in deeper layers of the peat show no marked seasonal variation (7); hence it is not possible to estimate bacterial production by this method at these depths. The number of bacteria in the 1–2 cm layer declined as rapidly as it rose, while numbers of testate protozoa remain relatively high throughout the short austral summer (59). Therefore it is possible that the production rate of bacteria remains at the initial level, but the standing crop is reduced following predation by the protozoa. Under these circumstances the total annual production of bacteria would be 7.5 mg dry weight m^{-2} at the 1–2 cm depth. Even allowing for the undoubted errors inherent in the assumptions underlying these calculations, bacterial production is negligible compared with primary production. However, if the microfungi have a rate of production similar to that of the bacteria, which is not unreasonable, then the much higher biomass (Table 4) would lead to considerably higher production.

Invertebrate biomass and production

A general appraisal of the composition, population numbers and in some cases biomass and respiration is possible for the fauna of a number of habitats. However, there is frequently considerable variation in community composition and population size and structure both spatially and seasonally within one site and between different examples of the same habitat type. Consequently, caution must be exercised when comparing the data presented here.

The mesofaunal groups represented at Signy Island are Rotifera, Nematoda, Tardigrada, Acari and Collembola. Representatives of both the Rotifera and Tardigrada are found in most habitats and, like the other invertebrates, their distribution is aggregated and their numbers fluctuate both spatially and temporally. Figures from four monthly samples (March–June) of the upper 6 cm of a moss turf give a mean density of 170×10^3 Rotifera and 27×10^3 Tardigrada (42), and these represent approximate median density values for the range of habitats examined. It seems likely that both biomass and respiration of these two groups will be low compared with other invertebrates. In the majority of habitats most nematodes are microbial feeders (65). The vast majority of Collembola consist of the ubiquitous species *Cryptopygus antarcticus* Willem, but the Acari are more diverse. Apart from the carnivore *Gamasellus racovitzai* (Trouessart), the majority in most habitats consist of tiny prostigmatids. The major exceptions occur in the crustose lichen and algal communities associated with bird and seal colonies, where the larger Cryptostigmata comprise 60 % and 50 % respectively of the total Acari numbers.

Values for mean annual biomass and respiration of Nematoda, Collembola and Acari have been calculated for each habitat (Table 5). It must be emphasised that many of these values are gross extrapolations and even the population estimates are based on varying numbers of samples of different sizes taken at different times of the year but they probably reflect fairly accurately the relative contributions of the different groups. There is no information on production. Within all three groups there is considerable variation in biomass and respiration between the different habitats and there is no direct relationship between these parameters and number of species. Totalling values for all three groups the highest biomass and respiration are found in the alga *Prasiola crispa* and from direct observation it is known that some patches of this alga support very high densities of Collembola and Acari. Examination of the data in Table 5 in conjunction with Table 2, indicates that those habitats with the highest biomass and respiration are the more specialised and restricted in total area.

Carnivorous invertebrates, with a predacious habit, include one species each of tardigrade, nematode and mite. Data on the population numbers, biomass and respiration of the latter two are given in Table 6. Reservations mentioned above regarding the accuracy of some estimates apply equally. Again the alga *Prasiola crispa* supports the highest biomass.

Rates of decomposition of litter and soil organic matter

Decomposition rates of mosses are variable but generally slow. Accumulation, an expression of the balance between production and decomposition, is also very variable. In the turf-forming moss *Chorisodontium aciphyllum*, three complementary methods used at one site indicate an annual loss of 2 %, the rate being linear to a depth of 10 cm, the

Table 5. Numbers of species, density, biomass and respiration of Nematoda, Collembola and Acari (excluding carnivorous species) in various habitats on Signy Island [†]

	Habitat		Crustose lichen	Fruticose lichen and moss cushion	Moss carpet	Moss turf	Alga	Grass and cushion chamaephyte	Seal wallows	Penguin rookery
						Vegetation subformations				
Nematoda	Number of species		n.d.	14	11	9	11	15	3	1
	Mean annual density ($\times 10^3$ m^{-2})		n.d.	1 866	2 721	1 314	1 257	6 027	576	4 040
	Mean annual biomass (mg wet weight m^{-2})		n.d.	1 580	1 329	296	–	4 097	–	8 249
	Total annual respiration (ml O$_2$ m^{-2})		n.d.	1 766	1 950	523	–	5 538	–	8 845
Collembola	Number of species		1	2	2	3	2	3	1	0
	Density ($\times 10^3$ m^{-2})	Summer	7	51	298	16	959	102	385	0
		Winter	<1	3	278	11	380	226	85	0
		Annual mean	4	27	288	14	670	164	235	0
	Vertical distribution (% of 0–6 cm in 3.6 cm layer)		–	–	19	25	1	17	1	–
	Mean annual biomass (mg wet weight m^{-2})		100	675	7 200	350	16 750	4 100	5 875	–
	Total annual respiration (ml O$_2$ m^{-2})		105	709	7 568	368	17 608	4 410	6 176	–
Acari	Number of species		6	8	3	4	4	4	3	0
	Density ($\times 10^3$ m^{-2})	Summer	39	1	1	19	13	11	17	0
		Winter	40	4	0	16	6	5	0	0
		Annual mean	40	3	1	18	10	8	9	0
	Vertical distribution (% of 0–6 cm in 3–6 cm layer)		–	–	18	45	2	37	<1	–
	Mean annual biomass (mg wet weight m^{-2})		2 408	2	<1	9	602	4	5	–
	Total annual respiration (ml O$_2$ m^{-2})		1 121	13	4	78	280	35	39	–
	Total annual biomass of Nematoda, Collembola and Acari (mg wet weight m^{-2})		2 508☆	2 257	8 529	655	17 352☆	8 201	5 880☆	8 249
	Total annual respiration of Nematoda, Collembola and Acari (ml O$_2$ m^{-2})		1 226☆	2 488	9 522	969	17 888☆	9 983	6 215☆	8 845

n.d. = not determined

☆ totals for Acari and Collembola only

† Population data for the arthropods are from (69). In view of its dominance in most habitats and the similar size of the other species, data for Cryptopygus antarcticus are used to estimate total biomass and respiration for the Collembola. Taking into account the approximate composition of C. antarcticus size classes throughout the year, the mean live weight and mean oxygen consumption at 6°C per individual have been calculated as 25 μg and 6 $\times 10^{-3}$ μl O$_2$ h^{-1} respectively, from (70). With the Acari, considering the species involved and where possible their life stage distribution, approximate mean figures for live weight per individual are estimated at 0.5 μg for prostigmatids and 100 μg for cryptostigmatids. Approximate mean respiratory rates per individual at 5°C have been estimated as 1 $\times 10^{-3}$ μl O$_2$ h^{-1} for prostigmatids and 10 $\times 10^{-3}$ μl O$_2$ h^{-1} for cryptostigmatids (72). All data for Nematoda are derived from (64, 65). A negligible respiration rate has been assumed during winter.

Table 6. Density, biomass and respiration for carnivorous Nematoda (*Clarkus gerlachei* (de Man) Tairajpuri) and Acari (*Gamasellus recovitzai*) on Signy Island †

		Vegetation subformations							
Habitat	Crustose lichen	Fruticose lichen and moss cushion	Moss carpet	Moss turf	Alga	Grass and cushion chamae-phyte	Seal wallows	Penguin rookery
Nematoda									
Number of species	n.d.	1	1	1	1	1	0	0
Mean annual density ($\times 10^3$ m^{-2})	n.d.	1	36	<1	237	3	–	–
Mean annual biomass (mg wet weight m^{-2})	n.d.	12	350	2	2 299	32	–	–
Total annual respiration (ml O$_2$ m^{-2})	n.d.	8	241	2	1 594	94	–	–
Acari									
Number of species	1	1	1	1	1	1	1	0
Density Summer ($\times 10^3$ m^{-2})	2	2	2	<1	2	7	<1	–
Winter	1	0	0	<1	<1	<1	0	–
Annual mean	1	1	1	<1	1	4	<1	–
Vertical distribution (% of 0–6 cm in 3–6 cm layer)	–	–	13	25	9	30	0	–
Mean annual biomass (mg wet weight m^{-2})	27	38	49	11	58	144	8	–
Total annual respiration	29	42	54	12	64	159	8	–
Total annual biomass of Nematoda and Acari (mg wet weight m^{-2})	27☆	50	399	13	2 357	176	8	0
Total annual respiration of Nematoda and Acari (ml O$_2$ m^{-2})	29☆	50	295	14	1 658	253	8	0

n.d. = not determined

☆ totals for Acari only

† The source of data is the same as for Table 5, except that the mean live weight per individual is estimated as 40 μg and the mean respiratory rate per individual at +5°C as 10×10^{-3} μl O$_2$ h^{-1} (72).

greatest depth of measurement (8). Below this depth the rate presumably decreases drastically because considerable accumulations up to 2 m deep occur at a number of sites. In moss carpets, production levels may be similar to those in moss turves but there is less accumulation, reflecting a higher rate of decomposition. In *Drepanocladus uncinatus* there was a dry weight loss of 25 % over the first year in a wet site and 14 % over the same period in a drier site (13). The greater physical instability in some wet habitats also leads to the removal of material. Decomposition rates of vascular plant material have not been measured, although since production is high and accumulation negligible, turnover is apparently fairly rapid.

Decomposition rates of cotton strips (97 % holocellulose) inserted vertically at three sites indicated that weight losses are greatest in *Deschampsia antarctica* swards (32). In addition there was a slight but consistent increase in decomposition rate with depth in the moss turves, which correlates with the increase in bacterial numbers with depth (7).

Anaerobic conditions are probably restricted to the wettest soils and plant communities, such as the ornithogenic soils, solifluction features and some moss carpets. The deep peat under moss turves is generally aerobic and the lower rate of decomposition of *Chorisodontium aciphyllum* peat compared with that formed by *Drepanocladus uncinatus* may well be a consequence of lack of water, as well as a general difference in substrate quality.

Microorganism — invertebrate interactions and trophic relationships

Trophic relationships are exceedingly complex and as yet only a general outline is possible. Because the soil fauna does not appear to include many microherbivores the animals probably feed mainly on the microorganisms. In this connection conflicting interpretations of Table 4 are possible. Because of the very high fungal biomass it may be suggested that fungi constitute an important part of microarthropod diets. On the other hand, the low bacterial biomass may be a reflection of invertebrate consumption. The complexity of relationships is illustrated by the fact that at least one species of nematode-trapping fungus and several species parasitic in nematodes have been isolated from a range of plant communities (19, 66).

NUTRIENT CYCLING

There are two main complementary sources of nutrients: the rocks of the island and the sea surrounding it (Fig. 5). Rock breakdown is predominantly a physical process but some chemical weathering occurs to produce clays. Most of the available K and Ca arises in this way. Na and Mg are derived directly from the sea in precipitation and spray, while P and N are derived indirectly from the sea, via birds and mammals (2, 40). Levels of water-extractable nutrients in bird guano can be extremely high (ammonium-N 1 790, phosphate 690, Na 1 210, Ca 82, K 612 mg 100 g^{-1}) (55). In some plant communities, notably those dominated by the moss turves and, to a lesser extent cushions, the main source of nutrients is in precipitation and dust. Supply of nutrients in windblown spray ceases when the sea freezes and winter snow is also low in Na, K and Ca.

Gradual accumulation of extractable phosphate (2 rising to 7 mg 100 g^{-1}) and ammonium-nitrogen (3 rising to 6 mg 100 g^{-1}) may occur during the winter (54, 55), probably as melting snow releases nutrients into the vegetation and underlying peat, rather than from release *in situ* by successive freeze-thaw cycles. Levels are reduced by leaching once the melt is under way but nitrate-nitrogen levels show no distinct seasonal variation.

High nutrient levels occur in summer precipitation (inorganic-N 0.65 ppm, organic-N 0.42 ppm, K > 1 ppm, Ca 1 ppm, P 0.03 ppm) and the mineral content of living mosses increases. At the same time there may be translocation of nutrients upwards from deeper levels in mosses such as *Polytrichum alpestre*. Certain mosses, such as *Grimmia* and *Tortula*, grow only in areas influenced by basic rocks and have high contents of Ca. Lower levels occur in peat-forming mosses such as *Polytrichum alpestre* and *Chorisodontium aciphyllum*, which have grown above any source of Ca (Table 7). Because the content of particular minerals in mosses decreases with increasing distance from the source of supply, as shown for example by the Na/K ratio in Fig. 5, variation in mineral content, as shown in Table 7, may have little functional significance (62).

In many vegetated areas, where decomposition can be extremely slow, especially in moss banks which are above the general groundwater level, considerable amounts of nutrients are effectively taken out of circulation, eventually being incorporated into the permafrost as the bank grows thicker. Loss of soil nutrients in melt water run-off is variable (33) and is dependent upon the substrate over or through which the water has passed. Concentrations of N and P are low (0.08 and 0.001 ppm respectively) when it has flowed over sparsely vegetated soil, unless there has been enrichment from bird or seal excrement (6.20 and 0.077 ppm N and P respectively). N and P levels are usually greater in water which has permeated moss stands (1.76 and 0.01 ppm respectively).

In most plant communities high concentrations of nutrients suggest little limitation on growth, with the possible exception of N. In some moss turves, however, N levels are often higher in the layer underlying the growing surface, suggesting a surplus. Whilst many areas are supplied with N from marine sources, *in situ* fixation of atmospheric N has been demonstrated in *Nostoc commune* and the lichens *Leptogium puberulum* and a species of *Stereocaulon*, in which *N. commune* is the phycobiont (27, 41), although they are confined to areas influenced by basic rocks.

Table 7. Summer mineral contents of bryophytes and a grass on Signy Island (40)

Growth form and species	Number of samples	pH	Loss on ignition (%)	Na	K	Ca	Mg	P	N	Organic C (%)
						Total (%)				
Moss cushions										
Andreaea sp.	1	–	63.8	0.14	0.50	0.66	0.70	0.08	1.11	38.4
Grimmia sp.	1	–	85.1	0.09	0.30	1.10	0.43	0.12	1.22	41.6
Tortula sp.	1	–	72.7	0.08	0.50	1.74	0.51	0.18	1.66	36.6
Moss carpets										
Brachythecium sp. & Drepanocladus sp.	4	5.2☆	80.0	0.13	0.87	0.19	0.34	0.29	1.53	39.5
Moss turfs										
Polytrichum alpestre & Chorisodontium aciphyllum										
0 – ca 8 cm green	9	–	93.8	0.13	0.29	0.27	0.31	0.10	0.83	45.3
brown	9	4.7	91.7	0.13	0.11	0.37	0.33	0.11	1.00	43.3
Grass sward										
Deschampsia antarctica										
green	3	–	71.9	0.11	0.48	0.47	0.51	0.29	2.22	38.4
brown	3	4.8	55.2	0.11	0.58	0.60	0.54	0.33	1.96	24.4

☆ Mean of 5 samples

INTERACTIONS BETWEEN TERRESTRIAL
AND AQUATIC ECOSYSTEMS

The most important transfers between ecosystems are those involved in nutrient cycling (38) either directly or indirectly from the sea and sometimes via the terrestrial ecosystem into freshwater lakes. All birds and mammals present on land for varying periods of the year are directly or indirectly dependent on the sea for their food. As well as the obvious colonies of surface breeding birds, such as penguins and the larger petrels, many of the smaller petrels nest within scree slopes (Fig. 3), sometimes burrowing through and under moss turves overlying scree slopes. Although, as shown in Table 2, the surface colonies only cover a small part of the snow-free ground, many are located at some distance inland (Fig. 1). During the breeding season peak biomass levels may reach 10 kg m^{-2} in chinstrap penguin rookeries (Fig. 7) (38) and deposition of penguin litter, i.e. guano and moulted feathers, amounts to as much as 16 g m^{-2} d^{-1} during moulting in March, although during the rest of the breeding season this does not rise much above 2 g m^{-2} d^{-1} (60). Extensive trampling of the vegetation may occur as seal wallows and bird colonies change position slightly from year to year, killing mosses or grass that may be present but often leading to the development of the algal subformation dominated by *Prasiola crispa*.

Figure 7. A colony of chinstrap penguins (*Pygoscelis antarctica*) on Moe Island, off the south west coast of Signy Island. Coronation Island, which has a mountainous interior rising to 1 200 m, lies in the background, with a glacier flowing into the sea along much of the rugged coastline.

OVERVIEW OF THE ECOSYSTEM AND MAN'S INFLUENCE UPON IT

The terrestrial ecosystem of Signy Island, in common with that of the rest of the maritime Antarctic, has developed under conditions of geographical isolation combined with a severe summer climate and a limited area free of snow and ice. Isolation has meant that the natural establishment of higher plants additional to the two native species is difficult, although it is known that other species can survive (74). The soils that have developed under the restricted grass stands are similar to temperate brown earths, with active populations of soil organisms, so that if further vascular plants could become established, such as *Poa annua* L., a common species in the sub-Antarctic, soil development might occur to a far greater extent and offer a larger and more amenable "target" habitat for immigrant organisms; it is known that microorganisms not recorded in the soil or vegetation arrive as propagules. However, the severe summer climate (Signy Island being the coldest of the IBP sites in this respect) is likely to restrict the viability of immigrant organisms. Moss turves and carpets experience temperatures of between $-5°C$ and $5°C$ for about 80 % of the summer (16) and this probably explains the absence of the otherwise cosmopolitan soil ciliate protozoan genus *Colpoda*, which occurs in the Arctic where summers are warmer (75). Invertebrates of temperate regions which contribute to soil mixing, such as earthworms and myriapods, are absent, as are higher insects. The lack of soil formation and slow decomposition shown by moss communities is probably a reflection of substrate quality, since mosses generally decompose slowly in other regions.

The maritime influence is considerable, partly because the island is small but also because of the presence in summer of large breeding populations of sea birds and moulting elephant seals. There are no truly terrestrial mammals.

Plant nutrients are seldom limiting but because of frost action creating instability many snow-free areas are more or less devoid of macroscopic organisms. The vegetation is characterized by the dominance of cryptogams, which have developed distinct communities because of lack of competition from flowering plants, locally favourable microclimate, and, in many areas, a supply of water throughout the summer. The most extensive vegetation occurs in lowland areas and on raised beaches. The larger part of the snow-free ground is composed of rock surfaces or skeletal soils, the former often being covered solely by lichens. These areas are rendered relatively unstable by frost action and cryoturbation but are locally colonized by mosses that have a relatively high rate of turnover and, unlike mosses of more stable habitats, often reproduce sexually. Mosses with a slower rate of turnover form closed communities in more favourable habitats with regular water availability, some degree of substrate stability and an insulating snow cover in winter. These factors are correlated with the length of time that a particular area of ground has been free of persistent snow. When persistent and seasonal snow cover decreases, desiccation of the vegetation and decreased winter insulation may rapidly lead to erosion. Although this occurs on Signy Island it is most marked on nearby Laurie Island where arid, snow-free hillsides support little vegetation other than the remnants of moss peat banks which were formerly much more extensive.

If net annual production, which locally reaches very high levels, is averaged over the whole snow- and ice-free area of the island it amounts to at most about 100 g m^{-2}. A minute fraction is allocated to consumers, judged from oxygen consumption as being between 4×10^{-3} and 4×10^{-4} % per season. Anything between 75 and 98 % is likely to persist into the following season, accumulation of material being prevented in many habitats by physical removal and catastrophic events. Although their study is extremely difficult, complex relationships are evident amongst invertebrates and microorganisms, with a variety of trophic levels (65).

Signy Island has experienced a sporadic human presence since the turn of the century but this has varied in intensity. A small shore-based whaling station operated on the site of the present British Antarctic Survey station between 1920–30 (53), but once pelagic whaling commenced in the southern oceans, the island was more or less deserted until the permanent station was established in 1947. So far man's influence on the ecosystem has been limited, but pressure on land may increase due to greater marine exploitation, requiring shore-based installations, and tourism. International recognition of the many problems is embodied in the Antarctic Treaty of 1959 (57). A number of specially protected areas have been designated, including Moe Island and Lynch Island (Fig. 1), and agreement has been reached with tour operators that no vessels will visit Signy Island. The pressure of scientific stations, situated in the biologically richest coastal areas, may affect both the vegetation and the breeding success of some birds, as well as being a vector of new organisms (39). Waste disposal also presents problems. The total area free of snow and ice in the maritime Antarctic is minute when compared with the land mass of arctic and alpine tundra, so that carefully planned conservation and management of this unique region is essential.

REFERENCES

1. Adie, R.J. 1964. Geological history. – In: Priesteley, R.D., Adie, R.J. & Robin, G. de Q. (eds.) Antarctic Research, pp. 118–162. London: Butterworth and Co. (Publishers) Ltd.
2. Allen, S.E., Grimshaw, H.M. & Holdgate, M.W. 1967. Factors affecting the availability of plant nutrients on an Antarctic island. – J. Ecol. 55: 381–396.
3. Allen, S.E. & Heal, O.W. 1970. Soils of the maritime Antarctic zone. – In: Holdgate, M.W. (ed.) Antarctic Ecology, 2: 693–696. London–New York: Academic Press.
4. Allison, J.S. & Smith, R.I.L. 1973. The vegetation of Elephant Island, South Shetland Islands. – Bull. Br. Antarc. Surv. 33 & 34: 185–212.
5. Bailey, A.D. Personal communication.
6. Baker, J.H. 1970. Yeasts, moulds and bacteria from an acid peat on Signy Island. – In: Holdgate, M.W. (ed.) Antarctic Ecology, 2: 717–722. London–New York: Academic Press.
7. Baker, J.H. 1970. Quantitative study of yeasts and bacteria in a Signy Island peat. Bull. Br. Antarc. Surv. 23: 51–55.
8. Baker, J.H. 1972. The rate of production and decomposition of Chorisodontium aciphyllum (Hook. f. and Wils.) Broth. – Bull Br. Antarc. Surv. 27: 123–129.
9. Baker, J.H. Unpublished data.
10. Baker, J.H. & Smith, D.G. 1972. The bacteria in an Antarctic peat. – J. Appl. Bact. 35: 589–596.
11. Callaghan, T.V. & Collins, N.J. In press. Life cycles, population dynamics and the growth of tundra plants. – In: Moore, J.J. (ed.) Tundra: Comparative Analysis of Ecosystems. Cambridge University Press.
12. Chambers, M.J.G. 1966. Investigations of patterned ground at Signy Island, South Orkney Islands: II. Temperature regimes in the active layer. – Bull. Br. Antarc. Surv. 10: 71–83.

13. Collins, N.J. 1973. The productivity of selected bryophyte communities in the maritime Antarctic. – In: Bliss, L.C. & Wielgolaski, F.E. (eds.) Primary Production and Production Processes, Tundra Biome, pp. 177–183. Edmonton: IBP Tundra Biome Steering Committee.

14. Collins, N.J. In press. The development of peat banks on Signy Island, against a background of changing climate and persistent snow and ice cover. – Bull. Br. Antarc. Surv.

15. Collins, N.J. In manuscript. Strategies of growth and population dynamics of tundra plants II. A moss, *Polytrichum alpestre* Hoppe in the maritime Antarctic. – Submitted to Oikos.

16. Collins, N.J. In press. The growth of mosses in two contrasting communities in the maritime Antarctic; measurement and prediction of net annual production. – In: Llano, G. (ed.) Adaptations within Antarctic Ecosystems, Proc. third symposium on Antarctic biology (in press).

17. Collins, N.J. Unpublished data.

18. Direccion General del Servicio Meteorologico Nacional. 1951. Datos climatologicos y geomagneticos Islas Orcadas del Sur (lat: 66°44'S, long: 44°44'W), periodo 1903–1950. – Direcc. gen. Serv. Met. Nac., Ser. B, Secc. 1ª, Pt. 1ª, No. 11.

19. Duddington, C.L., Wyborn, C.H.E. & Smith, R.I.L. 1973. Predacious fungi from the Antarctic. – Bull. Br. Antarc. Surv. 35: 87–90.

20. Edwards, J.A. 1972. Studies in *Colobanthus quitensis* (Kunth.) Barthl. and *Deschampsia antarctica* Desv.: V. Distribution, ecology and vegetative performance on Signy Island. – Bull. Br. Antarc. Surv. 28: 11–28.

21. Edwards, J.A. 1973. Vascular plant production in the maritime Antarctic. – In: Bliss, L.C. & Wielgolaski, F.E. (eds.) Primary Production and Production Processes, Tundra Biome, pp. 169–173. Edmonton: IBP Tundra Biome Steering Committee.

22. Edwards, J.A. 1974. Studies in *Colobanthus quitensis* (Kunth) Bartl. and *Deschampsia antarctica* Desv.: VI. Reproductive performance on Signy Island. – Bull. Br. Antarc. Surv. 39: (in press).

23. Edwards, J.A. 1974. Studies in *Colobanthus quitensis* (Kunth) Bartl. and *Deschampsia antarctica* Desv.: VII. Cyclic changes related to age in *Colobanthus*. – Bull. Br. Antarc. Surv. 40: (in press).

24. Edwards, J.A. Personal communication.

25. Fenton, J.H.C. Personal communication.

26. Fogg, G.E. 1967. Observations on the snow algae of the South Orkney Islands. – Phil. Trans. Roy. Soc. Ser. B 252: 279–287.

27. Fogg, G.E. & Stewart, W.D.P. 1968. *In situ* determinations of biological nitrogen fixation in Antarctica. – Bull. Br. Antarc. Surv. 15: 39–46.

28. Gimingham, C.H. & Smith, R.I.L. 1970. Bryophyte and lichen communities in the maritime Antarctic. – In: Holdgate, M.W. (ed.) Antarctic Ecology, 2: 752–785. London–New York: Academic Press.

29. Gimingham, C.H. & Smith, R.I.L. 1971. Growth form and water relations of mosses in the maritime Antarctic. – Bull. Br. Antarc. Surv. 25: 1–21.

30. Godwin, H. & Switsur, V.R. 1966. Cambridge University natural radiocarbon measurements VIII. – Radiocarbon 8: 390–400.

31. Heal, O.W., Bailey, A.D. & Latter, P.M. 1967. Bacteria, fungi and protozoa in Signy Island soils compared with those from temperate moorland. – Phil. Trans. Roy. Soc., Ser. B, 252: 191–197.

32. Heal, O.W., Howson, G., French, D.D. & Jeffers, J.N.R. 1974. Decomposition of cotton strips in tundra. – In: Holding, A.-J., Heal, O.W., MacLean, S.F. & Flanagan, P.W. (eds.) Soil Organisms and Decomposition in Tundra, pp. 341–362. Stockholm: IBP Tundra Biome Steering Committee.

33. Heywood, R.B. 1967. The freshwater lakes of Signy Island and their fauna. – Phil. Trans. Roy. Soc., Ser. B, 252: 347–362.

34. Heywood, R.B. 1970. Ecology of the fresh-water lakes of Signy Island, South Orkney Islands: I. Catchment areas, drainage systems and lake morphology. – Bull. Br. Antarc. Surv. 14: 25–43.

35. Holdgate, M.W. 1964. Terrestrial ecology in the maritime Antarctic. – In: Carrick, R., Holdgate, M. & Prévost, J. (eds.) Biologie Antarctique, pp. 181–194. Paris: Hermann.

36. Holdgate, M.W. 1965. Biological research by the British Antarctic Survey. – Polar Rec. 12: 553–573.

37. Holdgate, M.W. 1967. Signy Island. – Phil. Trans. Roy. Soc., Ser. B, 252: 173–177.

38. Holdgate, M.W. 1967. The Antarctic ecosystem. – Phil. Trans. Roy. Soc., Ser. B, 252: 363–383.
39. Holdgate, M.W. 1970. Conservation in the Antarctic. In: Holdgate, M.W. (ed.) Antarctic Ecology, 2: 924–945. London – New York: Academic Press.
40. Holdgate, M.W., Allen, S.E. & Chambers, M.J.G. 1967. A preliminary investigation of the soils of Signy Island, South Orkney Islands. – Bull. Br. Antarc. Surv. 12: 53–71.
41. Horne, A.J. 1972. The ecology of nitrogen fixation on Signy Island, South Orkney Islands. – Bull. Br. Antarc. Surv. 27: 1–18.
42. Jennings, P.G. Personal communication.
43. Light, J.J. & Heywood, R.B. 1973. Deep water mosses in Antarctic lakes. – Nature 242: 535–536.
44. Limbert, D. Personal communication from British Antarctic Survey meteorological data file.
45. Lindsay, D.C. 1971. Vegetation of the South Shetland Islands. – Bull. Br. Antarc. Surv. 25: 59–83.
46. Lindsay, D.C. 1973. Estimates of lichen growth rates in the maritime Antarctic. – Arctic and Alpine Res. 5: 341–346.
47. Longton, R.E. 1967. Vegetation in the maritime Antarctic. – Phil. Trans. Roy. Soc., Ser. B. 252: 213–35.
48. Longton, R.E. 1970. Growth and productivity of the moss *Polytrichum alpestre* Hoppe in Antarctic regions. – In: Holdgate, M.W. (ed.) Antarctic Ecology, 2: 818–837. London–New York: Academic Press.
49. Longton, R.E. 1972. Reproduction of Antarctic mosses in the genera *Polytrichum* and *Psilopilum* with particular reference to temperature. – Bull. Br. Antarc. Surv. 27: 51–96.
50. Longton, R.E. 1973. The occurrence of radial infection patterns in colonies of polar bryophytes. – Bull. Br. Antarc. Surv. 32: 41–49.
51. Longton, R.E. & Holdgate, M.W. 1967. Temperature relationships of Antarctic vegetation. – Phil. Trans. Roy. Soc., Ser. B. 252: 237–250.
52. McManmon, M. Personal communication.
53. Marr, J.W.S. 1935. The South Orkney Islands. – 'Discovery' Rep. 10: 283–382.
54. Northover, M.J. & Allen, S.E. 1967. Seasonal availability of chemical nutrients on Signy Island. – Phil. Trans. Roy. Soc., Ser. B. 252: 187–189.
55. Northover, M.J. & Grimshaw, H.M. 1967. Some seasonal trends in nutrient content of the soils of Signy Island, South Orkney Islands. – Bull. Br. Antarc. Surv. 14: 83–88.
56. Parinkina, O.M. 1973. Determination of bacterial growth rates in tundra soils. In: Rosswall, T. (ed.) Modern Methods in the Study of Microbial Ecology. Bull. Ecol. Res. Comm. (Stockholm) 17: 303–309.
57. SCAR Manual 1972. 2nd edition. Antarctic Treaty 1959, pp. 81–116. Cambridge: Scientific Committee of Antarctic Research.
58. Smith, H.G. 1973. The Signy Island terrestrial reference sites: II. The Protozoa. – Bull. Br. Antarc. Surv. 33 & 34: 83–87.
59. Smith, H.G. 1973. The population ecology of *Corythion dubium* (Rhizopoda: testacida). – Bull. Br. Antarc. Surv. 33 & 34: 123–125.
60. Smith, H.G. 1973. The ecology of Protozoa in chinstrap penguin guano. – Bull. Br. Antarc. Surv. 35: 33–50.
61. Smith, R.I.L. 1972. Vegetation of the South Orkney Islands with particular reference to·Signy Island. – Scient. Rep. Br. Antarc. Surv. 68: 1–124.
62. Smith. R.I.L. Personal communication.
63. Smith, R.I.L. & Corner, R.W.M. 1973. Vegetation of the Arthur Harbour – Argentine Islands regions of the Antarctic Peninsula. – Bull. Br. Antarc. Surv. 33 & 34: 89–122.
64. Spaul, V.W. 1973. Qualitative and quantitative distribution of soil nematodes of Signy Island, South Orkney Islands. – Bull. Br. Antarc. Surv. 33 & 34: 177–184.
65. Spaull, V.W. 1973. Distribution of nematode feeding groups at Signy Island, South Orkney Islands, with an estimate of their biomass and oxygen consumption. – Bull. Br. Antarc. Surv. 37: 21–32.
66. Spaull, V.W. Unpublished data.
67. Tilbrook, P.J. 1970. The terrestrial invertebrate fauna of the maritime Antarctic. – In: Holdgate, M.W. (ed.) Antarctic Ecology, 2: 886–896. London–New York: Academic Press.
68. Tilbrook, P.J. 1973. The Signy Island terrestrial reference sites: I. An introduction. – Bull. Br. Antarc. Surv. 33 & 34: 65–76.

69. Tilbrook, P.J. Unpublished data.
70. Tilbrook, P.J. & Block, W. 1972. Oxygen uptake in an Antarctic collembole, *Cryptopygus antarcticus*. – Oikos 23: 313–317.
71. Webb, R. 1973. Reproductive behaviour of mosses on Signy Island, South Orkney Islands. – Bull. Br. Antarc. Surv. 36: 61–77.
72. Wood, T.G. & Lawton, J.H. 1973. Experimental studies on the respiratory rates of mites (Acari) from beech-woodland leaf litter. – Oecologia 12: 169–191.
73. Wright, E.P. Personal communication.
74. Edwards, J.A. & Greene, D.M. 1973. The survival of Falkland Island transplants at South Georgia and Signy Island, South Orkney Islands. – Bull. Br. Antarc. Surv. 33 & 34: 33–45.
75. Smith, H.G. 1973. The temperature relations and bi-polar biogeography of the ciliate genus *Colpoda*. – Bull. Br. Antarc. Surv. 37: 7–13.

Rosswall, T. & Heal, O.W. (eds.) 1975.
Structure and Function of Tundra Ecosystems.
Ecol. Bull. (Stockholm) 20: 375–397.

MACQUARIE ISLAND, SUBANTARCTIC

J.F. JENKIN

INTRODUCTION

Macquarie Island (54°30'S, 158°57'E) is a small subantarctic island 1 500 km south-south-east of Tasmania. The island is approximately 34 x 2.5–5 km (120 km^2), comprising a long narrow plateau, 250–350 m above sea level, bounded on all sides by steep slopes (20–40°) or cliffs rising either directly from the coast or from a raised beach terrace (Figs. 1 and 2).

The rocks of Macquarie Island are mainly igneous; the island is considered to be composed of oceanic crust material of Miocene (24) or Pliocene age (29), uplifted during the Pleistocene (10) by faulting associated with tectonic activity along the Macquarie Ridge. There is evidence of past glacial activity, but there is no clear, current consensus as to the magnitude or time of occurrence of glaciation.

Macquarie Island was discovered in 1810 by the master of a ship involved in the sealing industry. During the next 110 years, gangs of men from Australia and New Zealand harvested the fur seals, elephant seals and penguins for their skins and oil, often with drastic effects on these populations. Sealers were also responsible for the introduction of rabbits, cats, rats and mice. Towards the end of the 19th century, scientists occasionally accompanied sealing vessels (16, 25) and various scientific expeditions have visited the island; their reports provide the earliest information on the island's biology. In 1948, a scientific and meteorological station was established on Macquarie Island by the Australian National Antarctic Research Expeditions (ANARE). This station, which has subsequently been permanently occupied, has been the site of many research projects (21).

ENVIRONMENTAL FACTORS

Climate

In view of the location of Macquarie Island, the dominant influence on its climate is the surface temperature of the surrounding ocean; this, in turn, is strongly influenced by ocean currents. Macquarie Island lies approximately 240 km north of the Antarctic Con-

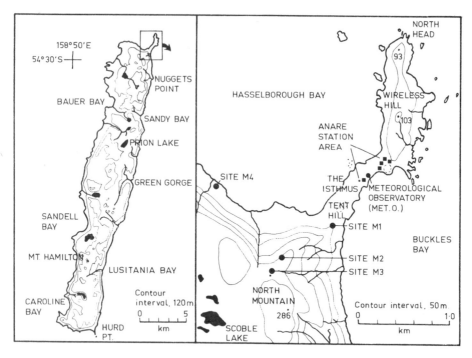

Figure 1. Macquarie Island, showing location of study sites and other places mentioned in text.

Figure 2. The isthmus and main body of the island viewed looking south from Wireless Hill. The ANARE station is visible on the isthmus; Buckles Bay to the left. In the background, grassland extends up the slopes leading up to the plateau, herbfield occurs on the beach terrace and in the upland valleys, and fell-field on the plateau.

vergence, which is the northern "boundary" of the cold, circumpolar, antarctic surface water, at which the cold water sinks below warmer and less dense subantarctic water. Near the Convergence, climatic conditions are determined not so much by latitude as by position north or south of the Convergence (30). Sea surface temperatures south of the Convergence vary seasonally, mainly due to the north-south movement of pack-ice around the antarctic continent. This variation, in association with changes in the temperature of the subtropical water, affects the sea surface temperature in the subantarctic zone. These changes are in turn reflected in changes in air temperature, which are, however, very small, both seasonally and diurnally. The climate of Macquarie Island is thus extremely oceanic with a very uniform temperature regime (Fig. 3).

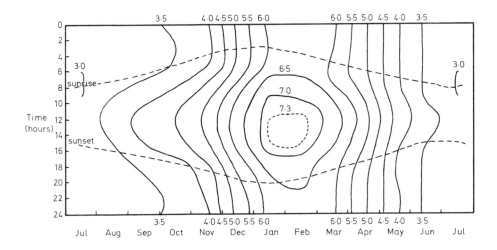

Figure 3. Mean air temperature ($^\circ$C) at 6 m altitude; thermo-isopleth diagram.

The meteorological observatory (subsequently referred to as Met. O.) is at 6 m altitude (Fig. 1). The mean minimum temperature isopleth (Fig. 4) emphasises the contrast between Macquarie Island and northern hemisphere areas where permafrost occurs.

Met. O. data (Table 1) show broad climatic comparisons but, in some respects, are atypical of much of the island. Air temperatures decrease by approximately 1°C per 100 m increase in altitude and on the plateau at 235 m altitude, the mean wind velocity is 32 % greater, and precipitation 16 % greater than at Met. O. Similarly, snow falls more frequently here and the snow cover lasts longer than at Met. O. The plateau thus experiences a more severe climate than is indicated by Met. O. data.

Leaf and plant canopy temperatures may exceed air temperature at 1 m. However, for most of the time, air-leaf temperature differences are probably quite small.

Table 1. Climate at Macquarie Island measured at the meteorological observatory (Met. O). Data to 1967 inclusive from Commonwealth Bureau of Meteorology (11); subsequent data from unpublished records.

Instruments and methods of observation: Radiation: "Rimco" silicon cell radiation integrator and "Eppley" pyranometer.

Air temperature and relative humidity: at 1 m above ground level in standard screen containing both dry- and wet-bulb thermometers.

Wind velocity: "Dines" anemograph and "Munro" 3-cup anemometer. Approximate height above ground: 1949–1956, 13 m, 1957–1969, 5 m.

Precipitation: standard 20 cm gauge with aperture at 30 cm above ground level, and "Casella" pluviograph.

Evaporation: based on data given by Loewe (20).   Sunshine duration: "Campbell-Stokes" recorder.

Variables	J	F	M	A	M	J	J	A	S	O	N	D	Year
Radiation (kJ cm^{-2}) (1967–1969)	47.8	36.3	25.8	13.9	6.5	3.3	5.3	9.5	21.1	32.5	41.5	49.4	292.9
Screen temperature (°C) (1948–1969) min	5.1	4.8	4.3	3.3	2.4	1.4	1.3	1.4	1.4	1.9	2.6	4.1	2.8
mean	6.7	6.6	6.1	5.1	4.2	3.3	3.1	3.3	3.5	3.8	4.4	5.9	4.7
max	8.4	8.2	7.5	6.6	5.6	4.8	4.6	4.8	5.2	5.4	6.2	7.6	6.2
Relative humidity (%) (1948–1969)	90.1	89.3	89.8	89.4	90.8	89.5	90.3	90.4	88.7	87.0	86.4	88.1	89.2
Wind velocity (m s^{-1}) (1949–1969)	8.0	8.5	8.9	8.9	8.4	8.7	8.3	9.0	9.5	8.9	7.9	7.4	8.6
Precipitation (mm) (1948–1969)	89.4	78.0	99.1	85.3	77.7	75.2	66.8	66.8	73.7	71.6	67.3	72.9	926.1
Evaporation (mm) (1948–1969)	44.9	37.5	31.0	30.5	26.5	30.0	29.0	27.9	32.5	55.5	46.4	48.6	445.2

Some form of precipitation occurs on 317 days per year (mean 1948–1969)

Snow depth: Not recorded, but rarely exceeds 20–30 cm, and rarely persists for more than a week. Snow and/or hail falls on an average 106 days per year (1965–1969) and may occur at any time, but shows a winter/spring maximum.

Fog: Not recorded. Mean total cloud cover (1960–1967) is 83 %.

Variables	J	F	M	A	M	J	J	A	S	O	N	D	Year
Sunshine duration (h) (1948–1953, 1964–1969)	105	106	81	54	31	21	25	43	69	84	93	93	814

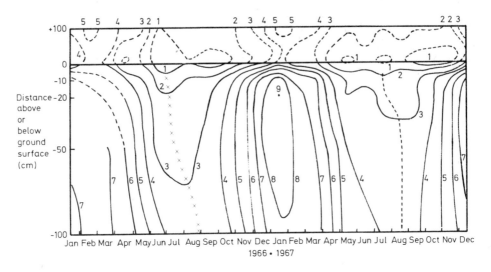

Figure 4. Mean minimum air and soil temperatures (°C) at 6 m altitude; thermo-isopleth diagram.

Soils

Soil formation is largely a function of vegetation growth as determined by wind exposure (28). With maximum wind exposure, e.g. on the plateau, the soils are mainly gravelly loams. Elsewhere, acid peats predominate, differentiated into various types according to drainage; the organic matter generally masks the effects of different parent materials. Many of the peats have a very high water content and show a marked and sharp reduction in oxygen content with increasing depth (Fig. 5). Soil data are summarised in Table 2.

The amount and frequency of precipitation, the excess of precipitation over evaporation and the consistent high humidity (Table 1) result in a constantly moist, drought-free environment. Drainage of water from the plateau is either directly via streams or via numerous lakes, some of which are drained by streams, others by subterranean drainage. Slow seepage of ground water is probably very common, particularly on the beach terraces. Periods of heavy rain usually result in increased erosion of the steep coastal slopes.

Table 2. Soil characteristics of the main sites at Macquarie Island

Site	M1 Grassland	M2 Grassland	M3 Herbfield	M4 Herbfield
Altitude (m)	45	230	235	15
Profile description	2.5–8 cm of brown, slightly fibrous peat overlying wind-blown, grey, basaltic beach sand. The sand contains only a small amount of organic matter, which decreases with increasing depth. The sand continues to between 50 and 75 cm depth, at which there is a sharply defined change to brown fibrous to pseudofibrous peat. The upper few centimetres of peat are soft, with a very high water content; below this the peat becomes hard and compressed, with clay content increasing with depth. Roots extend to approximately 50 cm.	Dark brown loamy peat, fibrous for the surface 7–12 cm. The colour darkens and the fibrous texture decreases with increasing depth. The soil becomes increasingly skeletal as depth increases to 60–75 cm, at which it grades into a very skeletal clay. Roots extend to approximately 30 cm.	Dark brown fibrous to pseudo-fibrous peat, containing very numerous fine roots in the surface 7–10 cm; larger roots extend to about 40 cm. At approximately 15 cm depth, there is a gradual change to a loamy peat. Between 40 and 60 cm, there is a marked increase in the sand and gravel content, and a skeletal grey-brown clay-loam is encountered between 45 and 75 cm. Below this a skeletal clay continues to bedrock at approximately 75–90 cm.	Light brown slightly fibrous peat, becoming darker and pseudo-fibrous at approximately 15–20 cm depth. Colour darkens and pseudofibrous nature increases with increasing depth. Roots are very numerous down to 15–20 cm, with larger roots extending to approximately 45 cm. The depth of the peat is unknown due to the high water table.
Soil type	Organic/mineral ☆	Organic ☆	Organic ☆	Organic ☆
pH	0–15 cm 6.4 ☆ (22) 7.5–38 cm 4.4 0–15 cm 4.3–6.8 (B6)	0–15 cm 5.4 ☆ 0–15 cm 4.0–6.6 (B5) 0–23 cm 5.4 (28)	0–15 cm 4.3 ☆ 0–15 cm 5.4–7.1 (B3) 0–12 cm 3.9 (28)	0–15 cm 4.4 ☆ 0–15 cm 4.7–6.6 (B4) 0–12 cm 3.9 (28)
Soil temperature ($^{\circ}$C). Approximate seasonal range of mean temperatures	–5 cm 1.8–6.5	–15 cm 0.5–4.0	–10 cm 0.5–4.5	
Soil moisture (% dw) 0–15 cm December Seasonal range	108 ☆ 5–400 (B6)	182 ☆ 95–900 (B5)	799 ☆ 400–770 (B3)	1027 ☆ 800–3000 (B4)

	Site 1	Site 2	Site 3	Site 4
Bulk density (g cm⁻³)		0–15 cm 0.28 ☆	0–15 cm 0.11 ☆	0–15 cm 0.07 ☆
Soil organic matter (% loss on ignition)	0–15 cm 5.9–31.2 ☆ (22); 7.5–38 cm 29.4–32.1 (22)	0–15 cm 21.4–22.2 ☆; 0–23 cm 89.3 (28)	0–15 cm 42.0–78.4 ☆; 0–12 cm 89.8 (28)	0–15 cm 79.1–96.1 ☆; 0–12 cm 89.8 (28)
Organic carbon (% dw)	0–15 cm 0.7–1.3 (B6)	0–15 cm 43.6–44.6 (B5)	0–15 cm 18.5–24.1 (B3)	0–15 cm 39.4 (B4)
Total nitrogen (% dw)	0–15 cm 0.11–0.16 (B6)	0–15 cm 3.33 (B5)	0–15 cm 1.56–2.19 (B3)	0–15 cm 1.79 (B4)
C/N ratio	0–15 cm 4.4–11.8 (B6)	0–15 cm 13.1–13.4 (B6)	0–15 cm 11.0–11.9 (B3)	0–15 cm 22.0 (B4)
Total P (ppm)	7.5–38 cm 1500 (22)			
Total K (ppm)	7.5–38 cm 1200 (22)			
Soluble (available) P (ppm)		0–23 cm 12.4 (28)	0–2.5 cm 4.2 (28)	0–2.5 cm 4.2 (28)
Exchangeable Ca⁺⁺	7.5–38 cm 6.11 (22)			
Exchangeable Mg⁺⁺	7.5–38 cm 8.50 (22)			
Na⁺	7.5–38 cm 5.42 (22)			
K⁺	7.5–38 cm 1.45 (22)			
Cation exchange capacity 100 g⁻¹) (meq)	7.5–38 cm 24.76 (22)			
Chloride content of ground water 0–45 cm (mg l⁻¹)			56 ☆	83 ☆

☆   indicates data recorded at study site. Other data from comparable sites.

(B3) data from Bunt (4, 5, 7), Bunt & Rovira (8, 9). The sample numbers correspond with the soil sample numbers in Table 6; the numbering of the various samples differs from that used by Bunt.

Methods of analysis

pH: determined electrometrically using glass electrode: 2:1 (Site M1) or 1:1 (Sites M3, M4) soil: water suspension of air-dried soil

Organic carbon: Walkley–Black method;

Total nitrogen: Kjeldahl digestion;

Total phosphorus, total potassium: extraction with concentrated hydrochloric acid

Exchangeable cations: not specified, determined after leaching with 40 % alcohol

Available phosphorus: colorimetric estimate of phosphate extracted by dilute acid solution of ammonium fluoride

Chloride: "Eel" silver electrode chloride meter.

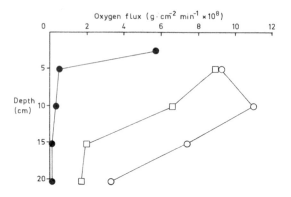

Figure 5. Oxygen flux in relation to soil depth. ● Herbfield, Site M3 (235 m altitude) □ Herbfield, Site M4 (15 m altitude) ○ In *Poa foliosa* stand in herbfield-grassland ecotone near Site M4. Soil oxygen fluxes were measured using an apparatus based on that of Poel (23), modified according to Black & West (3).

PRIMARY PRODUCTION

Macquarie Island is included in the botanical subantarctic zone, defined (17) as "from the southern limit of dwarf shrub vegetation to the southern limit of extensive, closed phanerogamic vegetation". The flora comprises approximately 40 vascular species of which three are introduced and three are endemic, 50 mosses, 30 liverworts and 55 lichens. Five vegetation formations are recognized (28) — grassland, herbfield, fen, bog and fell-field, and their distribution largely reflects the island's topography. In broad terms, grassland occurs on the coastal slopes, herbfield, fen and bog on the beach terrace and relatively flat, sheltered upland areas, and fell-field on the plateau. With increasing altitude or exposure, the vegetation in all formations shows a progressive reduction in size and vigour.

Grassland occurs on all steep slopes, both coastal and inland, up to an altitude of approximately 305 m, except where there is a high water table or high wind exposure. The vegetation cover is not continuous, being frequently interrupted by screes and landslips; seral communities are also of frequent occurrence. The dominant species is *Poa foliosa* Hook. f., commonly forming pure stands. *Stilbocarpa polaris* (Homb. & Jacq.) Gray, however, is often codominant and may also occur in pure stands. *Poa* forms a large tussock consisting of a crown of green shoots surmounting a peat pedestal which is surrounded by a dense mass of attached dead leaves and shoots (Fig. 6). *Stilbocarpa* has an approximately horizontal canopy formed by large leaves arising from a horizontal rhizome.

The herbfield formation occurs from near sea level to approximately 335 m in areas with a relatively high water table and moderate wind exposure. It is a closed community dominated by *Pleurophyllum hookeri* Buchan., with *Stilbocarpa polaris* variably present

Figure 6. Cross-section of a mature *Poa* pedestal at site M1, altitude 45 m. The mattock handle is approximately 0.9 m in length. The living roots and rhizomes in the top portion of the pedestal become less common towards the base, and similarly, the peat becomes less fibrous. The pedestal is overhung by a dense thatch of dead shoots, with the living shoots mainly confined to the top of the pedestal.

as a codominant. *Pleurophyllum* has a rosette form and a relatively short, mainly vertical rhizome.

Fen, dominated by *Juncus scheuchzerioides* Gaud., occurs locally in valley bottoms at all altitudes and on the beach terrace, and is associated with a neutral or alkaline water table at or above the ground surface. Bog, dominated mainly by bryophytes, especially *Breutelia* species, occurs locally where there is an acid water table at or above ground surface.

Fell-field, which occurs in areas subject to high wind velocities at all altitudes above approximately 180 m, is the most extensive formation. The vegetation, most commonly in stripes at right angles to the prevailing wind, is dominated by *Azorella selago* Hook. f. and *Rhacomitrium crispulum* (Hook. f. & Wils.) Hook. f. & Wils. Vegetation cover approximates 45 %; the intervening areas are covered with coarse gravel and stones, often variously sorted into polygons, stripes, etc.. Solifluction terraces are a common feature (Fig. 7).

IBP studies at Macquarie Island have been mainly located at four sites — two in each of the grassland and herbfield formations (Fig. 1).

Figure 7. Fell-field on the plateau in the northern part of the island, altitude 305 m. Solifluction terraces, with *Azorella selago* and *Rhacomitrium crispulum* on the terrace slopes and isolated *Ditrichum strictum* on the terrace flats, are visible in the foreground and to the centre right.

Grassland

Site M1. Altitude 45 m, situated on a flat saddle on a spur leading to the plateau. A small (6 m x 6 m) fenced plot at this site, from inside which all vegetation was completely removed, is designated Site M1A.

Site M2. Altitude 230 m, situated on the northern edge of the plateau below North Mountain.

Herbfield

Site M3. Altitude 235 m, situated on a relatively sheltered, almost flat area of the plateau leading up to North Mountain.

Site M4. Altitude 15 m, situated on the eastern end of the beach terrace which borders the south coast of Hasselborough Bay.

Sites M1 and M3 are the main study areas. Sites M2 and M4 represent, in the northern part of the island, the upper and lower limits of significant areas of grassland and herbfield respectively, and were selected to provide a contrast to the main study sites. Although the grassland and herbfield formations are extensive, and characteristic of

384

Macquarie Island, the majority of the island is covered by fell-field.

The pattern of annual variation in grassland and herbfield standing crop strongly suggests that the vegetation in mature communities has reached a steady-state equilibrium, in which the biomass varies seasonally, but shows little or no annual increase or decrease (19). The variation in total above-ground standing crop approximates a subdued sine-curve, which is the sum of analogous, but out-of-phase, variations in the dead and living components; the same features are apparent for individual species. The below-ground data neither confirm nor contradict the existence of a steady-state situation. This is apparent in both formations, and is consistent with the mosaic of developmental phases which exists. Communities in both grassland (1) and herbfield may be described in terms of a cyclic regeneration pattern of the dominant species, involving the progressive development of individuals of the species through pioneer, building, mature and degenerate phases (32). At low altitudes, the mature phase of *Poa* tussocks may develop in approximately 10 years and continue for a further 40 years; mature *Pleurophyllum* plants may be 40 years old. Regeneration in both formations is most commonly vegetative.

The grassland and herbfield communities have a large standing crop and annual production, particularly at lower altitudes (Table 3). At three of the four sites, one or two dominant species contribute more than 98 % of the total standing crop; at Site M3, however, six or seven species contribute the majority of the vascular plant standing crop. At all sites, there is only a very small vascular nonphotosynthetic component, and only at Site M3 do bryophytes and lichens contribute significantly to the total standing crop.

A number of factors contribute to the large annual production, which is due to the plants' ability to efficiently utilize low levels of radiation at temperatures which, although low and uniform, are rarely sufficiently low to limit metabolism (18). Seasonal variation in biomass is significantly related to radiation; 95 % of the annual total radiation is received during the nine months from August to April inclusive. The growing season for vascular species, based on the increase in above-ground living biomass, extends for 8 to 10 months. Leaf area index (LAI) varies seasonally, but remains high throughout the year. In the low altitude grassland LAI varies between 4.5 at midwinter and 7.6 in early summer; in the low altitude herbfield early summer LAI is 7.1. Rates of leaf production in on-growing *Poa* shoots show little seasonal variation; individual leaves function for 6–10 months. The dominant species approach photosynthetic saturation at low levels of illuminance, comparable to values commonly recorded in the field. The nutrient status of the soils limits plant growth, but there is little evidence of serious nutrient deficiency (see below). The plants are able to tolerate strong, salt-laden winds, and there is no evidence of transpiration stress.

Carbohydrate contents of the dominant species are relatively high, but are unlikely to limit assimilation. The annual carbohydrate cycle shows less variation than that reported for alpine and arctic species. Chlorophyll contents are relatively high and may have a compensatory role in the maintenance of photosynthesis under low levels of illuminance. Energy contents are intermediate between those reported for herbaceous temperate and alpine species.

Table 3. Standing crop and annual primary production (g m^{-2}) of the main grassland (M1, M2) and herbfield (M3, M4) sites at Macquarie Island

Site	M1	M2	M3	M4
Community plant cover %	90–100	90–100	97	87
Community LAI (live)	4.5 (midwinter)		n.d.	
	7.6 (early summer)	1.7 (early summer)		7.1 (early summer)
Standing crop				
Aboveground [1]				
Alive				
Monocotyledons	637	321	38	3
Forbs	262	1	85	733
Woody – green	5	2	8	1
– non-green	8	4	8	3
Bryophytes [2]	6	5	393	15
Lichens	0	0	9	<1
Standing dead [3]				
Monocotyledons	2560	936	104	14
Forbs	22	0	137	1570
Woody species	10	4	25	3
Litter	101			
Belowground [4]				
Alive	1690	n.d.	670	n.d.
Dead	3110	n.d.	1250	n.d.
Net production [5]				
Aboveground				
Monocotyledons	1440	n.d.	89	n.d.
Forbs	395	n.d.	174	n.d.
Woody – green		n.d.		n.d.
– non-green	55	n.d.	51	n.d.
Bryophytes	21	n.d.	146	n.d.
Lichens	0	n.d.	4	n.d.
Belowground	3670	n.d.	550	n.d.

1. Values for sites M1 and M3 are each based on a total of 35 quadrats (1 m^2). At each site, 5 quadrats were harvested on each of 7 occasions over a 13-month period. Data thus include seasonal variation. Values for Sites M2 and M4 are based on single December harvests of 5 and 4 quadrats (1 m^2) respectively.
2. Values for bryophytes and lichens refer to total living and dead biomass.
3. Separate values for standing dead and litter are available only for monocotyledons and forbs at Site 1. Values for woody species at Site M1, and for all species groups at other sites, are the sums of standing dead and litter.
4. Values are based on only 5 (Site M1) and 4 (Site M3) of the harvests referred to in (1) above. At each harvest, four cores (15 cm^2 area) were taken in each quadrat to a depth of 60 cm.
5. Production data are based on the difference between peak and minimum total biomass, regardless of times of occurrence, and therefore represent maximum estimates. Belowground values are based on only a small number of harvests (see (4) above), and may be unreliable.

n.d. = not determined

386

HERBIVORES

Little is known of the quantitative aspects of herbivory on Macquarie Island. Of the 119 arthropod species and genera recorded for Macquarie Island (31), approximately 100 are listed as being associated with plants, including plant litter. Snails and slugs are also present, but field observations suggest that invertebrate herbivory is of minor importance.

By far the most significant herbivore is the introduced rabbit (12). Since their introduction at Buckles Bay in 1879 or 1880 (13), the rabbits have flourished and now, apart from the more exposed areas of the plateau, abound all over the island. They vary locally in abundance from relatively sparse to plague proportions, and regions of maximum population density seem to vary in location from year to year. The introduced weka (*Gallirallus australis scotti* Ogilvie-Grant), rats and mice, are the only other vertebrates which could be classed as herbivores.

The effects of herbivores on nutrient turnover are unknown, but other animals, which can not be classed as herbivores (see below), probably have a significant effect on the nutrient budget of the vegetation.

Grazing by rabbits inevitably involves removal of vegetation. In lightly grazed areas or during the initial stages of grazing in a previously non-grazed area, selective feeding results in the partial or complete removal of *Stilbocarpa* and *Pleurophyllum* and only a slight effect on other species. There is, however, a whole spectrum of grazing effects. Continued heavy grazing can downgrade mature grassland and herbfield to a moss field or bare ground with consequent erosion (Fig. 8). Wekas turn over the surface vegetation in small local areas in their search for food, but their main diet is probably animal rather than plant. Removal of small amounts of vegetation in some areas has been attributed to rats or mice. Small amounts of plant material are removed by many bird species for use in nestbuilding.

Elephant seals (*Mirounga leonina* L.) and many bird species modify or damage vegetation over quite extensive areas (15). The elephant seals damage the vegetation, mainly in the grassland, simply by lying on it for variable periods whilst hauled out for breeding or moulting. The numerous royal penguin (*Eudyptes chrysolophus schlegeli* Finsch) rookeries are almost completely bare of vegetation (Fig. 9); the largest rookery covers approximately 6.5 ha. The position of gentoo penguin (*Pygoscelis papua* Forster) rookeries, approximately 50 m diameter, varies annually and the vegetation is often severely damaged by trampling. Less severe damage is caused locally by colonies of giant petrels (*Macronectes* spp.) and near the nests of several albatross species (*Phoebetria palpebrata* Forster and *Diomedea* spp.).

The effect on plant community structure depends on the severity of the initial damage, and the duration of the damaging influence. In broad terms, there appears to be a limit to the tolerance of vegetation to rabbit grazing, beyond which recovery, if it occurs at all, is extremely slow; below this limit, the vegetation is usually able to recover. Similarly, in areas permanently occupied by other animals, vegetation removal is virtually complete; in areas not permanently occupied, the vegetation usually recovers slowly, but may be considerably modified by the addition of animal feces.

Figure 8. The effects of rabbit grazing on a herbfield-grassland ecotone community on the west coast beach terrace. The dominant species, *Pleurophyllum hookeri* and *Poa foliosa*, have been largely eliminated, exposing the bare peat which is commencing to erode.

Figure 9. Royal penguin rookeries, extending to approximately 250 m altitude and 1.5 km inland from Nuggets Point. Redistribution, by wind and water, of organic material from extensive areas of animal activity such as these, is probably an important nutrient source.

CARNIVORES

Approximately fifty of the arthropod species recorded from Macquarie Island (31) are listed as being associated with animals, but there are no other data on carnivorous invertebrates. The total of 119 arthropod species and genera recorded for Macquarie Island includes 57 genera of Arachnida and 34 genera of Insecta (Collembola 12, Diptera 10).

The vertebrate populations of Macquarie Island are quite remarkable, both in diversity and abundance (21) (Table 4). However, most of the native animals are marine feeders, hence their roles as carnivores are not relevant here.

The southern skua (*Stercorarius skua lonnbergi* Mathews) and two species of giant petrel are probably the most significant terrestrial carnivores; they take a considerable toll of penguin eggs and chicks, and fulfil an important role by feeding on carrion – mainly elephant seal carcasses. Skua also prey on rabbits and smaller birds such as the dove prion (*Pachyptila desolata* Gmelin). A considerable part of the diet of wekas consists of kelp fly larvae (*Coelopa* spp.). The introduced feral cat preys on rabbits and ground-burrowing birds. Predation by cats has seriously affected the latter populations, and has probably contributed significantly to the extermination of two bird species.

There are no quantitative data on the consumption of prey or its effect on community structure. The interrelationships between feral cats, rabbits and ground-burrowing birds are being studied as an essential prerequisite to the introduction of measures for rabbit control, particularly to understand the likely effects of rabbit eradication on the subsequent predation by cats on the ground-burrowing birds.

DECOMPOSITION AND SOIL PROCESSES

The pattern of seasonal variation in grassland and herbfield standing crops suggests a steady-state situation, which implies a continuous production of dead biomass. Production of dead biomass varies seasonally, in relation to production of living biomass. There are, however, pronounced differences between species, both in the manner and in the seasonal pattern of aboveground dead biomass production. Unfortunately, very little is known about decomposition below the ground surface.

Up to 99 % of the *Poa* dead biomass may be attached to the tussock (Fig. 6), with usually only the terminal portions of some of the dead leaves in contact with the ground. Mature *Poa* pedestals grade from a tangled mass of living rhizomes and roots in the upper part, to a fibrous peat in the lower part. Senescent *Stilbocarpa* petioles collapse, and although approximately 20 % of the dead biomass may be still attached to the plant, approximately 90 % of the dead biomass is prostrate and in contact with the ground or litter surface. *Pleurophyllum* has a more marked winter die-back than *Poa* or *Stilbocarpa*. Most dead *Pleurophyllum* leaves remain attached and accumulate radially, forming a dense collar around the plant. The collars show a gradation in the extent of decomposition from the lower portions, where leaf remains are being incorporated into the soil, to the recently added dead leaves in the upper part. *Stilbocarpa* and *Pleurophyllum* rhizomes most commonly die back and decompose at one end,

Table 4. Vertebrates of Macquarie Island

Species		Ecosystem function ⊕	Density φ (No ha⁻¹)		Body weight (g) ♂	♀	Offspring (No yr⁻¹) ☆	Duration Days ‡
Macronectes giganteus (Gmelin)	giant petrel	$C_v\,C_s$	A	1.0	4640	3690	2800	365B
Macronectes halli Mathews	giant petrel	$C_v\,C_s$	A	0.2	4790	3580	700	365B
Gallirallus australis scotti (Ogilvie-Grant)+	weka or Maori-hen	$C_v\,C_s\,C_i$ O	C	—	—		—	365B
Anas superciliosa Gmelin	black duck	H_h	U	(0.03)	1300		—	365B
Stercorarius skua lonnbergi (Mathews)	southern skua	$C_v\,C_s$	C	0.15	1800		500	190B
Larus dominicanus Lichtenstein	dominican gull	C_s	C	0.07	1100	940	300	365B
Sterna vittata Gmelin	antarctic tern	C_i	R	—		120	—	365B
Carduelis flammea (P.L.S. Mueller)+	redpoll	H_g	U	—		~20	—	365B
Sturnus vulgaris L.+	starling	O	C	—		~50	—	365B
Oryctolagus cuniculus (L.)+ (26, 27)	rabbit	H_h	A	12.5	1300–1900	1200–2100	—	365B
Felis catus L.+	feral cat	C_v	C	(0.04)	4600	3200	—	365B
Rattus rattus L.+	rat	O	U	—	—		—	365B
Mus musculus L.+ (2)	mouse	$H_g\,C_i$	C	—	16		—	365B

+ Species introduced by man

⊕ H_h = grazing or browsing herbivores, H_g = granivores, C_v = carnivores on vertebrates, C_i = carnivores on invertebrates, C_s = consumers of carrion or scavengers, O = omnivores

φ A = abundant, C = common, U = uncommon, R = rare

‡ B = usually breeds

☆ Total number of offspring produced on the island annually. This value can also be expressed in terms of species population density; the area of the island is 12 000 ha.

All data for which no source is given can be referred to Antarctic Division, Department of Science, Melbourne, Australia.

while growth continues at the other.

The first year dry weight losses of early senescent above-ground material on the ground or litter surface were 63 % for *Poa* and 51 % for *Pleurophyllum*; both values differing significantly from the 90 % loss for *Stilbocarpa* (Table 5). Derived mean disappearance rates are 2.74, 1.99 and 6.52 mg g^{-1} day^{-1} respectively, and the pattern of weight loss is exponential. The placing of the litter during the experiment approximated normal field conditions for *Poa* and *Stilbocarpa* but the site (M1) was somewhat atypical for *Pleurophyllum*. The dry weight loss of *Poa* attached dead was examined in a separate experiment which extended over 18 months. The annual weight loss, based on an interpolated value for 365 days, was 57 %; the derived mean disappearance rate is 2.34 mg g^{-1} day^{-1}. These values do not differ significantly from those listed for *Poa* above. The annual dry weight loss of standard IBP wood pulp cellulose at Site M1 was 48 %; cellulose data for the other sites are shown in Table 5.

Table 5. Decomposition rates of natural litter and cellulose on Macquarie Island. Figures are mean % weight loss ± S.E.. Sites codes as in text.

	Site code	After 1 year	After 2 years
Native plant material			
(a) Standing dead (n=12)			
Poa foliosa, lamina		57.5 ± 10.8	
(b) Detached litter, in mesh folders on soil or litter surface (n=5)			
Poa foliosa, lamina	M1A	61.0 ± 2.7	84.2 ± 1.8
	M1	64.3 ± 4.3	84.5 ± 1.8
sheath	M1A	61.6 ± 6.5	n.d.
Stilbocarpa polaris, lamina	M1A	90.3 ± 2.8	100
	M1	90.5 ± 5.0	100
petiole	M1A	87.6 ± 2.2	n.d.
Pleurophyllum hookeri, lamina	M1A	35.7 ± 10.0	54.4 ± 5.3
	M1	66.3 ± 4.0	89.8 ± 2.0
Standard wood pulp on soil or litter surface (n=10)	M1	53.2 ± 5.5	
	M1A	42.2 ± 3.7	
	M2	70.7 ± 10.9	
	M3	51.2 ± 10.3	
	M4	62.2 ± 7.2	

n.d. = not determined

There is an apparent inconsistency between the relatively high rates of decomposition and the widespread occurrence of peat soils. Very little is known about decomposition below the ground surface but there is probably a considerable reduction in the decomposition rate of aboveground material once it is below the ground surface. Similarly, if belowground decomposition rates are less than aboveground rates, the belowground input of organic material from roots and rhizomes would be considerably greater than input from aboveground material. The organic matter content of soils increases with increasing water content (Table 2), which suggests that water-logging, and the consequent lack of aeration, are the main factors responsible for organic matter accumulation. Soil oxygen flux decreases sharply with increasing depth (Fig. 5), and may have very small values even above the water table.

There is little information on the organisms actually involved in decomposition (Table 6). Purple photosynthetic bacteria, filamentous sulphur bacteria and "iron" bacteria have also been described (6). There are no data concerned with microbial biomass or production although the respiration of a number of soils has been measured (8, 9). The broad sequence of events at Macquarie Island is probably similar to that in other comparable areas. "Parasitic and, more particularly, saprophytic fungi are both widespread and abundant, and fulfil an important function as primary agents of decay", and "the number of fungi recorded from soils are sufficient to warrant the assumption that they play some part in processes of decomposition" (7). Nematodes are considered to be of very minor importance in soil decomposition processes; seven of ten recorded genera are regarded as probable bacterial feeders and the remainder as algal feeders (4). Earthworms possibly have a significant local effect in some areas.

NUTRIENT CYCLING

Growth analysis of native species and a range of temperate agricultural species showed that plant growth is limited by the nutrient status of the grassland soil at Site M1. Plants which received only natural precipitation and distilled water grew as well on vermiculite as on natural soil, indicating the importance of atmospheric nutrients.

Large amounts of material are deposited in precipitation; the amounts decrease with increasing altitude and distance from the sea in an easterly direction. The annual deposition of total solids on the isthmus at 6 m altitude is 3.31 kg m^{-2} yr^{-1}; at Site M1 (45 m altitude), 0.20 kg m^{-2} yr^{-1}, and at Site M3 (235 m altitude), 0.09 kg m^{-2} yr^{-1}. The precipitation contains a wide range of essential plant nutrients, of which 92 % to 100 % are probably of marine origin.

The amount of nitrogen in the sea water around Macquarie Island is not known, but there are only very small traces of nitrate and nitrite. The amount of nitrogen in precipitation is, however, quite high (Table 7); the world-wide range for total nitrogen in precipitation is $0.07-2.35$ g m^{-2} yr^{-1} (14). The value for the sample from near the rookery (Table 7) is particularly high, and the relative magnitude of the tabulated values is in direct relation to the proximity of the collection sites to areas of animal activity. These results emphasise the likely importance, as a source of nitrogen, of material redistributed by wind and water from the extensive areas of animal activity – penguin

Table 6. Microbiological characteristics of a range of soils at Macquarie Island

Site and soil characteristics	Bacteria (4)	Fungi (4)	Algae (4)	Total (2) (4) microorganisms	Nematodes No. 100 g⁻¹ soil	Nematodes No. m⁻² × 10⁻⁶	Oxygen uptake μl g⁻¹ h⁻¹ 10°	20°	25°C
	No. per g soil × 10⁻⁶								
Fell-field (1)									
1. Mineral soil derived from glacial till. Grey-light brown. Gravelly									
(a) Underneath *Ditrichum* cushions	1.2	0.023	0.218	1.0–1.41(R)(3)	–	} 2.40	0.5	3.0	5.0
(b) From non-vegetated area	–	–	–	0.24–1.49(NR)	700		–	–	1.9–4.6
2. Organic soil, dark brown From underneath *Azorella* cushions	3.1	0.045	0.025	2.45–10.8(R)	5 300		15.5	13.5	21.0
Herbfield									
3. Very organic peat; plateau	4.3–9.6	0.004–0.012	<0.0001–1.0	–	–	4.10	–	–	65.0
4. Deep organic peat; beach terrace	11.7	0.141	0.091	–	–	3.55	–	–	96.0
Grassland									
5. Deep red-brown peat on slopes leading up to plateau									
(a) *Poa* root masses	7.1–17.9	0.013	<0.0001–0.004	–	10 084	} 4.58	83.5	108.0	191.0
(b) Peat between tussocks	–	–	–	–	15 016		–	–	–
6. Basaltic beach sand, near beach									
(a) *Poa* root masses	7.1	0.016	<0.0001	–	16 898	} 7.43	0.0	0.3	1.5
(b) Sand between tussocks	–	–	–	–	–		–	–	0.8
7. Peat, bog area near beach, between tussocks	15.2	0.141	0.031	–	5 071		–	–	37.0
Coastal									
8. Grey black mineral beach sand	–	–	–	2.53–5.09(NR)	–	2.92	–	–	–
9. Soil within root masses	–	–	–	8.82–15.60(R)	–	11.37	–	–	–
10.(a) Sandy organo-mineral material bound by roots, on rock pile, exposed to spray	0.4	0.046	0.025	–	–	5.32	17.0	26.5	45.0
(b) Organo-mineral soil under cushions	–	–	–	–	–	19.55	–	–	–
Origin of data	(7)			(8)		(4)		(8, 9)	

(1) Numbers correspond to Bunt's data in Table 2. All samples taken from surface 15 cm

(2) Bunt & Rovira (8) refer to "microorganisms". Bunt (7) states "no discrimination was made between bacteria and fungi"

(3) R and NR indicate rhizosphere and non-rhizosphere respectively. Rhizosphere considered as soil adhering firmly to belowground portions. Differences between R and NR are significant, and differences between soils are also significant.

(4) Fungi and bacteria, plate counts on Czapek's agar. Total microorganisms, plate counts on soil extract agar. Algae, direct count by fluorescent microscopy.

Table 7. The concentration and amount of nitrogen in precipitation

	Wireless Hill; within 50 m and downwind of penguin rookeries	Wireless Hill; western edge, north of (i.e. not downwind) and 200 m from penguin rookeries	Isthmus; meteorological enclosure
	Altitude 50 m	Altitude 100 m	Altitude 6 m
NH_3-N (mg l^{-1})	3.90	0.15	0.60
Organic–N (mg l^{-1})	5.48	1.54	2.34
Total N (mg l^{-1})	9.38	1.69	2.94
Total N (g m^{-2} yr^{-1})	8.69	1.57	2.72

rookeries and the beaches, which are constantly littered with innumerable seals. Ammonification, nitrification, and nitrogen-fixation occur in Macquarie Island soils, but are likely to be limitied by low soil temperatures and pH, and poor soil aeration.

Due to limited data, conclusions concerning the nutrient status of Macquarie Island soils are tentative. Experiments have shown that soil nutrients in the grassland at Site M1 limit plant growth with a possible deficiency in nitrogen and phosphorus (4, 5, 7, 8, 9, 22, 28). However, in view of the atmospheric input, and the abundance and healthy appearance of the vegetation, it is unlikely that nutrient deficiencies have a very significant effect on plant growth in natural grassland and herbfield communities.

The extremely high deposition of chloride, which amounts to approximately 50 % of the total deposition, seems to be without harmful effect. Plant chloride contents are high on a dry weight basis but, on a volume basis, are well below reported limits for concentrations causing damage in species with low salt tolerance. It is possible that the xeromorphic leaf characteristics of the dominant species contribute to their tolerance of strong, salt-laden winds. Analyses of the chloride content of precipitation, ground waters (Table 2), natural pools, and creeks indicate that input from precipitation is matched by output in drainage, and there is no evidence of chloride accumulation in soils. It is not known whether or not this conclusion applies to other elements.

OVERVIEW OF THE ECOSYSTEM AND MAN'S INFLUENCES ON IT

Macquarie Island is similar in many respects to its nearest neighbours — the New Zealand Shelf Islands — and to other more distant subantarctic islands. Nevertheless, it has its own distinctive features, not only biological, which set it quite apart.

The vegetation comprises a small number of well-adapted species which, given the prevailing climate, produce remarkably abundant growth. The high biomass and productivity of the grassland and herbfield formations are considered to result mainly from the ability of the vegetation to utilise efficiently low levels of irradiation at temperatures which, although low and uniform, are rarely sufficiently low to limit metabolism for any appreciable length of time. The small number of plant species also means that the botanical component of the ecosystem is extremely vulnerable to disturbing influences.

Fifty-seven bird species and seven seal species have been recorded, of which twenty-one bird species and two seal species breed on the island. Since Macquarie Island is virtually the only land in the vast expanse of ocean between Australia and the Antarctic continent, it is of vital importance as an animal breeding ground. It was this extreme abundance of animal life which first brought man to the island.

Unfortunately, man has drastically affected the island ecosystem. Fur seal and two bird species were exterminated and other animal populations severely depleted. This occurred by harvesting for commercial gain, use as food, or as a consequence of the predation of introduced dogs, cats, rats and wekas. Dogs are no longer present, but the other animals remain as an unfortunate legacy of the sealers' short-sighted self-interest. Grazing by rabbits, another animal introduced by the sealers, has severely damaged or drastically modified much of the island's vegetation.

Exploitation of the animal populations ceased in 1919, and the island was declared a sanctuary in 1933. The only current use of the island is as a base for scientific research. Apart from the two extinct bird species, other animal species threatened by the sealers' activities have now recovered or are recovering, although the fur seal species colonizing the island in recent years may not be the same as the original species. The present management policies, as administered by the Tasmanian National Parks and Wildlife Service, should preclude any future exploitation of the native animal populations, or at least, control it very strictly. It remains to be seen whether or not the current trials (27) to assess the suitability of the European rabbit flea as a myxomatosis vector will be successful.

Pressures for exploitation exist or will arise in future, e.g. tourism, mineral exploration, commercial harvesting of kelp, large-scale installations associated with non-biological research or other programmes. These and other possible types of exploitation will have varying degrees of compatibility with what should be the prime object of the management of the island, i.e. its maintenance as a nature reserve. It is to be hoped that past mistakes can and will be rectified, and avoided in future.

ACKNOWLEDGEMENTS

The Macquarie Island studies have been supported by the School of Botany, University of Melbourne, and the Antarctic Division, Department of Science. I am very grateful to Professor J.S. Turner, Professor T.C. Chambers and Dr. D.H. Ashton of the School of Botany, and to Mr. P. Sulzberger, Assistant Director (Scientific) of the Antarctic Division, for their continued interest, guidance and support. Dr. G.W. Johnstone of the Antarctic Division provided valuable assistance by collecting, from numerous sources, and collating the data in Table 4. I owe a great deal to innumerable ANARE personnel for their willing assistance at Macquarie Island.

REFERENCES

1. Ashton, D.H. 1965. Regeneration pattern of *Poa foliosa* Hook. f. on Macquarie Island. – Proc. Roy. Soc. Vict. 79: 215–233.
2. Berry, R.J. & Peters, J. 1975. Macquarie Island house mice: a genetical isolate on a sub-Antarctic island. – J. Zool. 176: 375–389.
3. Black, J.D.F. & West, D.W. 1969. Solid state reduction at a platinum microelectrode in relation to measurement of oxygen diffusion in soil. – Aust. J. Soil Res. 7: 67–72.
4. Bunt, J.S. 1954. The soil-inhabiting nematodes of Macquarie Island. – Aus. J. Zool. 2: 264–74.
5. Bunt, J.S. 1954. A comparative account of the terrestrial diatoms of Macquarie Island. – Proc. Linn. Soc. N.S.W. 79: 34–57.
6. Bunt, J.S. 1954. Notes on the bacteria belonging to the *Rhodobacteriineae* Breed, Murray and Hitchens, and the *Chlamydobacteriales* Buchanan occurring at Macquarie Island. – Proc. Linn. Soc. N.S.W. 79: 63–64.
7. Bunt, J.S. 1965. Observations on the fungi of Macquarie Island. – A.N.A.R.E. Rep. Series B (II), Publ. No. 78: 1–22.
8. Bunt, J.S. & Rovira, A.D. 1955. Microbiological studies of some subantarctic soils. – J. Soil Sci. 6: 119–28.
9. Bunt, J.S. & Rovira, A.D. 1955. The effect of temperature and heat treatment on soil metabolism. – J. Soil. Sci. 6: 129–36.
10. Colhoun, E.A. & Goede, A. 1973. Fossil penguin bones, C^{14} dates and the raised marine terrace of Macquarie Island: some comments. – Search 4: 499–501.
11. Commonwealth Bureau of Meteorology 1950–1970. – A.N.A.R.E. Rep. Series D, Meteorology. Vols. 1–20, 1948–1967.
12. Costin, A.B. & Moore, D.M. 1960. The effects of rabbit grazing on the grasslands of Macquarie Island. – J. Ecol. 48: 729–32.
13. Cumpston, J.S. 1968. Macquarie Island. Antarctic Division, Department of Supply, Australia. 380 pp.
14. Eriksson, E. 1952. Composition of atmospheric precipitation. I. Nitrogen compounds. – Tellus 4: 215–32.
15. Gillham, M. 1961. Modification of subantarctic flora on Macquarie Island by sea birds and sea elephants. – Proc. Roy. Soc. Vict. 74: 1–12.
16. Hamilton, A. 1894. Notes on a visit to Macquarie Island. – Trans. N.Z. Inst. 27: 559–79.
17. Holdgate, M.W. 1970. Introduction to Part XII. Vegetation. – In: Holdgate, M.W. (ed.) Antarctic Ecology, pp. 729–32. London: Academic Press.
18. Jenkin, J.F. 1972. Studies on Plant Growth in a Subantarctic Environment. – Ph. D. Thesis, University of Melbourne.
19. Jenkin, J.F. & Ashton, D.H. 1970. Productivity studies on Macquarie Island vegetation. – In: Holdgate, M.W. (ed.) Antarctic Ecology, pp. 851–63. London: Academic Press.
20. Loewe, F. 1957. Precipitation and evaporation in the Antarctic. – In: van Rooy, M.P. (ed.) Meteorology of the Antarctic, pp. 71–89. Pretoria: Weather Bureau.
21. Millett, M.R.O. 1972. List of publications resulting from the work of Australian National Antarctic Research Expeditions (to December 1970). – A.N.A.R.E. Rep. Series A, Publ. No. 121.
22. Piper, C.S. & Rountree, P.M. 1938. Soils from subantarctic islands. – Rep. British and N.Z. Antarct. Res. Exped. Rep. Series A, II, Part 7.
23. Poel, L.W. 1960. The estimation of oxygen diffusion rates in soil. – J. Ecol. 48: 165–73.
24. Quilty, P.G., Rubenach, M. & Wilcoxon, J.A. 1973. Miocene ooze from Macquarie Island. – Search, 4: 163–4.
25. Scott, J.H. 1882. Macquarie Island. – Trans. N.Z. Inst. 15: 484–93.
26. Shipp, E., Keith, K., Hughes, R.L. & Myers, K. 1963. Reproduction in a free-living population of domestic rabbits, *Oryctolagus cuniculus* (L), on a subantarctic island. – Nature, 200: 858–60.
27. Sobey, W.R., Adams, K.M., Johnston, G.C., Gould, L.R., Simpson, K.N.G. & Keith, K. 1973. Macquarie Island: the introduction of the European rabbit flea *Spilopsyllus cuniculi* (Dale) as a possible vector for myxomatosis. – J. Hyg. 71: 299–308.

28. Taylor, B.W. 1955. The flora, vegetation and soils of Macquarie Island. – A.N.A.R.E. Rep. Series B, II.
29. Varne, R., Gee, R.D. & Quilty, P.G.J. 1969. Macquarie Island and the cause of oceanic linear magnetic anomalies. – Science 166: 230–33.
30. Vowinckel, E. 1957. Climate of the Antarctic Ocean. – In: van Rooy, M.P. (ed.) Meteorology of the Antarctic, pp. 91–110. Pretoria: Weather Bureau.
31. Watson, K.C. 1967. The terrestrial Arthropoda of Macquarie Island. – A.N.A.R.E. Rep. Series B (I), Publ. No. 99.
32. Watt, A.S. 1947. Pattern and process in the plant community. – J. Ecol. 35: 1–22.

Rosswall, T. & Heal, O.W. (eds.) 1975.
Structure and Function of Tundra Ecosystems.
Ecol. Bull. (Stockholm) 20: 399–423.

SOUTH GEORGIA, SUBANTARCTIC

R.I. LEWIS SMITH and D.W.H. WALTON

INTRODUCTION

South Georgia (54–55°S, 36–38°W) is a subantarctic island situated ca 2 000 km east of Tierra del Fuego (Fig. 1). It is ca 160 km long and varies in width from 5 to 40 km, with its axis trending northwest to southeast. Much of its alpine topography lies above 1 000 m and most of the island is covered by extensive permanent ice with many large glaciers reaching the sea at the head of fiords.

The IBP study area occupies ca 2 km^2 on the south side of King Edward Cove, Cumberland East Bay (Fig. 1). It lies between sea level and 300 m in the lee of the 2 000 m high Allardyce Range. While part of the study area lies on the steep north slope of Brown Mountain, most of the sites are situated on an undulating area with several *roches moutonnées* and dissected by numerous small streams which frequently flow underground through the deeper peat deposits (Fig. 2). There are no permanent snow beds within the area although several patches persist until late January. Springs are abundant and give rise to extensive flushes and seepage slopes. There are several small freshwater pools and the west side of the study area is flanked by one of the island's largest lakes, ca 300 m wide. The area is composed of strongly folded tufaceous graywackes (44, 45). The youngest Pleistocene moraines which exist above the present sea level may be correlated with the post-Allerød moraines of northern Europe while three older series of moraines may represent the three phases of the Würm glaciation identified in the southern Andes (37), although they may have been deposited during irregular recession during one phase of glaciation (11). The glacial maxima are dated as at least 10 000 years B.P., ca 5 500 years B.P. and the most recent as around A.D. 1750–1800 (11) or as late as 1875 (37). A brief readvance occurred in the 1920s but all glaciers around the study area are currently receding.

Extensive exploitation of the fur and elephant seals and king penguins occurred during the 1800s (20, 32, 33). Besides several temporary encampments there was no permanent habitation until the early twentieth century (29). Several whaling stations were established between 1905 and 1920 (3) but all shore-based operations had ceased by 1965. Between about 1910 and 1930 the human population at the whaling stations during summer was several thousands although in the early 1800s there were over 3 000

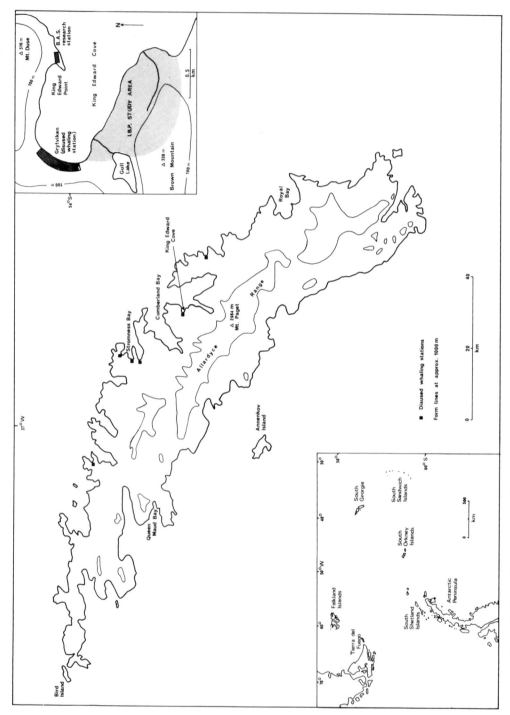

Figure 1. South Georgia, showing its position in relation to South America and the location of the IBP study area.

Figure 2. The IBP study area, King Edward Cove, South Georgia, looking south. The steep low slopes rising from the shore are dominated by tussock grass (*Poa flabellata*) and stands of *Acaena magellanica*. The undulating terrain extending from these coastal slopes to Brown Mountain (middle ground) and Gull Lake (far right) is covered by *Festuca contracta* grassland on the drier slopes and by *Rostkovia magellanica, Juncus scheuchzerioides* and bryophyte bogs in the depressions and valleys. Knoll and hill crests support sparse fell-field communities. Beyond the study area an extensive fluvio-glacial plain and glacial lakes extend from a hanging glacier near the centre of the photograph. The ice-covered Allardyce Range in the background, reaching 2 965 m in Mount Paget (left), lies ca 15 km southwest of the study area. (March 1971)

men operating from sealing vessels. However, over the past decade the permanent population has remained at only 15–50.

Scientific investigation of the island commenced with the German International Polar-Year Expedition of 1882–83 and continued sporadically as other expeditions visited South Georgia *en route* to the Antarctic. In 1925 the British Government established a marine biology station at King Edward Point, largely concerned with whale research. Besides the work of Skottsberg (35, 36) and Greene (14), largely within the IBP study area, little detailed botanical research had been undertaken prior to the commencement of the IBP Bipolar Botanical Project in 1967 (38). Other terrestrial biological sciences had been similarly neglected since most research had concentrated on the marine environment. However, in 1969 the King Edward Point settlement was taken over by the British Antarctic Survey and a multidisciplinary research station established.

401

ENVIRONMENTAL CONDITIONS

Climate

Evidence of long-term climatic fluctuations is provided by the series of glacial maxima over the past 10,000 years as indicated by the position of moraine systems. Despite the temporary re-advance of glaciers in the 1920s there has been a general recession since about the last major advance ca 100–200 years ago, suggesting a significant increase in mean air temperature (11, 37). The most recent period of advance for some glaciers coincided with a cold period commencing about 1924 (37). Ten-year running means of annual temperature reached a peak in the 1950s, but are now decreasing slightly (18). The extent of fresh-coloured rock, uncolonized by mosses or lichens, up to 3 m above the present permanent ice surface also indicates fairly rapid ice recession in recent times. Small climatic fluctuations, based on air temperature and precipitation data, have occurred over the past 65 years. Before 1938 and after 1957 the warmest month was frequently January, but between these years it was invariably February. Prior to the mid-1930s the coldest month was frequently July, or even June, but since then there has been a tendency for August to be the coldest month. Since 1945 there has been a marked increase in total annual precipitation.

The meteorological station at King Edward Cove was established in 1905 at ca 3 m above sea level. Continuous records have been maintained and summaries have been published for various periods (1, 2, 6, 30, 38, 52–56). Mean or total monthly data for several variables are presented in Table 1. Since South Georgia lies south of the Antarctic Convergence the climate is much colder than might be expected at this latitude. It has a cool oceanic climate with prevailing westerly winds. Winter and summer seasons are clearly defined although the annual range of mean monthly temperatures is barely 7°C; the absolute range of air temperatures is −19°C to 24°C. The weather recorded at King Edward Cove is strongly influenced by the high Allardyce Range to the windward which tends to create a "radiation window" on its lee side. It is representative of the IBP study area, but not of the island as a whole (31). Katabatic winds are frequent and are funnelled across the study area by deep glaciated valleys, while föhn winds also produce a localized rapid increase in air temperature (31). The radiation receipt is considerably reduced by frequent low cloud and the surrounding mountains, although the IBP sites receive little shading.

Sub-zero mean monthly air temperatures occur for 4–5 months, and summer frosts and snowfalls are frequent. Annual precipitation is high but varies greatly from year to year. Rain is frequent and often heavy during summer, with occasional daily falls exceeding 100 mm. There is a considerable winter snowfall which reduces the snow-free growing season near sea level to a maximum of ca 170 days although the corresponding period in late snow beds may not exceed 75 days. Pack ice occasionally reaches the southern part of the island in winter but there is no formation of fast ice although sheltered bays freeze over for periods of a few weeks.

Temperatures within vegetation during summer are normally well above ambient and can exceed 40°C in the litter layer of *Festuca contracta* T. Kirk grassland (47). Diurnal inversions are frequent within phanerogamic communities, with frost pockets commonly occurring in summer in stratified vegetation. Near-surface temperatures of moss banks seldom fall below 0°C in summer or for most of the winter when covered by snow (26,

Table 1. Mean monthly climatic data for King Edward Point, South Georgia

	J	F	M	A	M	J	J	A	S	O	N	D	Year
Screen temperature (°C)													
minimum (1944–64)	1.8	2.2	1.7	−0.3	−2.4	−3.6	−4.5	−4.6	−3.2	−1.1	−0.9	0.8	−1.1
mean (1905–73)	4.6	5.3	4.5	2.5	0.1	−1.1	−1.3	−1.5	0.1	1.5	2.8	3.8	1.8
maximum (1944–64)	8.3	9.5	8.5	5.8	3.4	2.0	1.3	1.5	3.0	5.4	6.5	7.0	5.2
Relative humidity (%) (1944–64)	74	72	73	77	78	78	77	76	75	75	70	73	75
Wind velocity (m s⁻¹) (1944–64, 1970–73)	4.2	4.6	4.8	4.2	4.0	4.0	4.0	4.2	4.4	4.2	4.4	4.1	4.3
Total precipitation (as equivalent rainfall) (mm) (1906–64, 1970–73)													
mean	102	124	133	135	149	130	139	135	104	77	89	88	1405
range of extremes	31–305	20–284	26–295	31–353	40–534	28–259	39–389	24–368	11–244	12–271	23–194	15–188	800–2237
Water fog (d) (1950–61)	1	2	2	2	3	2	1	1	1	1	1	1	18
Total sunshine duration (h) (1950–64, 1970–73)													
total	148	141	126	68	35	7	22	70	121	163	173	162	1236
daily mean	4.8	5.0	4.1	2.3	1.1	0.2	0.7	2.2	4.0	5.3	5.8	5.2	3.4
Theoretical day length (h)	16.5	14.7	12.6	10.4	8.4	7.4	7.9	9.5	11.6	13.8	15.8	17.0	12.1
Snow laying at midday (d) (1959–61)	4	4	4	18	28	30	31	31	30	25	8	8	221
Snowfall (d) (1950–61)	11	7	9	13	17	20	21	20	17	16	13	15	179
Snow depth on level ground	Frequent temporary cover, 1–5 cm, rarely 15–40 cm		Sporadic to continuous cover, 0–25 cm			Continuous cover, 25–100 cm			Sporadic to continuous cover, 10–50 cm		Frequent temporary cover, 1–5 cm, rarely 15–40 cm		

27). Severe and damaging frosts can occur in late autumn before winter snow accumulates, in early spring after the melt, and during winter if warm weather causes temporary melt. The growing season may be increased in some communities by the greenhouse effect caused by the warm pocket of air contained between the ground and the underside of the snow. The temperature within these air pockets is frequently more than 5°C above ambient whilst that of the plants may be 10°C higher than ambient.

Soils

The lower part of the study area has a typically glaciated topography overlain by a mantle of glacial tills and lithosols, with more mature soils and peat deposits where vegetation is well developed. The steeper slopes are extensively covered with loose fine scree. Such mineral soils are derived principally by weathering and past glacial action, chemical breakdown of rocks being relatively unimportant. Although there is no permafrost in South Georgia, the existence of vegetated hummock and hollow networks on level ground and ridge and trough systems on slopes are possibly relict phenomena of an era when permafrost existed. Small stone stripes, solifluction lobes and polygons are frequent while frost-heaving and differential sorting of mineral material occurs in most barren or sparsely vegetated terrain.

There are four principal groups of soils within the study area (Fig. 3):

(a) Organic soils. Deposits of peat exceeding 25 cm depth are formed (i) by oligotrophic bog communities in rock basins, at lake and pool margins and on valley floors where rushes and bryophytes predominate (peat depth 0.5–3.0 m); (ii) by tussock grass and associated turf-forming mosses on moist coastal plains and slopes (peat depth 0.25–2.5 m); (iii) by tall turf-forming mosses on well-drained but moist slopes (peat depth 0.25–1.0 m); (iv) by dense stands of a deciduous dwarf shrub on well-drained slopes (peat depth 0.25–0.75 m). The latter type is generally intermediate between peat and grassland brown soil. All peats are strongly acid with a pH range of 3.5–4.5. A ^{14}C date of 6 500 ± 500 years B.P. has been established for peat at ca 115 cm in a *Rostkovia magellanica* (Lam.) Hook. f. – *Sphagnum fimbriatum* Wils. bog near the study area (13), while a sample from 160 cm beneath a similar community within the study area has been dated as 8 537 ± 65 years B.P. (40).

(b) Meadow tundra soils. Soils comparable with this type occur beneath the eutrophic moss-dominated communities of seepage slopes and to a lesser extent below bryophyte marshes on more level ground. An upper peaty layer of 5–20 cm (pH 4.0–5.0) overlies a wet brown to grey band of fine clay up to 50 cm deep (pH 5.5–6.5), below which is usually a sandy or stony base.

A modified meadow tundra soil resembling the bog soils of the Alaskan tundra occurs below mesic grassland communities on wet or moist level ground. A fairly acid peat, 10–30 cm deep, overlies sandy soil or pebbles.

(c) Brown soils. Soils comparable with arctic brown soils occur on well-drained slopes or level ground beneath dry grassland. There is a superficial layer of litter overlying a more distinct peaty layer of 5–10 cm depth. This in turn overlies a dark brown to reddish-brown loamy, relatively acid soil (pH 4.2–5.2) in which there are frequently lenses of greyish clay. The depth of this loam increases to 30–40 cm where the vegetation is composed of closed stands of grass, and where a hummock and hollow system

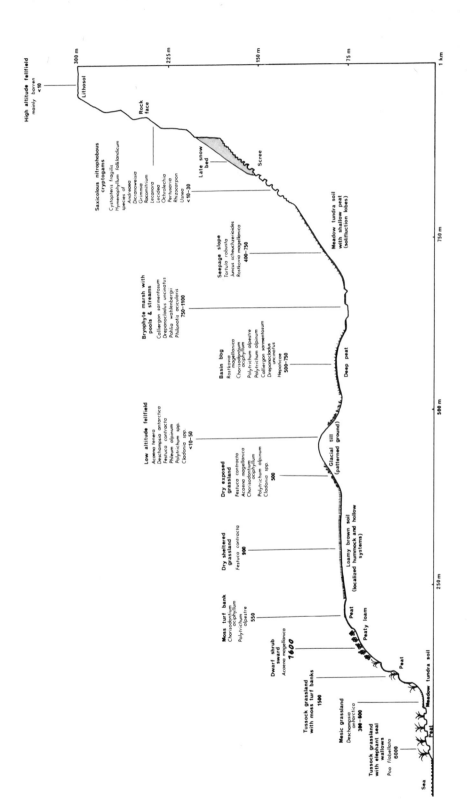

Figure 3. South Georgia IBP study area. Vegetation, soil types and estimated maximum net annual production for above and below ground living phytomass (g m^{-2} yr^{-1}).

405

has developed, it may reach about 1 m in depth beneath the earth hummocks. There is usually a basal layer of sandy debris and stones.

(d) Mineral soils. These range from fine clays, silts and sands to coarse gravels, pebbles and boulders. Where these soils exist as raw debris, vegetation is sparse or absent and virtually no organic layer has developed on the surface. Due to cryoturbic action the surface is littered with coarser material overlying fine soil varying in depth to ca 2 m. Particle and stone size increase again towards the base of the profile. They are mostly acidic in reaction (pH 4.5–5.5) but some more recently deposited morainic and fluvioglacial clays exceed pH 7.0.

The range of values for pH, loss on ignition, field moisture content, Na, K, Ca, Mg, P and N for each of the principal soil types together with the major sources of nutrient input and loss are indicated in Fig. 4. The organic soils have high levels of all major elements but the mineral soils are comparatively deficient in most, with the brown soils being intermediate. The proximity of the sea accounts for the relatively high Na levels. K, Ca and Mg are largely derived from the parent rock. The peats of bryophyte flushes and eutrophic mires have exceptionally high concentrations of Ca, although there are no calcareous rocks in this region of the island. While some P derives from rock weathering, both P and N are derived chiefly from biotic sources (seals and seabirds).

PRIMARY PRODUCTION

Community classification and dynamics

The floristic composition of the principal community types in the study area is summarized in Table 2. Besides the 24 native vascular species (14), three of which have a bipolar distribution, ca 50 alien species have been recorded around the former whaling stations (49). All the major community types are represented in the study area but since this region has been deglacierized longer than any other part of the island and has a more favourable climate, the extensive stands of closed vegetation are atypical of the island as a whole. While several species are almost restricted to this area, others, such as *Festuca contracta*, develop extensive closed grassland only in this region. Such grassland does not occur anywhere else in the geographical range of *F. contracta* although South Georgia represents the southernmost extremity of its distribution. *Acaena tenera* Alboff is also more abundant here than in any of its Fuegian habitats farther north.

There is an apparent gradation of major vegetation types occurring within an altitudinal range of 50–75 m. Each category can be ascribed to a different climatic zone in terms of northern hemisphere tundra sites. The coastal tussock grassland may be considered as maritime subpolar. Above this are dry meadow, dwarf shrub and mire communities more typical of low polar-alpine regions, while the exposed sparsely vegetated fell-field approaches that of high polar-alpine regions.

Because of the multidirectional gradients in topographic, edaphic, moisture, nutrient and microclimatic factors and the wide ecological amplitude of many species, the vegetation comprises an intricate continuum of interrelated noda (Fig. 3). Discrete community types are restricted to habitats exhibiting distinctive and relatively stable environmental conditions.

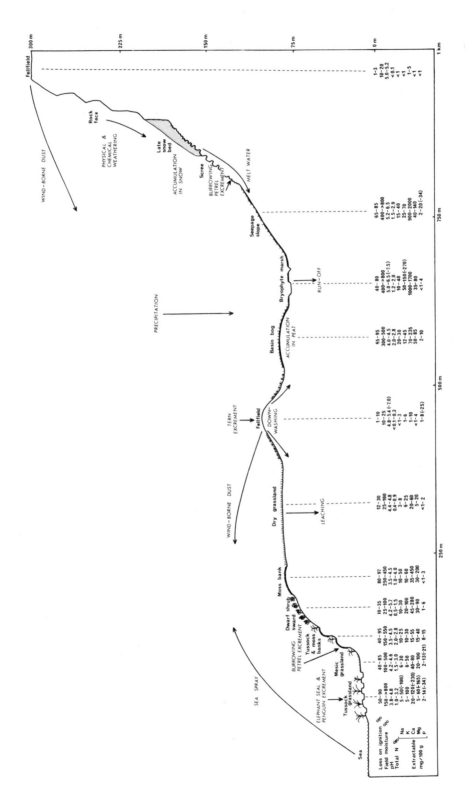

Figure 4. South Georgia IBP study area. Nutrient cycle and soil chemical data (All samples from 10–15 cm).

Table 2. Floristic composition of principal community types in IBP study area, South Georgia

Life form	Approx. total no. of species on South Georgia	Approx. no. of species which achieve dominance	Approx. number of species in principal community types (number of predominant species in brackets)							
			Dry meadow	Mesic meadow	Oligo-trophic mire	Eutrophic mire	Dwarf shrub heath	Tussock grassland	Fell-field	Rock face and crevice communities
			Festuca contracta grassland	*Deschampsia antarctica* grassland	*Rostkovia magellanica* bog	*Tortula ro-busta-Juncus scheuch-zerioides* bog	*Acaena magellanica* heath	*Poa flabel-lata* grass-land		
Grasses	5	3	2 (1)	1 (1)	3 (0)	3 (0)	1 (0)	3 (1)	3 (2)	0
Rushes	3	2	1 (0)	0	1 (1)	2 (1)	0	0	0	0
Sedges	1	0	1 (0)	0	0	1 (0)	0	0	0	0
Dwarf shrubs	2	1	2 (1)	1 (0)	2 (0)	1 (1)	1 (1)	1 (0)	2 (1)	0
Forbs	6	0	1 (0)	1 (0)	0	2 (0)	1 (0)	1 (0)	1 (0)	0
Pteridophytes	7	0	0	0	0	0	0	0	1 (0)	4 (1)
Acrocarpous mosses	100	12	9 (2)	3 (0)	6 (2)	5 (1)	2 (1)	4 (2)	18 (5)	25 (4)
Pleurocarpous mosses	20	3	0	4 (2)	0	2 (0)	0	2 (0)	0	2 (0)
Foliose liverworts	74	5	5 (1)	2 (0)	8 (2)	2 (0)	1 (0)	3 (0)	4 (0)	1 (0)
Thalloid liverworts	6	0	0	1 (0)	2 (1)	2 (1)	0	0	0	5 (2)
Fruticose lichens	45	5	9 (2)	0	7 (2)	0	1 (0)	5 (0)	14 (2)	5 (1)
Foliose lichens	25	3	2 (0)	0	1 (0)	0	0	1 (0)	2 (0)	5 (1)
Crustose and squamulose	80	14	0	0	0	0	0	0	18 (2)	25 (5)
Macro-algae	n.d.	0	0	1 (0)	0	0	0	1 (0)	0	0
% cover of IBP study area			30	<1	10	20	10	10	15	5

n.d. = not determined

The climax vegetation type and most widespread community is formed by dense stands of *Poa flabellata* (Lam.) Hook. f., individual plants of which may exceed 2 m in height (Fig. 5). Tussock grass occurs in wet to moderately dry coastal areas from sea level to ca 225 m, and is particularly luxuriant wherever there is nitrogen enrichment from birds and seals. Wet level ground amongst tussock or on raised beaches is locally dominated by *Deschampsia antarctica* Desv. forming small swards of mesic meadow. On wet valley floors, at lake margins and in rock basins extensive oligotrophic mires occur, dominated by a rush, *Rostkovia magellanica*, mosses and liverworts. Of these hydrophytic bryophytes *Calliergon sarmentosum* (Wahlenb.) Kindb. and *Drepanocladus uncinatus* (Hedw.) Warnst. locally develop large pure stands while *Pohlia wahlenbergii* (Web. et Mohr) Andrews and *Philonotis acicularis* (C. Muell.) Kindb. frequently dominate the margins of streams. Wet eutrophic seepage slopes receiving some degree of flushing are usually dominated by another rush, *Juncus scheuchzerioides* Gaudich., and the moss *Tortula robusta* Hook. et Grev., although *Rostkovia magellanica* and the dwarf shrub *Acaena magellanica* (Lam.) Vahl are often associated. Where drainage improves, *A. magellanica* and *Tortula robusta* predominate and on the drier stonier slopes the shrub forms dense pure stands. In similar but moister situations the tall turf-forming mosses, *Chorisodontium aciphyllum* (Hook. f. et Wils.) Broth. and *Polytrichum alpestre* Hoppe, develop deep bryophyte banks which also extend into the drier *Rostkovia* bogs and tussock communities.

Figure 5. *Poa flabellata* on a South Georgian beach. The exceptional height of the plants has been accentuated by erosion around the base of the tussock stools caused by elephant seals. The figure is 1.91 m tall. (December 1970)

In comparatively sheltered situations *Festuca contracta* forms extensive closed swards while on the drier, more exposed slopes it develops a mixed grassland with *Acaena magellanica* and abundant bryophytes and lichens, especially *Cladonia rangiferina* (L.) Web. All dry windswept mineral soils receiving little or no winter snow cover support a very open fell-field vegetation dominated by short cushion and turf-forming mosses (species of *Andreaea, Dicranoweisia, Grimmia, Polytrichum, Racomitrium*), crustose lichens (species of *Buellia, Lecidea, Lecanora, Rhizocarpon*) and malformed fruticose lichens (species of *Cladonia, Stereocaulon*), although scattered grasses (*Deschampsia antarctica, Festuca contracta, Phleum alpinum*) and dwarf shrubs (*Acaena magellanica, A. tenera*) are infrequent associates, particularly in the lee of large stones. A wide range of saxicolous lichen communities occur on most rock surfaces. Sheltered damp rocks support stands of short cushion and turf-forming mosses with abundant hepatics and occasionally ferns (*Cystopteris fragilis* (L.) Bernh., *Hymenophyllum falklandicum* Baker, *Polystichum mohrioides* (Bory) C. Presl.) in crevices. There are no aquatic or emergent vascular plants but dense growth of *Calliergon sarmentosum, Drepanocladus* cf. *aduncus* (Hedw.) Warnst., and *Campylium* sp. occurs down to at least 30 m in some nearby lakes (22). *Verrucaria* cf. *aethiobola* Wahlenb. ex Ach. (23) and filamentous algae are frequent in most freshwater systems.

The environmental pattern in the vegetation is related mainly to the moisture status of the substratum, which results from the local topography and drainage patterns, and gives rise to most of the seral variation exhibited by the vegetation (Fig. 3). The commonest type of succession is the gradient from wet mire to dry fell-field and usually includes several intergrading communities, seldom more than narrow ecotones. Such a continuum generally comprises a series of assemblages dominated successively by *Rostkovia, Juncus, Acaena, Festuca* and *Phleum*, together with a corresponding succession of cryptogams, e.g. *Drepanocladus uncinatus, Chorisodontium aciphyllum, Tortula robusta, Polytrichum alpinum* Hedw. and *Cladonia* spp. Another common gradient ranges from *Poa flabellata* grassland in wet biotically disturbed areas, through more open tussock with *Chorisodontium* banks on moist slopes and into dry *Festuca* grassland with and without abundant cryptogam associates, and ultimately into open fell-field. Ground subjected to cryoturbation often possesses a small-scale pattern comprising zones of cryptogams on the larger, more stable sorted stones arranged peripherally around the finer more mobile centres, and vascular species commencing on the stable earth ramps of solifluction lobes or frost heave phenomena. Coastal rocks also exhibit lichen zonations related to exposure to wind and salt deposition and to nitrogen enrichment from seabird excrement.

The morphological pattern is restricted to a few species with rhizomatous growth and is most prominent in open stony situations undergoing primary colonization. In sheltered habitats *Acaena magellanica* is often a pioneer colonist and quickly spreads by radial development of its rhizomes, while in fell-field habitats *A. tenera* forms similar but much smaller colonies. *Phleum alpinum* tends to produce tillers from rhizomes which, in exposed stony situations, appear to grow in a radiating pattern as the central part dies out. Such *Phleum* plants usually represent a stage in a small-scale succession initiated by a pioneer bryophyte colonist, usually *Polytrichum alpinum, P. juniperinum* Hedw. or *P. piliferum* Hedw., each of which also produces a circular pattern resulting from the radiating growth of underground stems. As organic matter accumulates, other bryophytes (mainly *Racomitrium austro-georgicum* (C. Muell.) Par. and hepatics) and lichens invade the developing moss hummock. As stability and moisture retention increase, vascular species (*Phleum alpinum, Acaena* spp. and occasionally *Festuca contracta*) become established. Depending on the degree of shelter and moisture a procumbent form of *A. magellanica* may eventually dominate the habitat. These small hummocks may be the initial stage of much larger hummock and hollow systems which occur in several areas of *Festuca* grassland. The rhizomatous growth of *Rostkovia* and *Juncus* in wet habitats often produces linear patterns of tillers extending over several metres but derived from a single parent.

Most vascular species and many mosses and lichens produce abundant seeds or spores but their viability is generally low and seedling or sporeling establishment sparse, both declining where environmental severity increases. There are few fertile species of liverworts. In all groups, vegetative propagules are the principal mode of dissemination, establishment and community development.

Standing crop, production and production rates

The IBP Bipolar Botanical Project (38) assessed various growth parameters for phytometric crop species grown at field sites of varying natural vegetation and microclimate, in an attempt to ascertain potential production and seasonal changes in growth rates, etc. For most parameters the values for South Georgia were appreciably lower than those obtained at Disko Island, West Greenland (lat. 69°N) (21).

In all vascular plant communities, peak production is not reached until late January— early February although new growth is produced from late October until late March in most species. Peak production in bryophytes and lichens (up to ca 1 000 g m^{-2} and 125 g m^{-2} respectively) tends to occur early in the summer before a dense canopy of vascular plants develops. Radiation receipt is greatest from October to December, reaching a maximum in November, but air temperatures are highest from January to March with February being the warmest month.

Extensive closed stands of the deciduous dwarf shrub *Acaena magellanica* occur on dry to moist slopes. Leaf production commences 1—2 weeks before the disappearance of the snow at many sites, as soon as the greenhouse cavity becomes effective. Growth is rapid although maximum dry weight production (850 g m^{-2} aboveground and 500 g m^{-2} belowground) is not achieved until late January when a leaf area index of at least 4 is attained (46). Maximum leaf size occurs in February by leaves initiated in January, while smaller leaves are produced until late March. Dry weight production of rhizomes increases until February as photosynthate is passed from the leaves to the rhizome system, although growth continues until late March. Rhizomes can grow up to 35 cm in a growing season and large numbers of inflorescences are produced. Inflorescences are initiated from mid-October onwards with the main periods of anthesis being mid-November—mid-December; mature seed is produced from late January onwards. Leaf fall occurs at the onset of winter and the foliage undergoes rapid decomposition so that by snow melt only a very small amount of litter has accumulated, comprising mainly petioles and rhizomes. Data for the peak production period in a dense *Acaena magellanica* stand are presented in Table 3. Seedlings of both *A. magellanica* and *A. tenera* have very slow growth rates and low production rates, those for the former species being ca 5 times greater than for *A. tenera* (47).

Table 3. Mid-season standing crop and net annual production data for three predominant community types.

Acaena magellanica site: Sheltered north-facing moist slope at ca 10 m. Data are maximum values for growing season, late January–early February (46).

Festuca contracta site: Moderately exposed north-facing gentle slope at ca 35 m. Data are for mid-March harvest, i.e. 4–6 weeks after peak production (48).

Poa flabellata site: Relatively sheltered, wet level ground with elephant seals wallowing between tussocks, at ca 3 m. Data are estimates for peak production around mid-January. Aboveground standing crop values of up to 15 kg m^{-2} living material and 10 kg m^{-2} dead material have been obtained for single plants of *P. flabellata* within 1 m^2 quadrats, but due to the openness of the community, the data in the table below have been reduced accordingly (17).

	Acaena magellanica dwarf shrub community	*Festuca contracta* meadow community	*Poa flabellata* grassland community
Community plant cover (%)	100	100	60
Community leaf area index	4	–	–
Standing crop (g m^{-2})			
Aboveground:			
Living Monocotyledons	0	208	7 500
Forbs	0	0	25
Woody green	362	85	0
non-green	938	132	0
Bryophytes	221	ca 500	0
Lichens	0	12	0
Algae	0	0	5
Dead (standing)			
Monocotyledons	0	1 598	5 000
Forbs	0	(mainly	5
Woody	517	*Festuca*)	0
Litter	4	140	250
Belowground:			
Living and dead	7 536	1 642	5 000
Total standing crop	9 573	4 317	17 785
Above: belowground standing crop	0.25	1.63	2.56
Net production (g m^{-2})			
Aboveground:			
Monocotyledons	0	160	5 000
Forbs	0	0	20
Woody green	350	80	0
non-green	505	100	0
Bryophytes	250	150	0
Lichens	0	2	0
Algae	0	0	5
Belowground:			
All groups	ca 500	ca 350	1 000
Total net production	1 605	840	6 025
Above: belowground net production	2.19	1.41	5.03

Leaf production in *Festuca contracta* grassland commences when soil temperatures exceed 0°C shortly after snow melt. Leaves begin to die back from the apices following peak production in February. A proportion of most leaves and of some inflorescences remain green through the winter but die completely early in the following season. Inflorescences are initiated by February of the previous summer and become visible as swellings in November, emerging in early January. Anthesis occurs a week or two later and mature seeds are produced in early March. Tiller and inflorescence production and above- and belowground net annual production is considerably lower at more exposed sites (43). Once dead grass material becomes detached, litter decomposition proceeds relatively quickly due to the high invertebrate and microbial populations and the frequent high summer temperatures at this level. Production data for *Festuca* grassland containing ca 30 % *Acaena magellanica* are given in Table 3. Corresponding data for almost pure grassland with < 5 % afforded by *Acaena* were considerably lower (41). Closed swards usually have a high proportion of the aboveground *Festuca* material (70–85 %) as standing dead foliage of the previous several years (15, 41, 48).

Tussock grass (*Poa flabellata*) is the most widespread and abundant vascular species on South Georgia. Individual plants develop a pedestal of dead and decomposing foliage and roots. In seal wallow areas the grass is dense, and few, if any, other species are associated; on steeper slopes the tussocks are smaller and are interspersed with moss banks and *Acaena magellanica*. Annual production of leaves, commonly exceeding 1 m in length, is high, particularly in enriched habitats (Table 3). Leaf production commences in October, possibly before snow melt occurs, reaching maximum production around January, but leaves die back towards the end of summer although the basal parts of many remain green for 1–3 years (17). Inflorescences are initiated by December of the previous season, developing rapidly in the new growing season. Anthesis occurs in early December and seeds are mature by late January.

Phleum alpinum is widespread on South Georgia but rarely forms closed swards. New leaves are produced shortly after the spring melt in sheltered, densely vegetated habitats but in the fell-field communities which have little or no snow cover in winter, leaf production does not commence until some time later. Flower initiation occurs in early spring and anthesis takes place during February, or later in fell-field sites, with seed set coinciding almost with the onset of winter. The relative growth rate, net assimilation rate and production of laterals decline with increasing exposure or altitude (7, 8, 9). Considerable differences exist in the standing crop of the grass in different habitats. Total dry weight of living above- plus belowground *Phleum* ranged from > 300 g m^{-2} in a sheltered pioneering community on enriched gravelly ground, > 80 g m^{-2} on a sheltered moist slope with negligible associated species, 33 g m^{-2} in a mire with high cover of *Rostkovia, Acaena* and *Tortula*, to 4.5 g m^{-2} in an exposed fell-field community with only scattered cryptogam associates. The mean number of flowering tillers m^{-2} at each of these sites was 260, 54, 21 and 13 respectively, and of vegetative tillers m^{-2} was > 1 000, > 250, 133 and 101 respectively (8, 10).

The tall acrocarpous mosses *Pohlia wahlenbergii* and *Philonotis acicularis* occur in flushes and at stream margins either as pure stands of either species or as mixed communities. The current year's growth arises from the horizontally aligned older shoots. Annual incremental growth is easily determined and is generally 4–5 cm. Net annual shoot production, as determined from cores, for *Pohlia* ranges from ca 380–850 g m^{-2} and for mixed stands from ca 960–1 055 g m^{-2}, the lower values being obtained from drier sites (12).

Polytrichum alpestre forms locally extensive deep banks on well-drained slopes often amongst tussock grass. The slow decomposition rate in these banks probably results from the relatively low microbial populations due to the high acidity of the peat. Net annual production ranges from 450–507 g m^{-2}, although these represent minimum values since dry weight losses due to decomposition were not considered (26).

The turf-forming acrocarp Tortula robusta predominates in eutrophic mires and in Acaena magellanica stands, but it is also associated with most phanerogamic vegetation. Growth occurs as an apical extension of the main shoot or by the occasional production of lateral shoots. Maximum growth in a dense Acaena sward occurs in early spring before the shrub canopy has developed. A standing crop of ca 500 g m^{-2} in October, shortly after melt, decreases steadily to 125 g m^{-2} by January–February, when the leaf area index of Acaena is about 4, as the lower portions of the shoots decompose. The decreasing leaf area index towards the end of summer permits further growth of Tortula, which reaches 425 g m^{-2} by late March (46).

The fruticose lichen Cladonia rangiferina is widespread and is abundant and locally dominant in dry, exposed Festuca contracta grassland. Cores of lichen, which excluded the blackish decomposing basal portion of the podetia, grown for 100 days at a Festuca grassland site at 30 m and at a fell-field site at 150 m, increased in dry weight by 127 g m^{-2} and 98 g m^{-2} respectively. Mean podetium length during this period increased by 5.3 mm and 4.6 mm for the low and high altitude sites respectively (25).

Production processes

Detached leaves of Acaena magellanica and A. tenera have maximum rates of photosynthesis of ca 9 mg CO_2 g^{-1} h^{-1} and 11 mg CO_2 g^{-1} h^{-1} respectively at an optimal temperature of ca 10°C. Photosynthesis at −2°C was over 40 % of the maximum in both species. A comparison between tetraploid A. magellanica from Tierra del Fuego and diploid material from South Georgia suggests that the upper compensation point could be much higher for the latter plants (ca 40°C) than for the tetraploid plants (ca 23°C), particularly at low light intensities (47).

Chlorophyll levels in Festuca contracta rise rapidly to a mid-growing season peak in late December–early January (4.75 and 4.14 mg g^{-1} for sheltered and exposed populations respectively). A maximum of 5.15 mg g^{-1} was attained in grassland treated with N fertilizer. Following a rapid decline there was a secondary peak in late February–early March after seed production was complete. During winter the level dropped to a mean of 1.75–2.00 mg g^{-1} and 1.68 mg g^{-1} for the sheltered and exposed sites respectively (43). Maximum values for the current year's vegetative shoots in Acaena spp. were attained in late January, being 6.75 mg g^{-1} in A. magellanica, 4.61 mg g^{-1} in A. tenera and 4.33 mg g^{-1} in A. magellanica x tenera (47). Data for other taxa were obtained shortly after mid-season and probably represent below-peak values, e.g. 3.59 and 2.46 mg g^{-1} for vegetative and flowering tillers respectively of Uncinia meridensis Steyermark, 4.45 and 4.81 mg g^{-1} for vegetative and flowering tillers respectively of Phleum alpinum, and 16.26 and 18.90 mg g^{-1} for vegetative tillers of Juncus scheuchzerioides and Rostkova magellanica respectively (47), while a maximum total chlorophyll

414

content of 6.25 mg g^{-1} has been obtained in mature leaves of *Poa flabellata*, with a maximum total carotenoid content of 0.48 mg g^{-1} (17).

Mid-season energy contents for the leaves and shoots of the principal species in the main communities in the study are listed in Table 4. The values for the inflorescences and scapes of *Acaena* spp. fell within the same range as for the leaves while the woody stem varied from 19.09 kJ g^{-1} (*A. tenera*) to 19.47 kJ g^{-1} (*A. magellanica*). For all fractions the values for the hybrid *A. magellanica x tenera* fell between those of the two parent taxa. Of the grasses, the leaves of *Poa flabellata* had a considerably higher energy value (21.06 kJ g^{-1}) than the other grasses. Grass inflorescences had lower values with the exception of *Festuca contracta* which still possessed immature seeds. Forbs and pteridophytes had relatively high values ranging from 19.55 kJ g^{-1} in *Callitriche antarctica* Engelm. to 21.31 kJ g^{-1} in *Galium antarcticum* Hook. f. With the exception of *Tortula robusta*, mosses had low energy values, particularly *Sphagnum fimbriatum* (18.25 kJ g^{-1}) (42). Total carbohydrate content in *Poa flabellata* leaves reaches an exceptional mid-season maximum of 73 %.

The nutrient contents of the shoots and leaves of the principal species in the main community types in the study area, sampled in early, mid and late growing season, are listed in Table 4. In most species the levels of N, P and K are high in new foliage but these decrease throughout the summer, while Ca tends to increase as the tissues mature. The cycling of Na and Mg appears to be less predictable although in the majority of species there is a decline in Mg as the plants age. Generally, species growing in wet acid bogs, moss peat banks, dry grassland and fell-field have low nutrient levels while those of eutrophic mires and biotically disturbed tussock areas have relatively high concentrations, especially of Na, P and N. The maximum levels obtained from 21 species analysed throughout a growing season were 1.2 %, 0.9 % and 5.4 % (dry weight) for Na, P and N respectively in *Callitriche antarctica*, 3.1 % and 0.6 % for Ca and Mg respectively in *Acaena magellanica*, and 4.8 % for K in *Galium antarcticum*.

HERBIVORES

There are no native grazing mammals in South Georgia, the largest native herbivores being beetles. Rats, introduced in the early 1800s are widespread in many coastal areas (19) and are fairly abundant in the study area where they eat the roots of *Poa flabellata*, leaves and rhizomes of *Acaena magellanica* and leaves of some grasses. The introduction of reindeer by whalers between 1909 and 1924 (5) to two regions several kilometres from the study area has led to serious damage to the vegetation by grazing and trampling and to the local eradication of many macro-lichens, bryophyte banks and *A. magellanica* and *P. flabellata* (24, 40). Some overgrazed communities have been replaced by swards of the alien grass *Poa annua* (49). The number of deer has increased from around a dozen to at least 2 500 over the past 60 years. Herbivorous arthropods are few in number of species (16), but shoot apices and sporophytes of mosses and leaves of *Acaena magellanica* and various grasses are grazed by several species of Coleoptera. Damage to the plants is sometimes considerable particularly at the base of grass shoots, and the insects may be partly responsible for the low flowering frequency of *Festuca contracta* in dense grassland (43). At least one mollusc species inhabits moss cushions on rock faces (40).

415

Table 4. Chemical analysis and energy contents of current year living shoots and leaves of principal species in the main community types in the study area of South Georgia

Community and species	Energy content (kJ g^{-1})	Total nutrient content (% dry weight)																
		Na			K			Ca			Mg			P			N		
Tussock grassland																			
Poa flabellata	21.06	0.37	0.17	0.11	1.70	1.40	0.94	0.01	0.16	0.31	0.06	0.12	0.13	0.19	0.20	0.44	1.80	1.40	2.00
Callitriche antarctica	19.55	0.65	0.78	0.46	2.40	1.90	3.10	0.56	0.63	0.44	0.30	0.28	0.18	0.86	0.62	0.45	5.40	3.20	3.00
Dry meadow																			
Festuca contracta	19.26	0.02	0.01	0.02	2.00	1.40	1.30	0.06	0.09	0.12	0.09	0.09	0.10	0.25	0.21	0.17	1.70	1.30	1.30
Galium antarcticum	21.31	0.08	0.05	0.06	4.00	4.40	3.10	0.91	1.10	1.00	0.36	0.30	0.31	0.49	0.34	0.30	4.10	2.40	2.30
Mesic meadow																			
Deschampsia antarctica	20.39	0.05	0.23	0.20	1.80	1.65	1.40	0.02	0.13	0.09	0.02	0.26	0.19	0.39	0.47	0.43	3.50	4.60	4.90
Dwarf shrub heath																			
Acaena magellanica	19.55	0.12	0.58	0.50	3.13	1.41	1.70	1.24	1.71	3.07	0.51	0.44	0.55	0.59	0.42	0.27	4.00	2.50	1.42
Oligotrophic mire																			
Rostkovia magellanica	20.35	0.05	0.04	0.04	1.60	1.60	1.80	0.31	0.22	0.23	0.09	0.09	0.09	0.39	0.25	0.26	2.00	2.10	2.40
Eutrophic mire																			
Juncus scheuchzerioides	20.52	0.28	0.35	0.32	4.30	3.00	2.70	0.30	0.48	0.65	0.34	0.17	0.19	0.58	0.30	0.20	2.90	2.50	1.70
Ranunculus biternatus	19.64	0.93	0.46	1.10	3.90	2.90	2.70	0.74	0.72	0.63	0.18	0.11	0.10	0.67	0.41	0.30	3.60	2.70	1.80
Tortula robusta	20.47	0.03	0.08	0.10	1.30	0.91	0.86	0.29	0.27	0.25	0.29	0.22	0.19	0.45	0.30	0.26	2.00	1.30	1.20
Pohlia wahlenbergii	–	0.10	0.10	0.10	2.10	1.50	0.78	0.94	0.81	0.62	0.21	0.26	0.19	0.58	0.30	0.21	2.20	1.30	0.90
Fell-field																			
Acaena tenera	20.14	0.15	0.62	0.55	2.70	1.24	1.10	0.51	0.94	1.00	0.42	0.41	0.39	0.10	0.35	0.36	0.89	2.45	2.80
Colobanthus quitensis	–	0.18	–	0.18	4.30	–	3.10	0.67	–	0.68	0.34	–	0.25	0.57	–	0.39	2.80	–	1.50
Phleum alpinum	19.72	0.04	0.01	0.01	2.60	1.30	1.20	0.04	0.05	0.03	0.09	0.14	0.09	0.51	0.28	0.28	2.80	2.10	1.20
Polystichum mohrioides	19.97	0.04	0.05	0.06	2.40	2.00	1.40	0.31	0.43	0.64	0.37	0.39	0.45	0.29	0.27	0.22	2.20	1.90	1.90
Moss turf bank																			
Chorisodontium aciphyllum	19.51	0.04	0.08	0.10	0.71	0.52	0.49	0.46	0.27	0.25	0.26	0.20	0.21	0.29	0.19	0.18	1.50	0.94	0.90
Polytrichum aplestre	19.55	0.38	0.08	0.06	0.56	0.60	0.68	0.03	0.05	0.07	0.14	0.15	0.17	0.09	0.12	0.13	1.00	1.20	1.30

For each element values in first column = early season sample (November); second column = mid season sample (January-February); third column = late season sample (early April); energy contents (ash-free weight basis) were obtained for mid season samples. Analyses undertaken by the Institute of Terrestrial Ecology, Merlewood Research Station, Grange-over-Sands, Cumbria, England.

Tardigrades, nematodes, enchytraeids, rotifers, etc. are often abundant in hydrophytic mosses, but these groups are negligible in terms of herbivory and biomass.

CARNIVORES AND INSECTIVORES

There are no obligate terrestrial carnivores in South Georgia. The introduced rats take eggs and chicks from nests of burrowing petrels (*Fregetta tropica* Gould, *Oceanites oceanicus* Kuhl, *Pelicanoides* spp.), ducks (*Anas flavirostris, A. georgica* Gm.) and pipits (*Anthus antarcticus*), while brown skuas (*Catharacta skua* Mathews) and sheathbills (*Chionis alba* Gm.) also take eggs, particularly from penguins (*Eudyptes chrysolophus* Brandt, *Pygoscelis* spp.). With the exception of the endemic South Georgian pipit and the two species of duck, all birds feed largely at sea on fish and crustacea (28). The skua and to a lesser extent the Dominican gull (*Larus dominicanus* Lichtenstein) are the only predatory birds, killing small petrels and occasionally taking chicks from nests. Skuas, gulls, sheathbills and giant petrels (*Macronectes* spp.) are also scavengers eating carrion in penguin rookeries or that washed up on the shore. The pipit and ducks are the only birds to feed on insects and other small arthropods.

Amongst the terrestrial arthropods predation is restricted almost entirely to beetles and spiders, although several species of Acarina, Collembola and Diptera are scavenging carnivores (16).

DECOMPOSITION AND SOIL PROCESSES

In hydric and mesic communities there is an abundant microfauna, but in the drier communities mites, collembola, spiders, beetles, various arthropod larvae, etc. are only locally abundant. In the more loamy soils and tussock peat lumbricid earthworms (*Acanthrodilus* sp.) are relatively common.

The maximum number of several invertebrate groups from various vegetation types is indicated in Table 5 (41). Relatively high numbers of arthropods occurred immediately following the spring melt then declined, but in *Festuca* grassland there was a second peak in the mid-growing season, whereas in an *Acaena magellanica* community mid-season numbers were low when canopy shading was greatest, with early and late season peaks when leaf area indices were low. Collembola and mites formed the great bulk of the biomass, particularly in the dwarf shrub and grass communities, while Coleoptera were most numerous in the latter. Numbers of all groups declined in the wetter and more exposed communities.

The numbers of bacteria per gramme dry weight in litter and sub-surface soil in a sheltered *Festuca* grassland, using a plate dilution technique, increased throughout the season following melt (41). In early summer the number of bacteria in litter and soil was approximately 0.08×10^6 g^{-1} and 0.01×10^6 g^{-1} respectively. Around midsummer these numbers increased to 0.66×10^6 g^{-1} and 0.02×10^6 g^{-1} respectively, and by late summer they had risen to 2.09×10^6 g^{-1} and 0.03×10^6 g^{-1}. The estimated wet

417

Table 5. Maximum numbers of some invertebrate groups extracted by the Tullgren funnel method from different closed vegetation types (numbers m^{-2})

Dominant plant species	Altitude (m)	Moisture regime of community	Sampling date	Enchytraeidae	Acarina	Araneida	Collembola	Coleoptera adults	+ larvae	Diptera
Acaena magellanica	20	moist	15.3.71	n.d.	31 080	960	56 500	60	510	230
Agrostis capillaris L. ☆	25	wet	13.3.70	1 410	7 230	960	10 740	570	1 130	110
Deschampsia antarctica	15	moist	24.2.70	170	16 500	850	8 760	60	280	226
Festuca contracta	35	moist	13.3.70	960	32 380	2 200	32 940	340	230	60
Festuca contracta	80	dry	8.2.71	280	22 370	110	22 880	0	0	60
Poa flabellata	15	moist	1.3.71	1 020	28 250	620	28 250	230	1 240	110
Phleum alpinum	15	moist	13.3.70	3 110	11 070	230	7 060	1 020	2 040	60
Rostkovia magellanica	15	wet	25.3.70	0	12 430	1 530	7 180	280	230	110
Chorisodontium aciphyllum	80	moist	25.1.71	110	11 300	0	9 040	0	0	60
Cladonia rangiferina	80	dry	25.1.71	280	6 440	0	5 590	0	0	230

☆ Naturalized alien grass (49)

n.d. = not determined

weight of bacteria in litter (wet weight) ranged from 0.02 μg g^{-1} early in the season to 0.63 μg (ww) g^{-1} (ww) late in the season, and the corresponding soil samples from 0.01 μg (ww) g^{-1} (ww) to 0.04 μg (ww) g^{-1} (ww). The numbers of bacteria and bacterial biomass at an exposed *Festuca* site were very much lower, e.g. the corresponding mid-summer levels were 0.06 x 10^6 g^{-1} and 0.001 x 10^6 g^{-1} for litter and soil (dw) respectively. Bacterial counts for litter in a *Poa flabellata* community were rather lower than those for the sheltered *Festuca* site although the more organic *Poa* soil had higher numbers than the corresponding samples from *Festuca* grassland. Late season data for the *Poa* samples were approximately 1.50 x 10^6 g^{-1} for litter and 0.07 x 10^6 g^{-1} for soil.

Deep deposits of wet acidic peat beneath some vegetation types suggests that decomposition is slow, particularly under anaerobic conditions where invertebrate and microbial populations are small. There is very little litter accumulation in *Acaena magellanica* stands due to rapid decomposition of foliage during winter. Over 90 % loss in dry weight occurs within 14 weeks, the remaining 10 % comprising mainly petioles (46). Litter bags containing *Festuca contracta* left for 1 year indicated that dry weight loss in current year green material was ca 56 % at sheltered and exposed grassland sites while loss in standing dead material ranged from 20 % at the more exposed sites to 25 % at a sheltered site (41). Loss in *Poa flabellata* standing dead material, however, ranged from 12 % at the sheltered site to 30 % at the most exposed site. These high values are probably overestimates since under natural conditions it takes several years before standing material becomes incorporated into the litter layer in the *Festuca* grassland ecosystem.

NUTRIENT CYCLING

Few data are available on nutrient cycling. Growth experiments using cereal crop species (39) and native plants grown in numerous local soil types within the study area have indicated a deficiency of nutrients in most soils but an excessive and possibly toxic amount in certain others. Although some organic soils have very high levels of most mineral nutrients, growth and performance were invariably improved by the addition of nutrients either in solution in pot experiments or as commercial N:P:K fertilizer in *Festuca* grassland ecosystem studies (43). Improved production and increased N, P and K levels in the foliage were also recorded in tussock grassland following burning (40). Aerial production in *Poa flabellata* grassland is considerably increased wherever stands are influenced by seal or bird colonies. This also occurs on a smaller scale where burrowing petrels nest in open *Festuca* grassland. Fell-field communities are locally enriched where there are colonies of terns (*Sterna vittata* Reichenow), while saxicolous cryptogamic communities are particularly well developed beneath colonies of cliff-breeding sea birds (*Daption capensis* (L.), *Phalacrocorax atriceps* Lönnberg). Principal nutrient sources are shown in Fig. 4.

In most vascular species the level of N, P, Mg and Na in litter and standing dead, particularly early in the season, is frequently as great as or greater than that in current year's living leaves. The level of K is about one sixth, and of Ca at least twice that found in the new growth. Therefore, in communities with a high proportion of litter and standing dead, e.g. *Poa flabellata* and *Festuca contracta* grassland, the total amount of nutrients retained in this dead material can be considerable and will be released at a rate determined by the rate of decomposition. Standing dead and litter in a typical *Festuca* grassland may contain over 10 g m^{-2} of N and over 3 g m^{-2} each of K and Ca, while these values for the total living plus dead aboveground vegetation can exceed 18 g m^{-2} and 8 g m^{-2} respectively (41). In *Acaena magellanica* and bryophyte marshes where decomposition proceeds quickly, nutrient turnover must be relatively rapid. Lichens containing blue-green algae may be important N-fixers in some habitats, e.g. *Leptogium menziesii* Mont. in *Tortula-Acaena* communities and *Stereocaulon glabrum* (Müll. Arg.) Vain. in exposed *Festuca* grassland and fell-field communities.

INTERACTIONS BETWEEN TERRESTRIAL AND AQUATIC ECOSYSTEMS

Almost all the South Georgian vertebrates, with the exception of the introduced reindeer and rats, are dependent on the marine ecosystem for their existence. All seabirds and seals come ashore to breed and moult in the summer. The large numbers of birds and seals around most coastal areas result in soil enrichment, which undoubtedly influences the distribution and development of the luxuriant stands of tussock grass (*Poa flabellata*). Besides fur and elephant seals (*Arctocephalus gazella* (Peters.), *Mirounga leonina* (Linn.)), tussock grass is also inhabited by several species of burrowing petrels which not only enrich the substratum but also aerate the root environment. Penguins have the greatest local effect on vegetation since their densely packed rookeries, severe trampling and excessive guano enrichment prevent all but a few lichens and algae from colonizing the rocks and mud. Farther inland, the nutrient-deficient mineral fell-field soils may be locally enriched by colonies of Dominican gulls, Antarctic terns or diving petrels. Coastal cliffs used as nesting sites by other petrels and rocks or boulders used as bird perches are often covered by stands of nitrophilous lichens. The activities of seals and penguins sometimes increase the nutrient status of freshwater pools near the shore. Duck populations are greatest in areas of such enriched pools where invertebrates and algae are more abundant (50, 51).

OVERVIEW OF THE ECOSYSTEM AND MAN'S INFLUENCE ON IT

The structure and composition of South Georgian terrestrial ecosystems are determined by two principal factors, namely isolation from any major land mass and the extension northwards of the Antarctic Convergence resulting in oceanic polar-alpine conditions at a relatively low latitude (54°S). Unlike most tundra regions of the world the comparatively long, wet and cold growing season permits high net annual production of several of its floristic components, particularly *Poa flabellata*, *Acaena magellanica* and some bryophytes.

In terms of diversity of plant and animal species and the extent of closed vegetation,

South Georgia is somewhat intermediate between other subantarctic islands and the maritime Antarctic region. The combination of comparatively severe environmental conditions and of a narrow range of plant and animal groups and species has produced relatively simple ecosystems.

Parts of South Georgia, notably the region in which the IBP study area is situated, have been free of glacial ice for at least 6 000 years, since peat deposits of that age are not uncommon. Provisional results from recent palynological studies indicate that the flora has changed little during this period although species abundance has fluctuated, presumably due to minor climatic changes (4). The island had experienced no human disturbance until around 1800. The long-term effect on the terrestrial ecosystem resulting from whaling activities has been the introduction of two thriving populations of reindeer and the establishment of now derelict stations at the heads of several of the most sheltered glacier-free bays. The unintentional introduction of rats around the island has also had a serious effect on several species of birds and to a lesser extent on the vegetation. Temporary introductions of domestic animals (sheep, cattle, horses, pigs, poultry, etc.) around some of the whaling stations have led to some minor changes in the vegetation while the imported foodstuffs have caused the introduction of many alien plants, several of which have become naturalised and compete aggressively with native vegetation (49).

Because of its isolation, South Georgia is relatively free from sources of pollution, except perhaps around some of the former whaling stations. The levels of heavy metals in the least affected areas may serve as an important base line with which the degree of pollution in other parts of the world may be compared. Samples of mosses and lichens from Queen Maud Bay, 60 km to the windward of any source of pollution, i.e. former whaling stations, had low but quite detectable levels of heavy metals, particularly Zn, although it is not known how much of these derives from the local rock and soil. Corresponding data for samples collected in the study area, close to the research and whaling stations had significantly higher levels of Pb and Zn, although Cd, Co, Cu and Ni were similar (40).

Although South Georgia does not come within the region protected by the Antarctic Treaty (34) it is subject to similar conservation laws. Since the cessation of whaling and sealing activities around the island in the early 1960s there has been a steady increase in elephant and fur seal numbers and in some bird populations, notably penguins, as well as in the number of reindeer; rats, which thrived on seal carcasses left on the beaches, are possibly declining. In recent years there has been an increasing interest in commercial pelagic fishing, including the harvesting of krill, by the Russians. Perhaps the greatest threat to southern polar ecosystems is that posed by tourism. Over the past few years the number of tourist ships visiting South Georgia and the Antarctic has risen steadily. In view of the effect of tourism on ecosystems in more accessible parts of the world, it is essential that certain areas representative of the region are set aside primarily for the benefit of tourists rather than for research and that their movements and activities are strictly controlled.

REFERENCES

1. Admiralty. 1948. Antarctic Pilot, 2nd ed. London: Hydrographic Department.
2. Admiralty. 1961. Antarctic Pilot, 3rd ed. London: Hydrographic Department.
3. Bannister, J.L. 1964. Whaling stations in South Georgia. – Polar Rec. 12: 207–209.
4. Barrow, C.J. Personal communication.
5. Bonner, W.N. 1958. The introduced reindeer of South Georgia. – Sci. Rep. Falkland Islands Dependencies Surv. 22, 8 pp.
6. Brooks, C.E.P. 1920. The climate and weather of the Falkland Islands and South Georgia. – Geophys. Mem., London, 15: 97–146.
7. Callaghan, T.V. 1973. Studies on the factors affecting the primary production of bi-polar *Phleum alpinum* L.– In: Bliss, L.C. & Wiegolaski F.E. (eds.) Primary Production and Production Processes, Tundra Biome, pp. 153–167. Edmonton: IBP Tundra Biome Steering Committee.
8. Callaghan, T.V. 1974. Interspecific variation in *Phleum alpinum* L. with specific reference to polar populations. – Arctic and Alpine Res. 6: 361–401.
9. Callaghan, T.V. & Lewis, M.C. 1971. The growth of *Phleum alpinum* L. in contrasting habitats at a sub-Antarctic station. – New Phytol. 70: 1143–1154.
10. Callaghan, T.V. & Lewis, M.C. 1971. Adaptation in the reproductive performance of *Phleum alpinum* L. at a sub-Antarctic station. – Bull. Br. Antarc. Surv. 26: 59–75.
11. Clapperton, C.M. 1971. Geomorphology of the Stromness Bay – Cumberland Bay area, South Georgia. – Scient. Rep. Br. Antarc. Surv. 70, 25 pp.
12. Clarke, G.C.S., Greene, S.W. & Greene, D.M. 1971. Productivity of bryophytes in polar regions. – Ann. Bot. 35: 99–108.
13. Fergusson, G.J. & Libbey, W.F. 1964. U.C.I.A. radiocarbon dates III, peat series South Georgia island. – Radiocarbon 6: 335.
14. Greene, S.W. 1964. The vascular flora of South Georgia. – Scient. Rep. Br. Antarc. Surv. 45, 58 pp.
15. Greene, D.M., Walton, D.W.H. & Callaghan, T.V. 1973. Standing crop in a *Festuca* grassland on South Georgia. – In: Bliss, L.C. & Wielgolaski, F.E. (eds). Primary Production and Production Processes, Tundra Biome, pp. 191–194. Edmonton: IBP Tundra Biome Steering Committee.
16. Gressitt, J.L. 1970. Subantarctic entomology and biogeography. – Pacific Insects Monograph 23: 295–374.
17. Gunn, T.C. Personal communication.
18. Heap, J.A. 1964. Pack ice. – In: Priestly, R.E., Adie, R.J. & Robin, G. de Q. (eds.) Antarctic Research, pp. 308–317. London: Butterworth & Co (Publishers) Ltd.
19. Holdgate, M.W. & Wace, N.M. 1961. The influence of Man on the floras and faunas of southern islands. – Polar Rec. 10: 475–493.
20. Jones, A.G.E. 1973. Voyages to South Georgia, 1795–1820. – Bull. Br. Antarc. Surv. 32: 15–22.
21. Lewis, M.C. & Greene, S.W. 1970. A comparison of plant growth at an Arctic and Antarctic station. – In: Holdgate, M.W. (ed.) Antarctic Ecology 2: 838–850. London–New York: Academic Press.
22. Light, J.J. & Heywood, R.B. 1973. Deep-water mosses in Antarctic lakes. – Nature 242: 535–536.
23. Lindsay, D.C. 1972. Lichens new to South Georgia. – Bull. Br. Antarc. Surv. 31: 41–43.
24. Lindsay, D.C. 1973. Effects of reindeer on plant communities in the Royal Bay area of South Georgia. – Bull. Br. Antarc. Surv. 35: 101–109.
25. Lindsay, D.C. 1975. Growth rates of *Cladonia rangiferina* (L.) Web. on South Georgia. – Bull. Br. Antarc. Surv. 40 (in press).
26. Longton, R.E. 1970. Growth and productivity of the moss *Polytrichum alpestre* Hoppe in Antarctic regions. – In: Holdgate, M.W. (ed.) Antarctic Ecology 2: 818–837. London–New York: Academic Press.
27. Longton, R.E. & Greene, S.W. 1967. The growth and reproduction of *Polytrichum alpestre* Hoppe on South Georgia. – In: Smith, J.E. (org.) A discussion on the Terrestrial Antarctic Ecosystem. Phil. Trans. R. Soc., Ser. B 252: 295–322.
28. Matthews, L.H. 1929. The birds of South Georgia. – "Discovery" Rep. 1: 561–592.
29. Matthews, L.H. 1931. South Georgia, the British Empire's sub-Antarctic outpost. Bristol: John Wright & Sons Ltd. and London: Simpkin Marshall Ltd.

30. Pepper, J. 1954. The Meteorology of the Falkland Islands and Dependencies 1944–50. London: Falkland Islands and Dependencies Meteorological Service.
31. Richards, P.A. & Tickell, W.L.N. 1968. Comparison between the weather at Bird Island and King Edward Point, South Georgia. – Bull. Br. Antarc. Surv. 15: 63–69.
32. Roberts, B. 1958. Chronological list of Antarctic expeditions. – Polar Rec. 9: 97–134.
33. Roberts, B. 1958. Chronological list of Antarctic expeditions. – Polar Rec. 9: 191–239.
34. SCAR Manual. 1972. 2nd edition. Antarctic Treaty 1959, p. 81–116. Cambridge: Scientific Committee of Antarctic Research.
35. Skottsberg, C.J.F. 1902. The geographical distribution of vegetation in South Georgia. – Geogr. J. 20: 498–502.
36. Skottsberg, C.J.F. 1912. The vegetation in South Georgia. – Wissenschaftliche Ergebnisse der Schwedischen Südpolar-Expedition 1901–03 Bd. 4, Botanik, Lief. 12: 1–36.
37. Smith, J. 1960. Glacier problems in South Georgia. – J. Glaciol. 3: 705–714.
38. Smith, R.I.L. 1971. An outline of the Antarctic programme of the Bipolar Botanical Project. – In: Heal, O.W. (ed.) Proceedings IBP Tundra Biome Working Meeting on Analyses of Ecosystems, Kevo, Finland, September 1970, pp. 50–71. Stockholm: IBP Tundra Biome Steering Committee.
39. Smith, R.I.L. 1975. Yield in oats and barley as a measure of soil fertility on a Subantarctic island. – J. Appl. Ecol. (in press).
40. Smith, R.I.L. Unpublished manuscripts.
41. Smith, R.I.L. & Stephenson, C. 1975. Preliminary growth studies on *Festuca contracta* T. Kirk and *Deschampsia antarctica* Desv. on South Georgia. – Bull. Br. Antarc. Surv. 41 & 42 (in press).
42. Smith, R.I.L. & Walton, D.W.H. 1973. Calorific values of South Georgian plants. – Bull. Br. Antarc. Surv. 36: 123–127.
43. Tallowin, J.R.B. 1975. The reproductive strategies of a subantarctic grass, *Festuca contracta* T. Kirk. – In: Llano, G.A. (ed.) Adaptations within Antarctic Ecosystems, Proc. third symposium on Antarctic biology (in press).
44. Trendall, A.F. 1953. The geology of South Georgia. I. – Sci. Rep. Falkland Islands Dependencies Surv. 7, 25 pp.
45. Trendall, A.F. 1959. The geology of South Georgia. II. – Sci. Rep. Falkland Islands Dependencies Surv. 19, 48 pp.
46. Walton, D.W.H. 1973. Changes in standing crop and dry matter production in an *Acaena* community on South Georgia. – In: Bliss, L.C. & Wielgolaski, F.E. (eds.) Primary Production and Production Processes, Tundra Biome, pp. 185–190. Edmonton: IBP Tundra Biome Steering Committee.
47. Walton, D.W.H. Unpublished manuscripts.
48. Walton, D.W.H., Greene, D.M. & Callaghan, T.V. 1974. An assessment of primary production in a sub-Antarctic grassland on South Georgia. – Bull. Br. Antarc. Surv. 41 & 42 (in press).
49. Walton, D.W.H. & Smith, R.I.L. 1973. The status of the alien vascular flora of South Georgia. – Bull. Br. Antarc. Surv. 36: 79–97.
50. Weller, M.W. 1972. Ecological studies of South Georgia pintail (*Anas g. georgica*). – Antarctic J. U.S. 7 (4): 77–78.
51. Weller, M.W. & Howard, R.L. 1972. Breeding of speckled teal *Anas flavirostris* on South Georgia. – Bull. Br. Antarc. Surv. 30: 65–68.
52. World Weather Records. 1927. Smithsonian Miscellaneous Collection 79: 1153–1154. City of Washington: The Smithsonian Institution.
53. World Weather Records 1921–30. 1934. Smithsonian Miscellaneous Collection 90: 425. City of Washington: The Smithsonian Institution.
54. World Weather Records 1931–40. 1947. Smithsonian Miscellaneous Collection 105: 477. City of Washington: The Smithsonian Institution.
55. World Weather Records 1941–50. 1959: 1288–1289. Washington D.C.: U.S. Department of Commerce Weather Bureau.
56. World Weather Records 1951–60. 1968. Vol. 6: 427–428. Antarctica, Australia, Oceanic Islands, and Ocean Weather stations. Washington D.C.: U.S. Department of Commerce Environmental Science Services Administration.

Rosswall, T. & Heal, O.W. (eds.) 1975.
Structure and Function of Tundra Ecosystems.
Ecol. Bull. (Stockholm) 20: 425–448.

ABISKO II
A COMPUTER SIMULATION MODEL
OF CARBON FLUX IN TUNDRA ECOSYSTEMS

F.L. BUNNELL and K.A. SCOULLAR

INTRODUCTION

The recognition that word models are an important initial step in the development of more rigorous mathematical models was explicit in the early stages of the International Biological Programme (16). In June 1972, efforts were initiated to transform the existing decomposition word model of the Tundra Biome into a mathematical simulation model that would operate at the community or ecosystem level. Under the critical eyes of the International Tundra Biome's Decomposition Working Group, with F. Bunnell and P. Dowding acting as midwives, that mathematical model was born in Abisko, Sweden (9, 10). In recognition of its birthplace it was christened the ABISKO model. Like all good models it evolved and matured; recently it has grown to become a mathematical expression of the major carbon fluxes in tundra ecosystems. The model, now termed ABISKO II, represents an unambiguous mathematical expression of the broad processes described by the different National word models in this volume. As it is presented here, the general form of the model is applicable to all National sites; in its specific detail it is applicable to a pure stand of *Dupontia fischeri* R.Br. at Barrow, Alaska. Although the model has continued to evolve, the present version still does not approach current limits of understanding for many ecosystem processes. This failing is due in part to deliberate constraints that were placed on the evolution of the model. Such constraints were necessary to retain the model's primary objective, the provision of a "consistent, biologically reasonable framework within which decomposition processes could be viewed for several distinctly different sites " (9).

From the earliest stage of model development we recognized that because the model was to serve as a vehicle for comparisons between National sites it was subject to certain limitations. In specific, it had to be sufficiently general to encompass the wide variety of sites included in the Tundra Biome and yet not so simply structured that it only reiterated the obvious. Thus we have been faced with a difficult compromise between extension of the biological detail in the model and retention of sufficient generality to encompass disparate National data bases. In several areas the model has been extended beyond the form described by Bunnell & Dowding (10). Such modifications have been retained only if they both add to the biological bases of the model and increase the realism of the model output. The incorporation of these features in the present model is therefore an explicit recognition that their omission would be biologically unreasonable and would reduce our potential understanding.

ABISKO II still considers only carbon. Transfers of carbon are converted to changes in biomass because biomass measures are the usual form of validation data. Processes affecting the patterns of carbon flux are computed daily, Thus, the equations simulating different processes must be general for any day of the year. The best supported version of the ABISKO II model is the one developed for *Dupontia fischeri* on the Barrow site. For this reason gaming with the Barrow version has generally served as the criterion determining whether a change should be made in the general model structure. Although the criterion is not broadly based, runs with data from other sites have proven it to be broadly applicable (11).

Given its appearance among the present collection of word models there are several features of ABISKO II which merit further elaboration. The model is oriented towards rigorous description of processes such as microbial respiration and photosynthesis rather than towards description of identifiable biomass pools such as basidiomycetes, enchytraeids or lichens. The word models of this volume are far more complete in their detail of structural description. In part the lack of structural detail in ABISKO II is a result of its heritage — development for comparison of decomposition processes between National sites (9).

Detailed information on microbial population dynamics are lacking for most sites. Acknowledging the limited information ABISKO II made and still makes the explicit assumption that rates of decomposition can be predicted from levels of temperature, oxygen and moisture without incorporating information on the size of microorganism populations which respond to these levels (14). Structural details of the decomposer groups are ignored. The accuracy of the simulation projections (Fig. 4 and 6) suggests that the assumption is not grossly incorrect, and that the concentration on processes rather than populations is justified.

Lack of structural detail is not limited to decomposer organisms. In its present form ABISKO II can only accommodate a single species of primary producer. Although the simulation projections may be realistic for a homogeneous sward of a particular species (Fig. 5 and 6) the model does not encompass the variety present on most tundra sites. Given these limitations it is important to recognize that the reduction in structural detail is not without its advantages. The major advantage lies in the explicit and unambiguous statement of process dynamics (e.g. Eq. 1, 6 and 7). Mathematical expressions of ecosystem processes are not only more formal and less ambiguous than most word models, but also lend themselves more conveniently to rigorous evaluation (6). The new biomass pools and processes incorporated into ABISKO II were incorporated because evaluation of their effects on ecosystem dynamics demonstrated their importance and not because data describing them were available. A comparison of this paper with that of Bunnell, MacLean & Brown (8) describing the Barrow site clarifies the differences between mathematical and word models. Although both discussions examine the Barrow site, the word model contains far more structural detail but achieves this

426

detail at the expense of rigorous definition of process dynamics.

The formalization of the ABISKO model as it is presented here concentrates on refinements made in the model since it was described by Bunnell & Dowding (10). These refinements involve conceptions of both the structural and functional aspects of tundra ecosystems. ABISKO II retains its decomposition-oriented heritage and concentrates on those aspects of the tundra ecosystem which are most relevant to decomposition processes. The relevant parts are viewed as discrete biomass pools which can change in magnitude. Structural features of the model involve the composition, boundaries and number of these biomass pools (compartments of Fig. 1). Functional features involve the manner in which processes affecting changes in the biomass pools are simulated (arrows of Fig. 1).

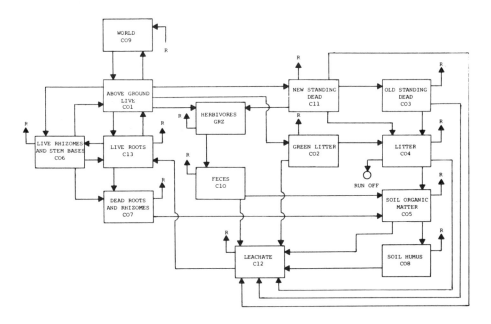

Figure 1. Biomass or carbon pools and transfers between pools simulated by ABISKO II. R = respiration.

STRUCTURAL FEATURES OF THE SIMULATED ECOSYSTEM

We initially considered 9 or 10 biomass pools to be the simplest representation of a tundra ecosystem which would allow informative analyses of the processes affecting carbon flux (10). Subsequent simulation runs with the model indicated that realism could be enhanced significantly by distinguishing 4 to 5 new biomass pools. Departures in the structure of the system from that described earlier are:

1. Roots are distinguished from rhizomes and stem bases.

Roots and rhizomes were initially treated as a common biomass pool. Using this approach the subsurface inputs of primary production to decomposition processes could not be simulated accurately. Differential translocation patterns associated with roots as compared to rhizomes, and the very different growth and death processes followed by roots and rhizomes necessitated that these components be treated separately.

2. Herbivore biomass is incorporated explicitly.

The original version of ABISKO incorporated grazing implicitly as a parameter which represented the potential feeding or grazing pressure during the ith week. In the implicit form effects of grazing were driven and could not be realistically simulated because there was no feedback between the forage and the grazing rates. Grazer biomass is now incorporated so that grazing effects can be more realistically examined.

3. Feces and green litter are treated separately.

Bunnell & Dowding (10) acknowledged that decomposition rates for lemming feces and green litter probably differed. Different decomposition rates between green litter and feces have since been documented for two tundra grazers — lemmings at the Barrow site and muskoxen on Devon Island. There are further reasons for separating feces and green litter beyond their different decomposition rates. Even at the same grazing rates, feces and litter are deposited differently in different seasons. Similarly, grazers have effects on biomass pools other than green vegetation, such as standing dead and rhizomes. These effects can also change seasonally and differentially affect the rates of deposition of green litter and feces. For all of these reasons feces and green litter are now treated as separate pools.

4. Different age classes of standing dead vegetation are distinguished.

Investigators at several sites have documented that substrates which are taxonomically identical but of different ages decompose at different rates (7, 17, 18). The largest differences occur between material which is less than one year dead and material which has experienced at least one winter and spring meltoff. These differences are probably related to more rapid leaching from the younger material. Separate age classes for standing dead material are incorporated in ABISKO II to permit differential rates of weight loss from these biomass pools.

5. Pools of soil carbon have been redefined.

The first ABISKO models considered two soil carbon pools, "below surface dead" and "soil carbon" (Fig. 1). "Below surface dead" represented plant and animal material that was located below the soil surface, but was derived from above-ground sources. Some structural integrity was still present and its origin was recognizable. "Soil carbon" represented carbon from all origins, and included all highly degraded plant and animal material as well as live and dead microorganisms. The differentiation of these two carbon pools has been abandoned for two reasons: they do not serve their intended purpose and they are unrealistically simplistic.

ABISKO I distinguished material that originated aboveground from material that originated belowground until their origins were no longer recognizable (and entered the "soil carbon" pool). The distinction was made on the premise that the predicted portions of soil organic matter originating above- and belowground would help evaluate model performance and lend insight into the processes forming peaty soils. Validation data have proven sparse and ABISKO II does not maintain the distinction between sources of soil organic matter.

Although the initial formulation of ABISKO distinguished the source of soil carbon, it did not separate less recalcitrant carbohydrates from humus; both were included in soil carbon. The differential capacity of microorganisms to attack or utilize these two substrates therefore could not be invoked. ABISKO II distinguishes between these two forms of carbon, and decomposition rates are more realistically simulated. Incorporation of a "soluble carbon" pool with its associated transfers lends a further advantage because it represents a major step necessary to permit incorporation of nutrients other than carbon into the ABISKO model.

In ABISKO II the two carbon pools of ABISKO I ("below surface dead" and "soil carbon") are represented by three pools: "soil organic matter" which includes carbon of above- and belowground origin, "soluble carbon" which represents dissolved carbon in the soil, and "soil humus" which represents the most resistant forms of soil carbon.

These five refinements represent major changes that are considered essential to the structure of the idealized tundra ecosystem simulated by ABISKO II. Their importance in the structure of the model implies that field studies of their magnitudes and dynamics are important to the understanding of decomposition and carbon flux in an ecosystem context. In summary, ABISKO II presently conceives of the tundra system as comprising 14 discrete biomass pools (Fig. 1). These pools are:

Above-ground live (C01): all living plant tissue exposed to light; only subdivided in the case of shrubs to separate green from non-green material.

Green litter (C02): any green plant parts dropped to the litter surface as a result of herbivore activity including clipping, trampling and defoliation by insects.

Old standing dead (C03): standing dead includes all above-ground parts which remain attached to the plant and above the ground surface after their death. The compartment includes dead heartwood and branches of shrubs if these are present. Old standing dead represents material which has passed through one winter and entered the subsequent growing season.

Litter (C04): plant material lying upon the ground surface; origin of the material is still recognizable. Litter may be derived from standing dead or from aboveground live via "green" litter.

Soil organic matter (C05): plant and animal matter found in the upper 10 cm of the soil. It is readily distinguishable from humus only where L, F and H layers are clearly defined. The structure of material in this compartment is still recognizable.

Live rhizomes and stem bases (C06): all living rhizomes present in the soil and stem bases of graminoids or other chamaephytes.

Dead roots and rhizomes (C07): all recognizable dead roots and rhizomes in the soil to a depth of 10 cm.

Soil humus (C08): all plant and animal material whose origin is no longer recognizable, as well as live and dead fungal hyphae and bacteria in the soil to a depth of 10 cm. Only clearly distinguished where identifiable L, F and H layers are present. Often merged together with C05. May be separated to distinguish different rates of microbial attack on material of varying resistance.

Atmospheric carbon dioxide (C09): a source for photosynthesis and a sink for all respiratory activity of plants and decomposer organisms. The compartment is included simply as a device for examining various respiration rates and allowing comparison between model output and data.

Feces (C10): all herbivore feces deposited on or in the litter layer.

New standing dead (C11): standing dead includes all aboveground plant parts which remain attached to the plant and aboveground after their death. New standing dead represents recently moribund and dead tissue which is entering or experiencing its first winter.

Soluble carbon (C12): all dissolved carbon in the upper 10 cm of the soil system.

Live roots (C13): all live roots present in the soil to a depth of 10 cm.

Herbivores (GRZ or C14): herbivore biomass.

FUNCTIONAL FEATURES OF THE SIMULATED ECOSYSTEM

The processes simulated by ABISKO II can be grouped under five headings: primary production (growth and death), herbivory, microbial respiration, leaching, and "ageing" including comminution. With the exception of ageing or comminution the basic formulation of each of these process groups has been refined since the model was described by Bunnell & Dowding (10). In some instances the refinement has resulted from new information or analyses, in other instances the original approach has proven dangerously unrealistic and the formulation has been altered without incorporating new data. The following discussion describes the processes in their general form with specific details given for the Barrow version. The Barrow version discussed here is that developed for a stand of *Dupontia fischeri.*

Primary production (growth and death)

The ABISKO II model was initially constructed to provide a consistent, biologically reasonable framework within which decomposition processes could be viewed for several distinctly different sites. Since the model was developed primarily to examine processes of carbon mineralization, the processes of primary production were of interest only to the extent that they provided realistic amounts of dead substrate. Bunnell & Dowding (9) noted "... we are not concerned with the primary production processes themselves. Provision for realistic input from primary production is, of course, critical to the biological integrity of the ABISKO model, and it is anticipated that primary production models will be coupled with it as they are developed."

Experience has proven that realistic primary production is indeed critical to the biological integrity of the model. It is impossible to incorporate primary production empirically and obtain useful insights into the role of decomposition in an ecosystem. Small

430

portions of the decomposer cycle, for example weight losses from litter, can be examined (11, 19), but whole system measures of carbon flux and estimates of the relative sensitivity of the simulated system to different variables are impossible to obtain. Even at the level of carbon flux, primary production and decomposition processes are too intimately coupled to be treated semi-independently. As well as demonstrating the futility of empirically forcing growth and death measures, the early simulations also demonstrated the extreme importance of patterns of growth and death. Inspired by these observations, we included a simple primary production submodel in ABISKO II. The constraints acknowledged for the decomposition transfers were retained and primary production processes were simulated at a level of resolution that appeared compatible with the different National data bases. With the incorporation of primary production ABISKO II evolved beyond a decomposition model to a relatively complete and dynamic carbon budget for tundra ecosystems.

The model simulates both photosynthesis and respiration. Growth and death result from the net balance between the two. Photosynthesis is assumed a multiplicative function of light intensity, temperature and shading, while respiration is assumed a function of temperature. Each of the potential modifiers of the photosynthetic rate assumes a value of 1.0 at optimal levels for that site and declines towards 0.0 as conditions worsen. Maximum photosynthetic rates (g biomass fixed g^{-1} biomass) are thus reduced independently by each of the potential influences as specific conditions depart from optimum.

Between the lower threshold temperature and optimal temperatures photosynthesis is assumed to increase as a half-saturation function, then to decline in the same manner towards zero as the optimum temperature is surpassed (Fig. 2).

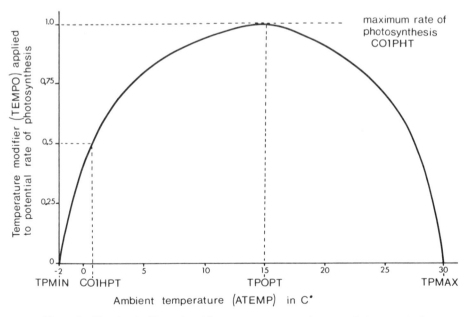

Figure 2. Simulated effect of ambient temperature on the rate of photosynthesis. (ATEMP, CO1HPT, TPMIN, TPOPT, TPMAX as in Eq. 2 and 4.)

The relationship thus has the form:

$$
TEMPO = \begin{cases}
0 & \text{if } ATEMP \leqslant TPMIN \\
& \text{or } ATEMP \geqslant TPMAX \\[2ex]
\dfrac{\dfrac{CO1HPT - TPMIN + TPOPT}{TPOPT}\,(ATEMP - TPMIN)}{CO1HPT - TPMIN + (ATEMP - TPMIN)} & \text{if } TPMIN \leqslant ATEMP \leqslant TPOPT \\[3ex]
\dfrac{\dfrac{CO1HPT - TPMIN + TPOPT}{TPOPT}\,(TPMAX - ATEMP)}{CO1HPT - TPMIN + (TPMAX - ATEMP)} & \text{if } TPOPT < ATEMP < TPMAX
\end{cases}
\tag{1}
$$

where TEMPO represents the temperature effect on photosynthesis, ATEMP represents air temperature ($^\circ$C), and TPMIN, TPMAX, and TPOPT represent the minimum, maximum and optimum temperatures for photosynthesis. CO1HPT represents the temperature at which the photosynthetic capacity of the foliage is half-saturated. In the summary form which more clearly reveals the half saturation relationship, the temperature effect at Barrow can be expressed as:

$$
TEMPO = \begin{cases}
0 & \text{if } ATEMP \leqslant TPMIN \\
& \text{or } ATEMP \geqslant TPMAX \\[2ex]
\dfrac{1.27 \times (ATEMP - 2.0)}{2.0 + (ATEMP + 4)} & \text{if } TPMIN \leqslant ATEMP \leqslant TPOPT \\[3ex]
\dfrac{1.27 \times (30 - ATEMP)}{2.0 + (ATEMP + 32)} & \text{if } TPOPT < ATEMP < TPMAX
\end{cases}
\tag{2}
$$

At high latitudes with prevailing low solar angles, snow meltoff coincides closely with the time of the summer solstice. Thus, light intensities are usually maximum at the onset of the growing season and decline progressively throughout the season. In such areas the leaves are seldom light saturated and truly optimal light environments are probably never attained. For the Barrow site "optimum" light conditions in the environment are equated with the highest light intensities observed. The effect of light on rates of photosynthesis, PLITE, is therefore arbitrarily set to the maximum value of 1.0 at highest seasonal light intensities (about 665 Langleys for Barrow), and allowed to decline linearly to 0.0 at zero light.

The shading effect on photosynthesis also varies between 0 and 1 and is computed by following some very simple assumptions. Measured interception efficiencies of green vegetation at Barrow range between 0.72 on 15 June to 1.0 at time of maximum standing crop. This empirical efficiency is assumed to represent the potential capacity of live green vegetation to utilize light. The actual percentage of light intercepted by live green is assumed proportional to the per cent of live green in the total standing biomass. The per cent intercepted by standing dead, or the shading effect, is thus

$$\left(1. - \frac{\text{live green}}{\text{total standing crop}} \right) \ 100 \ \%,$$

and the proportion of green biomass capable of photosynthesizing, SUNLIT, can be computed as:

$$\text{SUNLIT} = 1.0 - \left(\left(1.0 - \frac{\text{CO1}}{\text{BTOT}} \right) \left(\frac{\text{CO1}}{\text{BMX}} \right) \right) \tag{3}$$

where CO1 represents the live green biomass, BTOT represents live green plus standing dead (CO1 + CO3 + C11) and BMX represents the live biomass necessary for 100 % interception of incoming radiation. For sites other than Barrow or for different vegetative life forms the values in Equations 2 and 3 are different, but the general form of the expressions is unaltered.

After computation of the environmental influences of light, temperature and shade the total daily photosynthesis (including dark respiration), PHTGRO, is computed as

$$\text{PHTGRO} = \text{CO1PHT} \times \text{SUNLIT} \times \text{TEMPO} \times \text{PLITE} \times \text{CO1} \tag{4}$$

where SUNLIT, TEMP, PLITE and CO1 are as described previously and CO1PHT represents the maximum rate of photosynthesis (g g^{-1} live green). CO1PHT is estimated at 0.5 g g^{-1} (23). Available photosynthate is then allocated according to the hierarchy described below and in Fig. 3.

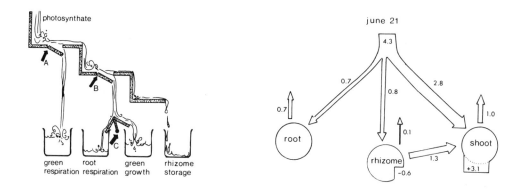

Figure 3. Postulated hierarchy of photosynthate allocation and simulated allocation patterns. Arrows moving downwards represent allocation patterns, upward arrows represent respiration and rectangels represent the next change (g m^{-2} d^{-1}).

1. The temperature-determined maintenance respiration of above ground live green is met to the extent that available photosynthate allows. When respiration demands exceed available photosynthate death of live green occurs.

2. After green maintenance respiration demands are met, green growth and root respiration share in the remaining photosynthate. When insufficient photosynthate is available to meet the demands of both green growth and root maintenance, available photosynthate is distributed to each in proportion to the amount demanded. Root maintenance respiration follows a geometric relationship with temperature, showing a twofold increase over the range 0 to $10°C$ and a respiration rate at $10°C$ of 0.007 g g^{-1} biomass d^{-1} for the Barrow site.

The model has had to assume a somewhat arbitrary constraint on the amount of photosynthate that can be allocated to daily growth of green material. Based on plant geometry and laboratory measures of photosynthetic potential, graminoids at Barrow appear to have the potential to incorporate 5 g m^{-2} of aboveground biomass per day. Resultant biomasses are too great when the value 5 g m^{-2} d^{-1} is permitted and the model arbitrarily restrains maximum growth at 3.5 g m^{-2} d^{-1}. The restriction can be considered analogous to nutrient limitation to growth rate and may not be unnatural (7, 8).

3. If photosynthate is still available for allocation after growth and maintenance respiration of green biomass and maintenance respiration of roots have been met, the remainder is allocated to rhizomes and stem bases.

Growth respiration is computed after photosynthate has been allocated to maintenance respiration and growth of live green, roots, rhizomes and stem bases. Green biomass can increase by three different means, but growth respiration is associated only with the incorporation of newly formed photosynthate. Respiration costs of growth are assumed to be 30 % of the amount of growth. Increment of green biomass also results from upwards translocation from rhizomes in the spring and from upwards translocation anytime that grazing is heavy and rhizome reserves are sufficient to replace losses due to grazing. Translocation from rhizomes in the spring is arbitrarily assumed to begin at snowmelt, increase to a maximum rate within five days, then decline linearly to zero over the next ten days. The maximum rate of upwards translocation from rhizomes, C06GNR % d^{-1} of rhizome biomass, is estimated to be 3 % d^{-1} for Barrow.

Use of the rhizomes for regrowth after grazing is somewhat more complicated. Regrowth of live green from rhizome and stem base reserves occurs only when the aboveground live biomass shows sufficient photosynthetic competence that it can generate a biomass increment of C01XAR g g^{-1} d^{-1}. Inefficient tissue is not replaced. The parameter C01XAR represents the level of biomass increment beyond which growth is assumed too rapid for senescence to occur (Eq. 5), and is estimated at 0.04 g g^{-1} d^{-1} for the Barrow site. If grazing has occurred and the above ground live biomass is photosynthetically competent, the model checks and updates the grazing history over the preceding seven days. Responses to grazing are assumed to follow a time lag with rhizomes replenishing about 20 % of the material removed on any date over the subsequent seven day period. The response of the rhizome to grazing is not uniformly distributed over the seven day period but peaks on the third day.

Translocations up from rhizomes and stem bases in the spring or in response to grazing depletes their biomass. The restoration or growth of this biomass may occur through any of three pathways: first, on days when sufficient photosynthate is produced to meet all other needs the remainder is allocated to rhizome biomass; second, as live green materi-al undergoes senescence a portion, C01RHZ, of the amount becoming moribund is with-drawn to the rhizome; and third, as roots die a portion of their biomass, C13RHZ, is simi-larly withdrawn to rhizome biomass.

Roots grow either by receiving newly formed photosynthate from aboveground live or from reserves present in the rhizomes. No root growth from rhizomes occurs until the rhi-zomes have been replenished after the period of spring depletion and translocation upwards. Replenishment need not be complete and in fact is established at an arbitrary percent, C06NPC, of the biomass prior to the period of spring translocation. For the Barrow site the value of C06NPC is estimated to be 95 %. Once this portion of the early season rhi-zome biomass is reattained the potential rate of translocation from rhizomes to roots is assumed to increase linearly to a maximum value, C06ROT %, at rhizome biomass levels greater or equal to 100 % of the early season levels.

The potential amount of transfer computed by this formulation is not all allocated to new roots. Carbon translocated from rhizomes to roots is respired at the root respiration rate computed for that day and the potential allocation to roots is reduced accordingly. All other growth of both aerial and subsurface plant parts is assumed to have the same re-spiratory cost of 30 % the amount of growth.

For all plants parts death results when maintenance respiration for that part exceeds the amount of photosynthate allocated. Some death and senescence of live green occurs when-ever growth rates decline below C01XAR $g\ g^{-1}\ d^{-1}$. At growth rates less than C01XAR $g\ g^{-1}\ d^{-1}$ the death rate increases linearly with decreasing growth to a threshold value of C01DXR $g\ g^{-1}\ d^{-1}$ at biomass increments of C01MAR or less. At growth rates greater than C01XAR $g\ g^{-1}\ d^{-1}$ there is no senescence of aboveground live vegetation. Death rates of live green thus have the form:

$$
\text{Death rate} = \begin{cases} 0 & \text{if BIOINC} \geq \text{C01XAR} \\[2ex] \text{C01DXR}\left(\dfrac{\text{C01XAR} - \text{BIOINC}}{\text{C01XAR} - \text{C01MAR}}\right) & \text{if C01MAR} < \text{BIOINC} < \text{C01XAR} \quad (5) \\[2ex] \text{C01DXR} & \text{if BIOINC} \leq \text{C01MAR} \end{cases}
$$

where BIOINC is the computed biomass increment for that day before mortality is applied.

Roots die when they respire more carbon than they acquire through uptake or allo-cation of newly formed photosynthate. The rate of death increases linearly from zero when the net carbon flux in roots is zero to a maximum value C13XDR $g\ g^{-1}\ d^{-1}$ at some negative carbon balance C13MAR. Carbon flux deficits greater than C13MAR ($-0.007\ g\ g^{-1}\ d^{-1}$ for Barrow) do not further increase root death rates. Rhizome death proceeds simply as a daily rate whenever soil temperatures exceed $0°C$ (C06DR = 0.001 $g\ g^{-1}\ d^{-1}$ for Barrow).

ABISKO II accumulates leached carbon in the soluble soil carbon compartment (C12). The potential for root uptake of soluble carbon is included as one of the two possible outputs from this carbon pool, the second being microbial uptake and subsequent respi-ration.

On any specific day soluble carbon is incorporated into growth as a function of the photosynthate allocated to growth on that day. Small percentages of the photosynthate allocated to above-ground live, roots, and rhizomes (5 %, 2 %, and 5 % respectively) are withdrawn from the soluble soil carbon compartment and incorporated into live plant biomass. Deficiency of soluble soil carbon serves only to reduce root uptake from this compartment and does not restrict photosynthate-induced growth. Differentiation of the root uptake among nutrients could provide insight into nutrient limitation, but data are too sparse to simulate nutrient uptake over different sites.

Herbivory

The original version of ABISKO expressed herbivory as an intervention or driving variable $HERB_i$ (i = 1, 2, ... , 52 weeks), where $HERB_i$ represented the g m^{-2} of vegetative material that were removed but not assimilated by the herbivore under conditions of unlimited forage. At that time it was assumed that grazing had relatively little influence on the decomposition or broad carbon flux patterns and could be treated superficially. Simulation runs since made with the model indicate that for some sites grazing is an important modifier of rates of weight loss or carbon flux.

There are a number of ways in which herbivory influences carbon flux and decomposition patterns in an ecosystem. Green vegetation aboveground is intercepted before it can become standing dead or litter and is deposited as feces, incorporated as grazer biomass, respired or rejected and transferred to the litter layer. The removal of green vegetation aboveground alters the translocation patterns and thus influences the dynamics of vegetation belowground and subsurface inputs into the decomposer cycle. Microtine grazers incorporate vegetation into winter nests, further redistributing aboveground vegetation and altering the seasonal patterns of green and dead vegetation of various ages. Because the amount of wastage or rejecta that accompanies feeding appears correlated with the phenology of the forage, the seasonal patterns of grazing influence the deposition of litter in a complex fashion.

Each of the phenomena mentioned has been examined within the framework of ABISKO II. All influences of herbivory are made a function of herbivore biomass (g m^{-2}). The biomass is either set at a specific level, driven by a Fourier series or generated by a simple population dynamics model.

Other models simulating herbivory in tundra systems (5, 12) have made ingestion rate a function of forage biomass. Because herbivores can compensate for a reduction in ingestion rate over a wide range of forage biomass by extending their grazing period, the relationship between ingestion rate and forage biomass appears unnecessary and potentially confusing within the broad formulation of ABISKO II. ABISKO II simulates lemming food intake in a straightforward fashion. Average daily metabolic rate of a lemming out of its nest (ADMR; Kcal d^{-1}) is calculated as:

$$ADMR = 1.28 \ W^{0.75} - 0.45 \ T + 6.4 \tag{6}$$

where W is wet weight in grams and T is ambient temperature in °C (15). Thus, we need to know only the weight of the average lemming and ambient temperature to predict the amount of respiration at any time. Data of Batzli (2) have been employed to estimate the average weight of lemmings in each month of the year. These weights vary from 30 g in September when the population is dominated by juveniles and sub-adults, to 57 g in June and July when adults and sub-adults dominate the age structure. The

436

data in this form do not allow for the increase in weight of adult males that is observed during lemming "highs", but the error is assumed to be unimportant.

Given the weight of the average lemming and the ambient temperature, the calculated respiration (Eq. 6) is converted to biomass ingested by the ingestion: respiration ratio of 3.33 (1) and the average calorific content of the vegetation (4.5 Kcal g^{-1}). Actual amounts ingested are computed by multiplying by the number of lemmings per hectare. Amounts ingested thus vary with the population age structure (average weight), ambient air temperature and lemming density. Lemming densities excluding nestlings vary from 1 to 200 per hectare during the course of a lemming cycle.

Lemmings do not ingest all the vegetative material that they clip (7, 22). Moribund and senescing portions of the leaf or stem are rejected. The Barrow version of ABISKO II therefore assumes the proportion of rejecta to vary seasonally, increasing throughout the growing season as graminoids become senescent to some maximum value in late fall when only the stem bases are palatable. The palatable portion, C01ED, thus assumes a value of 100 % during much of the growing season and declines to to a value of 9 % during fall and winter.

The computed grazing rate (g d^{-1}) is subsequently distributed as green litter or rejecta, herbivore biomass and feces. Since the estimated digestibility of *Dupontia fischeri* by lemmings appears to be about 35 % (2, 21), the Barrow version assumes that feces represent 65 % of dry matter intake. Lemmings also influence the distribution of vegetation and thus carbon flux by nest building. Although the impact of lemming nest building may be important locally (7), on a hectare basis it is insignificant. The highest nest densities reported (20) were 42 ha^{-1}. Given an average nest weight of about 80 g, nest building activities account for only 0.34 g m^{-2} or about 0.3 % of the annual primary production. The present version of ABISKO II ignores lemming nest building activities.

Decomposition and soil processes

ABISKO II treats only those decomposition and soil processes most intimately associated with carbon flux. These processes include leaching, comminution and respiration by microorganisms utilizing the substrate as an energy source.

Microbial respiration

The model assumes that activity rates of the microbial populations are more important than microbial biomass in determining carbon flux. These activity or respiration rates were initially generated from temperature and moisture levels by a complex fitting function (see Eq. 7, 8, 9 and 10 in (10)). Subsequently a model of microbial respiration that is both simpler and more biologically meaningful has been developed (13) and is employed in ABISKO II.

Bunnell & Tait (13) provide a detailed discussion of the rationale and structure of the microbial respiration model. The model applies only to aerobic respiration and assumes microbial activity to be a function of the supply rates of water, oxygen and nutrients, particularly organic nutrients. Moisture, oxygen, temperature, and the nature of the substrate are the major determinants of microbial respiration rates and each can reduce the rate of respiration independently of the other factors. Thus, the respiration rate determinants are combined multiplicatively and a formal statement of the model is:

437

$$R(T,M) = \frac{M}{a_1 + M} \times \frac{a_2}{a_2 + M} \times a_3 \times a_4^{\left(\frac{T-10}{10}\right)} \tag{7}$$

where

R (T,M) = the respiration rate at temperature T and moisture level M

a_1 = % moisture content at which the substrate is half-saturated with water

a_2 = % moisture content at which half the channels are saturated or blocked with water

a_3 = the respiration rate that occurs at 10°C when neither oxygen nor moisture is limiting

a_4 = the Q_{10} coefficient.

The respiration model has been evaluated for a number of tundra substrates including muskoxen dung, lemming feces, litter, and standing dead of various ages and species (14). Its general applicability has been demonstrated and its accuracy illustrated (Fig. 4). ABISKO II employs Eq. 7 to simulate all transfers involving microbial respiration.

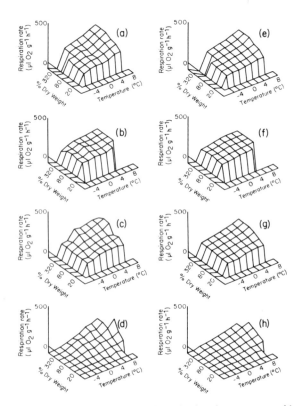

Figure 4. Measured and simulated rates of microbial respiration for: one-year-old standing dead of *Carex aquatilis* (a) and (e); two-year-old standing dead of *Carex aquatilis* (b) and (f); two-year-old standing dead of *Eriophorum angustifolium* (c) and (g); mixed graminoid litter from Barrow, Alaska (d) and (h). Simulated surfaces are generated by Eq. 7; data are from (14).

438

Leaching

Leaching from above-ground material is known to occur and has been documented but not quantified for Barrow and Devon Island (17; P. Widden, pers. comm.). Despite its acknowledged existence, accurate simulation of the leaching process has proven extremely difficult. The formulation employed in ABISKO II has not evolved beyond that reported earlier (9, 10) (see their Eq. 5 and 6) with one exception: microbial activity is assumed to generate leachable material beyond that present at death of the substrate. The value of this refinement is questionable because we have been unable to quantify the role of temperature, precipitation, and other forms of moisture in modifying the leaching rate. Presently the model assumes free-flowing water to be the dominant influence and the leaching rate increases linearly above zero to a maximum rate as free flowing water increases. The effect is assumed bounded by substrate characteristics such that beyond a specific threshold a further increase in flowing water has no further effect (Eq. 5 of (10)). Over a narrow temperature range, temperature is assumed to modify the leaching rate, decreasing the rate to zero as the temperature declines to zero. Above temperatures of 2°C (Table 1), the leaching rate is controlled solely by moisture levels (Eq. 6 of (10)). Microbial activity is assumed to generate leachable material in direct proportion to the respiration rate.

Comminution and physical "ageing"

Comminution by abiotic and biotic agents has not been simulated realistically. The combination of losses from simulated leaching and losses to microbial respiration are usually insufficient to explain the observed rates of carbon loss. It is assumed that comminution, physical transport, and, in some instances, anaerobic respiration contribute the remaining losses. ABISKO II incorporates physical transport for some sites (e.g., Devon Island), but ignores losses to anaerobic respiration. Comminution of the substrate is treated in the fashion described by Bunnell & Dowding (10) (see their Eq. 4 and 11). The approach assumes that physical and biological comminution of a substrate proceeds in direct proportion to the rates of leaching and respiration losses from the substrate. Thus if a substrate has typically lost x proportion of its weight (on a unit area basis) before entering the next oldest and more degraded biomass pool, the transfer due to comminution or ageing can be expressed as:

$$\text{transfer to next oldest biomass pool} = \frac{1-x}{x} \text{ (leaching and respiration losses)} \tag{8}$$

It has proven impossible to evaluate alternative approaches to simulating comminution rates.

SIMULATED CARBON FLUX

The relationships discussed above have proven adequate to simulate carbon flux realistically for a variety of tundra ecosystems (11). Here we wish to present the parameter values for only one site, Barrow, Alaska, and to indicate some patterns predicted by the

439

Table 1. Parameter values for the Barrow Site version of ABISKO II

Fortran Variable Name	Value	Meaning	Source ☆
PGWTL	0.40	Weight loss of green litter before becoming old litter (proportion of original weight)	17
PNSDWL	0.30	Weight loss of new standing dead before becoming old standing dead (proportion of original weight)	17
RSDBQ	5.0	Rate of graminoid collapse relative to microbial respiration of old stem bases	E ☆☆
PSDWL	0.4	Weight loss of litter before becoming soil organic matter (proportion of weight as litter)	E
PBGDL	0.8	Weight loss of soil organic matter before becoming humus (proportion of original weight)	E
BGCOM	0.0001	Daily rate of below ground comminution (g g^{-1} d^{-1})	E
RCOMX	1.0	Rate of dead root comminution relative to root respiration	E
SNOMLT	166	Day of snow melt (Julian day number)	24 (long term average)
SNOFAL	274	First day of permanent snow cover (Julian day number)	24 (long term average)
BMX	100	Maximum standing biomass for shading effects	7
C01PHT	0.5	Maximum photosynthetic rate (g g^{-1} live green d^{-1})	23 (modified)
C01XGR	3.5	Maximum daily biomass increment of live green (g m^{-2} d^{-1})	P.C. Miller pers. comm. suggests 5.0
C01HPT	2.0	Temperature allowing half maximum photosynthetic rate ($^{\circ}$C)	23
C01A3	0.06	Respiration rate of green biomass at 10°C (g g^{-1} d^{-1})	About 1/9 photosynthesis at 10°C (Miller, pers. comm.)
C01A4	2.0	Q$_{10}$ value for respiration of live green	assumed same as roots
C01XDR	0.15	Maximum daily death rate of live green (g g^{-1} d^{-1})	E
C01MAR	−0.05	Green biomass increment at which green death rate maximum (g g^{-1} d^{-1})	E
C01XAR	0.04	Green growth rate at and above which green death = 0 (g g^{-1} d^{-1})	E
C01WS	0.07	Maximum survival of green through winter (proportion of BMX)	7
C01RHZ	0.25	Proportion of green translocated to rhizome at time of death	E
C01ED	0.09	Proportion of live green edible by grazers in winter	7
C01CNR	0.05	Proportion of green biomass that originates as soil nutrients	E
C02A1	4.16	g H$_2$O g^{-1} green litter at half field capacity	14
C02A2	4.16	g H$_2$O g^{-1} green litter at half maximum retentive capacity	14
C02A3	777	Respiration rate of green litter at 10°C (μl O$_2$ g^{-1} h^{-1}) when moisture not limiting	14
C02A4	8.79	Q$_{10}$ value for green litter	14
C02LMX	0.03	Maximum leaching rate of green litter (g g^{-1} d^{-1})	E
C02MNM	1.0	Minimum moisture for leaching from green litter (g H$_2$O g^{-1} dw)	E

440

Table 1 cont.

Fortran Variable Name	Value	Meaning	Source ☆
C02MXM	5.0	Optimum moisture for leaching green litter ($g\ H_2O\ g^{-1}$ dw)	E
C02MNT	−0.5	Minimum temperature for leaching green litter (°C)	E
C02MXT	5.0	Optimum temperature for leaching green litter (°C)	E
C03A1	0.19	$g\ H_2O\ g^{-1}$ old standing dead at half field capacity	14
C03A2	30000	$g\ H_2O\ g^{-1}$ old standing dead at half maximum retentive capacity	14
C03A3	107	Respiration rate of old standing dead $10°C$ ($\mu l\ O_2\ g^{-1}\ h^{-1}$) when moisture not limiting	14
C03A4	2.79	Q_{10} value for old standing dead	14
C03LMX	0.0	Maximum leaching rate of old standing dead ($g\ g^{-1}\ d^{-1}$) (without microbial activity)	E
C03MNM	2.0	Minimum moisture for leaching old standing dead ($g\ H_2O\ g^{-1}$ dw)	E
C03MXM	7.5	Optimum moisture for leaching old standing dead ($g\ H_2O\ g^{-1}$ dw)	E
C03MNT	−0.5	Minimum temperature for leaching old standing dead (°C)	E
C03MXT	5.0	Optimum temperature for leaching old standing dead (°C)	E
C03LCH	0.05	Leachable material generated by microbial respiration ($g\ g^{-1}$ respired)	E
C04A1	1.16	$g\ H_2O\ g^{-1}$ litter at half field capacity	14
C04A2	28.20	$g\ H_2O\ g^{-1}$ litter at half maximum retentive capacity	14
C04A3	232	Respiration rate for litter at $10°C$ ($\mu l\ O_2\ g^{-1}\ h^{-1}$) when moisture not limiting	14
C04A4	3.74	Q_{10} value for litter	14
C04LMX	0.005	Maximum leaching rate for litter ($g\ g^{-1}\ d^{-1}$)	E
C04MNM	2.0	Minimum moisture for leaching litter ($g\ H_2O\ g^{-1}$ dw)	E
C04MXM	7.5	Optimum moisture for leaching litter ($g\ H_2O\ g^{-1}$ dw)	E
C04MNT	−0.5	Minimum temperature for leaching litter (°C)	E
C04MXT	5.0	Optimum temperature for leaching litter (°C)	E
C04LCH	0.1	Leachable material generated by microbial respiration ($g\ g^{-1}$ respired)	E
C05A1	0.90	$g\ H_2O\ g^{-1}$ soil carbon at half field capacity	E
C05A2	25	$g\ H_2O\ g^{-1}$ soil carbon at half maximum retentive capacity	E
C05A3	40	Respiration rate of soil carbon at $10°C$ ($\mu l\ O_2\ g^{-1}\ h^{-1}$) when moisture not limiting	E
C05A4	4.0	Q_{10} value for soil carbon	E
C05LCH	0.1	Leachable material generated by microbial respiration ($g\ g^{-1}$ respired)	E
C06A4	2.0	Q_{10} value for live rhizomes	4
C06A3	0.005	Respiration rate of rhizomes at $10°C$ ($g\ g^{-1}\ d^{-1}$)	E, 4 (modified)
C06GRN	0.03	Maximum rhizome translocation rate to shoots ($g\ g^{-1}\ d^{-1}$)	E
C06NPC	0.95	Minimum proportion of full rhizome biomass for new root growth	E

Table 1 cont.

Fortran Variable Name	Value	Meaning	Source ☆
C06ROT	0.21	Maximum translocation from rhizomes to new root growth ($g\ g^{-1}\ d^{-1}$)	E
C06CNR	0.05	Proportion of rhizome biomass that originates as soil nutrients	E
C06DR	0.001	Death rate for rhizomes ($g\ g^{-1}\ d^{-1}$)	
C07A1	0.75	$g\ H_2O\ g^{-1}$ dead root at half field capacity	E
C07A2	20	$g\ H_2O\ g^{-1}$ dead root at half maximum retentive capacity	E
C07A3	80	Respiration of dead roots at $10^{\circ}C$ ($\mu l\ O_2\ g^{-1}\ h^{-1}$) when moisture not limiting	E
C07A4	6.0	Q_{10} value for dead roots	E
C08A1	0.9	$g\ H_2O\ g^{-1}$ soil humus at half field capacity	E
C08A2	2.50	$g\ H_2O\ g^{-1}$ soil humus at half maximum retentive capacity	E
C08A3	5.0	Respiration rate of soil humus at $10^{\circ}C$ ($\mu l\ O_2\ g^{-1}\ h^{-1}$) when moisture not limiting	E
C08A4	1.8	Q_{10} value for soil humus	Benoit (pers. comm.)
C08LCH	0.1	Leachable material generated from soil humus by microbial respiration ($g\ g^{-1}$ respired)	
C10A1	4.16	$g\ H_2O\ g^{-1}$ feces at half field capacity	14
C10A1	4.16	$g\ H_2O\ g^{-1}$ feces at half maximum retentive capacity	14
C10A3	777	Respiration rate of lemming feces at $10^{\circ}C$ ($\mu l\ O_2\ g^{-1}\ h^{-1}$)	14
C10A4	8.0	Q_{10} value for lemming feces	E
C11A1	0.74	$g\ H_2O\ g^{-1}$ new standing dead at half field capacity	14
C11A2	127	$g\ H_2O\ g^{-1}$ new standing dead at half maximum retentive capacity	14
C11A3	184	Respiration rate of new standing dead at $10^{\circ}C$ ($\mu l\ O_2\ g^{-1}\ h^{-1}$) when moisture not limiting	14
C11A4	2.56	Q_{10} value for new standing dead	14
C11LMX	0.05	Maximum leaching rate of new standing dead ($g\ g^{-1}\ d^{-1}$)	E
C11MNM	1.0	Minimum moisture for leaching from new standing dead ($g\ H_2O\ g^{-1}$ dw)	E
C11MXM	5.0	Optimum moisture for leaching from new standing dead ($g\ H_2O\ g^{-1}$ dw)	E
C11MNT	−0.5	Minimum temperature for leaching from new standing dead ($^{\circ}C$)	E
C11MXT	5.0	Optimum temperature for leaching from new standing dead ($^{\circ}C$)	E
C11ED	0.09	Proportion of new standing dead edible by grazers	E
C12A1	0.0	$g\ H_2O\ g^{-1}$ of soluble carbohydrates at half field capacity	E
C12A2	30000	$g\ H_2O\ g^{-1}$ of soluble carbohydrates at half maximum retentive capacity	E
C12A3	1000	Respiration rate of soluble carbohydrates at $10^{\circ}C$ ($\mu l\ O_2\ g^{-1}\ h^{-1}$) when moisture not limiting	E
C12A4	2.0	Q_{10} value for soluble carbohydrates	E
C13A4	2.0	Q_{10} value for live roots	3
C13A3	0.007	Respiration rate of live roots at $10^{\circ}C$ ($g\ g^{-1}\ d^{-1}$)	3
C13MAR	−0.007	Carbon flux at which root death is maximum ($g\ g^{-1}\ d^{-1}$)	E

Table 1 cont.

Fortran Variable Name	Value	Meaning	Source ☆
C13XDR	0.05	Maximum death rate of roots (g g^{-1} d^{-1})	E
C13RHZ	0.1	Proportion translocated to rhizome at time of root death	E
C13CNR	0.02	Proportion biomass that originates as soil nutrients	E

☆   Sources cited frequently never measured the parameter directly but provided data which have been interpreted.

☆☆   E = Estimated
Although many parameters in the model have never been directly quantified, we often have reasonable estimates of their magnitude. For example, we have no direct measurements of mortality of live green during the growing season, but we do know the pattern of increase in LAI of the standing dead vegetation. Other estimates are guesses which have been somewhat modified on the basis of simulation projections.

model using these parameter values. The derivations and magnitudes of parameter values employed by the Barrow version of ABISKO II are summarized in Table 1. Simulated results are compared with field data in Fig. 5 and 6. Initial compartment sizes for these runs are presented in Table 2. Abiotic data employed in a specific run are chosen from the same year as the validation data examined during that run.

Table 2. Initial compartment sizes for simulation runs illustrated in Figures 5, 6 and 7

Compartment	Biomass pool	Initial value (g biomass m^{-2})
C01	Aboveground live	6.0
C02	Green litter	0.1
C03	Old standing dead	5.0
C04	Litter	25.0
C05	Soil organic matter	1 400.0
C06	Live rhizomes and stem bases	50.0
C07	Dead roots and rhizomes	1 250.0
C08	Soil humus	12 600.0
C09	World	10 000 000.0 (g C)
C10	Feces	3.0
C11	New standing dead	30.0
C12	Leachate	0.0
C13	Live roots	400.0
C14 or GRZ	Grazers	0.06

In Fig. 5. carbon has been converted to leaf area index to facilitate comparison with field measures. The close agreement between observed and simulated values suggests that both life and death processes of aboveground graminoid parts are realistically simulated by ABISKO II. The transients illustrated are the product of photosynthesis, carbon allocation, and respiration. Admittedly errors in the fomulation of one process could compensate for errors in another, but the close agreement between simulated projections and field observations is encouraging. It is particularly noteworthy that the independently simulated photosynthetic and respiratory processes produce simulated death rates that approximate the timing and magnitude of observed death rates extremely closely. The projections and data illustrated in Figs. 5 and 6 are for the Barrow site. The formulation of primary production processes described above is apparently general and holds for at least two life forms and three widely different tundra sites (Barrow, Alaska; Devon Island, Canada; Moor House, United Kingdom) (11).

Fig. 6 illustrates the simulated transients of some of the belowground processes as these compare with field measures. The field data employed in the comparison were obtained by daily KOH titration of gas collected from plastic cores sunk into the soil. These data are compared with the cumulated totals of simulated respiration from relevant system components. Root respiration includes that of microbes associated with the rhizosphere while microbial respiration is that of microorganisms utilizing soluble carbon, soil organic matter, and soil humus as an energy source.

Simulated microbial respiration follows a pattern closely similar to that of the field measures of respiration, but shows a greater depression early in the season. The early

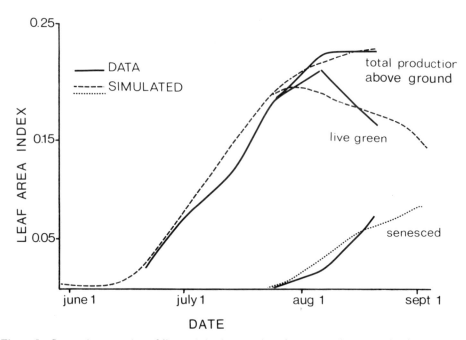

Figure 5. Seasonal progression of live and dead vegetation above ground: measured values compared with simulated values (measured values courtesy of L.L. Tieszen).

season depression is more evident in the pattern of simulated microbial plus root respi- ration (Fig. 6). There are at least two reasons for this early season disparity between simulated and measured values. The soil temperature employed in the model is that at 5 cm depth. Early in the season field surface temperatures permit respiration while simulated temperatures (at 5 cm depth) are too cold to allow significant respiration. Because the lower threshold for root respiration is higher than that for microbes, the disparity between simulated and measured values is more obvious when roots are con- sidered. The release of carbon dioxide trapped during freeze-up is not simulated but will appear in field measures, and thus contributes to the early spring disparity between field and simulated values.

Over the 85 day sample period the accumulated totals of measured respiration and simulated respiration are 159 and 165 g C m^{-2} respectively. The cumulative dispari- ty between measured and simulated values over this period is thus 6 g C m^{-2} or 3.7 % of the measured values. A disparity of less than 5 % is well within the sample error as- sociated with root biomass data; thus the respiration dynamics of microbe, root and other contributing compartments must be assumed realistic within the accuracy of avail- able data. The proportion of total simulated soil respiration that originates with the roots on any given day varies between 33 % and 70 %, and lies at the lower end of the range of reported values (50 to 93 %) (3).

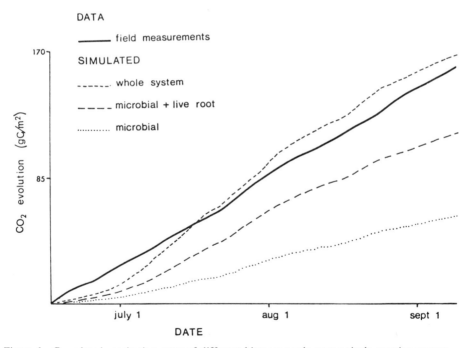

Figure 6. Cumulated respiration rates of different biomass pools over a single growing season: measured values compared with simulated values (measured values for 1973 courtesy of R.E.Benoit; abiotic data from 1973).

LOW GRAZING

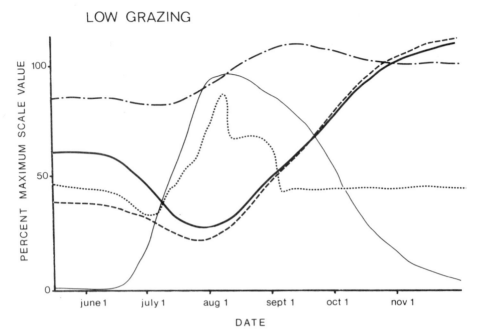

Figure 7. Simulated seasonal progression of biomass pools for Barrow, Alaska (abiotic data from 1972). Maximum scale value varies between biomass pools: live green (100 g m^{-2}) ———; all dead vegetation including litter and standing dead of various age classes (110 g m^{-2}) ———; all standing dead vegetation (100 g m^{-2}) — — —; rhizomes and stem bases (120 g m^{-2}) ------; live roots (2 000 g m^{-2}) — · —.

Comparisons of simulated and measured values (Fig. 4, 5 and 6) suggest that the mathematical expressions presented in this paper represent a general, realistic and rigorous statement of carbon flux processes in tundra ecosystems. When these relationships are combined within the bookkeeping system of ABISKO II they produce biomass transients of the form shown in Fig. 7. The realism of these transients mirrors the realism of the mathematical expressions constituting the model. Although many processes could have been simulated in more detail, ABISKO II presently represents the least ambiguous and best quantified general statement of carbon dynamics within tundra ecosystems.

In summary, we must note that the apparent accuracy of the model does not obviate discussion of its failings. Processes of physical degradation are treated implicitly and without rigor. The important effects of small changes in microclimate within the plant canopy and at depth in the soil are not encompassed. Changing quality of decomposing substrates is handled only implicitly and also without rigor. For example, the differences between simulated and measured patterns of soil respiration may be caused by seasonal changes in substrate quality (6) that are not encompassed by ABISKO II. Potential interactions between different primary producer species or decomposer populations are not incorporated. Most constraining, however. is the model's consideration of the single element, carbon. While rigorous description of carbon dynamics within tundra ecosystems is gratifying, it is limited and may ignore controlling influences of phosphorous or other nutrients (8).

ACKNOWLEDGEMENTS

The development of the ABISKO model has been truly international. In North America research and development has been supported by the National Science Foundation under grant 29342 to the University of Alaska through a subcontract to the University of British Columbia. The subcontract was fulfilled under the joint NSF sponsorship of the International Biological Programme and the Office of Polar Programs and was directed under the auspices of the U.S. Tundra Biome. Field and laboratory activities at Barrow were supported by the Naval Arctic Research Laboratory of the Office of Naval Research. Some Canadian contributions were supported by the Canadian National Research Council and Canadian Department of Environment through their grants supporting the Canadian Tundra Biome studies. For that portion of the model simulating lichen growth forms further Canadian support was received from the Canadian Department of Indian and Northern Affairs under its grant to the Arctic and Alpine Research Committee of the University of British Columbia through a subcontract to F. Bunnell.

REFERENCES

1. Batzli, G.O. In manuscript. Populations and energetics of small mammals in tundra ecosystem. – In: Moore, J.J. (ed.) Tundra: Comparative analysis of ecosystems. IBP Series. Cambridge University Press.
2. Batzli, G.O. In press. The role of small mammals in arctic ecosystems. – In: Petrusewicz, K., Golley, K.F. & Ryszkowski, L. (eds.) Small Mammals: Their Productivity and Population Dynamics. IBP Series. Cambridge University Press.
3. Billings, W.D., Peterson, K.M., Shaver, G.R. & Trent, A.W. In press. Effect of temperature on root growth and respiration in a tundra ecosystem, Barrow, Alaska. – In: Marshal, J.K. (ed.) The Below-ground Ecosystem. Proc. Fort Collins IBP Symp., September 1973.
4. Billings, W.D., Shaver, G.R. & Trent A.W. 1974. Temperature effects of growth and respiration of roots and rhizomes in tundra graminoids. – In: Bliss, L.C. & Wielgolaski, F.E. (eds.) Primary Production and Production Processes, Tundra Biome, pp. 57–63. Edmonton: IBP Tundra Biome Steering Committee.
5. Bunnell, F. 1972. Lemmings – models and the real world. – In: Proc. Summer Computer Simulation Conference, 1972, pp. 1183–1193 and 1203–1204. San Diego.
6. Bunnell, F. 1973. Decomposition: models and the real world. – In: Rosswall, T. (ed.) Modern Methods in the Study of Microbial Ecology. Bull. Ecol. Res. Comm. 17: 407–415. (Stockholm.)
7. Bunnell, F. 1973. Computer simulation of nutrient and lemming cycles in an arctic tundra wet meadow ecosystem. – Ph. D. Thesis, Univ. of California, Berkeley. 312 pp.
8. Bunnell, F.L., MacLean, S.F. & Brown J. 1975. Barrow, Alaska, USA. – In: Rosswall, T. & Heal, O.W. (eds.) Structure and Function of Tundra Ecosystems. Ecol. Bull. Vol. 20. Stockholm: Swedish National Science Research Council.
9. Bunnell, F.L. & Dowding, P. 1973. ABISKO model. Mimeo Rept., IBP Tundra Biome, 23 pp.
10. Bunnell, F.L. & Dowding, P. 1974. ABISKO – a generalized decomposition model for comparison between tundra sites. – In: Holding, A.J., Heal, O.W., MacLean, Jr., S.F. & Flanagan, P.W. (eds.) Soil Organisms and Decomposition in Tundra, pp. 227–247. Stockholm: IBP Tundra Biome Steering Committee.
11. Bunnell, F.L., Scoullar, K.A. & Dowding, P. In manuscript. Between site comparison of carbon flux using simulation models. – In: Moore, J.J. (ed.) Tundra: Comparative analysis of ecosystems. IBP Series. Cambridge University Press.
12. Bunnell, F.L., Kärenlampi, L. & Russell, D.E. 1973. A simulation model of lichen – *Rangifer* interactions in Northern Finland. – Rep. Kevo Subarctic Res. Stat. 10: 1–8.

13. Bunnell, F.L. & Tait, D.E.N. 1974. Mathematical simulation models of decomposition processes. – In: Holding, A.J., Heal, O.W., MacLean, Jr., S.F. & Flanagan, P.W. (eds.) Soil Organisms and Decomposition in Tundra, pp. 207–225. Stockholm: IBP Tundra Biome Steering Committee.
14. Bunnell, F.L., Tait, D.E.N., Flanagan, P.W. & Van Cleve, K. Submitted. Microbial respiration and weight loss: a general model of the influence of abiotic variables. – Soil Biol. Biochem.
15. Collier, B.D., Stenseth, N., Osborn, R. & Barkley, S. 1974. A simulation model of energy acquisition and utilization by the brown lemming (*Lemmus trimucronatus*) at Barrow, Alaska. – Oikos 26 (In press).
16. Coulombe, H.N. & Brown, J. 1970. The synthesis and modeling of the Barrow, Alaska ecosystem. – In: Proc. of the Conf. on Productivity and Conservation in Northern Circumpolar Lands, October 15–17, 1969, pp. 44–49. Morges, Switzerland: IUCN.
17. Flanagan, P.W. & Veum, A.K. 1974. The influence of temperature and moisture on decomposition rates in tundra. – In: Holding, A.J., Heal, O.W., MacLean, Jr., S.F. & Flanagan P.W. (eds.) Soil Organisms and Decomposition in Tundra, pp. 249–277. Stockholm: IBP Tundra Biome Steering Committee.
18. Heal, O.W., Latter, P.M. & Howson, G. In press. A study of the decomposition of organic matter. – In: Heal, O.W. & Perkins, D.F. (eds.) The Ecology of some British Moors and Montane Grasslands. Berlin–Heidelberg–New York: Springer Verlag.
19. Lohammar, T. & Rosswall, T. 1974. Use of the 'ABISKO model' for simulating *Rubus chamaemorus* litter decomposition. – In: Flower-Ellis, J.G.K. (ed.) Progress Report, 1973. IBP Swedish Tundra Biome Project Tech. Rep. 16: 97–107.
20. MacLean, S.F., Jr., Fitzgerald, B.M. & Pitelka, F.A. 1974. Population cycles in arctic lemmings: winter production and predation by weasels. – Arctic and Alpine Res. 6: 1–12.
21. Melchior, H.R. 1972. Summer herbivory by the brown lemming at Barrow, Alaska. – In: Proc. 1972 U.S. Tundra Biome Symposium, Lake Wilderness, Washington, pp. 136–138.
22. Thompson, D.Q. 1955. The role of food and cover in population fluctuations of the brown lemming at Point Barrow, Alaska. Trans. – 20th N. Amer. Wildl. Conf., Bol. 20: 166–176.
23. Tieszen, L.L. 1973. Photosynthesis and respiration in arctic tundra grasses: field light intensity and temperature responses. – Arctic and Alpine Res. 5: 233–251.
24. U.S. Department of Commerce. Local Climatological Data, Barrow, Alaska. National Climate Center, Ashville, NC 28801.

LIST OF AUTHORS

J.H. Baker, The Freshwater Biological Association, River Laboratory, East Stoke, Wareham,
  Dorset BH20 6BB, UK
A. Berg, Botanical Laboratory, University of Oslo, Blindern, Oslo 3, Norway
O. Blehr, The Hardangervidda Project, University of Bergen, N−5000 Bergen, Norway
L.C. Bliss, Department of Botany, University of Alberta, Edmonton, Alberta T6G 2E1, Canada
L.G. Bogatyrev, Faculty of Pedology, Moscow State University, Moscow, USSR
J. Brown, U.S. Army Cold Regions Research and Engineering Laboratory, Hanover, NH 03755, USA
F.L. Bunnell, Faculty of Forestry, University of British Columbia, Vancouver, B.C. V6T 1W5, Canada
A. Cernusca, Institute für Allgemeine Botanik der Universität Innsbruck, Sternwartestrasse 15,
  A−6020 Innsbruck, Austria
Yu. I. Chernov, A.N. Sewertzoff Institute of Evolutionary Morphology and Animal Ecology, Leninskie
  prospekt 33, Moscow, USSR
N.J. Collins, Institute of Terrestrial Ecology, The Edinburgh Laboratory, Bush Estate, Pencuik, Mid-
  lothian EH26 0QB, U.K.
E.V. Dorogostaiskaya, Komarov Botanical Institute, Popova street 2, Leningrad, USSR
P. Dowding, Department of Botany, Trinity College, Dublin 2, Ireland
M. Espeland, Zoological Institute, University of Oslo, Blindern, Oslo 3, Norway
J.G.K. Flower-Ellis, College of Forestry, S−901 87 Umeå, Sweden
E. Gaare, Direktoratet for Vilt og Ferskvannsfisk, Elgeseter gt. 10, N−7000 Trondheim, Norway
T.V. Gerasimenko, Komarov Botanical Institute, Popova street 2, Leningrad, USSR
G. Grabherr, Institut für Allgemeine Botanik der Universität Innsbruck, Sternwartestrasse 15,
  A−6020 Innsbruck, Austria
L.A. Grishina, Faculty of Pedology, Moscow State University, Moscow, USSR
A. Hagen, Zoological Institute, University of Oslo, Blindern, Oslo 3, Norway
O.W. Heal, The Institute of Terrestrial Ecology, Merlewood Research Station, Grange-over-Sands,
  Cumbria LA11 6JU, UK
B. Healy, Department of Zoology, University College, Belfield, Dublin 4, Ireland
O. Hesjedal, Telemark Distrikthøgskole, N−3800 Bø i Telemark, Norway
S. Hågvar, Zoological Institute, University of Oslo, Blindern, Oslo 3, Norway
I.V. Ignatenko, North-Eastern Complex Scientific Institute, K. Marx Street 11, Magadan, USSR
V.V. Ivanov, Faculty of Pedology, Moscow State University, Moscow, USSR
J.F. Jenkin, School of Botany, University of Melbourne, Parkville, Victoria 3052, Australia
L.-G. Johansson, Department of Plant Physiology, University of Umeå, S−901 87 Umeå, Sweden
H.E. Jones, Institute of Terrestrial Ecology, Merlewood Research Station, Grange-over-Sands,
  Cumbria LA11 6JU, UK
S. Jonsson, Department of Entomology, University of Uppsala, P.O. Box 561, S−751 22 Uppsala 1,
  Sweden
P. Kallio, The Subarctic Research Station of the University of Turku, SF−20500 Turku 50, Finland
S. Kjelvik, Botanical Laboratory, University of Oslo, Blindern, Oslo 3, Norway
W. Larcher, Institut für Allgemeine Botanik der Universität Innsbruck, Sternwartestrasse 15,
  A−6020 Innsbruck, Austria
L. Lien, Zoological Museum, University of Oslo, Sarsgaten 1, Oslo 5, Norway
S.F. MacLean, Jr., Institute of Arctic Biology, University of Alaska, Fairbanks, Alaska 99701, USA
N.V. Matveyeva, Komarov Botanical Institute, Popova street 2, Leningrad, USSR
J.J. Moore, Department of Botany, University College, Belfield, Dublin 4, Ireland
I. Mysterud, Zoological Institute, University of Oslo, Blindern, Oslo 3, Norway
B.N. Norin, Komarov Botanical Laboratory, Popova street 2, Leningrad, USSR
E. Nötzel, Institut für Allgemeine Botanik der Universität Innsbruck, Sternwartestrasse 15,
  A−6020 Innsbruck, Austria
E. Østbye, Zoological Institute, University of Oslo, Blindern, Oslo 3, Norway
O.M. Parinkina, Central Museum of Pedology, Birjevoi Drive 6, Leningrad, USSR
T.G. Polozova, Komarov Botanical Institute, Popova street 2, Leningrad, USSR

E.B. Pospelova, Faculty of Pedology, Moscow State University, Moscow, USSR

T. Rosswall, Department of Microbiology, Agricultural College, S–750 07 Uppsala 7, Sweden

B.-E. Rydén, Department of Hydrology, University of Uppsala, P.O. Box 554, S–751 22 Uppsala 1, Sweden

A. Sandhaug, Botanical Laboratory, University of Oslo, Blindern, Oslo 3, Norway

V.F. Schamurin, Komarov Botanical Institute, Popova street 2, Leningrad, USSR

L. Schulz-Schmidt, Kärntner Institut für Seenforschung, Flatschacherstrasse 70, A–9020 Klagenfurt, Austria

K.A. Scoullar, Faculty of Forestry, University of British Columbia, Vancouver, B.C. V6T 1W5, Canada

N.M. Shalaeva, Faculty of Pedology, Moscow State University, Moscow, USSR

H.-J. Skar, Zoological Institute, University of Oslo, Blindern, Oslo 3, Norway

A. Skartveit, Geophysical Institute, University of Bergen, N–5000 Bergen, Norway

T. Skogland, Direktoratet for Vilt og Ferkvannsfisk, Elgeseter gt. 10, N–7000 Trondheim, Norway

O. Skre, Botanical Laboratory, University of Oslo, Blindern, Oslo 3, Norway

N. Smeets, Institut für Allgemeine Botanik der Universität Innsbruck, Sternwartestrasse 15, A–6020 Innsbruck, Austria

N.V. Smirnova, Central Geophysical Observatory, Leningrad USSR

R.I.L. Smith, British Antarctic Survey, Botanical Section, Life Sciences Division, Monks Wood Experimental Station, Abbots Ripton, Huntingdon, Cambridgeshire DE 17 2LS, UK

T. Solhøy, Zoological Museum, University of Bergen, Musepl. 3, N–5000 Bergen, Norway

M. Sonesson, Abisko Natural Science Research Station, S–980 24 Abisko, Sweden

N.C. Stenseth, Zoological Institute, University of Oslo, Blindern, Oslo 3, Norway

I.V. Stepanova, Komarov Botanical Institute, Popova street 2, Leningrad, USSR

P.J. Tilbrook, British Antarctic Survey, Monks Wood Experimental Station, Abbots Ripton, Huntingdon PE17 2LS, UK

B.A. Tomilin, Komarov Botanical Institute, Popova street 2, Leningrad, USSR

V.D. Vassiljevskaya, Faculty of Pedology, Moscow State University, Moscow, USSR

A.A. Vinokurov, Central Laboratory of Nature Conservation, Kravchenko street 12, Moscow, USSR

D.W.H. Walton, British Antarctic Survey, Botanical Section, Life Sciences Division, Monks Wood Experimental Station, Abbots Ripton, Huntingdon, Cambridgeshire PE17 2LS, UK

J.B. Whittaker, Department of Biology, University of Lancaster, Lancaster, UK

F.E. Wielgolaski, Botanical Laboratory, University of Oslo, Blindern, Oslo 3, Norway

O.V. Zalensky, Komarov Botanical Institute, Popova street 2, Leningrad, USSR